THE MOLECULAR BASIS OF LIFE

READINGS FROM
**SCIENTIFIC
AMERICAN**

THE MOLECULAR BASIS OF LIFE

An Introduction to Molecular Biology

WITH INTRODUCTIONS BY

Robert H. Haynes
YORK UNIVERSITY, TORONTO

and

Philip C. Hanawalt
STANFORD UNIVERSITY

W. H. FREEMAN AND COMPANY
SAN FRANCISCO AND LONDON

Each of the SCIENTIFIC AMERICAN articles in *The Molecular Basis of Life* is available as a separate Offprint at twenty cents each. For a complete listing of approximately 650 articles now available as Offprints, write to W. H. Freeman and Company, 660 Market Street, San Francisco, California 94104.

Exploring the concepts and theories that provide insight into the nature of matter and of life can be a delectable mental experience. Unfortunately, it is often difficult to get the best ideas out of the heads of scientists and bring them into general circulation where they can be understood and appreciated by everyone. Throughout the years the editors of *Scientific American* have been unusually successful in conveying contemporary science to the public in a style that is at once elegant and clear. *The Molecular Basis of Life* is another in a series of collections of *Scientific American* articles devoted to a well-defined area of modern biology.

Although the articles in this volume were originally addressed primarily to the scientifically sophisticated layman, we have found them very effective as readings for courses in molecular biology, and in the new general biology "core curricula." Because of their unique pedagogical style these articles often stimulate the interest of students more effectively than traditional textbooks. Their usefulness persists: we have even noticed some of our graduate students studying them in preparation for their Ph.D. qualifying exams. (Evidently they realize that their professors sometimes obtain their own broader knowledge of molecular biology as much from *Scientific American* as from the technical journals.)

This volume is a logical introduction to two earlier collections of *Scientific American* articles, *The Living Cell* and *From Cell to Organism* (both with introductions written by Donald Kennedy of Stanford University).

The two branches of science that contain much of our basic understanding of matter and of life are quantum mechanics and molecular biology. The rise of the quantum theory in the early decades of this century transformed thinking in physics and chemistry; the mid-century advent of molecular biology brought an equally far-reaching revolution to biology. Now, even though the fever of creativity is past, and the new doctrines have been accorded the dangerous status of received truth, we can still recapture some of the excitement that surrounded each of the new advances as it occurred. Most of the crucial developments were described in *Scientific American* by scientists who were intimately connected with them. We have organized 34 of these articles in a logically coherent sequence and have provided introductory material to make the collection up to date and self-contained. The articles span the period from 1948 to 1968. The two articles from the year 1948—that on the bacteriophage by Max and Mary Delbrück and the one describing the birth of biochemical genetics by George Beadle—set the stage for the great drama that followed. From these beginnings the reader should be able to trace the development of the major concepts of molecular biology through the ensuing 20-year period of intellectual ferment. (One should note the year in which each article was written in order to place it in proper historical perspective.)

Both quantum mechanics and molecular biology are the sources of strong ecumenical forces in science, and this tendency toward integration has had a profound effect on the relations among its several branches. Quantum mechanics unified the physical sciences, and molecular biology provided the life sciences with a firm basis in physics and chemistry. Future advances in neurobiology and animal behavior might well effect a further unification of science by narrowing the gap that now exists between biology and the social sciences.

May 1968

ROBERT H. HAYNES
PHILIP C. HANAWALT

CONTENTS

THE MOLECULAR BASIS OF LIFE

*L*IFE — and the Advent of Molecular Biology

*W*HAT IS LIFE? Is it the harmonious working of an intricate bio-chemical engine, or the very Breath of God that gives form to dust? This question of high romance is asked by anyone who ever pauses to wonder; and not surprisingly, philosophers, theologians, and scientists have responded eloquently with answers that range from the mystic's sublime to Everyman's ridiculous. It has been asserted that life is a general property of matter: Spinoza believed that all natural bodies were animate and that stones could think; and Diderot would endow with life even the molecules of which organic substances are composed. Others maintain that life is an introspective conception, and that each person is alive only unto himself, all other creatures being automata. Unfortunately, such speculations, however interesting in themselves, are of no value to biologists in their research, or to physicians in their practice, and we must pass them by in favor of more useful conjectures about what life may be.

Plants and animals are remarkably well adapted to their environments; they exhibit goal-directed behavior, and the structure of each part seems to be of optimal design for its particular function. For these reasons organisms have long been compared with contemporary machines: with clocks in the eighteenth century, with heat engines in the nineteenth, and with computers today. For the romantic, such comparison seems to justify the existence of a Designer, or perhaps a "vital force" within the living machine that makes it go, although common sense is content to let the machine run itself according to the ordinary laws of physics and chemistry, without benefit of the extra metaphysical baggage. (The claim that living organisms contain "something more" than material components bound by physical laws would presuppose a complete understanding of the behavior of molecules and the whole variety of processes they can support. Yet such a total understanding of physics and chemistry is seldom claimed, even by the most sagacious.) With or without vital forces, the machine analogy remains weak because organisms differ profoundly in *origin* and *composition* from even the most accomplished robots that the imagination can devise. However, these very shortcomings in the analogy suggest that we should focus our attention as much upon those two aspects of organisms as upon their function and behavior. That such an emphasis now prevails in modern biology will become evident in the articles that follow in this volume.

When reduced to honesty, few will profess to know what life is, and some will argue that the word is meaningless, and the question ill-conceived. Most attempted definitions of life have been functional and based upon such obvious phenomena as growth, reproduction, motility, irritability, or consciousness; or, alternatively, upon such abstract characteristics of these processes as their "purposiveness" or "adaptability." (The almost perfect adaptation of organisms to their environments was once considered to be quasimystical, until Darwin showed how it might arise in the course of evolution through the mechanism of natural selection.) All such definitions have been destructively criticized on the grounds that there are some living things that do not possess the property in question — spermatozoa do not grow, mules do not reproduce, plants are nonmotile; and, conversely, that certain obviously inanimate objects can successfully mimic each of the allegedly definitive activities — crystals grow, automata reproduce, machines are goal-directed or adaptable, and so on. Nonetheless, we all share a common intuition that enables us to distinguish a man from his corpse, a tree from a log, or a whistling bird from a babbling brook, even though it may be difficult to specify all the fine distinctions in such a way as to provide a straightforward answer to our question. Thus, it becomes evident that much of the difficulty is semantic because, in common parlance, "life" is a collective word that subsumes a vast panorama of complex phenomena associated with all of the organisms that exist. This carries the awesome suggestion that if we are to gain a really proper understanding of what life is, we may have to study in detail the many diverse forms in which it occurs, as well as to enquire into its origin. One is relieved of this impracticable assignment by the prospect that there are certain basic characteristics to be found in the simplest creatures and that are yet essential for even the most complex. The idea that such properties exist first arose with the realization that the many diverse species of plants and animals share a common evolutionary past, and that they are composed of cells containing relatively few types of molecules, primarily proteins, nucleic acids, carbohydrates, and fats. The simplest organisms consist of but a single cell, and even the most complex are constructed of relatively few cell types. Thus, the cell has come to be regarded as the simplest independent structure that possesses all of the essential properties of life, and, if we are to understand life, we must first understand the molecular basis of cellular activities.

The life history of the typical unspecialized cell consists of endless cycles of growth and division into identical daughter cells. To the casual observer, the only thing that simple organisms such as bacteria ever do is to grow and divide. Furthermore, these two processes must be very closely coupled; otherwise cells would either grow enormously in size (growth without division), or they would become vanishingly small after relatively few divisions unaccompanied by growth. Regulated cell growth and division is thus the *sine qua non* of life, and these processes are the essential consequences of the particular chemical nature and evolutionary history of cell components.

Growth requires the synthesis of new cell substance and, since cells are composed primarily of proteins, this must of necessity be based upon protein synthesis. The macromolecules known as proteins consist entirely of smaller units, called amino acids, that are either derived directly from the environment or synthesized from other nutrient materials. The newly assembled proteins may be used in a number of ways. For example, they may function as structural elements in the cell's architecture, or as catalysts (enzymes) for the various chemical reactions responsible for cellular activity, including protein synthesis itself. If one were to frame a contemporary definition of life it would surely be in terms of the unique and vital role of protein synthesis in living organisms. Although biochemists have recently learned how to initiate limited protein synthesis *in vitro*, in nature it occurs only in cells and no inanimate structure, however complicated, is capable of it. For some of us, this is a rather disconcerting reminder of Engel's nineteenth-century definition of the fundamental nature of life as the "mode of existence of albuminous substances (i.e., proteins), and this essentially consists in the constant self-renewal of the chemical constituents of these substances."

The synthesis of cell components, together with the breakdown of nutrients to yield the energy and molecular subunits required for these syntheses, involves lengthy interconnected sequences of biochemical reactions. These enzyme-catalyzed reaction sequences are known collectively as "metabolic pathways." In addition to studying the structure and function of proteins as units, it is equally important to learn how they are organized into those special configurations within the cell that provide for the most efficient movement of materials along the pathways.

The problem of the regulation of cellular activities has only recently been attacked in a concerted fashion. However, these studies should ultimately resolve the old conflict between the Democritean, or atomistic, approach to biology and the Aristotelian, or holistic, approach. The former is concerned primarily with the reduction or analysis of organisms into their respective parts; the latter, with the integration and interaction of these parts within the whole. Yet it is clear that insofar as any complex system is more than the sum of its parts, it is so by virtue of the controlled interactions or modes of regulation of these parts. These opposing methodologies will ultimately complement one another in our efforts to understand life, and, although the reductionist approach has dominated the recent history of molecular biology, it is becoming increasingly evident that regulation and integration will be a major theme in the biology of the immediate future.

The structures of proteins are well adapted to their individual roles in the economy of the cell. Despite the great complexity of these molecules, the detailed three-dimensional configuration of several proteins has recently been worked out by the technique of X-ray diffraction. Even seemingly trivial alterations or errors in the assembly of proteins can destroy their biochemical function and render them useless to the cell. For example, substitution of certain critical amino acids by others in the protein hemoglobin is sufficient to change the shape of red blood cells into the abnormal form characteristic of sickle-cell anemia. Clearly, proteins must interact with other molecules with such intimate "lock-and-key" precision that even small structural defects may be sufficient to destroy the essential stereochemical specificity of the interaction.

It is the sum total of proteins within a cell that confers upon it its individuality and the unique characteristics that must somehow be recreated in each of the two daughter cells that arise upon division. Since the hereditary traits in any individual depend on the nature of the proteins it contains, it is clear that the mechanism of heredity must be related to that of protein synthesis. What then is the material basis of heredity? Does it reside in these ubiquitous proteins, or perhaps might we here discover a mysterious "vital force"?

One hundred years ago Gregor Mendel analyzed the quantitative distribution of hereditary characters among the offspring of pea plants that he was able to cross in his garden. On the basis of certain regularities in the reappearance of parental characters in subsequent generations, he concluded that there must exist in plants certain particulate units or "genetic factors" that control the hereditary traits of individuals and that are passed on intact to their offspring. These particulate units, whose existence was at first purely inferential, were later christened *genes* at about the time that the significance of Mendel's work finally impressed itself upon geneticists at the turn of the century. Mendel's atomistic theory of heredity was the conceptual opposite of the then current "fluid blending" theory of inheritance that so dismayed Darwin as he sought to construct a plausible explanation for the genetic variability upon which the mechanism of natural selection depends. However, genes remained abstract entities whose very location was a mystery until the early years of this century, when it was concluded that they resided in the chromosomes that had recently been discovered by cytologists in cell nuclei.

In the early years of classical genetics there was little interest in the chemical nature of the gene, for it was by no means obvious that its chemical structure would also reveal the mechanism of its action in cells. It was known that chromosomes consisted almost entirely of protein and a second, rather uninteresting, substance called nucleic acid that had been discovered by Miescher in 1868, only two years after Mendel's first paper was published. Thus it was commonly assumed that a gene was some kind of nucleoprotein particle, although it was thought that the nucleic acid component could not possibly have enough specificity built into its structure to be capable of carrying the primary genetic information.

Not only was the chemical nature of the gene unknown during the first half of this century, but its mode of action was also obscure. The first conceptual advance that heralded the advent of molecular biology was the "one gene, one enzyme" hypothesis of Beadle, Tatum, and Ephrussi, which asserted that a gene functions by directing the synthesis of a particular enzyme. It was then but a short step to the further generalization that genes direct *all* protein synthesis. This formed the essential link between proteins and the mechanism of heredity.

Despite the great insight provided by the "one gene, one enzyme" hypothesis, the remarkable ability of genes to duplicate themselves accurately in preparation for each new cell generation, and their great stability against change or mutation throughout many generations remained as mysterious as ever. The stability of genes was particularly impressive to physicists such as Bohr, Delbrück, and Schrödinger, who found it paradoxical that genes, being of molecular dimensions, should be stabilized against the expected statistical-mechanical fluctuations in their physical state. For this and other reasons several interesting but subsequently discounted notions arose: first, that there might exist a kind of biological "uncertainty principle," formally analogous to that of Heisenberg in physics, which would ultimately forbid our penetration into the fine details of genetics; another was that the gene might be an exceptional state of matter subject to laws that were complementary with the laws of atomic physics but not reducible to them. Although such simple analogies between the laws of quantum mechanics and those of genetics proved to be of no heuristic value for biology, they did suggest to many young physicists that the gene was every bit as interesting and challenging an object for study as the atomic nucleus. Since many of these physicists were later to become prominent molecular biologists, it is for this reason, if no other, that quantum mechanics has been regarded by some as an intellectual progenitor of molecular biology.

The mystery of the gene was dramatically dispelled in the early 1950's with the discovery that it is composed of DNA, and that the genetic information that specifies protein structure is encoded in the linear sequence of nucleotide bases contained in the double-stranded, helical DNA structure proposed by Watson and Crick. In biology the implications of the model of DNA structure are matched only by the insights arising from Darwin's theory of evolution by natural selection. Many of the developments that followed with great speed in the later 1950's and early 1960's are described in detail in the articles in this volume. However, to complete our story here, we should perhaps mention a few of these important advances: the mode of replication of DNA and, *ipso facto*, of the gene; the detailed nature of the genetic code; the structural and biochemical basis of protein synthesis; the principal mechanisms for the regulation of gene function in microorganisms; and the discovery of DNA repair mechanisms in cells.

But what of our original question? Do these revolutionary advances add up to an understanding of the fundamental nature of life? Certainly we do have an understanding of its material basis that would have been thought unattainable only a few years ago. But our search for the nature of life seems to have been something like a hunt for a creature we could not describe, although we had a rough idea of its whereabouts. Now, to many, the hunt seems to have been successful, but can we be sure we have found what we were looking for? This the reader will have to evaluate for himself. And, what remains for the future, now that so much has been accomplished so quickly?

As we pointed out above, life encompasses not only growth and division, those minimal vital properties of individual cells, but also a number of more complex phenomena that are found in multicellular organisms. The most impressive of these are, first, the processes of cellular differentiation and morphogenesis that occur during embryological development of plants and animals, and, second, such neural processes as sensory perception, learning, memory, and consciousness. At present, differentiation appears to depend largely upon gene regulation: that is, the genes controlling those proteins that enable a particular cell to become specialized in its functions are activated at the appropriate time in the developmental sequence by a combination of intracellular and extrinsic signals of largely unknown origin. An analogy of one facet of this process might be contained in the Jacob-Monod "operon hypothesis" for the control of enzyme synthesis in bacteria. However, the discovery of the nature of the developmental signals in higher organisms may well generate another series of revolutionary advances in biology.

The fundamental problems of brain function are more elusive. Neurophysiology is an old and well-established field, and we already understand many aspects of the behavior of neurons. However, even the application of the most sophisticated techniques of molecular biology, electrophysiology, and cybernetics may be insufficient to provide any genuine insight into the nature of memory and consciousness. It has been suggested, by Gunther Stent and others, that perhaps such mental phenomena can *never* be understood, since the brain, being a finite engine, may be incapable of providing an explanation for itself. However, a century ago, Thomas Henry Huxley argued that man might yet break through this ultimate dialectical paradox and come to see how, in their complementary ways, thought is a property of matter, just as matter has been regarded as a form of thought! But would this be a synthesis or a dissolution of intellect?

Suggestions for Further Reading

It is interesting to discover how little, as well as how much, our ideas on the nature of life developed during the century preceding the advent of molecular biology. Developments during this period can be conveniently surveyed in the following brief works, all with the same title, by three scientists prominently associated with the speculations of their times: T. H. Huxley, *The Physical Basis of Life* (Lay Sermon, Edinburgh, 1868; reprinted in *Methods and Results,* Macmillan, London, 1893, pp. 130–165); E. B. Wilson, *The Physical Basis of Life* (Yale University Press, New Haven, 1923); J. D. Bernal, *The Physical Basis of Life* (Routledge and Kegan Paul, London, 1951).

The annunciation of molecular biology was proclaimed in a book by Erwin Schrödinger, *"What is Life? The Physical Aspect of the Living Cell"* (Cambridge University Press, 1944); its epitaph has been written by Gunther Stent in "That Was The Molecular Biology That Was" (*Science, 160,* 390, 1968).

I

MACROMOLECULES

*Molecular Structure
as the Key
to Biological Activity*

The structure and function of any cell is largely determined by the totality of protein molecules it contains, and the structure and function of a protein is in turn determined by the particular linear sequence of amino acid subunits from which it is built up. Such large molecules are referred to as polymers, and the amino acid subunits of protein polymers are monomers. It is convenient to think of the sequence of amino acid units in proteins as embodying a certain amount of "information," just as the meaning, or information, contained in a sentence is determined by the particular sequence of words in the sentence. The sum total of all the information associated with all the proteins in a cell is stored or encoded in the genes, there being one gene for each distinct type of protein. The constellation of all the genes in a cell is referred to as the "genome," which is a kind of "blueprint" of the genetic information required for the duplication of the cell. Hence the gene is regarded as the principal unit of continuity and inheritance in living cells. But whereas proteins are built up of amino acid sequences, genes consist of linear sequences of molecular subunits called *nucleotides*. A polymer resulting from a combination of nucleotides is a nucleic acid. The nucleic acids (DNA and RNA) and proteins together make up as much as 90 percent of the dry weight of many cell types. DNA is often referred to as the *primary genetic material* of cells. The functions of both genes and proteins are revealed in, and appear to be a consequence of, their particular three-dimensional structures as *macromolecules*. Thus it is appropriate, and indeed necessary, to begin our study of fundamental life processes by reviewing the recent advances that have given us unprecedented insight into the detailed structures of these giant molecules. The remarkable mechanism whereby the information contained in the nucleotide sequence of the gene is used to generate the amino acid sequence in a protein is outlined in Part III.

The most direct approach to the investigation of an experimental problem is often the best one, even though it may be very laborious and time-consuming. Direct observation is the classical approach to the description and analysis of biological systems. With the aid of the optical microscope, such observations can be extended to structures with dimensions as small as 0.2 micron, the limit of resolution of that instrument. A simple living cell, the bacterium *Escherichia coli*, has dimensions of about 1 to 2 microns (1 micron $= 10^{-4}$ cms). In order to visualize the finest details of subcellular organization, higher magnification is necessary. This can be achieved with the electron microscope, which can resolve structures as small as a few Angstroms in size (1A $= 10^{-4}$ microns) and thus extend our view into the realm of molecular biology.

PROTEINS

Our story begins with the observation of the fibrils of the protein collagen in electron micrographs as described by Francis O. Schmitt in "Giant Molecules in Cells and Tissues."

In this article Schmitt shows that biological organization consists basically of ordered aggregates of very large molecules. Some of these aggregates may be visible even in the light microscope, as are the giant salivary gland chromosomes of the fruit fly *Drosophila*. These structures consist of both protein and nucleic acids in a highly organized array, and for many years they have provided cytologists with a most important system for studying genetic phenomena.

Great excitement attended the first reported determination of the complete amino acid sequence of a purified protein. The protein analyzed was the pancreatic hormone, insulin. This amazing feat of chemical virtuosity was accomplished by Frederick Sanger at Cambridge University and is described in "The Insulin Molecule" by one of his coworkers, E. O. P. Thompson. It was made possible in part by a considerable sophistication in the art of chromatography, the separation of substances by their relative solubilities or interactions in different solvents (see Stein and Moore, *Sci. Amer.*, March 1951; Offprint 81). These techniques have since been further developed so that the amino acid sequencing of a protein can now be carried out almost entirely by automatic procedures. Insulin was found to consist of two chains of amino acids held together by several cross-links between the chains. These cross-links are covalent disulfide bonds, and the bonds between successive amino acids in the chains are peptide bonds. The sequence of amino acids in a polypeptide chain is called the primary structure of the protein. However, this primary linear structure is subject to further coiling and folding in the so-called "secondary" and "tertiary" structures that constitute the final shape of the protein. The particular amino acids present in any given polypeptide chain determine its secondary and tertiary folding patterns.

Paul Doty discusses the three-dimensional configurations of proteins in his article "Proteins," in which he points out that at that time (that is, 1957) no one knew the complete three-dimensional structure of any protein. However, he does describe the physical technique whereby this might be accomplished: X-ray diffraction. Applying this technique, Linus Pauling found that the polypeptide backbone of proteins was often coiled in a definite helical form stabilized by hydrogen bonds between certain atoms in the backbone. The amino acid "side groups" have relatively little influence in the stabilization of this secondary "alpha-helix" structure (see Pauling, Corey, and Hayward, *Sci. Amer.*, July 1954; Offprint 31). Some proteins such as collagen have been shown to consist of a triple helix of three polypeptide strands. The forces that hold such strands together are generally weaker than the peptide bonds that make up the strands themselves. For this reason, it is possible to change the configurations of polypeptide chains in solution without changing the amino acid sequence. Doty describes the technique of optical rotation and its usefulness for measuring the helical content of a protein and for following reversible transitions from the helix form to other more random configurations.

The next step in working out the details of protein structure was to determine the complete three-dimensional configuration of a protein. This enormous task was first completed for myoglobin by John Kendrew (*Sci. Amer.*, Dec. 1961; Offprint 121). Simultaneously, Kendrew's colleague Max Perutz, mapped the locations of the 10,000 atoms that constitute hemoglobin. In this work the technique of X-ray diffraction was utilized to its utmost. In "The Hemoglobin Molecule," M. F. Perutz describes some of the necessary refinements in technique, in particular the treatment of the "phase problem." With the detailed knowledge of the locations of all of the atoms in a protein, one should be able to figure out how it works. Hemoglobin functions as a carrier of oxygen, and the locations of the "heme" groups that bind the oxygen can be accurately fixed from the X-ray information. The apparent lack of symmetry in the tertiary folding pattern of hemoglobin and other proteins is especially striking: the polypeptide chain is coiled and convoluted about itself in what would appear to be a quite haphazard arrangement, with distant portions of the chain folded so as to be in proximity with one another. However, it is now clear that this folding is not haphazard at all and that the simple specification of the primary sequence of amino acids is adequate to ensure the precise mode of folding in the functional protein. The sensitivity of the X-ray diffraction technique is emphasized further by the fact that it is actually possible to measure a slight change in position of some of the atoms when the oxygen molecule is bound.

Oxygen-carrying is just one of the many specialized functions of proteins. Insulin is a hormone that regulates sugar metabolism in the body. Others, such as collagen, belong to the important class of structural proteins. However, the most intriguing class of proteins are the enzymes. These proteins are highly specific catalysts and they are responsible for most of the metabolic activity in the living cell. As catalysts they do not actually enter into the biochemical reaction as reactants, but rather they affect the *rate* at which such reactions approach an equilibrium condition. Long before the structure of any enzyme was known, the general plan for its operation was understood in principle. For example, it was suspected that an enzyme which catalyzed the cleavage of a particular chemical bond might do so by somehow grasping the substrate molecule, thereby placing a strain upon the bond and reducing the amount of energy required to break it.

This principle can now be illustrated by the enzyme, lysozyme. The detailed tertiary structure of this macromolecule has been worked out with the use of X-ray diffraction, as described in "The Three-dimensional Structure of an Enzyme Molecule" by David C. Phillips. Lysozyme contains regions coiled in the alpha-helix configuration, but it possesses another configuration—the antiparallel pleated sheet stabilized by *interchain* hydrogen bonds.

Phillips also discusses the important question of how a protein is folded into its final configuration. In an outline of the mechanism of synthesis of the polypeptide chain, it is suggested that the protein may in fact fold as it is sequentially synthesized. This would explain why some enzymes lose their activity if unfolded in solution even though they may refold. The correct folding may require that only part of the chain be available as folding begins. Yet other proteins, notably the enzyme ribonuclease whose structure is also known, can be unfolded in solution and then refolded to regain maximum activity of the intact enzyme molecule. Incidentally, ribonuclease is an enzyme that specifically attacks and hydrolyzes one class of the nucleic acids, the ribonucleic acids (RNA).

NUCLEIC ACIDS

The article by F. H. C. Crick entitled "The Structure of the Hereditary Material" was written just a year after his first report with J. D. Watson on their now famous model of DNA structure. This model, which ultimately proved to be correct, was based upon the X-ray diffraction data of Rosalind Franklin and Maurice Wilkins. Once its complementary, double-helical structure had been established, the mode of replication of DNA was immediately evident: the two strands simply unwind as new nucleotides are added to growing daughter strands. It is interesting to note that Crick's 1954 article ends with the prediction that "If we knew the monomers from which nature makes DNA . . . we might be able to carry out very spectacular experiments in the test tube." It was just four years later that Arthur Kornberg and his associates accomplished just that, the synthesis of DNA in a test tube by means of an enzyme, DNA polymerase, purified from the bacterium *Escherichia coli*.

As the primary genetic material, DNA must perform another function just as important as its own replication. This is the process of transcription, by which the nucleotide sequence corresponding to each gene is used as a template for producing "working copies" of the genes. These working copies are molecules called *messenger RNA*. The translation of the genetic message from the nucleotide language of the messenger RNA into the amino acid sequence of a protein requires still another type of RNA called *transfer RNA*. The way in which this is accomplished is described by Robert W. Holley in "The Nucleotide Sequence of a Nucleic Acid." However, the important landmark highlighted by this article is the first determination of the nucleotide sequence in a nucleic acid. This is analogous to the primary sequence determination of a protein. In the nucleotide sequence determination, however, the technical problem was considerably more complex, because of the difficulty in obtaining a homogenous preparation of transfer RNA molecules.

When DNA is isolated from simple cells, such as the bacterium *Escherichia coli*, it is found to exist as a number (generally several hundred) of pieces in the molecular weight range of 30 million. However, the findings of bacterial geneticists had indicated that these pieces of DNA had a unique relationship to each other and that the bacterial chromosome consisted of a continuous sequence of genes arranged in a circle. Were these DNA pieces physically held together by some sort of linker, or were they simply breakage fragments of some still larger DNA molecule? The answer was provided in the elegant experiments of John Cairns and reported in his article on "The Bacterial Chromosome." Using the technique of tritium autoradiography, a considerable amount of ingenuity, and still more patience, Cairns succeeded in isolating intact the entire bacterial chromosome. The finding that it did indeed consist of one DNA molecule nearly 1000 times the length of the cell was a most striking confirmation of the genetic analysis. These autoradiographs also verified that the mode of normal replication consisted in the sequential progress of a single growing point at which the parental DNA strands separate as the new daughter DNA strands are formed. An important topological problem arises from the fact that the DNA must rotate in order for the strands to unwind and come apart. From the known number of turns in the DNA helix and the limiting time that it takes a bacterium to replicate its DNA, it is possible to calculate the unwinding rate of DNA: this gives the unbelievable figure of 15,000 revolutions per minute. In his article, Cairns proposes one possible unwinding mechanism in which a "rotor" continually applies a torque to the molecule at the origin, the point at which replication begins. Another interesting finding about the bacterial chromosome, also predicted from the results of genetic analysis, is that the DNA molecule does indeed exist as a closed circle.

The "semiconservative" mode of normal DNA replication was demonstrated in experiments of Matthew Meselson and Franklin Stahl at Cal Tech in 1957. Since then, a new, nonconservative mode of DNA replication has been discovered. This was demonstrated by the same method that was used to show semiconservative replication and it is described in our article on "The Repair of DNA." As the title implies, this type of DNA synthesis appears to operate for the specific purpose of correcting defects or damaged regions in DNA. Living cells that are deficient in repair are much more sensitive to radiation and other deleterious agents. The existence of this repair system also provides at least one possible explanation for the fact that the information in DNA is redundant. Each strand is a mirror image of the other. Thus, if one strand is damaged, the other strand can be used to retrieve the information needed for its repair.

The last article in this section on "The Duplication of Chromosomes" by J. Herbert Taylor returns us to the realm of microscopically visible structures. The discussion is concerned with the chromosomes of cells much more complex than the bacteria. These chromosomes also carry their genetic information in the form of DNA, but it is very likely that they contain more than one DNA molecule. One human chromosome (the human cell contains 48 chromosomes) contains as much DNA as do 100 bacterial cells. That amount would be equivalent to a DNA molecule about 10 centimeters long. This quantity is sufficient to code for 3,000,000 different proteins. The basic mode of replication of the DNA in these large chromosomes is the same as that in the simpler cells. The experiments of Taylor are consistent with the semiconservative model of replication proposed by Watson and Crick a few years before.

The chromosome in the cell of a multicellular organism is a complex of nucleic acid and protein. In the next section we will consider in detail the simplest sort of protein nucleic acid complex, namely the virus.

FIBRILS OF COLLAGEN, the principal protein of skin, are enlarged 60,000 diameters in this electron micrograph made by Jerome Gross of the Massachusetts General Hospital. The fibrils have been shadowed with a heavy metal to bring out their banded structure.

Giant Molecules in Cells and Tissues

1

FRANCIS O. SCHMITT · September 1957

Two giant molecules, the proteins and the nucleic acids, provide the principal structural and dynamic constituents of the living cell. Each is made up of smaller, simpler molecular units (monomers), which are joined together, or polymerized, in the subtle chemical processes which taken together express the cell's identity as a living system. In this article it will be seen that the process of polymerization, by which proteins and nucleic acids are synthesized, provides a model for understanding how they in turn organize themselves into the higher structures of cells and tissues. This spontaneous process apparently depends upon specific properties built into these molecules. Proteins and nucleic acids, in short, may be regarded as the monomers of the living cell.

These giant monomers may be polymerized in the cell where they are made, or they may be transported in inactive form to another part of the organism. There they may be activated and polymerized as the occasion demands. For example, the soluble protein fibrinogen is always present in the blood, but it is polymerized into the insoluble fibrin of a blood clot only when bleeding must be stopped.

The function of a natural high polymer is of course reflected in its properties. The protein keratin has great tensile strength; it forms the principal structure of hair, horn and fingernail. The protein collagen serves a similar purpose in skin and tendon. Elastin is a springy protein; it occurs in ligaments and the elastic fibers of connective tissue.

These three types of polymer are more or less passive; others respond actively to changes in their chemical environment. Under the influence of such changes the protein of muscle contracts. Contraction is a property not only of muscle but also of many other biological structures, from the rapidly oscillating tail of the sperm cell to the flowing pseudopods of the amoeba. Indeed, contractility is an essential feature of all living cells, and probably employs a common molecular mechanism.

The threadlike chromosomes of the cell nucleus, made up of protein and nucleic acid, are polymers with another function: the maintenance of the specific linear sequence of the genes. We should also reserve a category for natural high polymers whose purpose is not known. A good example is the fibrous protein of nerve cells. These so-called neurofibrils are very long and less than a millionth of an inch thick. They run through the core of all nerve fibers; in the light microscope they are seen as bundles of coagulated filaments. Their presence in all nerve tissue indicates that they must serve some function, but to date no one has been able to show what it might be. Considerable effort is currently being made to isolate this protein (from the giant nerve fibers of the squid) and to determine its composition and function.

The idea that biological fibers are composed of fibrous molecules is not new. In the 19th century microscopists observed that such fibers tended to fray into finer fibers, and assumed that the hierarchy continued downward in scale. At the same time natural fibers were analyzed with polarized light, and the analysis indicated that their molecules were organized in regular structures. In

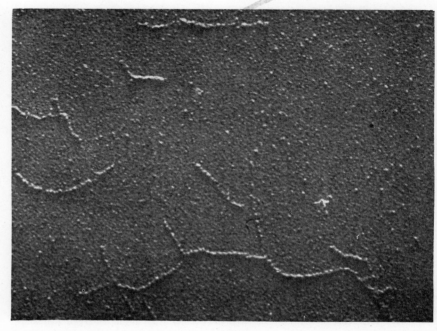

MOLECULES OF COLLAGEN, enlarged 100,000 diameters, appear as long, thin threads in this electron micrograph made by Cecil E. Hall of the Massachusetts Institute of Technology.

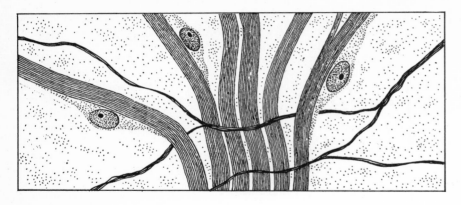

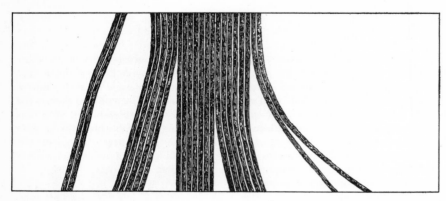

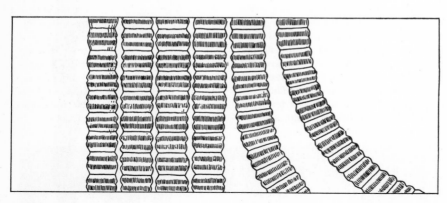

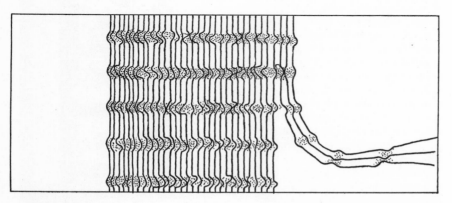

HIERARCHY OF FIBERS is outlined in these drawings of collagen as seen at four different magnifications. At top are collagen fibers in a bit of connective tissue as they appear under the light microscope. In a light microscope of higher power a single frayed collagen fiber is seen to consist of many fibrils (*second drawing from top*). Enlarged still more with an electron microscope, the same fibrils show cross-bands and other details (*third drawing from top*). X-ray diffraction methods permit even finer analyses revealing that a single fibril is made up of parallel chains of collagen molecules (*fourth drawing*).

the 1920s and 1930s polarization analysis showed that the cellular fibers were very thin. Today we know that they are the molecules themselves; they can actually be visualized in the electron microscope. Used in conjunction with X-ray diffraction and other older methods, this instrument has provided significant information on the molecular organization of structures in living cells.

When a thin section of a muscle cell is observed in the electron microscope, it is resolved into finer fibers called myofibrils, each of which consists of many thin filaments. A striking feature of the fibrils is the striations that occur regularly along their length. These cross-bands are brought out by staining the muscle tissue with compounds of heavy metals, which scatter electrons more than do the lighter elements of which the tissue is composed. Thus the bands are regions that combine well with the stains. When the fibrils are shadowed with metal so that they can be seen in relief, adjacent bands have slightly different thicknesses and hence are more visible.

The band pattern provides a kind of molecular fingerprint by which the protein can be identified in the electron microscope and which provides important clues to how giant molecules are organized into fibers. Let us consider in detail collagen, the protein of skin and tendon. Collagen, which is also present in bone, teeth and loose connective tissue, represents as much as a third of all the protein in an animal. In compact form such as tendon it will resist a pull of as much as 100,000 pounds per square inch, roughly the strength of steel wire. Intensively studied by electron microscopists, X-ray crystallographers and chemists, it is now one of the best-known fibrous proteins.

If we tease a bit of tendon or skin with fine needles, or break it up in a blendor, its fibers are split into fibrils. We can see under the light microscope that the fibrils have a fairly uniform width: usually from 200 to 1,000 Angstrom units (an Angstrom unit is a hundred millionth of a centimeter). The fibrils are composed of still finer strands: protofibrils. These are thought to consist of fibrous molecules strung end to end.

When undried native collagen fibrils are examined in the electron microscope, they show cross-bands which repeat at intervals of about 700 Angstroms. Richard S. Bear of the Massachusetts Institute of Technology has offered the following explanation for this banding. The molecular chain of collagen consists of amino acid units in specific sequence. Thus the characteristic side chains of the amino acids also occur in regular sequence. When protofibrils lie side by side, certain side chains, especially the short ones, fit together in regions of relative order. The longer side chains, on the other hand, do not fit well, and give rise to less orderly regions. Bear concluded that the regions of relative disorder correspond to bands (the regions which are slightly thicker and take on more stain); the regions of relative order, to the space between bands (interbands). The banding of collagen would thus reflect the sequence of amino acid units along the molecular chains.

Now when a collagenous tissue, such as the tendon of a rat's tail, is placed in dilute acid, it swells up and eventually dissolves; the resulting solution is as clear as water but relatively viscous. The solution can then be spun in an ultracentrifuge to remove the larger aggregates of collagen. The molecules in the remaining solution were measured by Paul Doty of Harvard University, using the methods of the physical chemist. He determined that they are 14 Angstroms wide and 2,900 Angstroms long. The molecules were visualized directly by Cecil E. Hall of M.I.T., who found that their dimensions were roughly the same [see illustration on page 17].

The dispersed molecules can be reassembled into fibrils by changing the character of the solution. The crossbands of the artificial fibrils can then be studied in the electron microscope. Depending on the nature of the treatment, the band patterns show considerable variation. First, the bands may be entirely absent. Second, the principal bands may repeat about every 700 Angstroms, as in the native fibril. Third, the bands may repeat in about a third of this distance. Fourth, they may repeat about every 2,800 Angstroms, a distance four times that of the normal spacing. This "long spacing" occurs in two forms: "fibrous" and "segment" [see illustrations on pages 20 and 21].

Reflecting on these band patterns, Jerome Gross of the Massachusetts General Hospital and John H. Highberger of the United Shoe Machinery Corporation, working in collaboration with the author, deduced that they represent different ways in which the collagen molecules can come together under different conditions. When the molecules are lined up side by side with their ends "in register," their principal bands will re-peat about every 2,800 Angstroms. In other words, the distance between the principal bands is about the same as the length of the molecule. If adjacent molecules are in register and pointing in the same direction, the pattern will be of the segment long-spacing type. If adjacent molecules are in register but pointing in opposite directions, the pattern will be fibrous long-spaced. If the adjacent molecules are pointing in the same direction, but are regularly staggered by about a fourth of their length, they will form bands with the native spacing of 700 Angstroms. If the ends of neighboring molecules have no orderly arrangement, no bands at all are formed.

These observations will explain why it seems likely that the organization of protoplasm depends on highly specific properties built into its giant monomers. The collagen molecule consists of three chains of amino acid units wound in a helix around a common axis. Side chains extending from this molecule interact with similarly placed side chains on adjacent collagen molecules. The molecules will "recognize" each other even if much foreign material is present.

This interaction is significantly influenced by the chemical environment of the molecules. Thus an artificial fibril of collagen with its band pattern repeating every 2,800 Angstroms cannot be made in a solution of pure collagen. A second constituent, such as adenosine triphosphate (ATP), must be added. Presumably the ATP, by combining with certain side chains of the collagen molecule, changes the pattern of the side chains still available for interaction with neighboring molecules.

The cross-bands of various kinds of muscle-protein also have been analyzed, though not in such detail as those of collagen. When the muscle that holds shut the shell of a clam is minced in a dilute salt solution, it breaks up into fibrils of the protein paramyosin. In the electron microscope the stained fibrils have a band pattern which repeats about every 145 Angstroms. By means of X-ray diffraction Bear has demonstrated that a unit five times this length also repeats along the fibrils.

Paramyosin fibrils can be dissolved and reconstituted so that the pattern of their bands repeats at the length of the paramyosin molecule. The Australian electron microscopist Alan J. Hodge, working at M.I.T., has shown that this distance is about twice the X-ray period, or about 1,500 Angstroms. It would be interesting to know the connection be-tween the structure of the paramyosin fibril and the long-lasting contraction of the clam's muscle.

A fast muscle of the sort that causes the blink of an eyelid has a rather different construction. The fibrils consist of parallel filaments made up of at least two kinds of protein: actin and myosin. They are segmented into alternating regions, in one of which the filaments are more highly organized than in the other. Throughout both regions a finer band pattern repeats about every 400 Angstroms. The bands of isolated actin fibrils have a similar length, as do those of light meromyosin (a derivative of myosin). How this length is related to the repeating pattern of the fibril and its constituent protein molecules is not yet clear.

In contractile structures other than muscle the filaments may be specialized. The hairlike cilia of microorganisms and higher animals, for example, consist of two fine filaments surrounded by nine thicker filaments or pairs of filaments,

SIDE CHAINS of collagen molecules lying side by side may be long or short. The long side chains sometimes end in an electrically charged group (+ or −). The short side chains tend to fit together in an orderly manner; the long, to interact in a disorderly manner. These disordered regions correspond to the bands in electron micrographs.

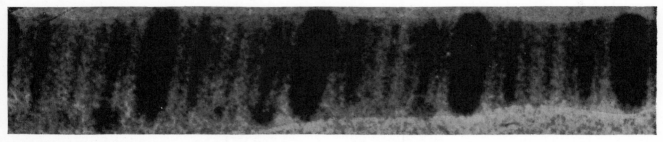

COLLAGEN RECONSTITUTED in a solution containing certain organic substances has a band pattern which repeats at intervals of about 2,800 Angstroms. The electron micrograph at left, made by Gross, shows reconstituted fibrils with "fibrous long-spacing";

RECONSTITUTED PARAMYOSIN, *i.e.*, paramyosin dissolved in salt solution and then made to reassemble, is enlarged 67,000 diameters in an electron micrograph by J. W. Jacques of M.I.T. Here the band pattern repeats every 1,600 to 1,800 Angstrom units.

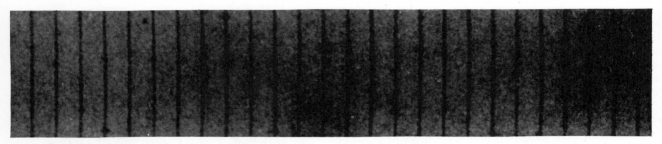

LIGHT MEROMYOSIN, derived from the muscle protein myosin, is enlarged 160,000 diameters in an electron micrograph furnished by Andrew G. Szent-Gyorgyi of the Marine Biological Laboratory in Woods Hole, Mass. The pattern repeats every 420 Angstroms.

NATIVE COLLAGEN FIBRIL has a band pattern which repeats at intervals of about 640 Angstroms. Collagen fibrils dissolved in acid and reconstituted in salt solution may also have this pattern. The electron micrograph enlarges the fibril 170,000 diameters.

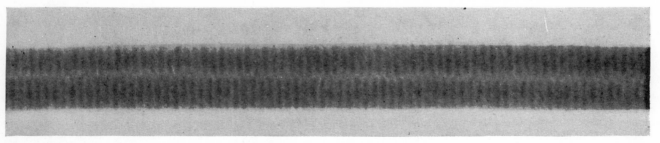

FIBRIL OF PARAMYOSIN, a protein from the muscle of a clam, is enlarged 160,000 diameters in this electron micrograph by Hall. The pattern of bands visible in the fibril repeats every 145 Angstrom units, roughly a 10th the length of the paramyosin molecule.

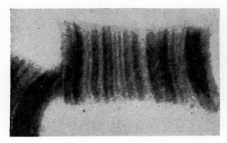

the micrograph at right, made by Alan J. Hodge at M.I.T., "segment long-spacing."

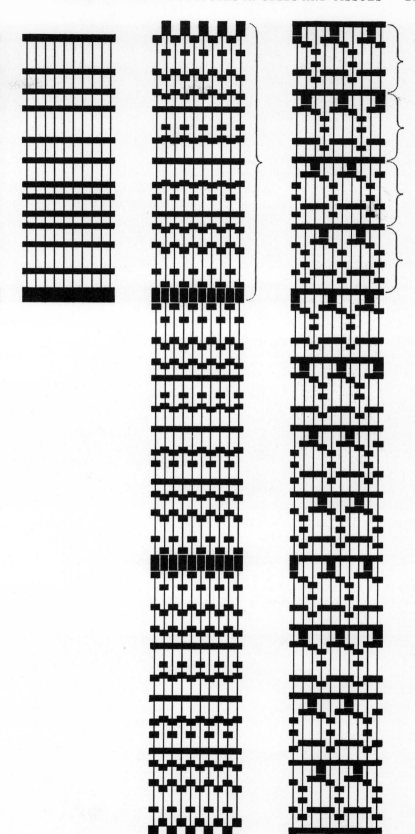

the whole encased in a cylindrical sheath. It is not yet known whether such filaments are composed, like those of muscle, of several types of protein.

What makes contractile polymers contract? We can only sketch the process in rough outline. In the case of muscle there must be a protein which forms filaments extending the length of the muscle. This protein transmits tension to the connective-tissue sheath of the muscle and thus to the tendon; it may be actin or a complex of actin and other proteins. In close proximity to these filaments is a second set of filaments, presumably consisting primarily of myosin. The Nobel laureate Albert Szent-Gyorgyi and his school have shown that muscular contraction and relaxation involve a quick change in the relationship between these two proteins. The relationship is influenced by ions of potassium, sodium, calcium and magnesium, and by the energy-rich substance ATP We must discover what this relationship is if we are to understand what makes fibrous systems contract. According to some workers, contraction occurs when one set of filaments slides past the other. It is believed by others that during contraction a filament of one kind coils in a helix around a filament of the other.

Whatever the mechanism, it seems likely that it is governed by complementary patterns or chemical groups built into both kinds of protein molecule. This complementarity is expressed or suppressed by the presence or absence of substances such as ATP. The function of ATP in turn is regulated by the enzyme adenosine triphosphatase (ATPase), which is an integral part of the myosin filament. This enzyme is localized in such a way that it can act on ATP only at one specific moment during the cycle of contraction and relaxation.

Another example of this subtle interaction between specific natural polymers and their chemical environment is the fibrinogen-fibrin system of blood clot-

BAND PATTERNS of collagen are explained by means of a schematic collagen molecule (*upper left*) marked at regions where it interacts with other collagen molecules. If adjacent molecules point in the same direction and are in register (*second from left*), their pattern is "segment long-spaced." If adjacent molecules point in opposite directions and are in register (*third from left*), the pattern is "fibrous long-spaced." If they point in the same direction but are regularly staggered (*fourth*), the pattern repeats at a shorter interval.

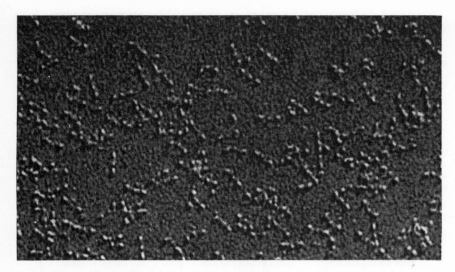

MOLECULES OF FIBRINOGEN are enlarged 130,000 diameters in this electron micrograph by Hall. Each of the molecules consists of three tiny spheres joined by a fine thread.

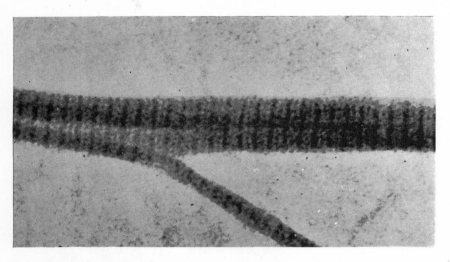

FIBRIL OF FIBRIN, the insoluble protein made up of fibrinogen, is enlarged 180,000 diameters in this electron micrograph by Hall. Its band pattern repeats every 235 Angstroms.

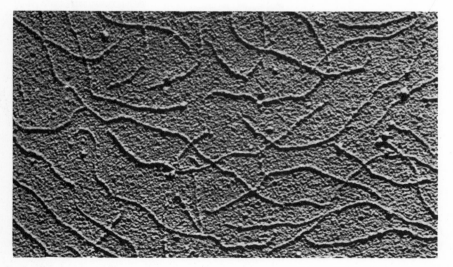

NERVE FILAMENTS are enlarged 26,000 diameters in this electron micrograph by Myles Maxfield of M.I.T. Filaments of this kind are found in the central core of all nerve fibers.

ting. When measured in solution, fibrinogen molecules are about 40 Angstroms in diameter and 550 Angstroms long. In the electron microscope they are about 400 Angstroms long and consist of three spheres, each 30 to 40 Angstroms in diameter, joined by a delicate thread [*see illustration at left*].

When blood clots, a peptide segment is split out of the fibrinogen molecules. The molecules are thus activated and combine to form a so-called intermediate polymer, the length of which is 4,000 to 5,000 Angstroms. The intermediate polymers, which have been observed in the electron microscope by B. M. Siegel of Cornell University, now come together to form fibrils of the insoluble protein fibrin. These fibrils prevent bleeding by clogging the broken blood vessels. In the electron microscope the fibrils of fibrin have a band pattern which repeats every 235 Angstroms. This distance is not clearly related to the length of the fibrinogen molecule. John D. Ferry of the University of Wisconsin has suggested that the bands may be related to activated fibrinogen molecules which are lined up side by side but staggered.

The mechanism by which soluble fibrinogen is activated and converted into the intermediate polymer is extremely complicated. Like the contraction of muscle, it involves not only the interacting protein molecules but also ions, enzymes and other substances. Some of these facilitate the reaction; others inhibit it. Only by such delicate feed-back mechanisms can the organism maintain high-polymer systems which go into action when they are needed but remain inactive when they are not.

We now come to the most remarkable high-polymer system of all. This is the system that enables the organism to reproduce itself: the nucleic acid and protein of the chromosomes.

The structure of chromosomes has been studied intensively and fruitfully under the light microscope, but reliable information about their molecular organization is scanty. In the electron microscope chromosomes of many kinds appear to have the same basic structure: a relatively dense, smooth-edged filament from 100 to 200 Angstroms wide. On this scale no bands or discontinuities are apparent.

This lack of bands or discontinuities does not mean that the chromosome threads are not made up of long molecules which specifically interact with one another. It is due to the fact that nucleic acid molecules, unlike protein molecules, have no long side chains which, by interacting with the side chains of neighboring molecules, can form bands. It is well known, however, that under the light microscope the giant chromosomes in the salivary gland of the fruit fly have pronounced bands. The darker bands represent regions in which the ratio of DNA to protein is high; the lighter bands, regions in which the ratio is low. From this it is obvious that the position of the DNA and protein molecules is precisely determined. What is perhaps more to the point, geneticists have related the hereditary traits of the fruit fly and other insects to specific segments of their chromosomes.

I should like to suggest that the lessons learned from the organization of a protein such as collagen can be applied profitably to the study of the chromosome and the gene. Let us for the moment neglect the internal structure of DNA and its protein partners in the chromosome, and merely make some reasonable deductions from other facts.

First, DNA can be dissolved out of the nucleus of the cell by salt solution. This is a very weak chemical treatment, yet it effectively breaks the bonds that link DNA molecules to protein molecules and to one another. The fact that these bonds can be broken so easily makes it seem rather unlikely that, in its replication and in exerting its biochemical effects, the chromosome is an indivisible unit with all its macromolecules in an unchanging array.

An alternative is that the genetic specificity resides ultimately in the individual giant molecules of the chromosomes and determines the manner in which they interact. Since DNA molecules preserve their chemical pattern from one generation to the next, they must be capable of precise replication. If they can perform such a difficult feat, they may also be capable of highly specific interactions with other kinds of DNA molecules and with protein molecules. Thus they might spontaneously aggregate into the specific patterns characteristic of native chromosomes.

In this picture the chromosome is an aggregation of DNA and protein molecules which is stable in a particular chemical environment in the nucleus of the cell. A change in this immediate environment may alter not only the structural relationship of the molecules but also their biochemical and genetic activity. These possibilities are now being investigated in our laboratory at M.I.T. by applying the techniques used in the study of collagen to DNA, to the protein of chromosomes and to the giant banded chromosomes of fruit flies.

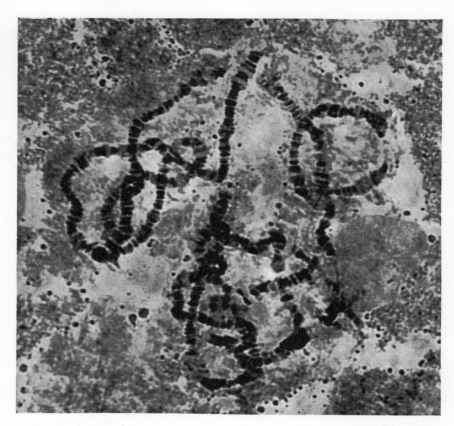

GIANT CHROMOSOMES of the fruit fly *Drosophila* are enlarged 500 diameters in this light-microscope photograph made by Herman W. Lewis of M.I.T. Cross-bands are visible.

MOLECULES OF DNA are enlarged 100,000 diameters in this electron micrograph made by Hall. The material for the micrograph was extracted from the sperm cells of the salmon.

2 | The Insulin Molecule

E. O. P. THOMPSON · May 1955

Proteins, the keystone of life, are the most complex substances known to man, and their chemistry is one of the great challenges in modern science. For more than a century chemists and biochemists have labored to try to learn their composition and solve their labyrinthine structure [see "Proteins," by Joseph S. Fruton; SCIENTIFIC AMERICAN Offprint 10]. In the history of protein chemistry the year 1954 will go down as a landmark, for last year a group of investigators finally succeeded in achieving the first complete description of the structure of a protein molecule. The protein is insulin, the pancreatic hormone which governs sugar metabolism in the body.

Having learned the architecture of the insulin molecule, biochemists can now go on to attempt to synthesize it and to investigate the secret of the chemical activity of this vital hormone, so important in the treatment of diabetes. Furthermore, the success with insulin has paved the way toward unraveling the structure of other proteins with the same techniques, and work on some of them has already begun.

The insulin achievement was due largely to the efforts of the English biochemist Frederick Sanger and a small group of workers at Cambridge University. Sanger had spent 10 years of intensive study on this single molecule. When he commenced his investigation of protein structure in 1944, he chose insulin for several reasons. Firstly, it was one of the very few proteins available in reasonably pure form. Secondly, chemists had worked out a good estimate of its atomic composition (its relative numbers of carbon, hydrogen, nitrogen, oxygen and sulfur atoms). Thirdly, it appeared that the key to insulin's activity as a hormone lay in its

structure, for it contained no special components that might explain its specific behavior.

Insulin is one of the smallest proteins. Yet its formula is sufficiently formidable. The molecule of beef insulin (from cattle) is made up of 777 atoms, in the proportions 254 carbon, 377 hydrogen, 65 nitrogen, 75 oxygen and 6 sulfur. Certain general features of the organization of a protein molecule have been known for a long time, thanks to the pioneering work of the German chemist Emil Fischer and others. The atoms form building units called amino acids, which in turn are strung together in long chains to compose the molecule. Of the 24 amino acids, 17 are present in insulin. The total number of amino acid units in the molecule is 51.

Sanger's task was not only to discover the over-all chain configuration of the insulin molecule but also to learn the sequence of all the amino acids in the chains. The sequence is crucial: a change in the order of amino acids

changes the nature of the protein. The number of possible arrangements of the amino acids of course is almost infinite. One can get some notion of the complexity of the protein puzzle by remembering that the entire English language is derived from just 26 letters (two more than the number of amino acids) combined in various numbers and sequences.

Sanger followed the time-honored method used by chemists to investigate large molecules: namely, breaking them down into fragments and then attempting to put the pieces of the puzzle together. A complete breakdown into the amino acid units themselves makes it possible to identify and measure these components. But this gives no clue to how the units are combined and arranged. To investigate the structure a protein chemist shatters the molecule less violently and then examines these larger fragments, consisting of combinations of two, three or more amino acids. The procedure is somewhat like dropping a pile of plates on the floor. The

COMPLETE MOLECULE of insulin is depicted in this structural formula. Each amino acid in the molecule is represented by an abbreviation rather than its complete atomic structure. The key to these abbreviations is in the chart on page 27. The molecule consists

first plate may break into 10 pieces; the second plate may also give 10 pieces but with fractures at different places; the next plate may break into only eight fragments, and so on. Since the sample of protein contains billions of molecules, the experiment amounts to dropping billions of plates. The chemist then pores through this awesome debris for recognizable pieces and other pieces that overlap the breaks to show how the broken sections may be combined.

An amino acid consists of an amino group (NH_3^+), a carboxyl group (COO^-) and a side chain attached to a carbon atom. All amino acids have the amino and carboxyl groups and differ only in their side chains. In a protein molecule they are linked by combination of the carboxyl group of one unit with the amino group of the next. In the process of combination two hydrogen atoms and an oxygen atom drop out in the form of a water molecule and the link becomes CO–NH. This linkage is called the peptide bond. Because of loss of the water molecule, the units linked in the chain are called amino acid "residues." A group of linked amino acids is known as a peptide: two units form a dipeptide, three a tripeptide and so on.

When a peptide or protein is hydrolyzed—treated chemically so that the elements of water are introduced at the peptide bonds—it breaks down into amino acids. The treatment consists in heating the peptide with acids or alkalis. To break every peptide bond and reduce a protein to its amino acids it must be heated for 24 hours or more. Less prolonged or drastic treatment, known as partial hydrolysis, yields a mixture of amino acids, peptides and some unbroken protein molecules. This is the plate-breaking process by which the de-

tailed structure of a protein is investigated.

One of the key inventions that enabled Sanger to solve the jigsaw puzzle was a method of labeling the end amino acid in a peptide. Consider a protein fragment, a peptide, which is composed of three amino acids. On hydrolysis it is found to consist of amino acids A, B and C. The question is: What was their sequence in the peptide? The first member of the three-part chain must have had a free (uncombined) amino (NH_3) group. Sanger succeeded in finding a chemical marker which could be attached to this end of the chain and would stay attached to the amino group after the peptide was hydrolyzed. The labeling material is known as DNP (for dinitrophenyl group). It gives the amino acid to which it is attached a distinctive yellow color. The analysis of the tripeptide sequence proceeds as follows. The tripeptide is treated with the labeling material and is then broken down into its three amino acids. The amino acid which occupied the end position, say B, is now identified by its yellow color. The process is repeated with a second sample of the tripeptide, but this time it is only partly hydrolyzed, so that two amino acids remain as a dipeptide derivative colored yellow. If B is partnered with, say, A in this fragment, one knows that the sequence must be BA, and the order in the original tripeptide therefore was BAC.

Another tool that played an indispensable part in the solution of the insulin jigsaw puzzle was the partition chromatography method for separating amino acids and peptides, invented by the British chemists A. J. P. Martin and R. L. M. Synge [see "Chromatography," by William H. Stein and Stanford Moore; SCIENTIFIC AMERICAN Offprint 81]. Ob-

viously Sanger's method of analysis required separation and identification of extremely small amounts of material. With paper chromatography, which isolates peptides or amino acids in spots on a piece of filter paper, it is possible to analyze a mixture of as little as a millionth of a gram of material with considerable accuracy in a matter of days. As many as 40 different peptides can be separated on a single sheet.

With the knowledge that the insulin molecule was made up of 51 amino acid units, Sanger began his attack on its structure by investigating whether the units were strung in a single long chain or formed more than one chain. Among the components of insulin were three molecules of the amino acid cystine. The cystine molecule is unusual in that it has an amino and a carboxyl group at each end [see its formula in table on page 27]. Since such a molecule could crosslink chains, its presence in insulin suggested that the protein might consist of more than one chain. Sanger succeeded in proving that there were indeed two chains, which he was able to separate intact by splitting the sulfur links in the cystine molecule. Using the DNP labeling technique, he also showed that one chain began with the amino acid glycine and the other with phenylalanine.

Sanger proceeded to break each chain into fragments and study the pieces —especially overlaps which would permit him to build up a sequence. Concentrating on the beginning of the glycine chain, Sanger labeled the glycine with DNP and examined the peptide fragments produced by partial hydrolysis. In the debris of the broken glycine chains he found these sequences attached to the labeled glycine molecules: glycine-isoleucine;   glycine-isoleucine-

of 51 amino acid units in two chains. One chain (top) has 21 amino acid units; it is called the glycyl chain because it begins with glycine (Gly). The other chain (bottom) has 30 amino acid units; it is called the phenylalanyl chain because it begins with phenylalanine (Phe). The chains are joined by sulfur atoms (S-S). The dotted lines indicate the fragments which located the bridges.

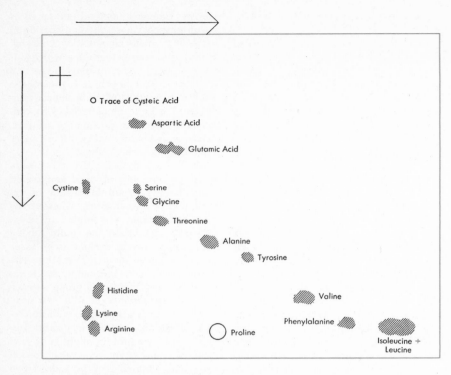

PAPER CHROMATOGRAPHY separates the 17 amino acids of insulin. In the chromatogram represented by this diagram insulin was broken down by hydrolysis and a sample of the mixture placed at the upper left on the sheet of paper. The sheet was hung from a trough filled with solvent which carried each amino acid a characteristic distance down the paper. The sheet was then turned 90 degrees and the process repeated. The amino acids, with the exception of proline, appear as purple spots when sprayed with ninhydrin.

valine; glycine-isoleucine-valine–glutamic acid; glycine-isoleucine-valine–glutamic acid–glutamic acid. Thus it was evident that the first five amino acids in the glycine chain were glycine, isoleucine, valine and two glutamic acids. Similar experiments on the phenylalanine chain established the first four amino acids in that sequence: phenylalanine, valine, aspartic acid and glutamic acid.

Sanger and a colleague, Hans Tuppy, then undertook the immense task of analyzing the structure of the entire phenylalanine chain. It meant breaking down the chain by partial hydrolysis, separating and identifying the many fragments and then attempting to put the pieces of the puzzle together in proper order. The chain, made up of 30 amino acids, was by far the most complex polypeptide on which such an analysis had ever been attempted.

The bewildering mixture of products from partial breakdown of the chain—amino acids, dipeptides, tripeptides, tetrapeptides and so on—was much too complicated to be sorted out solely by chromatography. Sanger and Tuppy first employed other separation methods (electrophoresis and adsorption on charcoal and ion-exchange resins) which divided the peptide fragments into groups. Then they analyzed these simpler mixtures by paper chromatography. They succeeded in isolating from the fractured chain 22 dipeptides, 14 tripeptides and 12 longer fragments [see chart on pages 28 and 29]. Although these were obtained only in microscopic amounts, they were identified by special techniques and the sequences of their amino acids were determined.

These were the jigsaw pieces that had to be reassembled. Just as in a jigsaw puzzle there are key pieces around which the picture grows, so in this case there were some key pieces as starting points. For instance, the chain was known to contain just one aspartic acid. Six peptides with this amino acid were found in the debris from partial breakdown of the chain [see chart]. The aspartic acid was attached to from one to four other amino acids in these pieces. Their sequences showed that in the original make-up of the chain the order must have been phenylalanine-valine–aspartic acid–glutamic acid–histidine.

Other sequences were pieced together in a similar way until five long sections of the chain were reconstructed. But this

still left several gaps in the chain. Sanger and Tuppy now resorted to another method to find the missing links. They split the phenylalanine chain with enzymes instead of by acid hydrolysis. The enzyme splitting process yields longer fragments, and it leaves intact certain bonds that are sensitive to breakage by acid treatment. Thus the investigators obtained long chain fragments which bridged the gaps and revealed the missing links.

After about a year of intensive work Sanger and Tuppy were able to assemble the pieces and describe the structure of insulin's phenylalanine chain. Sanger then turned to the glycine chain and spent another year working out its structure, with the assistance of the author of this article. The glycine chain is shorter (21 amino acids) but it provided fewer clues: there were fewer key pieces that occurred only once, and two amino acids (glutamic acid and cystine) cropped up in so many of the fragments that it was difficult to place them unequivocally in the sequence.

One detail that remained to be decided before the structure could be completed was the actual composition of two amino acids in the chain. Certain amino acids may occur in two forms: e.g., glutamic acid and glutamine. Glutamic acid has two carboxyl (COO^-) groups, whereas glutamine has an amide ($CONH_2$) group in the place of one of the carboxyls [see opposite page]. The difference gives them completely different properties in the protein. Similarly there are aspartic acid and asparagine. Now acid hydrolysis changes glutamine to glutamic acid and asparagine to aspartic acid. Consequently after acid hydrolysis of a protein one cannot tell which form these amino acids had in the original chain. The question was resolved by indirect investigations, one of which involved comparing the products obtained when the same peptide was broken down by acid hydrolysis and by enzymes which do not destroy the amide groups.

By the end of 1952 the two chains were completely assembled. There remained only the problem of determining how the two chains were linked together to form the insulin molecule. But this was easier said than done. As so often happens, what looked simple in theory had complications in practice.

The bridges between the chains, as we have noted, must be cystine, because this amino acid has symmetrical bonds at both ends. The fact that insulin

FORMULA	NAME	ABBREVIATION	PHENYLALANYL	GLYCYL
$CH_2(NH_3{}^+) \cdot COO^-$	Glycine	Gly	3	1
CH_3——$CH(NH_3 \quad \cdot COO^-$	Alanine	Ala	2	1
CH_2OH——$CH(NH_3{}^+) \cdot COO^-$	Serine	Ser	1	2
$CH_3 \cdot CHOH$——$CH(NH_3{}^+) \cdot COO^-$	Threonine	Thr	1	0
$\begin{matrix}CH_3 \\ \quad \searrow CH\text{——}CH(NH_3{}^+) \cdot COO^- \\ CH_3\end{matrix}$	Valine	Val	3	2
$\begin{matrix}CH_3 \\ \quad \searrow CH \cdot CH_2\text{——}CH(NH_3{}^+) \cdot COO^- \\ CH_3\end{matrix}$	Leucine	Leu	4	2
$\begin{matrix}CH_3 \cdot CH_2 \\ \qquad\qquad \searrow CH\text{——}CH(NH_3{}^+) \cdot COO^- \\ CH_3\end{matrix}$	Isoleucine	Ileu	0	1
$\begin{matrix}CH_2\text{—}CH_2 \\ | \qquad | \\ CH_2 \quad CH\text{—}COO^- \\ \searrow \, \diagup \\ NH^+\end{matrix}$	Proline	Pro	1	0
$\begin{matrix}CH=CH \\ \diagup \qquad\qquad \searrow \\ CH \qquad\qquad\qquad C \cdot CH_2\text{—}CH(NH_3{}^+) \cdot COO^- \\ \diagdown \qquad\qquad \diagup \\ CH\text{—}CH\end{matrix}$	Phenylalanine	Phe	3	0
$\begin{matrix}CH=CH \\ \diagup \qquad\qquad \searrow \\ HO\text{—}C \qquad\qquad\qquad C \cdot CH_2\text{—}CH(NH_3{}^+) \cdot COO^- \\ \diagdown \qquad\qquad \diagup \\ CH\text{—}CH\end{matrix}$	Tyrosine	Tyr	2	2
$NH_2CO \cdot CH_2\text{—}CH(NH_3{}^+) \cdot COO^-$	Asparagine	Asp (NH$_2$)	1	2
$COOH \cdot CH_2 \cdot CH_2\text{—}CH(NH_3{}^+) \cdot COO^-$	Glutamic Acid	Glu	2	2
$NH_2 \cdot CO \cdot CH_2 \cdot CH_2\text{—}CH(NH_3{}^+) \cdot COO^-$	Glutamine	Glu (NH$_2$)	1	2
$\begin{matrix}NH_2\text{—}C\text{—}NH \cdot CH_2 \cdot CH_2 \cdot CH_2\text{—}CH(NH_3{}^+) \cdot COO^- \\ \| \\ NH\end{matrix}$	Arginine	Arg	1	0
$\begin{matrix}CH=C \cdot CH_2\text{—}CH(NH_3{}^+) \cdot COO^- \\ | \qquad | \\ NH \quad N \\ \diagdown \, \| \\ CH\end{matrix}$	Histidine	His	2	0
$CH_2NH_2 \cdot CH_2 \cdot CH_2 \cdot CH_2\text{—}CH(NH_3{}^+) \cdot COO^-$	Lysine	Lys	1	0
$\begin{matrix}COO^- \qquad\qquad\qquad\qquad\qquad COO^- \\ \diagdown CH\text{—}CH_2\text{—}S\text{—}S\text{—}CH_2\text{—}CH \diagup \\ NH_3{}^+ \qquad\qquad\qquad\qquad\qquad NH_3{}^+\end{matrix}$	Cystine	$\begin{matrix}CyS \\ | \\ CyS\end{matrix}$	2	4
			30	21

AMINO ACIDS of insulin are listed in this chart. Their chemical formulas are at the left. The dots in the formulas represent chemical bonds other than those suggested by the atoms adjacent to each other. The number of amino acid units of each kind found in the phenylalanyl chain are listed in the fourth column of the chart. The fifth column comprises a similar listing for the glycyl chain.

PEPTIDES FROM ACID HYDROLYZATES	Phe · **Val**			**Glu** · His			CySO₃H	**Gly**			His · Leu			Glu · **Ala**		

PEPTIDES FROM ACID HYDROLYZATES

Phe · **Val**   **Glu** · His   CySO₃H · **Gly**   His · Leu   Glu · **Ala**

Val · Asp   His · **Leu**   Leu · **Val**   **Ala** · Leu

Asp · **Glu**   Leu · CySO₃H   Ser · **His**   Val · Glu

Phe · **Val** · Asp   Leu · CySO₃H · **Gly**   Val · Glu · Ala   Tyr

Glu · His · **Leu**   Ser · **His** · Leu

Val · Asp · **Glu**   Leu · **Val** · Glu

His · **Leu** · CySO₃H   Ala · Leu · Tyr

Phe · **Val** · Asp · **Glu**   Ser · **His** · Leu · Val   Tyr

His · **Leu** · CySO₃H · **Gly**   Leu · **Val** · Glu · **Ala**

Phe · **Val** · Asp · **Glu** · His   Ser · **His** · Leu · **Val** · Glu

Glu · His · **Leu** · CySO₃H   **His** · Leu · **Val** · Glu

Ser · **His** · Leu · **Val** · Glu · **Ala**

SEQUENCES DEDUCED FROM THE ABOVE PEPTIDES

Phe · **Val** · Asp · **Glu** · His · **Leu** · CySO₃H · **Gly**   Tyr

Ser · **His** · Leu · **Val** · Glu · **Ala**

PEPTIDES FROM PEPSIN HYDROLYZATE

Phe · **Val** · Asp · **Glu** · His · **Leu** · CySO₃H · **Gly** · Ser · **His** · Leu
                  | |
                 NH₂   NH₂

                                                  Val · Glu · Ala · Leu

His · **Leu** · CySO₃H · **Gly** · Ser · **His** · Leu

PEPTIDES FROM CHYMOTRYPSIN HYDROLYZATE

Phe · **Val** · Asp · **Glu** · His · **Leu** · CySO₃H · **Gly** · Ser · **His** · Leu · **Val** · Glu · **Ala** · Leu · Tyr
                  | |
                 NH₂   NH₂

PEPTIDES FROM TRYPSIN HYDROLYZATE

STRUCTURE OF PHENYLALANYL CHAIN OF OXIDIZED INSULIN

Phe · **Val** · Asp · **Glu** · His · **Leu** · CySO₃H · **Gly** · Ser · **His** · Leu · **Val** · Glu · **Ala** · Leu · **Tyr**
                  | |
                 NH₂   NH₂

- -

STRUCTURE OF GLYCYL CHAIN OF OXIDIZED INSULIN

Gly · Ileu · Val · Glu · Glu · CySO₃H · CySO₃H · Ala · Ser · Val · CySO₃H · Ser · Leu · Tyr ·
                              |
                             NH₂

SEQUENCE OF AMINO ACIDS in the phenylalanyl chain was deduced from fragments of the chain. The entire sequence is at the bottom above the dotted line. Each fragment is indicated by a horizontal sequence of amino acids joined by dots. The fragments are arranged so that each of their amino acids is in the vertical column above the corresponding amino acid in the entire chain.

CySO₃H · Gly   Arg · Gly   Lys · Ala
Leu · Val   Gly · Glu   Gly · Phe   Thr · Pro
Val · CySO₃H   Glu · Arg
Leu · Val   Gly · Glu · Arg   Pro · Lys · Ala
Val · CySO₃H · Gly
Leu · Val · CySO₃H
Leu · Val · CySO₃H   Thr · Pro · Lys · Ala
Leu · Val · CySO₃H · Gly

Leu · Val · CySO₃H · Gly   Thr · Pro · Lys · Ala
Gly · Glu · Arg · Gly

Leu · Val · CySO₃H · Gly · Glu · Arg · Gly · Phe   Tyr · Thr · Pro · Lys · Ala

Tyr · Thr · Pro · Lys · Ala
Leu · Val · CySO₃H · Gly · Glu · Arg · Gly · Phe · Phe

Gly · Phe · Phe · Tyr · Thr · Pro · Lys
Ala

Leu · Val · CySO₃H · Gly · Glu · Arg · Gly · Phe · Phe · Tyr · Thr · Pro · Lys · Ala

u · Leu · Glu · Asp · Tyr · CySO₃H · Asp
                    | |
H₂   NH₂   NH₂

The shorter fragments (*group at the top*) were obtained by hydrolyzing insulin with acid. The longer fragments (*groups third, fourth and fifth from the top*) were obtained with enzymes. The same method was used to deduce the sequence in the glycyl chain (*bottom*).

contains three cystine units suggested that there might be three bridges, or cross-links, between the chains. It appeared that it should be a simple matter to locate the positions of the bridges by a partial breakdown of the insulin molecule which gave cystine-containing fragments with sections of the two chains still attached to the "bridge" ends.

When Sanger began this analysis, he was puzzled to find that the cystine-containing peptides in his broken-down mixtures showed no significant pattern whatever. Cystine was joined with other amino acids in many different combinations and arrangements, as if the chains were cross-linked in every conceivable way. Sanger soon discovered the explanation: during acid hydrolysis of the insulin molecule, cystine's sulfur bonds opened and all sorts of rearrangements took place within the peptides. Sanger and his associate A. P. Ryle then made a systematic study of these reactions and succeeded in finding chemical inhibitors to prevent them.

By complex analyses which employed both acid hydrolysis and enzyme breakdown, Sanger and his co-workers L. F. Smith and Ruth Kitai eventually fitted the bridges into their proper places and obtained a complete picture of the structure of insulin [*see diagram at bottom of pages 24 and 25*]. So for the first time the biochemist is able to look at the amino-acid arrangement in a protein molecule. The achievement seems astounding to those who were working in the field 10 years ago.

To learn how insulin's structure determines its activity as a hormone is still a long, hard road. It will be difficult to synthesize the molecule, but once that has been accomplished, it will be possible to test the effect of changes in the structure on the substance's physiological behavior. Evidently slight variations do not affect it much, for Sanger has shown that the insulins from pigs, sheep and steers, all equally potent, differ slightly in structure.

The methods that proved so successful with insulin, plus some newer ones, are already being applied to study larger proteins. Among the improvements are promising new techniques for splitting off the amino acids from a peptide chain one at a time—clearly a more efficient procedure than random hydrolysis. The rate of progress undoubtedly will be speeded up as more biochemists turn their attention to the intriguing problem of relating the structure of proteins to their physiological functions.

3 | Proteins

PAUL DOTY · September 1957

Thousands of different proteins go into the make-up of a living cell. They perform thousands of different acts in the exact sequence that causes the cell to live. How the proteins manage this exquisitely subtle and enormously involved process will defy our understanding for a long time to come. But in recent years we have begun to make a closer acquaintance with proteins themselves. We know they are giant molecules of great size, complexity and diversity. Each appears to be designed with high specificity for its particular task. We are encouraged by all that we are learning to seek the explanation of the function of proteins in a clearer picture of their structure. For much of this new understanding we are indebted to our experience with the considerably simpler giant molecules synthesized by man. High-polymer chemistry is now coming forward with answers to some of the pressing questions of biology.

Proteins, like synthetic high polymers, are chains of repeating units. The units are peptide groups, made up of the monomers called amino acids [*see diagram below*]. There are more than 20 different amino acids. Each has a distinguishing cluster of atoms as a side group [*see next two pages*], but all amino acids have a certain identical group. The link-

ing of these groups forms the repeating peptide units in a "polypeptide" chain. Proteins are polypeptides of elaborate and very specific construction. Each kind of protein has a unique number and sequence of side groups which give it a particular size and chemical identity. Proteins seem to have a further distinction that sets them apart from other high polymers. The long chain of each protein is apparently folded in a unique configuration which it seems to maintain so long as it evidences biological activity.

We do not yet have a complete picture of the structure of any single protein. The entire sequence of amino acids has been worked out for insulin [see "The Insulin Molecule," by E. O. P. Thompson, beginning on page 24 in this book]; the determination of several more is nearing completion. But to locate each group and each atom in the configuration set up by the folded chain is intrinsically a more difficult task; it has resisted the Herculean labors of a generation of X-ray crystallographers and their collaborators. In the early 1930s W. T. Astbury of the University of Leeds succeeded in demonstrating that two X-ray diffraction patterns, which he called alpha and beta, were consistently associated with certain fibers, and he identified a third with collagen, the pro-

tein of skin, tendons and other structural tissues of the body. The beta pattern, found in the fibroin of silk, was soon shown to arise from bundles of nearly straight polypeptide chains held tightly to one another by hydrogen bonds. Nylon and some other synthetic fibers give a similar diffraction pattern. The alpha pattern resisted decoding until 1951, when Linus Pauling and R. B. Corey of the California Institute of Technology advanced the notion, since confirmed by further X-ray diffraction studies, that it is created by the twisting of the chain into a helix. Because it is set up so naturally by the hydrogen bonds available in the backbone of a polypeptide chain [*see top diagram on page 34*], the alpha helix was deduced to be a major structural element in the configuration of most proteins. More recently, in 1954, the Indian X-ray crystallographer G. N. Ramachandran showed that the collagen pattern comes from three polypeptide helixes twisted around one another. The resolution of these master plans was theoretically and esthetically gratifying, especially since the nucleic acids, the substance of genetic chemistry, were concurrently shown to have the structure of a double helix. For all their apparent general validity, however, the master plans did not give us the complete configuration in three dimensions

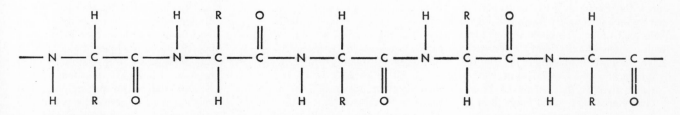

POLYPEPTIDE CHAIN is a repeating structure made up of identical peptide groups (CCONHC). The chain is formed by amino acids, each of which contributes an identical group to the backbone plus a distinguishing radical (R) as a side group.

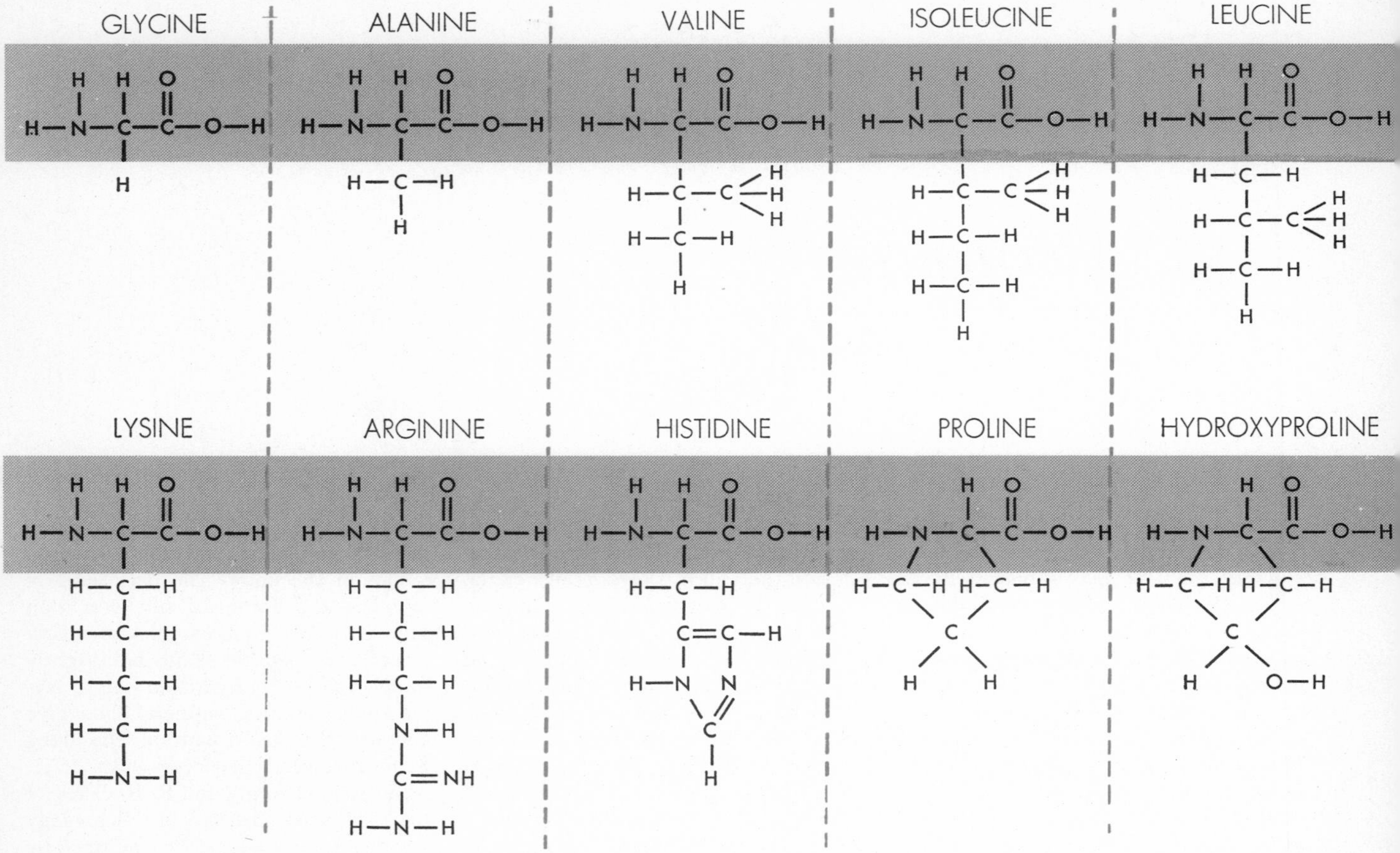

GLYCINE   ALANINE   VALINE   ISOLEUCINE   LEUCINE

LYSINE   ARGININE   HISTIDINE   PROLINE   HYDROXYPROLINE

AMINO ACIDS, the 20 commonest of which are shown in this chart, have identical atomic groups (*in colored bands*) which react to form polypeptide chains. They are distinguished by their unique side groups. In forming a chain, the amino group (NH_2) of one

of any single protein.

The X-ray diffraction work left a number of other questions up in the air. Since the alpha helix had been observed only in a few fibers, there was no solid experimental evidence for its existence elsewhere. There was even a suspicion that it could occur only in fibers, where it provides an economical way to pack polypeptides together in crystalline structures. Many proteins, especially chemically active ones such as the enzymes and antibodies, are globular, not linear like those involved in fibers and structural tissues. In the watery solutions which are the natural habitat of most proteins, it could be argued, the affinity of water molecules for hydrogen bonds would disrupt the alpha helix and reduce the chain to a random coil. These doubts and suppositions have prompted investigations by our group at Harvard University in collaboration with E. R. Blout of the Children's Cancer Research Foundation in Boston.

In these investigations we have employed synthetic polypeptides as laboratory models for the more complex and sensitive proteins. When Blout and coworkers had learned to polymerize them to sufficient length—100 to 1,000 amino acid units—we proceeded to observe their behavior in solution.

Almost at once we made the gratifying discovery that our synthetic polypeptides could keep their helical coils wound up in solutions. Moreover, we found that we could unwind the helix of some polypeptides by adjusting the acidity of our solutions. Finally, to complete the picture, we discovered that we could reverse the process and make the polypeptides wind up again from random coils into helixes.

The transition from the helix to the random coil occurs within a narrow range as the acidity is reduced; the hydrogen bonds, being equivalent, tend to let go all at once. It is not unlike the melting of an ice crystal, which takes place in a narrow temperature range. The reason is the same, for the ice crystal is held together by hydrogen bonds. To complete the analogy, the transition from the helix to the random coil can also be induced by heat. This is a true melting process, for the helix is a one-dimensional crystal which freezes the otherwise flexible chain into a rodlet.

From these experiments we conclude that polypeptides in solution have two natural configurations and make a reversible transition from one to the other, depending upon conditions. Polypeptides in the solid state appear to prefer the alpha helix, though this is subject to the presence of solvents, especially water. When the helix breaks down here, the transition is to the beta configuration, the hydrogen bonds now linking adjacent chains. Recently Blout and Henri Lenormant have found that fibers of polylysine can be made to undergo the alpha-beta transition reversibly by mere alteration of humidity. It is tempting to speculate that a reversible alpha-beta transition may underlie the process of muscle contraction and other types of

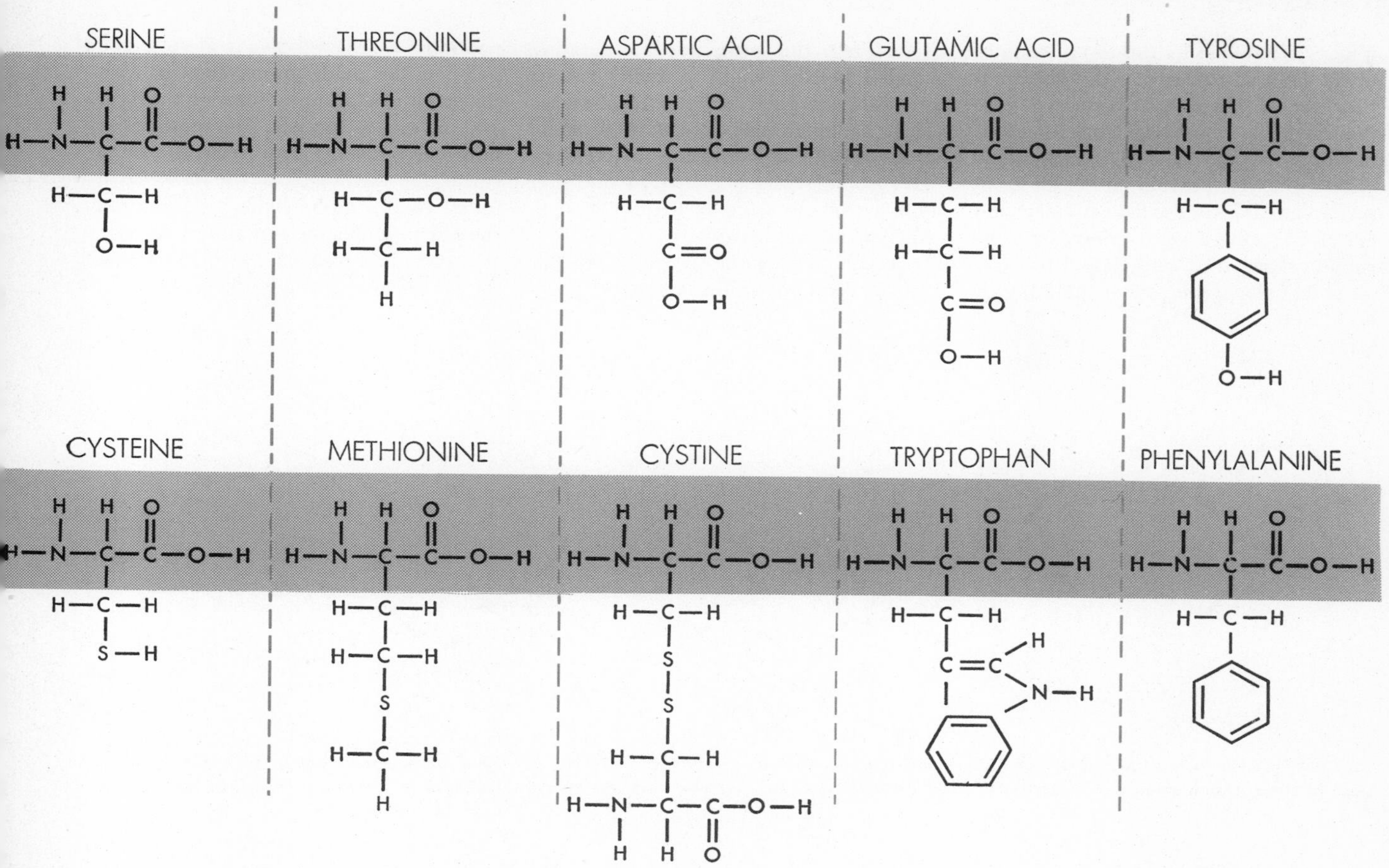

SERINE	THREONINE	ASPARTIC ACID	GLUTAMIC ACID	TYROSINE

CYSTEINE	METHIONINE	CYSTINE	TRYPTOPHAN	PHENYLALANINE

molecule reacts with the hydroxyl group (OH) of another. This reaction splits one of the amino hydrogens off with the hydroxyl group to form a molecule of water. The nitrogen of the first group then forms the peptide bond with the carbon of the second.

movement in living things.

Having learned to handle the polypeptides in solution we turned our attention to proteins. Two questions had to be answered first: Could we find the alpha helix in proteins in solution, and could we induce it to make the reversible transition to the random coil and back again? If the answer was yes in each case, then we could go on to a third and more interesting question: Could we show experimentally that biological activity depends upon configuration? On this question, our biologically neutral synthetic polypeptides could give no hint.

For the detection of the alpha helix in proteins the techniques which had worked so well on polypeptides were impotent. The polypeptides were either all helix or all random coil and the rodlets of the first could easily be distinguished from the globular forms of the second by use of the light-scattering technique. But we did not expect to find that any of the proteins we were going to investigate were 100 per cent helical in configura-

tion. The helix is invariably disrupted by the presence of one of two types of amino acid units. Proline lacks the hydrogen atom that forms the crucial hydrogen bond; the side groups form a distorting linkage to the chain instead. Cystine is really a double unit, and forms more or less distorting cross-links between chains. These units play an important part in the intricate coiling and folding of the polypeptide chains in globular proteins. But even in globular proteins, we thought, some lengths of the chains might prove to be helical. There was nothing, however, in the over-all shape of a globular protein to tell us whether it had more or less helix in its structure or none at all. We had to find a way to look inside the protein.

One possible way to do this was suggested by the fact that intact, biologically active proteins and denatured proteins give different readings when observed for an effect called optical rotation. In general, the molecules that exhibit this effect are asymmetrical in

atomic structure. The side groups give rise to such asymmetry in amino acids and polypeptide chains; they may be attached in either a "left-handed" or a "right-handed" manner. Optical rotation provides a way to distinguish one from the other. When a solution of amino acids is interposed in a beam of polarized light, it will rotate the plane of polarization either to the right or to the left [see diagrams at top of page 36]. Though amino acids may exist in both forms, only left-handed units, thanks to some accident in the chemical phase of evolution, are found in proteins. We used only the left-handed forms, of course, in the synthesis of our polypeptide chains.

Now what about the change in optical rotation that occurs when a protein is denatured? We knew that native protein rotates the plane of the light 30 to 60 degrees to the left, denatured protein 100 degrees or more to the left. If there was some helical structure in the protein, we surmised, this shift in rotation might be induced by the disappearance of the helical structure in the denaturation process. There was reason to believe that the helix, which has to be either left-handed or right-handed, would have optical activity. Further, although it appeared possible for the helix to be wound either way, there were grounds for assuming that nature had chosen to make all of its helixes one way or the other. If it had not, the left-handed and right-handed helixes would mutually cancel out their respective optical rotations. The change in the optical rotation of proteins with denaturation would then have some other explanation entirely, and we would have to invent another way to look for helixes.

To test our surmise we measured the optical rotation of the synthetic poly-peptides. In the random coil state the polypeptides made an excellent fit with the denatured proteins, rotating the light 100 degrees to the left. The rotations in both cases clearly arose from the same cause: the asymmetry of the amino acid units. In the alpha helix configuration the polypeptides showed almost no rotation or none at all. It was evident that the presence of the alpha helix caused a

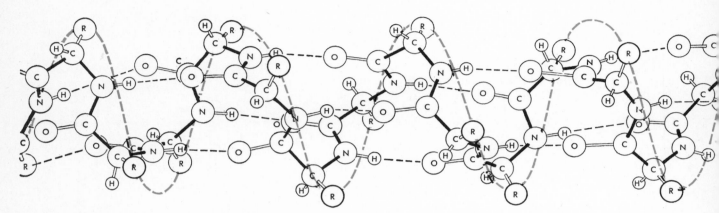

ALPHA HELIX gives a polypeptide chain a linear structure shown here in three-dimensional perspective. The atoms in the repeating unit (CCONHC) lie in a plane; the change in angle between one unit and the next occurs at the carbon to which the side group

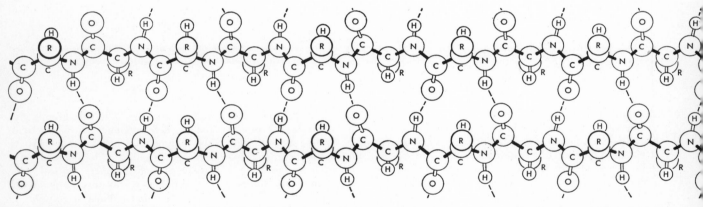

BETA CONFIGURATION ties two or more polypeptide chains to one another in crystalline structures. Here the hydrogen bonds do not contribute to the internal organization of the chain, as in the alpha helix, but link the hydrogen atoms of one chain to the oxygen

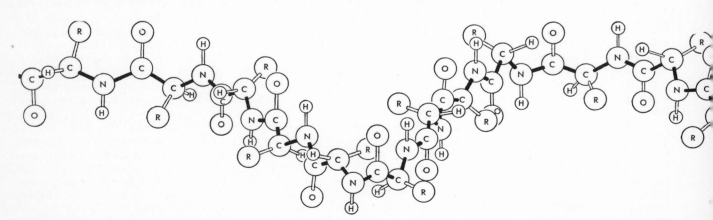

RANDOM CHAIN is the configuration assumed by the polypeptide molecule in solution, when hydrogen bonds are not formed. The flat configuration of the repeating unit remains, but the chain rotates about the carbon atoms to which the side groups are at-counter-rotation to the right which nearly canceled out the leftward rotation of the amino acid units. The native proteins also had shown evidence of such counter-rotation to the right. The alpha configuration did not completely cancel the leftward rotation of the amino acid units, but this was consistent with the expectation that the protein structures would be helical only in part. The experiment thus strongly indicated the presence of the alpha helix in the structure of globular proteins in solution. It also, incidentally, seemed to settle the question of nature's choice of symmetry in the alpha helix: it must be right-handed.

When so much hangs on the findings of one set of experiments, it is well to double check them by observations of another kind. We are indebted to William Moffitt, a theoretical chemist at Harvard, for conceiving of the experiment that provided the necessary confirmation. It is based upon another aspect of the optical rotation effect. For a given substance, rotation varies with the wavelength of the light; the rotations of most substances vary in the same way. Moffitt predicted that the presence of

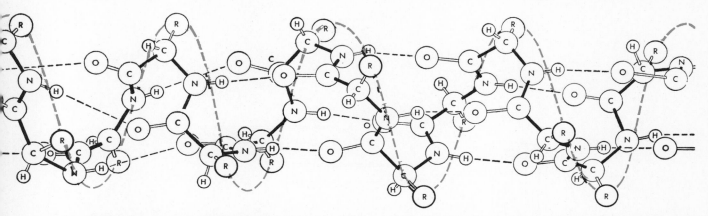

(R) is attached. The helix is held rigid by the hydrogen bond (*broken black lines*) between the hydrogen attached to the nitrogen in one group and the oxygen attached to a carbon three groups along the chain. The colored line traces the turns of the helix.

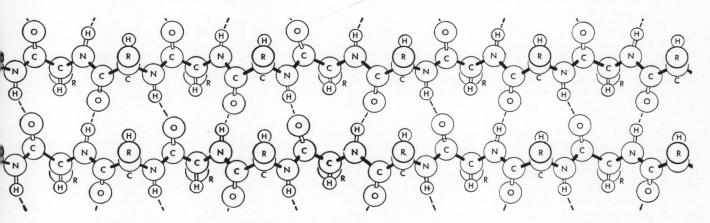

atoms in the adjoining chain. The beta configuration is found in silk and a few other fibers. It is also thought that polypeptide chains in muscle and other contractile fibers may make reversible transitions from alpha helix to beta configuration when in action.

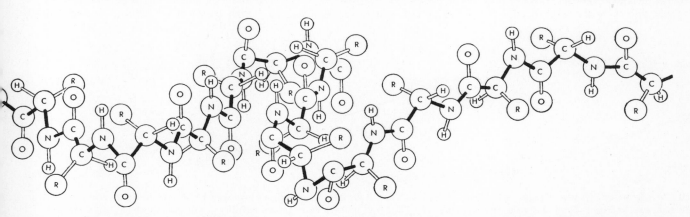

tached. The random chain may be formed from an alpha helix when hydrogen bonds are disrupted in solution. A polypeptide chain may make a reversible transition from alpha helix to random chain, depending upon the acid-base balance of the solution.

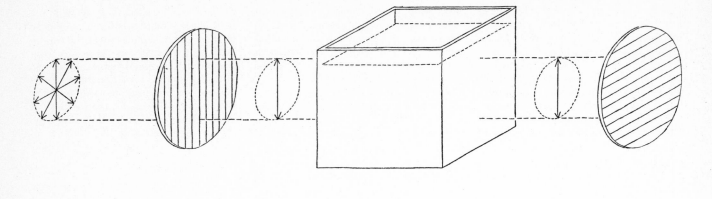

OPTICAL ROTATION is induced in a beam of polarized light by molecules having certain types of structural asymmetry. At top a beam of light is polarized in the vertical plane and transmitted unchanged through a neutral solution. At bottom asymmetrical molecules in the solution cause the beam to rotate from the vertical plane. The degree of rotation may be determined by turning the second polarizing filter (*right*) to the point at which it cuts off the beam. The alpha helix in a molecule causes such rotation.

the alpha helix in a substance would cause its rotation to vary in a different way. His prediction was sustained by observation: randomly coiled polypeptides showed a normal variation while the helical showed abnormal. Denatured and native proteins showed the same contrast. With the two sets of experiments in such good agreement, we could conclude with confidence that the alpha

helix has a significant place in the structure of globular proteins. Those amino acid units that are not involved in helical configurations are weakly bonded to each other or to water molecules, probably in a unique but not regular or periodic fashion. Like synthetic high-polymers, proteins are partly crystalline and partly amorphous in structure.

The optical rotation experiments also

provided a scale for estimating the helical content of protein. The measurements indicate that, in neutral solutions, the helical structure applies to 15 per cent of the amino acid units in ribonuclease, 50 per cent of the units in serum albumin and 85 per cent in tropomyosin. With the addition of denaturing agents to the solution, the helical content in each case can be reduced to zero. In

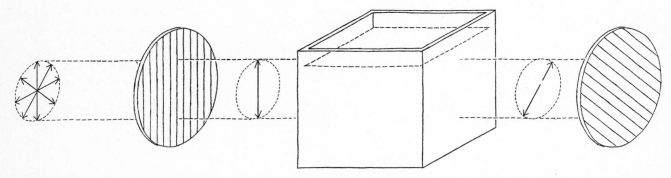

COLLAGEN MOLECULE is a triple helix. The colored broken line indicates hydrogen bonds between glycine units. The black broken lines indicate hydrogen bonds which link hydroxyproline units and give greater stability to collagens in which they are found.

some proteins the transition is abrupt, as it is in the synthetic polypeptides. On the other hand, by the use of certain solvents we have been able to increase the helical content of some proteins—in the case of ribonuclease from 15 to 70 per cent. As in the polypeptides, the transition from helix to random coil is reversible. The percentage of helical structure in proteins is thus clearly a variable. In their natural environment, it appears, the percentage at any given time represents the equilibrium between the inherent stability of the helix and the tendency of water to break it down.

In a number of enzymes we have been able to show that biological activity falls off and increases with helical content. Denaturation is now clearly identified with breakdown of configuration, certainly insofar as it involves the integrity of the alpha helix. This is not surprising. It is known that catalysts in general must have rigid geometrical configurations. The catalytic activity of an enzyme may well require that its structure meet similar specifications. If this is so, the rigidity that the alpha helix imposes on the otherwise flexible polypeptide chain must play a decisive part in establishing the biological activity of an enzyme. It seems also that adjustability of the stiffness of structure in larger or smaller regions of the polypeptide chain may modify the activity of proteins in response to their environment. Among other things, it could account for the versatility of the gamma globulins; without any apparent change in their amino acid make-up, they are able somehow to adapt themselves as antibodies to a succession of different infectious agents.

The next step toward a complete anatomy of the protein molecule is to determine which amino acid units are in the helical and which in the nonhelical regions. Beyond that we shall want to know which units are near one another as the result of folding and cross-linking, and a myriad of other details which will supply the hues and colorings appropriate to a portrait of an entity as intricate as protein. Many such details will undoubtedly be supplied by experiments that relate change in structure to change in function, like those described here.

In the course of our experiments with proteins in solution we have also looked into the triple-strand structure of collagen. That structure had not yet been resolved when we began our work, so we did not know how well it was designed for the function it serves in structural tissues. Collagen makes up one third of the proteins in the body and 5 per cent of its total weight; it occurs as tiny fibers or fibrils with bonds that repeat at intervals of about 700 Angstroms. It had been known for a long time that these fibrils could be dissolved in mild solvents such as acetic acid and then reconstituted, by simple precipitation, into their original form with their bandings restored. This remarkable capacity naturally suggested that the behavior of collagen in solution was a subject worth exploring.

Starting from the groundwork of other investigators, Helga Boedtker and I were able to demonstrate that the collagen molecule is an extremely long and thin rodlet, the most asymmetric molecule yet isolated. A lead pencil of comparable proportions would be a yard long. When a solution of collagen is just slightly warmed, these rodlets are irreversibly broken down. The solution will gel, but the product is gelatin, as is well known to French chefs and commercial producers of gelatin. The reason the dissolution cannot be reversed was made clear when we found that the molecules in the warmed-up solution had a weight about one third that of collagen. It appeared that the big molecule of collagen had broken down into three polypeptide chains.

At about the same time Ramachandran proposed the three-strand helix as the collagen structure. Not long afterward F. H. C. Crick and Alexander Rich at the University of Cambridge and Pauline M. Cowan and her collaborators at King's College, London, worked out the structure in detail. It consists of three polypeptide chains, each incorporating three different amino acid units—proline, hydroxyproline and glycine. The key to the design is the occurrence of glycine, the smallest amino acid unit, at every third position on each chain. This makes it possible for the bulky proline or hydroxyproline groups to fit into the links of the triple strand, two of these nesting in each link with the smaller glycine unit [see diagram on page 36].

One question, however, was left open in the original model. Hydroxyproline has surplus hydrogen bonds, which, the model showed, might be employed to reinforce the molecule itself or to tie it more firmly to neighboring molecules in a fibril. Independent evidence seemed to favor the second possibility. Collagen in the skin is irreversibly broken down in a first degree burn, for example, at a temperature of about 145 degrees Fahrenheit. This is about 60 degrees higher than the dissolution temperature of the collagen molecule in solution. The obvious inference was that hydroxyproline lends its additional bonding power to the tissue structure. Moreover, tissues with a high hydroxyproline content withstand higher temperatures than those with lower; the skin of codfish, with a low hydroxyproline content, shrivels up at about 100 degrees. Tomio Nishihara in

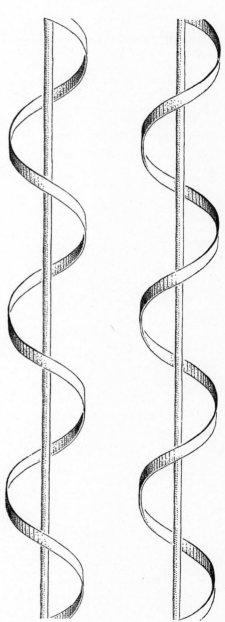

ASYMMETRY of a helix is either left-handed (left) or right-handed. Helix in proteins appears to be exclusively right-handed.

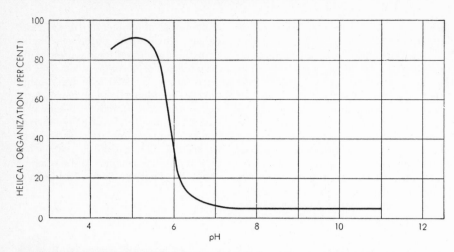

ALPHA HELIX BREAKDOWN is induced in solutions of some polypeptides when the pH (acidity or alkalinity) reaches a critical value at which hydrogen bonds are disrupted.

our laboratory has compared the breakdown temperatures of collagen molecules and tissues from various species and found that the tissue temperature is uniformly about 60 degrees higher. Thus we must conclude that the extra stability conferred by hydroxyproline goes directly to the molecule and not to the fibril.

The structure of collagen demonstrates three levels in the adaptation of polypeptide chains to fit the requirements of function. First there are the chains as found in gelatin, with their three amino acids lined up in just the right sequence. These randomly coiled and quite soluble molecules are transformed into relatively insoluble, girderlike building units when united into sets of three by hydrogen bonds. The subtly fashioned collagen molecules are still too fragile to withstand body temperatures. When arranged side by side, however, they form a crystalline structure which resists comparatively high temperatures and has fiber-like qualities with the vast range of strengths and textures required in the different types of tissues that are made of collagen.

The story of collagen, like that of other proteins, is still far from complete. But it now seems that it will rank among the first proteins whose molecular structure has been clearly discerned and related in detail to the functions it serves.

4 | The Hemoglobin Molecule

M. F. PERUTZ · November 1964

In 1937, a year after I entered the University of Cambridge as a graduate student, I chose the X-ray analysis of hemoglobin, the oxygen-bearing protein of the blood, as the subject of my research. Fortunately the examiners of my doctoral thesis did not insist on a determination of the structure, otherwise I should have had to remain a graduate student for 23 years. In fact, the complete solution of the problem, down to the location of each atom in this giant molecule, is still outstanding, but the structure has now been mapped in enough detail to reveal the intricate three-dimensional folding of each of its four component chains of amino acid units, and the positions of the four pigment groups that carry the oxygen-combining sites.

The folding of the four chains in hemoglobin turns out to be closely similar to that of the single chain of myoglobin, an oxygen-bearing protein in muscle whose structure has been elucidated in atomic detail by my colleague John C. Kendrew and his collaborators. Correlation of the structure of the two proteins allows us to specify quite accurately, by purely physical methods, where each amino acid unit in hemoglobin lies with respect to the twists and turns of its chains.

Physical methods alone, however, do not yet permit us to decide which of the 20 different kinds of amino acid units occupies any particular site. This knowledge has been supplied by chemical analysis; workers in the U.S. and in Germany have determined the sequence of the 140-odd amino acid units along each of the hemoglobin chains. The combined results of the two different methods of approach now provide an accurate picture of many facets of the hemoglobin molecule.

In its behavior hemoglobin does not resemble an oxygen tank so much as a molecular lung. Two of its four chains shift back and forth, so that the gap between them becomes narrower when oxygen molecules are bound to the hemoglobin, and wider when the oxygen is released. Evidence that the chemical activities of hemoglobin and other proteins are accompanied by structural changes had been discovered before, but this is the first time that the nature of such a change has been directly demonstrated. Hemoglobin's change of shape makes me think of it as a breathing molecule, but paradoxically it expands, not when oxygen is taken up but when it is released.

When I began my postgraduate work in 1936 I was influenced by three inspiring teachers. Sir Frederick Gowland Hopkins, who had received a Nobel prize in 1929 for discovering the growth-stimulating effect of vitamins, drew our attention to the central role played by enzymes in catalyzing chemical reactions in the living cell. The few enzymes isolated at that time had all proved to be proteins. David Keilin, the discoverer of several of the enzymes that catalyze the processes of respiration, told us how the chemical affinities and catalytic properties of iron atoms were altered when the iron combined with different proteins. J. D. Bernal, the X-ray crystallographer, was my research supervisor. He and Dorothy Crowfoot Hodgkin had taken the first X-ray diffraction pictures of crystals of protein a year or two before I arrived, and they had discovered that protein molecules, in spite of their large size, have highly ordered structures. The wealth of sharp X-ray diffraction spots produced by a single crystal of an enzyme such as pepsin could be explained only if every one, or almost every one, of the 5,000 atoms in the pepsin molecule occupied a definite position that was repeated in every one of the myriad of pepsin molecules packed in the crystal. The notion is commonplace now, but it caused a sensation at a time when proteins were still widely regarded as "colloids" of indefinite structure.

In the late 1930's the importance of the nucleic acids had yet to be discovered; according to everything I had learned the "secret of life" appeared to be concealed in the structure of proteins. Of all the methods available in chemistry and physics, X-ray crystallography seemed to offer the only chance, albeit an extremely remote one, of determining that structure.

The number of crystalline proteins then available was probably not more than a dozen, and hemoglobin was an obvious candidate for study because of its supreme physiological importance, its ample supply and the ease with which it could be crystallized. All the same, when I chose the X-ray analysis of hemoglobin as the subject of my Ph.D. thesis, my fellow students regarded me with a pitying smile. The most complex organic substance whose structure had yet been determined by X-ray analysis was the molecule of the dye phthalocyanin, which contains 58 atoms. How could I hope to locate the thousands of atoms in the molecule of hemoglobin?

The Function of Hemoglobin

Hemoglobin is the main component of the red blood cells, which carry oxygen from the lungs through the arteries to the tissues and help to carry carbon dioxide through the veins back to the lungs. A single red blood cell contains about 280 million molecules of hemoglobin. Each molecule has 64,500 times the weight of a hydrogen atom and is

molecule

made up of about 10,000 atoms of hydrogen, carbon, nitrogen, oxygen and sulfur, plus four atoms of iron, which are more important than all the rest. Each iron atom lies at the center of the group of atoms that form the pigment called heme, which gives blood its red color and its ability to combine with oxygen. Each heme group is enfolded in one of the four chains of amino acid units that collectively constitute the protein part of the molecule, which is called globin. The four chains of globin consist of two identical pairs. The members of one pair are known as alpha chains and those of the other as beta chains. Together the four chains contain a total of 574 amino acid units.

In the absence of an oxygen carrier a liter of arterial blood at body temperature could dissolve and transport no more than three milliliters of oxygen. The presence of hemoglobin increases this quantity 70 times. Without hemoglobin large animals could not get enough oxygen to exist. Similarly, hemoglobin is responsible for carrying more than 90 percent of the carbon dioxide transported by venous blood.

Each of the four atoms of iron in the hemoglobin molecule can take up one molecule (two atoms) of oxygen. The reaction is reversible in the sense that oxygen is taken up where it is plentiful, as in the lungs, and released where it is scarce, as in the tissues. The reaction is accompanied by a change in color: hemoglobin containing oxygen, known as oxyhemoglobin, makes arterial blood look scarlet; reduced, or oxygen-free, hemoglobin makes venous blood look purple. The term "reduced" for the oxygen-free form is really a misnomer because "reduced" means to the chemist that electrons have been added to an atom or a group of atoms. Actually, as James B. Conant of Harvard University demonstrated in 1923, the iron atoms in both reduced hemoglobin and oxyhemoglobin are in the same electronic condition: the divalent, or ferrous, state. They become oxidized to the trivalent, or ferric, state if hemoglobin is treated with a ferricyanide or removed from the red cells and exposed to the air for a considerable time; oxidation also occurs in certain blood diseases. Under these conditions hemoglobin turns brown and is known as methemoglobin, or ferrihemoglobin.

Ferrous iron acquires its capacity for binding molecular oxygen only through its combination with heme and globin. Heme alone will not bind oxygen, but the specific chemical environment of the globin makes the combina-

HEMOGLOBIN MOLECULE, as deduced from X-ray diffraction studies, is shown from above (*top*) and side (*bottom*). The drawings follow the representation scheme used in three-dimensional models built by the author and his co-workers. The irregular blocks represent electron-density patterns at various levels in the hemoglobin molecule. The molecule is built up from four subunits: two identical alpha chains (*light blocks*) and two identical beta chains (*dark blocks*). The letter "N" in the top view identifies the amino ends of the two alpha chains; the letter "C" identifies the carboxyl ends. Each chain enfolds a heme group (*colored disk*), the iron-containing structure that binds oxygen to the molecule.

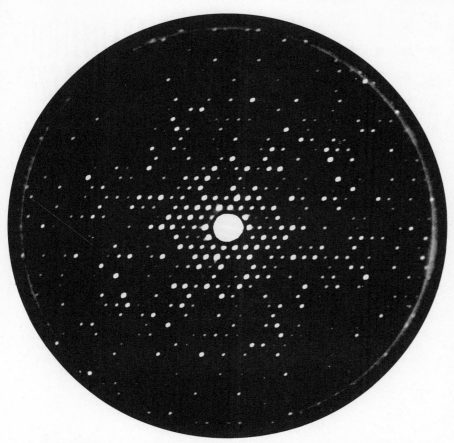

X-RAY DIFFRACTION PATTERN was made from a single crystal of hemoglobin that was rotated during the photographic exposure. Electrons grouped around the centers of the atoms in the crystal scatter the incident X rays, producing a symmetrical array of spots. Spots that are equidistant from the center and opposite each other have the same density.

ing. To preserve this order during X-ray analysis crystals are mounted wet in small glass capillaries. A single crystal is then illuminated by a narrow beam of X rays that are essentially all of one wavelength. If the crystal is kept stationary, a photographic film placed behind it will often exhibit a pattern of spots lying on ellipses, but if the crystal is rotated in certain ways, the spots can be made to appear at the corners of a regular lattice that is related to the arrangement of the molecules in the crystal [*see illustration at left*]. Moreover, each spot has a characteristic intensity that is determined in part by the arrangement of atoms inside the molecules. The reason for the different intensities is best explained in the words of W. L. Bragg, who founded X-ray analysis in 1913—the year after Max von Laue had discovered that X rays are diffracted by crystals—and who later succeeded Lord Rutherford as Cavendish Professor of Physics at Cambridge:

"It is well known that the form of the lines ruled on a [diffraction] grating has an influence on the relative intensity of the spectra which it yields. Some spectra may be enhanced, or reduced, in intensity as compared with others. Indeed, gratings are sometimes ruled in such a way that most of the energy is thrown into those spectra which it is most desirable to examine. The form of the line on the grating does not influence the positions of the spectra, which depend on the number of lines to the centimetre, but the individual lines scatter more light in some directions than others, and this enhances the spectra which lie in those directions.

"The structure of the group of atoms which composes the unit of the crystal grating influences the strength of the various reflexions in exactly the same way. The rays are diffracted by the electrons grouped around the centre of each atom. In some directions the atoms conspire to give a strong scattered beam, in others their effects almost annul each other by interference. The exact arrangement of the atoms is to be deduced by comparing the strength of the reflexions from different faces and in different orders."

Thus there should be a way of reversing the process of diffraction, of proceeding backward from the diffraction pattern to an image of the arrangement of atoms in the crystal. Such an image can actually be produced, somewhat laboriously, as follows. It will be noted that spots on opposite sides of the center of an X-ray picture have the same

tion possible. In association with other proteins, such as those of the enzymes peroxidase and catalase, the same heme group can exhibit quite different chemical characteristics.

The function of the globin, however, goes further. It enables the four iron atoms within each molecule to interact in a physiologically advantageous manner. The combination of any three of the iron atoms with oxygen accelerates the combination with oxygen of the fourth; similarly, the release of oxygen by three of the iron atoms makes the fourth cast off its oxygen faster. By tending to make each hemoglobin molecule carry either four molecules of oxygen or none, this interaction ensures efficient oxygen transport.

I have mentioned that hemoglobin also plays an important part in bearing carbon dioxide from the tissues back to the lungs. This gas is not borne by the iron atoms, and only part of it is bound directly to the globin; most of it is taken up by the red cells and the noncellular fluid of the blood in the form of bicarbonate. The transport of bicarbonate is facilitated by the disappearance of

an acid group from hemoglobin for each molecule of oxygen discharged. The reappearance of the acid group when oxygen is taken up again in the lungs sets in motion a series of chemical reactions that leads to the discharge of carbon dioxide. Conversely, the presence of bicarbonate and lactic acid in the tissues accelerates the liberation of oxygen.

Breathing seems so simple, yet it appears as if this elementary manifestation of life owes its existence to the interplay of many kinds of atoms in a giant molecule of vast complexity. Elucidating the structure of the molecule should tell us not only what the molecule looks like but also how it works.

The Principles of X-Ray Analysis

The X-ray study of proteins is sometimes regarded as an abstruse subject comprehensible only to specialists, but the basic ideas underlying our work are so simple that some physicists find them boring. Crystals of hemoglobin and other proteins contain much water and, like living tissues, they tend to lose their regularly ordered structure on dry-

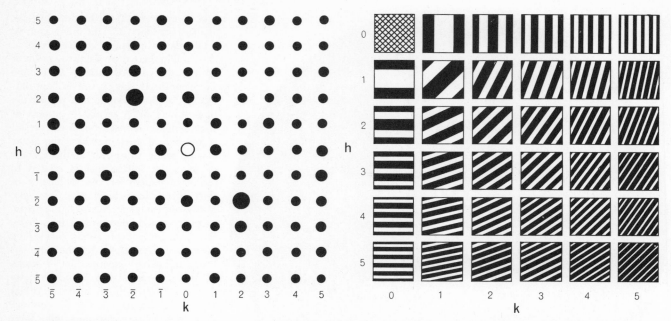

INTERPRETATION OF X-RAY IMAGE can be done with a special optical device to generate a set of diffraction fringes (*right*) from the spots in an X-ray image (*left*). Each pair of symmetrically related spots produces a unique set of fringes. Thus the spots indexed $2,\bar{2}$ and $\bar{2},2$ yield the fringes indexed 2,2. A two-dimensional image of the atomic structure of a crystal can be generated by printing each set of fringes on the same sheet of photographic paper. But the phase problem (*below*) must be solved first.

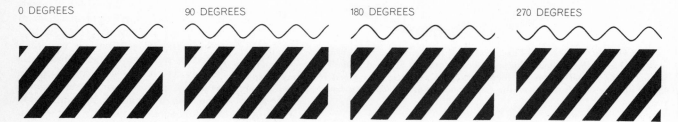

0 DEGREES   90 DEGREES   180 DEGREES   270 DEGREES

PHASE PROBLEM arises because the spots in an X-ray image do not indicate how the fringes are related in phase to an arbitrarily chosen common origin. Here four identical sets of fringes are related by different phases to the point of origin at the top left corner. The phase marks the distance of the wave crest from the origin, measured in degrees. One wavelength is 360 degrees.

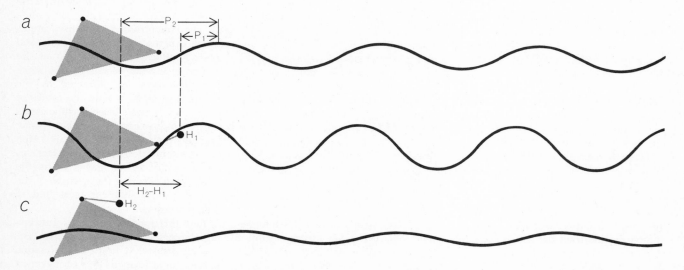

HEAVY-ATOM REPLACEMENT METHOD provides information about phases by changing the intensities of the X-ray diffraction pattern. In *a* a highly oversimplified protein (a triangle of three atoms) scatters a sinusoidal wave that represents the amplitude and phase of a single set of fringes. In *b* and *c*, after heavy atoms H_1 and H_2 are attached to the protein in different positions, the wave is changed in amplitude and phase. The heavy atoms can serve as points of common origin for measuring the magnitude of the phases (P_1 and P_2) of waves scattered by the unaltered protein. The distance between H_1 and H_2 must be accurately known.

degree of intensity. With the aid of a simple optical device each symmetrically related pair of spots can be made to generate a set of diffraction fringes, with an amplitude proportional to the square root of the intensity of the spots. The device, which was invented by Bragg and later developed by H. Lipson and C. A. Taylor at the Manchester College of Science and Technology, consists of a point source of monochromatic light, a pair of plane-convex lenses

and a microscope. The pair of spots in the diffraction pattern is represented by a pair of holes in a black mask that is placed between the two lenses. If the point source is placed at the focus of one of the lenses, the waves of parallel light emerging from the two holes will interfere with one another at the focus of the second lens, and their interference pattern, or diffraction pattern, can be observed or photographed through the microscope.

Imagine that each pair of symmetrically related spots in the X-ray picture is in turn represented by a pair of holes in a mask, and that its diffraction fringes are photographed. Each set of fringes will then be at right angles to the line joining the two holes, and the distance between the fringes will be inversely proportional to the distance between the holes. If the spots are numbered from the center along two mutually perpendicular lines by the indices h and k, the relation between any pair of spots and its corresponding set of fringes would be as shown in the top illustration on the preceding page.

The Phase Problem

An image of the atomic structure of the crystal can be generated by printing each set of fringes in turn on the same sheet of photographic paper, or by superposing all the fringes and making a print of the light transmitted through them. At this point, however, a fatal complication arises. In order to obtain the right image one would have to place each set of fringes correctly with respect to some arbitrarily chosen common origin [see middle illustration on preceding page]. At this origin the amplitude of any particular set of fringes may show a crest or trough or some intermediate value. The distance of the wave crest from the origin is called the phase. It is almost true to say that by superposing sets of fringes of given amplitude one can generate an infinite number of different images, depending on the choice of phase for each set of fringes. By itself the X-ray picture tells us only about the amplitudes and nothing about the phases of the fringes to be generated by each pair of spots, which means that half the information needed for the production of the image is missing.

The missing information makes the diffraction pattern of a crystal like a hieroglyphic without a key. Having spent years hopefully measuring the intensities of several thousand spots in the diffraction pattern of hemoglobin, I found myself in the tantalizing position of an explorer with a collection of tablets engraved in an unknown script. For some time Bragg and I tried to develop methods for deciphering the phases, but with only limited success. The solution finally came in 1953, when I discovered that a method that had been developed by crystallographers for solving the phase problem in simpler structures could also be applied to proteins.

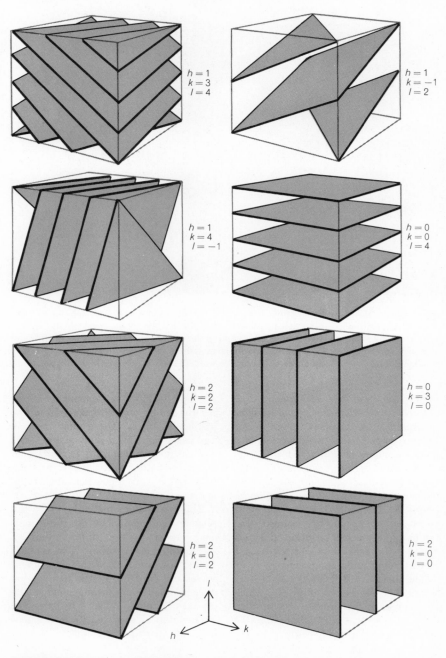

THREE-DIMENSIONAL FRINGES are needed to build up an image of protein molecules. For this purpose many different X-ray diffraction images are prepared and symmetrically related pairs of spots are indexed in three dimensions: h, k and l and h̄, k̄ and l̄. Each pair of spots yields a three-dimensional fringe like those shown here. Fringes from thousands of spots must be superposed in proper phase to build up an image of the molecule.

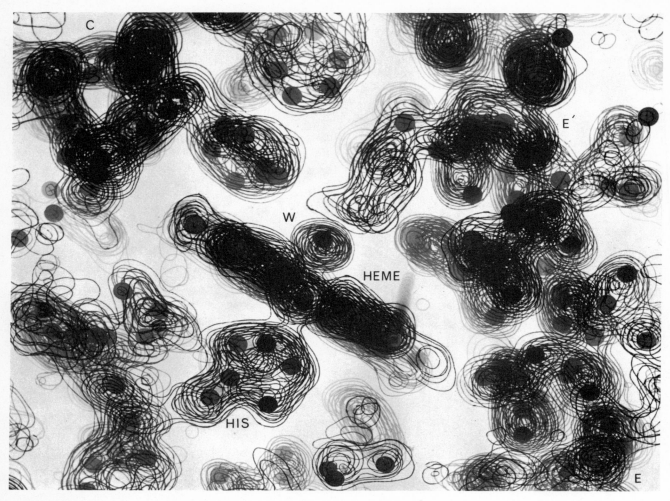

CONTOUR MAPS, drawn on stacked sheets of clear plastic, show a portion of the myoglobin molecule as revealed by superposition of three-dimensional fringe patterns. The maps were made by John C. Kendrew and his associates at the University of Cambridge. Myoglobin is very similar to the beta chain of hemoglobin. The heme group is seen edge on. *His* is an amino acid subunit of histidine that is attached to the iron atom of the heme group. *W* is a water molecule linked to the iron atom. The region between *E* and *E'* represents amino acid subunits arranged in an alpha helix. *C* is an alpha helix seen end on. The black dots mark atomic positions.

In this method the molecule of the compound under study is modified slightly by attaching heavy atoms such as those of mercury to definite positions in its structure. The presence of a heavy atom produces marked changes in the intensities of the diffraction pattern, and this makes it possible to gather information about the phases. From the difference in amplitude in the absence or presence of a heavy atom, the distance of the wave crest from the heavy atom can be determined for each set of fringes. Thus with the heavy atom serving as a common origin the magnitude of the phase can be measured. The bottom illustration on page 42 shows how the phase of a single set of fringes, represented by a sinusoidal wave that is supposedly scattered by the oversimplified protein molecule, can be measured from the increase in amplitude produced by the heavy atom H_1.

Unfortunately this still leaves an am-

biguity of sign; the experiment does not tell us whether the phase is to be measured from the heavy atom in the forward or the backward direction. If n is the number of diffracted spots, an ambiguity of sign in each set of fringes would lead to 2^n alternative images of the structure. The Dutch crystallographer J. M. Bijvoet had pointed out some years earlier in another context that the ambiguity could be resolved by examining the diffraction pattern from a second heavy-atom compound.

The bottom illustration on page 42 shows that the heavy atom H_2, which is attached to the protein in a position different from that of H_1, diminishes the amplitude of the wave scattered by the protein. The degree of attenuation allows us to measure the distance of the wave crest from H_2. It can now be seen that the wave crest must be in front of H_1; otherwise its distance from H_1 could not be reconciled with its distance from

H_2. The final answer depends on knowing the length and direction of the line joining H_2 to H_1. These quantities are best calculated by a method that does not easily lend itself to exposition in nonmathematical language. It was devised by my colleague Michael G. Rossmann.

The heavy-atom method can be applied to hemoglobin by attaching mercury atoms to the sulfur atoms of the amino acid cysteine. The method works, however, only if this attachment leaves the structure of the hemoglobin molecules and their arrangement in the crystal unaltered. When I first tried it, I was not at all sure that these stringent demands would be fulfilled, and as I developed my first X-ray photograph of mercury hemoglobin my mood alternated between sanguine hopes of immediate success and desperate forebodings of all the possible causes of failure. When the diffraction spots ap-

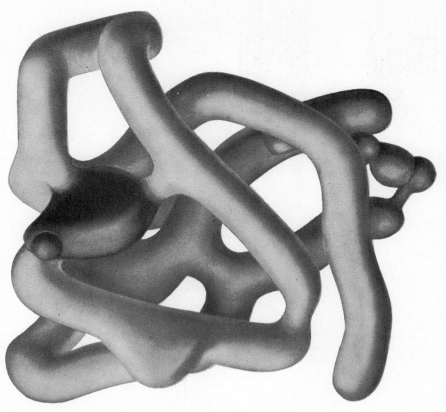

MYOGLOBIN MOLECULE, as first reconstructed at low resolution by Kendrew and his co-workers in 1957, had this rather repulsive visceral appearance. The sausage-like knot marks the path of the amino acid chain of the molecule. The dark disklike shape (here placed at an incorrect angle) is the heme group. A more detailed and more correct view of myoglobin, as seen from the other side, appears at bottom right on the preceding page.

peared in exactly the same position as in the mercury-free protein but with slightly altered intensities, just as I had hoped, I rushed off to Bragg's room in jubilant excitement, expecting that the structure of hemoglobin and of many other proteins would soon be determined. Bragg shared my excitement, and luckily neither of us anticipated the formidable technical difficulties that were to hold us up for another five years.

Resolution of the Image

Having solved the phase problem, at least in principle, we were confronted with the task of building up a structural image from our X-ray data. In simpler structures atomic positions can often be found from representations of the structure projected on two mutually perpendicular planes, but in proteins a three-dimensional image is essential. This can be attained by making use of the three-dimensional nature of the diffraction pattern. The X-ray diffraction pattern on page 41 can be regarded as a section through a sphere that is filled with layer after layer of diffraction spots. Each pair of spots can be made to generate a set of three-dimensional fringes like the ones shown on page 6. When their phases have been measured, they can be superposed by calculation to build up a three-dimensional image of the protein. The final image is represented by a series of sections through the molecule, rather like a set of microtome sections through a piece of tissue, only on a scale 1,000 times smaller [see illustration on preceding page].

The resolution of the image is roughly equal to the shortest wavelength of the fringes used in building it up. This means that the resolution increases with the number of diffracted spots included in the calculation. If the image is built up from part of the diffraction pattern only, the resolution is impaired.

In the X-ray diffraction patterns of protein crystals the number of spots runs into tens of thousands. In order to determine the phase of each spot accurately, its intensity (or blackness) must be measured accurately several times over: in the diffraction pattern from a crystal of the pure protein and in the patterns from crystals of several compounds of the protein, each with heavy atoms attached to different positions in the molecule. Then the results have to be corrected by various geometric factors before they are finally used to build up an image through the superposition of tens of thousands of fringes. In the final calculation tens of millions of numbers may have to be added or subtracted. Such a task would have been quite impossible before the advent of high-speed computers, and we have been fortunate in that the development of computers has kept pace with the expanding needs of our X-ray analyses.

While I battled with technical difficulties of various sorts, my colleague John Kendrew successfully applied the heavy-atom method to myoglobin, a protein closely related to hemoglobin [see "The Three-dimensional Structure of a Protein Molecule," by John C. Kendrew; SCIENTIFIC AMERICAN Offprint 121]. Myoglobin is simpler than hemoglobin because it consists of only one chain of amino acid units and one heme group, which binds a single molecule of oxygen. The complex interaction phenomena involved in hemoglobin's dual function as a carrier of oxygen and of carbon dioxide do not occur in myoglobin, which acts simply as an oxygen store.

Together with Howard M. Dintzis and G. Bodo, Kendrew was brilliantly successful in managing to prepare as many as five different crystalline heavy-atom compounds of myoglobin, which meant that the phases of the diffraction spots could be established very accurately. He also pioneered the use of high-speed computers in X-ray analysis. In 1957 he and his colleagues obtained the first three-dimensional representation of myoglobin [see illustration on this page].

It was a triumph, and yet it brought a tinge of disappointment. Could the search for ultimate truth really have revealed so hideous and visceral-looking an object? Was the nugget of gold a lump of lead? Fortunately, like many other things in nature, myoglobin gains in beauty the closer you look at it. As Kendrew and his colleagues increased the resolution of their X-ray analysis in the years that followed, some of the intrinsic reasons for the molecule's strange shape began to reveal themselves. This shape was found to be not a freak but a fundamental pattern of nature, probably common to myoglobins and hemoglobins throughout the vertebrate kingdom.

In the summer of 1959, nearly 22 years after I had taken the first X-ray

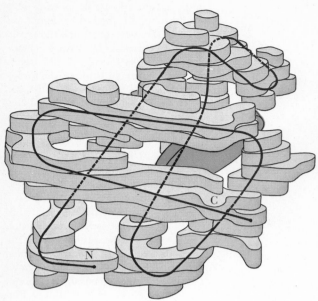

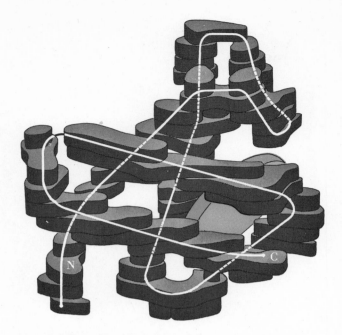

HEMOGLOBIN CHAINS, alpha at left and beta at right, are re-drawn from models built by the author and his colleagues. The superposed lines show the course of the central chain. A heme group (*color*) is partly visible, tucked in the back of each model.

pictures of hemoglobin, its structure emerged at last. Michael Rossmann, Ann F. Cullis, Hilary Muirhead, Tony C. T. North and I were able to prepare a three-dimensional electron-density map of hemoglobin at a resolution of 5.5 angstrom units, about the same as that obtained for the first structure of myoglobin two years earlier. This resolution is sufficient to reveal the shape of the chain forming the backbone of a protein molecule but not to show the position of individual amino acids.

As soon as the numbers printed by the computer had been plotted on contour maps we realized that each of the four chains of hemoglobin had a shape closely resembling that of the single chain of myoglobin. The beta chain and myoglobin look like identical twins, and the alpha chains differ from them merely by a shortcut across one small loop [*see illustration below*].

Kendrew's myoglobin had been extracted from the muscle of the sperm whale; the hemoglobin we used came from the blood of horses. More recent observations indicate that the myoglobins of the seal and the horse, and the hemoglobins of man and cattle, all have the same structure. It seems as though the apparently haphazard and irregular folding of the chain is a pattern specifically devised for holding a heme group in place and for enabling it to carry oxygen.

What is it that makes the chain take up this strange configuration? The extension of Kendrew's analysis to a high-

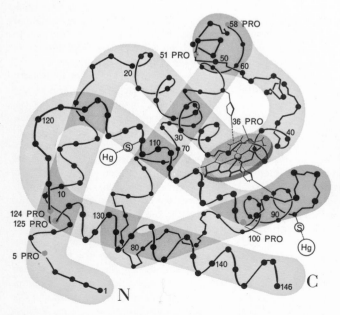

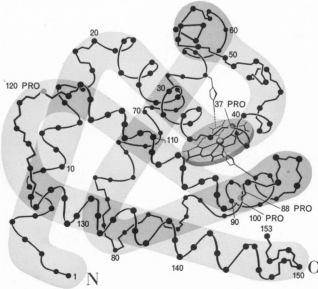

BETA CHAIN AND MYOGLOBIN appear at left and right. Every 10th amino acid subunit is marked, as are proline subunits (*color*), which often coincide with turns in the chain. Balls marked "Hg" show where mercury atoms can be attached to sulfur atoms (S).

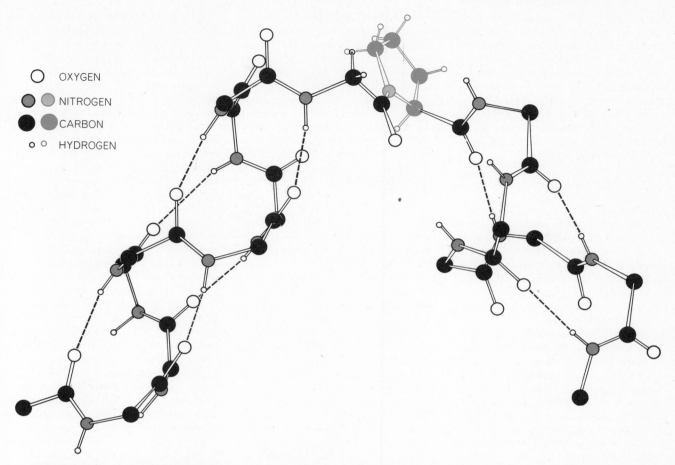

OXYGEN

NITROGEN

CARBON

HYDROGEN

CORNER IN HEMOGLOBIN MOLECULE occurs where a subunit of the amino acid proline (*color*) falls between two helical regions in the beta chain. The chain is shown bare; all hydrogen atoms and amino acid side branches, except for proline, are removed.

er resolution shows that the chain of myoglobin consists of a succession of helical segments interrupted by corners and irregular regions. The helical segments have the geometry of the alpha helix predicted in 1951 by Linus Pauling and Robert B. Corey of the California Institute of Technology. The heme group lies embedded in a fold of the chain, so that only its two acid groups protrude at the surface and are in contact with the surrounding water. Its iron atom is linked to a nitrogen atom of the amino acid histidine.

I have recently built models of the alpha and beta chains of hemoglobin and found that they follow an atomic pattern very similar to that of myoglobin. If two protein chains look the same, one would expect them to have much the same composition. In the language of protein chemistry this implies that in the myoglobins and hemoglobins of all vertebrates the 20 different kinds of amino acid should be present in about the same proportion and arranged in similar sequence.

Enough chemical analyses have been done by now to test whether or not this is true. Starting at the Rockefeller Institute and continuing in our laboratory, Allen B. Edmundson has determined the sequence of amino acid units in the molecule of sperm-whale myoglobin. The sequences of the alpha and beta chains of adult human hemoglobin have been analyzed independently by Gerhardt Braunitzer and his colleagues at the Max Planck Institute for Biochemistry in Munich, and by William H. Konigsberg, Robert J. Hill and their associates at the Rockefeller Institute. Fetal hemoglobin, a variant of the human adult form, contains a chain known as gamma, which is closely related to the beta chain. Its complete sequence has been analyzed by Walter A. Schroeder and his colleagues at the California Institute of Technology. The sequences of several other species of hemoglobin and that of human myoglobin have been partially elucidated.

The sequence of amino acid units in proteins is genetically determined, and changes arise as a result of mutation. Sickle-cell anemia, for instance, is an inherited disease due to a mutation in one of the hemoglobin genes. The mu-

tation causes the replacement of a single amino acid unit in each of the beta chains. (The glutamic acid unit normally present at position No. 6 is replaced by a valine unit.) On the molecular scale evolution is thought to involve a succession of such mutations, altering the structure of protein molecules one amino acid unit at a time. Consequently when the hemoglobins of different species are compared, we should expect the sequences in man and apes, which are close together on the evolutionary scale, to be very similar, and those of mammals and fishes, say, to differ more widely. Broadly speaking, this is what is found. What was quite unexpected was the degree of chemical diversity ·among the amino acid sequences of proteins of similar three-dimensional structure and closely related function. Comparison of the known hemoglobin and myoglobin sequences shows only 15 positions—no more than one in 10—where the same amino acid unit is present in all species. In all the other positions one or more replacements have occurred in the course of evolution.

What mechanism makes these diverse

chains fold up in exactly the same way? Does a template force them to take up this configuration, like a mold that forces a car body into shape? Apart from the topological improbability of such a template, all the genetic and physico-chemical evidence speaks against it, suggesting instead that the chain folds up spontaneously to assume one specific structure as the most stable of all possible alternatives.

Possible Folding Mechanisms

What is it, then, that makes one particular configuration more stable than all others? The only generalization to emerge so far, mainly from the work of Kendrew, Herman C. Watson and myself, concerns the distribution of the so-called polar and nonpolar amino acid units between the surface and the interior of the molecule.

Some of the amino acids, such as glutamic acid and lysine, have side groups\ of atoms with positive or negative electric charge, which strongly attract the surrounding water. Amino acid side groups such as glutamine or tyrosine, although electrically neutral as a whole, contain atoms of nitrogen or oxygen in which positive and negative charges are sufficiently separated to form dipoles; these also attract water, but not so strongly as the charged groups do. The attraction is due to a separation of charges in the water molecule itself, making it dipolar. By attaching themselves to electrically charged groups, or to other dipolar groups, the water molecules minimize the strength of the electric fields surrounding these groups and stabilize the entire structure by lowering the quantity known as free energy.

The side groups of amino acids such as leucine and phenylalanine, on the other hand, consist only of carbon and hydrogen atoms. Being electrically neutral and only very weakly dipolar, these groups repel water as wax does. The reason for the repulsion is strange and intriguing. Such hydrocarbon groups, as they are called, tend to disturb the haphazard arrangement of the liquid water molecules around them, making it ordered as it is in ice. The increase in order makes the system less stable; in physical terms it leads to a reduction of the quantity known as entropy, which is the measure of the disorder in a system. Thus it is the water molecules' anarchic distaste for the orderly regimentation imposed on them by the hydrocarbon side groups that forces these side groups to turn away from water and to stick to one another.

Our models have taught us that most electrically charged or dipolar side groups lie at the surface of the protein molecule, in contact with water. Nonpolar side groups, in general, are either confined to the interior of the molecule or so wedged into crevices on its surface as to have the least contact with water. In the language of physics, the distribution of side groups is of the kind leading to the lowest free energy and the highest entropy of the protein molecules and the water around them. (There is a reduction of entropy due to the orderly folding of the protein chain itself, which makes the system less stable, but this is balanced, at moderate temperatures, by the stabilizing contributions of the other effects just described.) It is too early to say whether these are the only generalizations to be made about the forces that stabilize one particular configuration of the protein chain in preference to all others.

At least one amino acid is known to be a misfit in an alpha helix, forcing the chain to turn a corner wherever the unit occurs. This is proline [see illustration on preceding page]. There is, however, only one corner in all the hemoglobins and myoglobins where a proline is always found in the same position: position No. 36 in the beta chain and No. 37 in the myoglobin chain [see bottom illustration on page 46]. At other corners the appearance of prolines is haphazard and changes from species to species. Elkan R. Blout of the Harvard Medical School finds that certain amino acids such as valine or threonine, if present in large numbers, inhibit the formation of alpha helices, but these do not seem to have a decisive influence in myoglobin and hemoglobin.

Since it is easier to determine the sequence of amino acid units in proteins than to unravel their three-dimensional structure by X rays, it would be useful to be able to predict the structure from the sequence. In principle enough is probably known about the forces between atoms and about the way they tend to arrange themselves to make such predictions feasible. In practice the enormous number of different ways in which a long chain can be twisted still makes the problem one of baffling complexity.

Assembling the Four Chains

If hemoglobin consisted of four identical chains, a crystallographer would expect them to lie at the corners of a regular tetrahedron. In such an arrangement each chain can be brought into congruence with any of its three neighbors by a rotation of 180 degrees about one of three mutually perpendicular

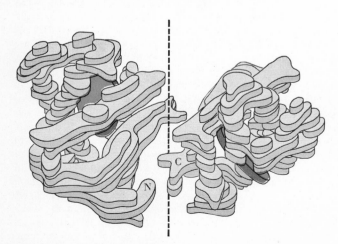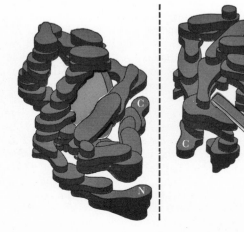

FOUR CHAINS OF HEMOGLOBIN are arranged in symmetrical fashion. Two alpha chains (left) and two beta chains (right) face each other across an axis of symmetry (broken vertical lines). In the assembled molecule the two alpha chains are inverted over the two beta chains and nested down between them. When arranged in this manner, the four chains lie at the corners of a tetrahedron.

axes of symmetry. Since the alpha and beta chains are chemically different, such perfect symmetry is unattainable, but the actual arrangement comes very close to it. As a first step in the assembly of the molecule two alpha chains are placed near a twofold symmetry axis, so that a rotation of 180 degrees brings one chain into congruence with its partner [*see illustration on preceding page*].

Next the same is done with the two beta chains. One pair, say the alpha chains, is then inverted and placed over the top of the other pair so that the four chains lie at the corners of a tetrahedron. A true twofold symmetry axis now passes vertically through the molecule, and "pseudo-axes" in two directions perpendicular to the first relate the alpha to the beta chains. Thus the arrangement is tetrahedral, but because of the chemical differences between the alpha and beta chains the tetrahedron is not quite regular.

The result is an almost spherical molecule whose exact dimensions are $64 \times 55 \times 50$ angstrom units. It is astonishing to find that four objects as irregular as the alpha and beta chains can fit together so neatly. On formal grounds one would expect a hole to pass through the center of the molecule because chains of amino acid units, being asymmetrical, cannot cross any symmetry axis. Such a hole is in fact found [*see top illustration on page 40*].

The most unexpected feature of the oxyhemoglobin molecule is the way the four heme groups are arranged. On the basis of their chemical interaction one would have expected them to lie close together. Instead each heme group lies in a separate pocket on the surface of the molecule, apparently unaware of the existence of its partners. Seen at the present resolution, therefore, the structure fails to explain one of the most important physiological properties of hemoglobin.

In 1937 Felix Haurowitz, then at the German University of Prague, discov-

ered an important clue to the molecular explanation of hemoglobin's physiological action. He put a suspension of needle-shaped oxyhemoglobin crystals away in the refrigerator. When he took the suspension out some weeks later, the oxygen had been used up by bacterial infection and the scarlet needles had been replaced by hexagonal plates of purple reduced hemoglobin. While Haurowitz observed the crystals under the microscope, oxygen penetrated between the slide and the cover slip, causing the purple plates to dissolve and the scarlet needles of hemoglobin to re-form. This transformation convinced Haurowitz that the reaction of hemoglobin with oxygen must be accompanied by a change in the structure of the hemoglobin molecule. In myoglobin, on the other hand, no evidence for such a change has been detected.

Haurowitz' observation and the enigma posed by the structure of oxyhemoglobin caused me to persuade a graduate student, Hilary Muirhead, to attempt an X-ray analysis at low resolution of the reduced form. For technical reasons human rather than horse hemoglobin was used at first, but we have now found that the reduced hemoglobins of man and the horse have very similar structures, so that the species does not matter here.

Unlike me, Miss Muirhead succeeded in solving the structure of her protein in time for her Ph.D. thesis. When we examined her first electron-density maps, we looked for two kinds of structural change: alterations in the folding of the individual chains and displacements of the chains with respect to each other. We could detect no changes in folding large enough to be sure that they were not due to experimental error. We did discover, however, that a striking displacement of the beta chains had taken place. The gap between them had widened and they had been shifted sideways, increasing the distance between their respective iron atoms from 33.4 to 40.3 angstrom units [*see illustration on page 50*]. The arrangement of the two alpha chains had remained unaltered, as far as we could judge, and the distance between the iron atoms in the beta chains and their nearest neighbors in the alpha chains had also remained the same. It looked as though the two beta chains had slid apart, losing contact with each other and somewhat changing their points of contact with the alpha chains.

F. J. W. Roughton and others at the University of Cambridge suggest that the change to the oxygenated form of

RESIDUE NUMBER	HEMOGLOBIN			MYOGLOBIN
	ALPHA	BETA	GAMMA	
81	MET	LEU	LEU	HIS
82	PRO	LYS	LYS	GLU
83	ASN	GLY	GLY	ALA
84	ALA	THR	THR	GLU
85	LEU	PHE	PHE	LEU
86	SER	ALA	ALA	LYS
87	ALA	THR	GLN	PRO
88	LEU	LEU	LEU	LEU
89	SER	SER	SER	ALA
90	ASP	GLU	GLU	GLN
91	LEU	LEU	LEU	SER
92	HIS	HIS	HIS	HIS
93	ALA	CYS	CYS	ALA
94	HIS	ASP	ASN	THR
95	LYS	LYS	LYS	LYS
96	LEU	LEU	LEU	HIS
97	ARG	HIS	HIS	LYS
98	VAL	VAL	VAL	ILEU
99	ASP	ASP	ASP	PRO
100	PRO	PRO	PRO	ILEU
101	VAL	GLU	GLU	LYS
102	ASP	ASN	ASN	TYR

ALA ALANINE	GLY GLYCINE	PRO PROLINE
ARG ARGININE	HIS HISTIDINE	SER SERINE
ASN ASPARAGINE	ILEU ISOLEUCINE	THR THREONINE
ASP ASPARTIC ACID	LEU LEUCINE	TYR TYROSINE
CYS CYSTEINE	LYS LYSINE	VAL VALINE
GLN GLUTAMINE	MET METHIONINE	
GLU GLUTAMIC ACID	PHE PHENYLALANINE	

AMINO ACID SEQUENCES are shown for corresponding stretches of the alpha and beta chains of hemoglobin from human adults, the gamma chain that replaces the beta chain in fetal human hemoglobin and sperm-whale myoglobin. Colored bars show where the same amino acid units are found either in all four chains or in the first three. Site numbers for the alpha chain and myoglobin are adjusted slightly because they contain a different number of amino acid subunits overall than do the beta and gamma chains. Over their full length of more than 140 subunits the four chains have only 20 amino acid subunits in common.

hemoglobin takes place after three of the four iron atoms have combined with oxygen. When the change has occurred, the rate of combination of the fourth iron atom with oxygen is speeded up several hundred times. Nothing is known as yet about the atomic mechanism that sets off the displacement of the beta chains, but there is one interesting observation that allows us at least to be sure that the interaction of the iron atoms and the change of structure do not take place unless alpha and beta chains are both present.

Certain anemia patients suffer from a shortage of alpha chains; the beta chains, robbed of their usual partners, group themselves into independent assemblages of four chains. These are known as hemoglobin H and resemble normal hemoglobin in many of their properties. Reinhold Benesch and Ruth E. Benesch of the Columbia University College of Physicians and Surgeons have discovered, however, that the four iron atoms in hemoglobin H do not interact, which led them to predict that the combination of hemoglobin H with oxygen should not be accompanied by a change of structure. Using crystals grown by Helen M. Ranney of the Albert Einstein College of Medicine, Lelio Mazzarella and I verified this prediction. Oxygenated and reduced hemoglobin H both resemble normal human reduced hemoglobin in the arrangement of the four chains.

The rearrangement of the beta chains must be set in motion by a series of atomic displacements starting at or near the iron atoms when they combine with oxygen. Our X-ray analysis has not yet reached the resolution needed to discern these, and it seems that a deeper understanding of this intriguing phenomenon may have to wait until we succeed in working out the structures of reduced hemoglobin and oxyhemoglobin at atomic resolution.

Allosteric Enzymes

There are many analogies between the chemical activities of hemoglobin and those of enzymes catalyzing chemical reactions in living cells. These analogies lead one to expect that some enzymes may undergo changes of structure on coming into contact with the substances whose reactions they catalyze. One can imagine that the active sites of these enzymes are moving mechanisms rather than static surfaces magically endowed with catalytic properties.

Indirect and tentative evidence suggests that changes of structure involv-

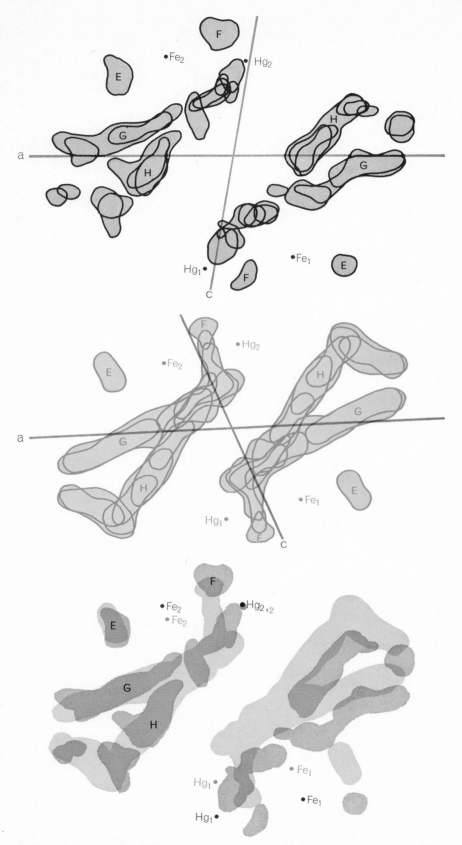

MOVEMENT OF HEMOGLOBIN CHAINS was discovered by comparing portions of the two beta chains in "reduced" (oxygen-free) human hemoglobin (*top*) with the same portions of horse hemoglobin containing oxygen (*middle*). The bottom illustration shows the outlines of the top and middle pictures superposed so that the mercury atoms (Hg_2) and helical regions (*E, F, G, H*) of the two chains at left coincide. The iron atoms (Fe_2) do not quite match. The chains at right are now seen to be shifted with respect to each other.

ing a rearrangement of subunits like that of the alpha and beta chains of hemoglobin do indeed occur and that they may form the basis of a control mechanism known as feedback inhibition. This is a piece of jargon that biochemistry has borrowed from electrical engineering, meaning nothing more complicated than that you stop being hungry when you have had enough to eat.

Constituents of living matter such as amino acids are built up from simpler substances in a series of small steps, each step being catalyzed by an enzyme that exists specifically for that purpose. Thus a whole series of different enzymes may be needed to make one amino acid. Such a series of enzymes appears to have built-in devices for ensuring the right balance of supply and demand. For example, in the colon bacillus the amino acid isoleucine is made from the amino acid threonine in several steps. The first enzyme in the series has an affinity for threonine: it catalyzes the removal of an amino group from it. H. Edwin Umbarger of the Long Island Biological Association in Cold Spring Harbor, N.Y., discovered that the action of the enzyme is inhibited by isoleucine, the end product of the last enzyme in the series. Jean-Pierre Changeux of the Pasteur Institute later showed that isoleucine acts not, as one might have expected, by blocking the site on the enzyme molecule that would otherwise combine with threonine but probably by combining with a different site on the molecule.

The two sites on the molecule must therefore interact, and Jacques Monod, Changeux and François Jacob have suggested that this is brought about by a rearrangement of subunits similar to that which accompanies the reaction of hemoglobin with oxygen. The enzyme is thought to exist in two alternative structural states: a reactive one when the supply of isoleucine has run out and an unreactive one when the supply exceeds demand. The discoverers have coined the name "allosteric" for enzymes of this kind.

The molecules of the enzymes suspected of having allosteric properties are all large ones, as one would expect them to be if they are made up of several subunits. This makes their X-ray analysis difficult. It may not be too hard to find out, however, whether or not a change of structure occurs, even if it takes a long time to unravel it in detail. In the meantime hemoglobin will serve as a useful model for the behavior of more complex enzyme systems.

The Three-dimensional Structure of an Enzyme Molecule

DAVID C. PHILLIPS · November 1966

One day in 1922 Alexander Fleming was suffering from a cold. This is not unusual in London, but Fleming was a most unusual man and he took advantage of the cold in a characteristic way. He allowed a few drops of his nasal mucus to fall on a culture of bacteria he was working with and then put the plate to one side to see what would happen. Imagine his excitement when he discovered some time later that the bacteria near the mucus had dissolved away. For a while he thought his ambition of finding a universal antibiotic had been realized. In a burst of activity he quickly established that the antibacterial action of the mucus was due to the presence in it of an enzyme; he called this substance lysozyme because of its capacity to lyse, or dissolve, the bacterial cells. Lysozyme was soon discovered in many tissues and secretions of the human body, in plants and most plentifully of all in the white of egg. Unfortunately Fleming found that it is not effective against the most harmful bacteria. He had to wait seven years before a strangely similar experiment revealed the existence of a genuinely effective antibiotic: penicillin.

Nevertheless, Fleming's lysozyme has proved a more valuable discovery than he can have expected when its properties were first established. With it, for example, bacterial anatomists have been able to study many details of bacterial structure [see "Fleming's Lysozyme," by Robert F. Acker and S. E. Hartsell; SCIENTIFIC AMERICAN, June, 1960]. It has now turned out that lysozyme is the first enzyme whose three-dimensional structure has been

determined and whose properties are understood in atomic detail. Among these properties is the way in which the enzyme combines with the substance on which it acts—a complex sugar in the wall of the bacterial cell.

Like all enzymes, lysozyme is a protein. Its chemical makeup has been established by Pierre Jollès and his colleagues at the University of Paris and by Robert E. Canfield of the Columbia University College of Physicians and Surgeons. They have found that each molecule of lysozyme obtained from egg white consists of a single polypeptide chain of 129 amino acid subunits of 20 different kinds. A peptide bond is formed when two amino acids are joined following the removal of a molecule of water. It is customary to call the portion of the amino acid in-

corporated into a polypeptide chain a residue, and each residue has its own characteristic side chain. The 129-residue lysozyme molecule is cross-linked in four places by disulfide bridges formed by the combination of sulfur-containing side chains in different parts of the molecule [see illustration on opposite page].

The properties of the molecule cannot be understood from its chemical constitution alone; they depend most critically on what parts of the molecule are brought close together in the folded three-dimensional structure. Some form of microscope is needed to examine the structure of the molecule. Fortunately one is effectively provided by the techniques of X-ray crystal-structure analysis pioneered by Sir Lawrence Bragg and his father Sir William Bragg.

ALA	ALANINE	GLY	GLYCINE	PRO	PROLINE
ARG	ARGININE	HIS	HISTIDINE	SER	SERINE
ASN	ASPARAGINE	ILEU	ISOLEUCINE	THR	THREONINE
ASP	ASPARTIC ACID	LEU	LEUCINE	TRY	TRYPTOPHAN
CYS	CYSTEINE	LYS	LYSINE	TYR	TYROSINE
GLN	GLUTAMINE	MET	METHIONINE	VAL	VALINE
GLU	GLUTAMIC ACID	PHE	PHENYLALANINE		

TWO-DIMENSIONAL MODEL of the lysozyme molecule is shown on the opposite page. Lysozyme is a protein containing 129 amino acid subunits, commonly called residues (see key to abbreviations above). These residues form a polypeptide chain that is cross-linked at four places by disulfide (–S–S–) bonds. The amino acid sequence of lysozyme was determined independently by Pierre Jollès and his co-workers at the University of Paris and by Robert E. Canfield of the Columbia University College of Physicians and Surgeons. The three-dimensional structure of the lysozyme molecule has now been established with the help of X-ray crystallography by the author and his colleagues at the Royal Institution in London. A painting of the molecule's three-dimensional structure appears on pages 54 and 55. The function of lysozyme is to split a particular long-chain molecule, a complex sugar, found in the outer membrane of many living cells. Molecules that are acted on by enzymes are known as substrates. The substrate of lysozyme fits into a cleft, or pocket, formed by the three-dimensional structure of the lysozyme molecule. In the two-dimensional model on the opposite page the amino acid residues that line the pocket are shown in dark green.

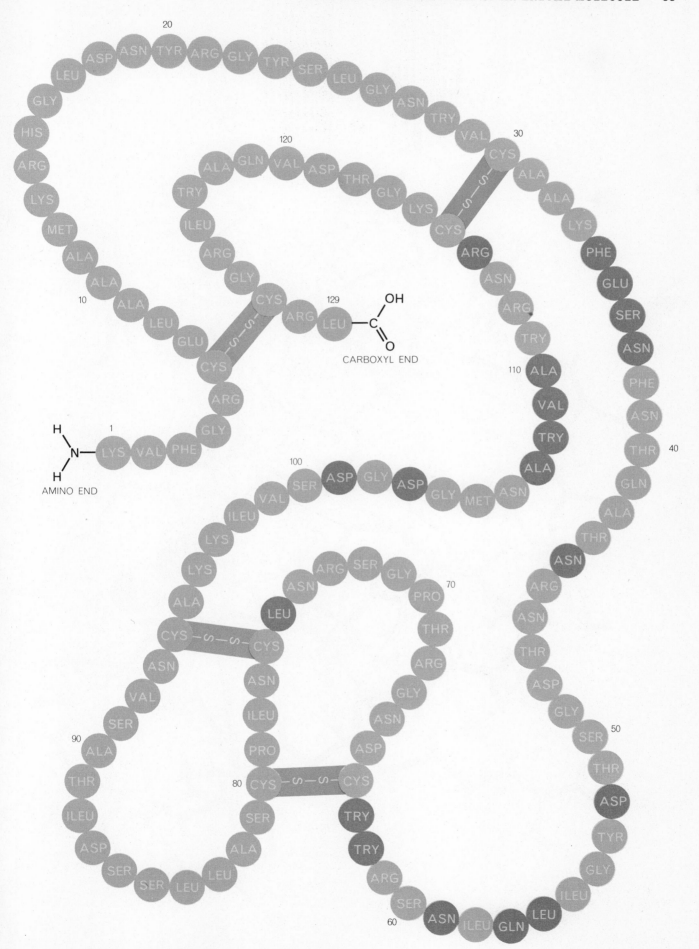

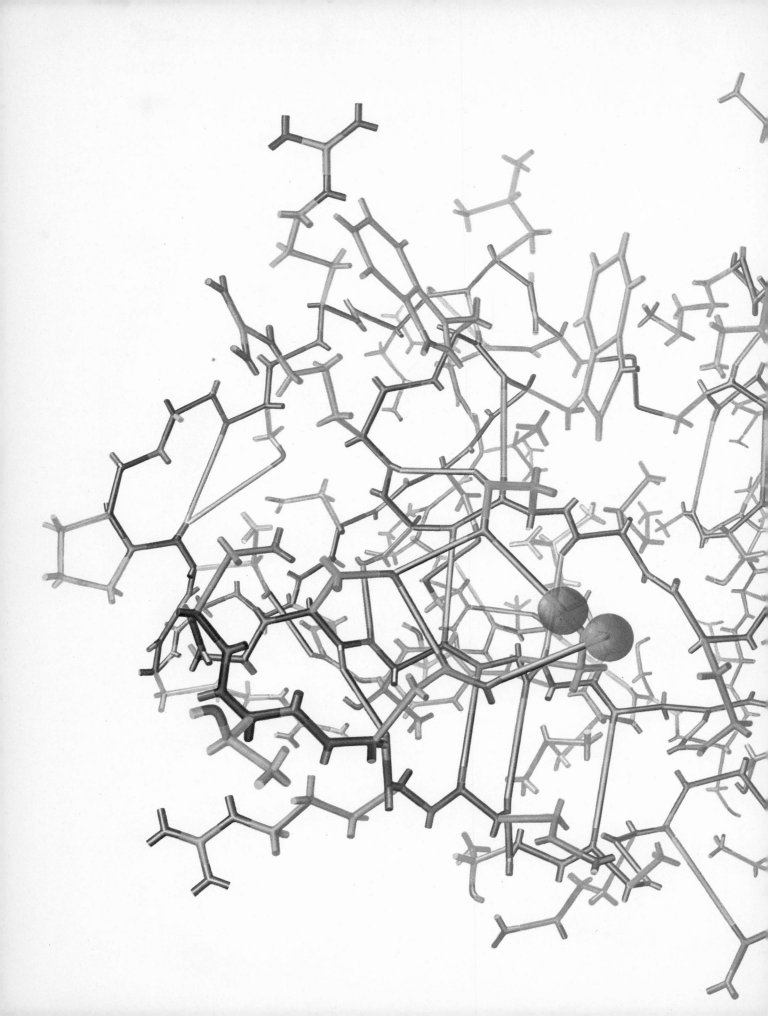

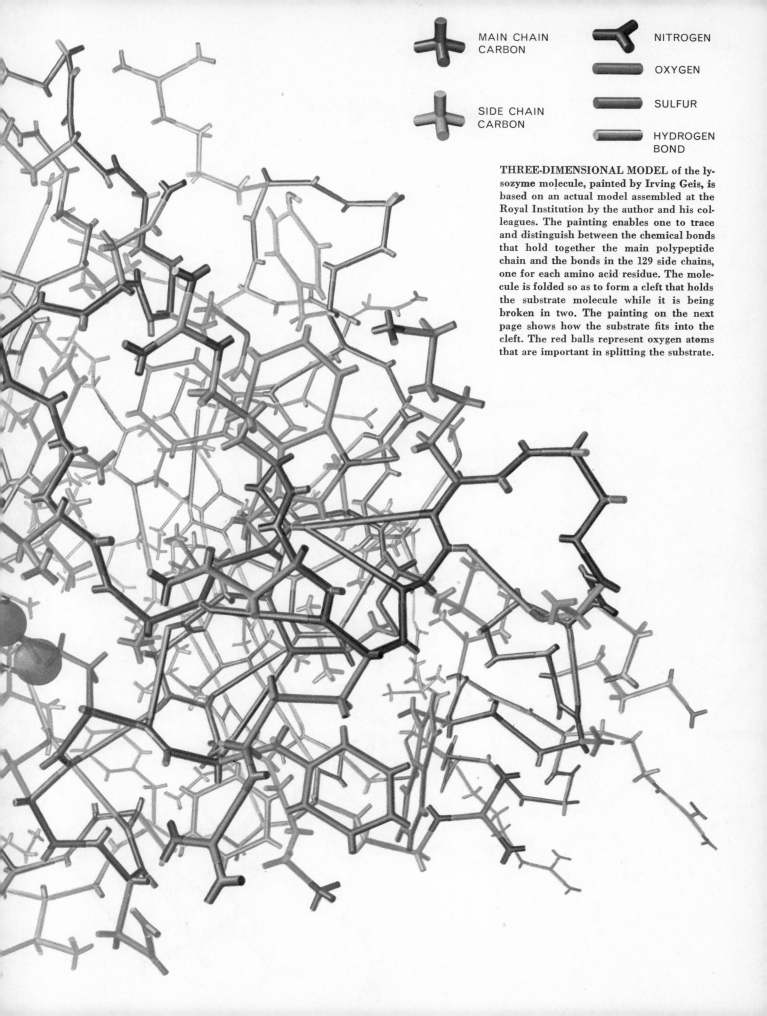

MAIN CHAIN CARBON

SIDE CHAIN CARBON

NITROGEN

OXYGEN

SULFUR

HYDROGEN BOND

THREE-DIMENSIONAL MODEL of the lysozyme molecule, painted by Irving Geis, is based on an actual model assembled at the Royal Institution by the author and his colleagues. The painting enables one to trace and distinguish between the chemical bonds that hold together the main polypeptide chain and the bonds in the 129 side chains, one for each amino acid residue. The molecule is folded so as to form a cleft that holds the substrate molecule while it is being broken in two. The painting on the next page shows how the substrate fits into the cleft. The red balls represent oxygen atoms that are important in splitting the substrate.

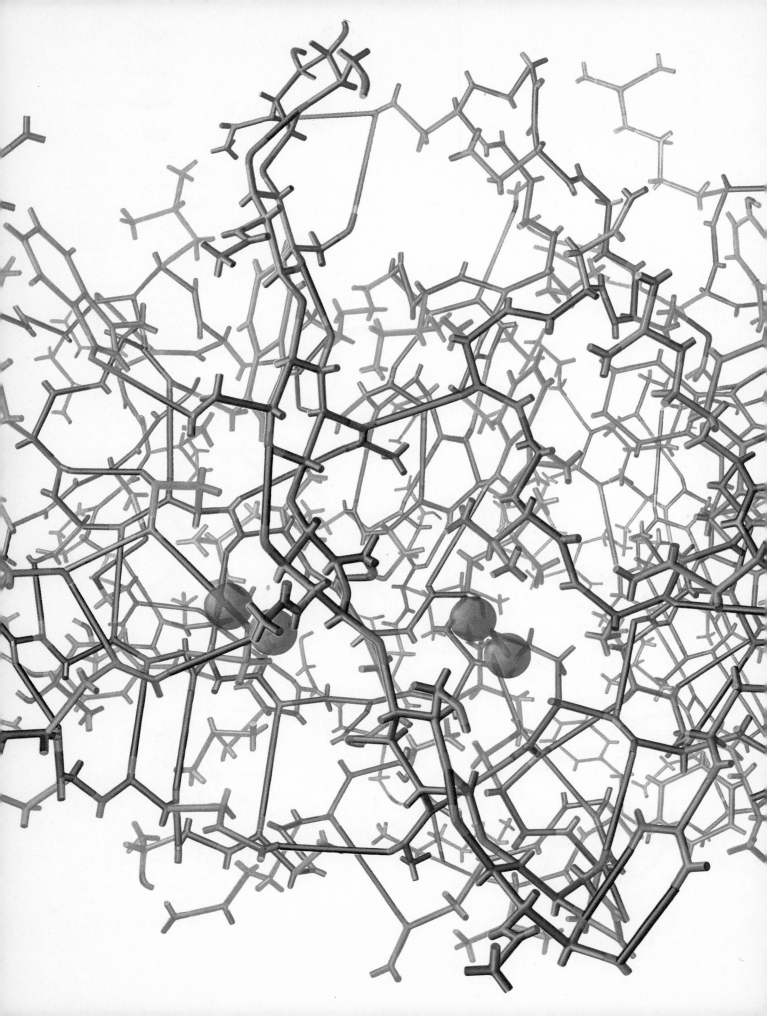

The difficulties of examining molecules in atomic detail arise, of course, from the fact that molecules are very small. Within a molecule each atom is usually separated from its neighbor by about 1.5 angstrom units (1.5×10^{-8} centimeter). The lysozyme molecule, which contains some 1,950 atoms, is about 40 angstroms in its largest dimension. The first problem is to find a microscope in which the atoms can be resolved from one another, or seen separately.

The resolving power of a microscope depends fundamentally on the wavelength of the radiation it employs. In general no two objects can be seen separately if they are closer together than about half this wavelength. The shortest wavelength transmitted by optical microscopes (those working in the ultraviolet end of the spectrum) is about 2,000 times longer than the distance between atoms. In order to "see" atoms one must use radiation with a much shorter wavelength: X rays, which have a wavelength closely comparable to interatomic distances. The employment of X rays, however, creates other difficulties: no satisfactory way has yet been found to make lenses or mirrors that will focus them into an image. The problem, then, is the apparently impossible one of designing an X-ray microscope without lenses or mirrors.

Consideration of the diffraction theory of microscope optics, as developed by Ernst Abbe in the latter part of the 19th century, shows that the problem can be solved. Abbe taught us that the formation of an image in the microscope can be regarded as a two-stage process. First, the object under examination scatters the light or other radiation falling on it in all directions, forming a diffraction pattern. This pattern arises because the light waves scattered from different parts of the object combine so as to produce a wave of large or small amplitude in any direction

according to whether the waves are in or out of phase—in or out of step—with one another. (This effect is seen most easily in light waves scattered by a regularly repeating structure, such as a diffraction grating made of lines scribed at regular intervals on a glass plate.) In the second stage of image formation, according to Abbe, the objective lens of the microscope collects the diffracted waves and recombines them to form an image of the object. Most important, the nature of the image depends critically on how much of the diffraction pattern is used in its formation.

X-Ray Structure Analysis

In essence X-ray structure analysis makes use of a microscope in which the two stages of image formation have been separated. Since the X rays cannot be focused to form an image directly, the diffraction pattern is recorded and the image is obtained from it by calculation. Historically the method was not developed on the basis of this reasoning, but this way of regarding it (which was first suggested by Lawrence Bragg) brings out its essential features and also introduces the main difficulty of applying it. In recording the intensities of the diffracted waves, instead of focusing them to form an image, some crucial information is lost, namely the phase relations among the various diffracted waves. Without this information the image cannot be formed, and some means of recovering it has to be found. This is the well-known phase problem of X-ray crystallography. It is on the solution of the problem that the utility of the method depends.

The term "X-ray crystallography" reminds us that in practice the method was developed (and is still applied) in the study of single crystals. Crystals suitable for study may contain some

10^{15} identical molecules in a regular array; in effect the molecules in such a crystal diffract the X radiation as though they were a single giant molecule. The crystal acts as a three-dimensional diffraction grating, so that the waves scattered by them are confined to a number of discrete directions. In order to obtain a three-dimensional image of the structure the intensity of the X rays scattered in these different directions must be measured, the phase problem must be solved somehow and the measurements must be combined by a computer.

The recent successes of this method in the study of protein structures have depended a great deal on the development of electronic computers capable of performing the calculations. They are due most of all, however, to the discovery in 1953, by M. F. Perutz of the Medical Research Council Laboratory of Molecular Biology in Cambridge, that the method of "isomorphous replacement" can be used to solve the phase problem in the study of protein crystals. The method depends on the preparation and study of a series of protein crystals into which additional heavy atoms, such as atoms of uranium, have been introduced without otherwise affecting the crystal structure. The first successes of this method were in the study of sperm-whale myoglobin by John C. Kendrew of the Medical Research Council Laboratory and in Perutz' own study of horse hemoglobin. For their work the two men received the Nobel prize for chemistry in 1962 [see "The Three-dimensional Structure of a Protein Molecule," by John C. Kendrew, SCIENTIFIC AMERICAN Offprint 121, and "The Hemoglobin Molecule," by M. F. Perutz, which begins on page 39 in this book.

Because the X rays are scattered by the electrons within the molecules, the image calculated from the diffraction pattern reveals the distribution of electrons within the crystal. The electron density is usually calculated at a regular array of points, and the image is made visible by drawing contour lines through points of equal electron density. If these contour maps are drawn on clear plastic sheets, one can obtain a three-dimensional image by assembling the maps one above the other in a stack. The amount of detail that can be seen in such an image depends on the resolving power of the effective microscope, that is, on its "aperture," or the extent of the diffraction pattern that has been included in the formation of the image. If the waves diffracted through sufficiently high angles are included

MODEL OF SUBSTRATE shows how it fits into the cleft in the lysozyme molecule. All the carbon atoms in the substrate are shown in purple. The portion of the substrate in intimate contact with the underlying enzyme is a polysaccharide chain consisting of six ringlike structures, each a residue of an amino-sugar molecule. The substrate in the model is made up of six identical residues of the amino sugar called N-acetylglucosamine (NAG). In the actual substrate every other residue is an amino sugar known as N-acetylmuramic acid (NAM). The illustration is based on X-ray studies of the way the enzyme is bound to a trisaccharide made of three NAG units, which fills the top of the cleft; the arrangement of NAG units in the bottom of the cleft was worked out with the aid of three-dimensional models. The substrate is held to the enzyme by a complex network of hydrogen bonds. In this style of model-making each straight section of chain represents a bond between atoms. The atoms themselves lie at the intersections and elbows of the structure. Except for the four red balls representing oxygen atoms that are active in splitting the polysaccharide substrate, no attempt is made to represent the electron shells of atoms because they would merge into a solid mass.

(corresponding to a large aperture), the atoms appear as individual peaks in the image map. At lower resolution groups of unresolved atoms appear with characteristic shapes by which they can be recognized.

The three-dimensional structure of lysozyme crystallized from the white of hen's egg has been determined in atomic detail with the X-ray method by our group at the Royal Institution in Lon-don. This is the laboratory in which Humphry Davy and Michael Faraday made their fundamental discoveries dur-ing the 19th century, and in which the X-ray method of structure analysis was developed between the two world wars by the brilliant group of workers led by William Bragg, including J. D. Ber-nal, Kathleen Lonsdale, W. T. Astbury, J. M. Robertson and many others. Our work on lysozyme was begun in 1960 when Roberto J. Poljak, a visiting work-er from Argentina, demonstrated that suitable crystals containing heavy atoms could be prepared. Since then C. C. F. Blake, A. C. T. North, V. R. Sarma, Ruth Fenn, D. F. Koenig, Louise N. Johnson and G. A. Mair have played important roles in the work.

In 1962 a low-resolution image of the structure was obtained that revealed the general shape of the molecule and

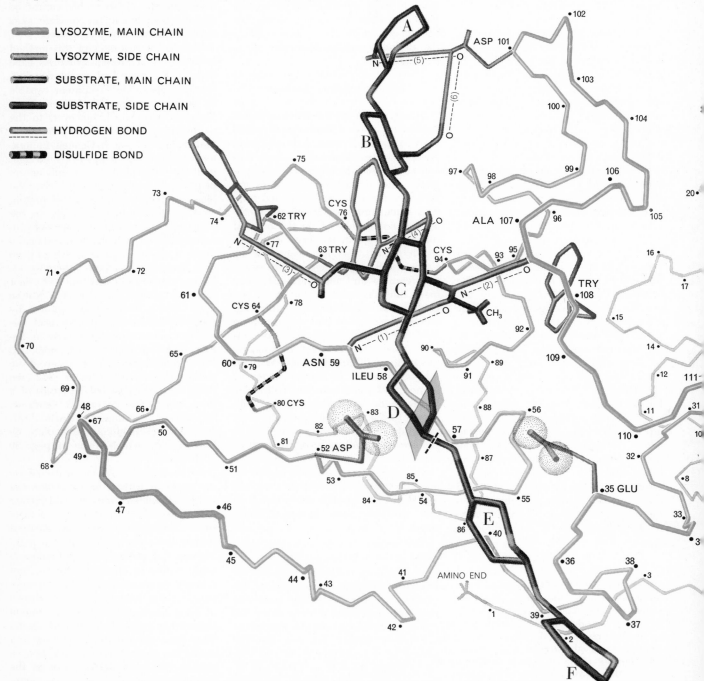

MAP OF LYSOZYME AND SUBSTRATE depicts in color the central chain of each molecule. Side chains have been omitted ex-cept for those that produce the four disulfide bonds clipping the lysozyme molecule together and those that supply the terminal con-nections for hydrogen bonds holding the substrate to the lysozyme. The top three rings of the substrate (A, B, C) are held to the un-derlying enzyme by six principal hydrogen bonds, which are iden-tified by number to key with the description in the text. The lyso-

showed that the arrangement of the polypeptide chain is even more complex than it is in myoglobin. This low-resolution image was calculated from the amplitudes of about 400 diffraction maxima measured from native protein crystals and from crystals containing each of three different heavy atoms. In 1965, after the development of more efficient methods of measurement and computation, an image was calculated on the basis of nearly 10,000 diffraction maxima, which resolved features separated by two angstroms. Apart from showing a few well-separated chloride ions, which are present because the lysozyme is crystallized from a solution containing sodium chloride, the two-angstrom image still does not show individual atoms as separate maxima in the electron-density map. The level of resolution is high enough, however, for many of the groups of atoms to be clearly recognizable.

The Lysozyme Molecule

The main polypeptide chain appears as a continuous ribbon of electron density running through the image with regularly spaced promontories on it that are characteristic of the carbonyl groups (CO) that mark each peptide bond. In some regions the chain is folded in ways that are familiar from theoretical studies of polypeptide configurations and from the structure analyses of myoglobin and fibrous proteins such as the keratin of hair. The amino acid residues in lysozyme have now been designated by number; the residues numbered 5 through 15, 24 through 34 and 88 through 96 form three lengths of "alpha helix," the conformation that was proposed by Linus Pauling and Robert B. Corey in 1951 and that was found by Kendrew and his colleagues to be the most common arrangement of the chain in myoglobin. The helixes in lysozyme, however, appear to be somewhat distorted from the "classical" form, in which four atoms (carbon, oxygen, nitrogen and hydrogen) of each peptide group lie in a plane that is parallel to the axis of the alpha helix. In the lysozyme molecule the peptide groups in the helical sections tend to be rotated slightly in such a way that their CO groups point outward from the helix axes and their imino groups (NH) inward.

The amount of rotation varies, being slight in the helix formed by residues 5 through 15 and considerable in the one formed by residues 24 through 34. The effect of the rotation is that each NH group does not point directly at the CO group four residues back along the chain but points instead between the CO groups of the residues three and four back. When the NH group points directly at the CO group four residues back, as it does in the classical alpha helix, it forms with the CO group a hydrogen bond (the weak chemical bond in which a hydrogen atom acts as a bridge). In the lysozyme helixes the hydrogen bond is formed somewhere between two CO groups, giving rise to a structure intermediate between that of an alpha helix and that of a more symmetrical helix with a three-fold symmetry axis that was discussed by Lawrence Bragg, Kendrew and Perutz in 1950. There is a further short length of helix (residues 80 through 85) in which the hydrogen-bonding arrangement is quite close to that in the three-fold helix, and also an isolated turn (residues 119 through 122) of three-fold helix. Furthermore, the peptide at the far end of helix 5 through 15 is in the conformation of the three-fold helix, and the hydrogen bond from its NH group is made to the CO three residues back rather than four.

Partly because of these irregularities in the structure of lysozyme, the proportion of its polypeptide chain in the alpha-helix conformation is difficult to calculate in a meaningful way for comparison with the estimates obtained by other methods, but it is clearly less than half the proportion observed in myoglobin, in which helical regions make up about 75 percent of the chain. The lysozyme molecule does include, however, an example of another regular conformation predicted by Pauling and Corey. This is the "antiparallel pleated sheet," which is believed to be the basic structure of the fibrous protein silk and in which, as the name suggests, two lengths of polypeptide chain run parallel to each other in opposite directions. This structure again is stabilized by hydrogen bonds between the NH and CO groups of the main chain. Residues 41 through 45 and 50 through 54 in the lysozyme molecule form such a structure, with the connecting residues 46 through 49 folded into a hairpin bend between the two lengths of comparatively extended chain. The remainder of the polypeptide chain is folded in irregular ways that have no simple short description.

Even though the level of resolution achieved in our present image was not enough to resolve individual atoms, many of the side chains characteristic of the amino acid residues were readily identifiable from their general shape. The four disulfide bridges, for example, are marked by short rods of high electron density corresponding to the two relatively dense sulfur atoms within them. The six tryptophan residues also were easily recognized by the extended electron density produced by the large double-ring structures in their

zyme molecule fulfills its function when it cleaves the substrate between the *D* and the *E* ring. Note the distortion of the *D* ring, which pushes four of its atoms into a plane.

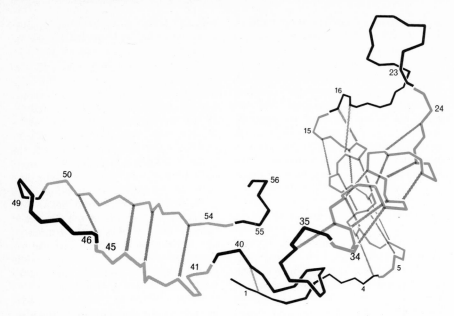

FIRST 56 RESIDUES in lysozyme molecule contain a higher proportion of symmetrically organized regions than does all the rest of the molecule. Residues 5 through 15 and 24 through 34 (*right*) form two regions in which hydrogen bonds (*gray*) hold the residues in a helical configuration close to that of the "classical" alpha helix. Residues 41 through 45 and 50 through 54 (*left*) fold back against each other to form a "pleated sheet," also held together by hydrogen bonds. In addition the hydrogen bond between residues 1 and 40 ties the first 40 residues into a compact structure that may have been folded in this way before the molecule was fully synthesized (*see illustration at the bottom of these two pages*).

liquid. Such "polar" side chains are hydrophilic—attracted to water; they are found in aspartic acid and glutamic acid residues and in lysine, arginine and histidine residues, which have basic side groups. On the other hand, most of the markedly nonpolar and hydrophobic side chains (for example those found in leucine and isoleucine residues) are shielded from the surrounding liquid by more polar parts of the molecule. In fact, as was predicted by Sir Eric Rideal (who was at one time director of the Royal Institution) and Irving Langmuir, lysozyme, like myoglobin, is quite well described as an oil drop with a polar coat. Here it is important to note that the environment of each molecule in the crystalline state is not significantly different from its natural environment in the living cell. The crystals themselves include a large proportion (some 35 percent by weight) of mostly watery liquid of crystallization. The effect of the surrounding liquid on the protein conformation thus is likely to be much the same in the crystals as it is in solution.

It appears, then, that the observed conformation is preferred because in it the hydrophobic side chains are kept out of contact with the surrounding liquid whereas the polar side chains are generally exposed to it. In this way the system consisting of the protein and the solvent attains a minimum free energy, partly because of the large number of favorable interactions of like groups within the protein molecule and between it and the surrounding liquid, and partly because of the relatively high disorder of the water molecules that are in contact only with other polar groups of atoms.

Guided by these generalizations, many workers are now interested in the possibility of predicting the conforma-

side chains. Many of the other residues also were easily identifiable, but it was nevertheless most important for the rapid and reliable interpretation of the image that the results of the chemical analysis were already available. With their help more than 95 percent of the atoms in the molecule were readily identified and located within about .25 angstrom.

Further efforts at improving the accuracy with which the atoms have been located is in progress, but an almost complete description of the lysozyme molecule now exists [*see illustration on pages 54 and 55*]. By studying it and the

results of some further experiments we can begin to suggest answers to two important questions: How does a molecule such as this one attain its observed conformation? How does it function as an enzyme, or biological catalyst?

Inspection of the lysozyme molecule immediately suggests two generalizations about its conformation that agree well with those arrived at earlier in the study of myoglobin. It is obvious that certain residues with acidic and basic side chains that ionize, or dissociate, on contact with water are all on the surface of the molecule more or less readily accessible to the surrounding

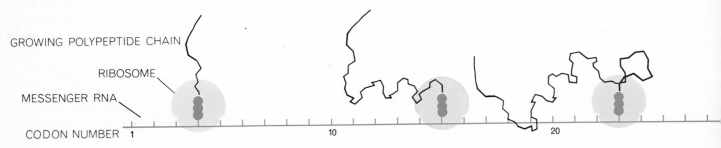

FOLDING OF PROTEIN MOLECULE may take place as the growing polypeptide chain is being synthesized by the intracellular particles called ribosomes. The genetic message specifying the amino acid sequence of each protein is coded in "messenger" ribonucleic acid (RNA). It is believed several ribosomes travel simultaneously along this long-chain molecule, reading the message as they go.

tion of a protein molecule from its chemical formula alone [see "Molecular Model-building by Computer," by Cyrus Levinthal; SCIENTIFIC AMERICAN Offprint 1043]. The task of exploring all possible conformations in the search for the one of lowest free energy seems likely, however, to remain beyond the power of any imaginable computer. On a conservative estimate it would be necessary to consider some 10^{129} different conformations for the lysozyme molecule in any general search for the one with minimum free energy. Since this number is far greater than the number of particles in the observable universe, it is clear that simplifying assumptions will have to be made if calculations of this kind are to succeed.

The Folding of Lysozyme

For some time Peter Dunnill and I have been trying to develop a model of protein-folding that promises to make practicable calculations of the minimum energy conformation and that is, at the same time, qualitatively consistent with the observed structure of myoglobin and lysozyme. This model makes use of our present knowledge of the way in which proteins are synthesized in the living cell. For example, it is well known, from experiments by Howard M. Dintzis and by Christian B. Anfinsen and Robert Canfield, that protein molecules are synthesized from the terminal amino end of their polypeptide chain. The nature of the synthetic mechanism, which involves the intracellular particles called ribosomes working in collaboration with two forms of ribonucleic acid ("messenger" RNA and "transfer" RNA), is increasingly well understood in principle, although the detailed environment of the growing protein chain remains unknown. Nevertheless,

it seems a reasonable assumption that, as the synthesis proceeds, the amino end of the chain becomes separated by an increasing distance from the point of attachment to the ribosome, and that the folding of the protein chain to its native conformation begins at this end even before the synthesis is complete. According to our present ideas, parts of the polypeptide chain, particularly those near the terminal amino end, may fold into stable conformations that can still be recognized in the finished molecule and that act as "internal templates," or centers, around which the rest of the chain is folded [see illustration at bottom of these two pages]. It may therefore be useful to look for the stable conformations of parts of the polypeptide chain and to avoid studying all the possible conformations of the whole molecule.

Inspection of the lysozyme molecule provides qualitative support for these ideas [see top illustration on opposite page]. The first 40 residues from the terminal amino end form a compact structure (residues 1 and 40 are linked by a hydrogen bond) with a hydrophobic interior and a relatively hydrophilic surface that seems likely to have been folded in this way, or in a simply related way, before the molecule was fully synthesized. It may also be important to observe that this part of the molecule includes more alpha helix than the remainder does.

These first 40 residues include a mixture of hydrophobic and hydrophilic side chains, but the next 14 residues in the sequence are all hydrophilic; it is interesting, and possibly significant, that these are the residues in the antiparallel pleated sheet, which lies out of contact with the globular submolecule formed by the earlier residues. In the light of our model of protein fold-

ing the obvious speculation is that there is no incentive to fold these hydrophilic residues in contact with the first part of the chain until the hydrophobic residues 55 (isoleucine) and 56 (leucine) have to be shielded from contact with the surrounding liquid. It seems reasonable to suppose that at this stage residues 41 through 54 fold back on themselves, forming the pleated-sheet structure and burying the hydrophobic side chains in the initial hydrophobic pocket.

Similar considerations appear to govern the folding of the rest of the molecule. In brief, residues 57 through 86 are folded in contact with the pleated-sheet structure so that at this stage of the process—if indeed it follows this course—the folded chain forms a structure with two wings lying at an angle to each other. Residues 86 through 96 form a length of alpha helix, one side of which is predominantly hydrophobic, because of an appropriate alternation of polar and nonpolar residues in that part of the sequence. This helix lies in the gap between the two wings formed by the earlier residues, with its hydrophobic side buried within the molecule. The gap between the two wings is not completely filled by the helix, however; it is transformed into a deep cleft running up one side of the molecule. As we shall see, this cleft forms the active site of the enzyme. The remaining residues are folded around the globular unit formed by the terminal amino end of the polypeptide chain.

This model of protein-folding can be tested in a number of ways, for example by studying the conformation of the first 40 residues in isolation both di-

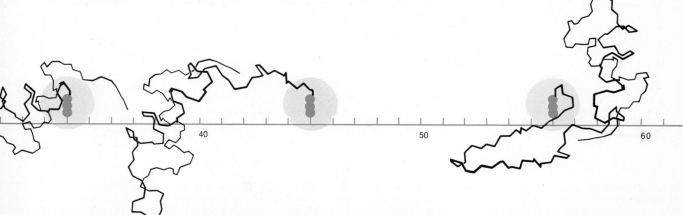

Presumably the messenger RNA for lysozyme contains 129 "codons," one for each amino acid. Amino acids are delivered to the site of synthesis by molecules of "transfer" RNA (dark color). The illustration shows how the lysozyme chain would lengthen as a ribosome travels along the messenger RNA molecule. Here, hypothetically, the polypeptide is shown folding directly into its final shape.

rectly (after removal of the rest of the molecule) and by computation. Ultimately, of course, the model will be regarded as satisfactory only if it helps us to predict how other protein molecules are folded from a knowledge of their chemical structure alone.

The Activity of Lysozyme

In order to understand how lysozyme brings about the dissolution of bacteria we must consider the structure of the bacterial cell wall in some detail. Through the pioneer and independent studies of Karl Meyer and E. B. Chain, followed up by M. R. J. Salton of the University of Manchester and many others, the structures of bacterial cell walls and the effect of lysozyme on them are now quite well known. The important part of the cell wall, as far as lysozyme is concerned, is made up of glucose-like amino-sugar molecules linked together into long polysaccharide chains, which are themselves cross-connected by short lengths of polypeptide chain. This part of each cell wall probably forms one enormous molecule—a "bag-shaped macromolecule," as W. Weidel and H. Pelzer have called it.

The amino-sugar molecules concerned in these polysaccharide structures are of two kinds; each contains an acetamido (–NH · CO · CH₃) side group, but one of them contains an additional major group, a lactyl side chain [see illustration below]. One of these amino sugars is known as N-acetylglucosamine (NAG) and the other as N-acetylmuramic acid (NAM). They occur alternately in the polysaccharide chains, being connected by bridges that include an oxygen atom (glycosidic linkages) between carbon atoms 1 and 4 of consecutive sugar rings; this is the same linkage that joins glucose residues in cellulose. The polypeptide chains that cross-connect these polysaccharides are attached to the NAM residues through the lactyl side chain attached to carbon atom 3 in each NAM ring.

Lysozyme has been shown to break the linkages in which carbon 1 in NAM is linked to carbon 4 in NAG but not the other linkages. It has also been shown to break down chitin, another common natural polysaccharide that is found in lobster shell and that contains only NAG.

Ever since the work of Svante Arrhenius of Sweden in the late 19th century enzymes have been thought to work by forming intermediate compounds with their substrates: the substances whose chemical reactions they catalyze. A proper theory of the enzyme-substrate complex, which underlies all present thinking about enzyme activity, was clearly propounded by Leonor Michaelis and Maude Menton in a remarkable paper published in 1913. The idea, in its simplest form, is that an enzyme molecule provides a site on its surface to which its substrate molecule can bind in a quite precise way. Reactive groups of atoms in the enzyme then promote the required chemical reaction in the substrate. Our immediate objective, therefore, was to find the structure of a reactive complex between lysozyme and its polysaccharide substrate, in the hope that we would then be able to recognize the active groups of atoms in the enzyme and understand how they function.

Our studies began with the observation by Martin Wenzel and his colleagues at the Free University of Berlin that the enzyme is prevented from functioning by the presence of NAG itself. This small molecule acts as a competitive inhibitor of the enzyme's activity and, since it is a part of the large substrate molecule normally acted on by the enzyme, it seems likely to do this by binding to the enzyme in the way that part of the substrate does. It prevents the enzyme from working by preventing the substrate from binding to the enzyme. Other simple amino-sugar molecules, including the trisaccharide made of three NAG units, behave in the same way. We therefore decided to study the binding of these sugar molecules to the lysozyme molecules in our crystals in the hope of learning something about the structure of the enzyme-substrate complex itself.

My colleague Louise Johnson soon found that crystals containing the sugar molecules bound to lysozyme can be prepared very simply by adding the sugar to the solution from which the lysozyme crystals have been grown and in which they are kept suspended. The small molecules diffuse into the protein crystals along the channels filled with water that run through the crystals. Fortunately the resulting change in the crystal structure can be studied quite simply. A useful image of the electron-density changes can be calculated from

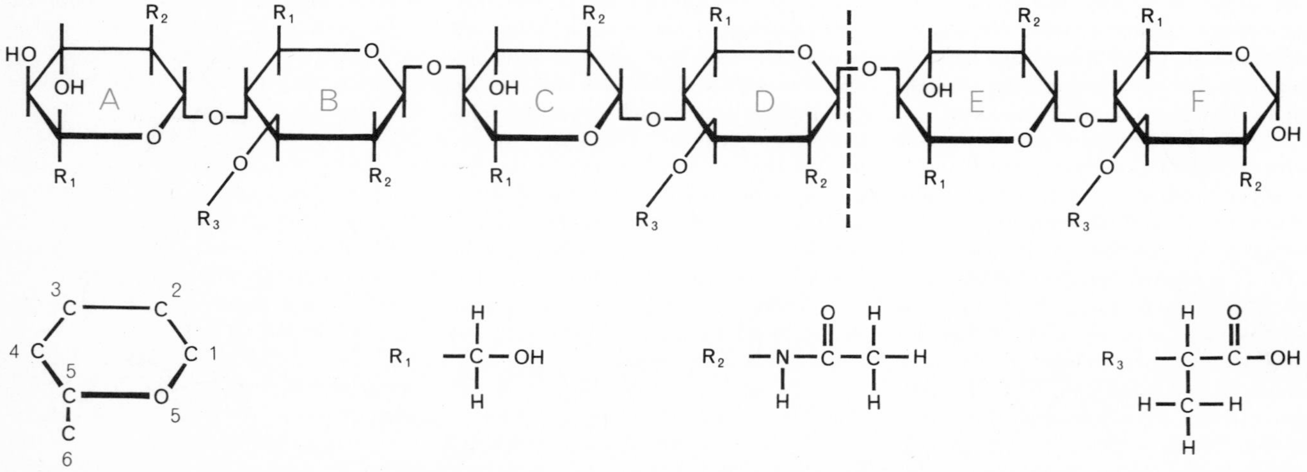

POLYSACCHARIDE MOLECULE found in the walls of certain bacterial cells is the substrate broken by the lysozyme molecule. The polysaccharide consists of alternating residues of two kinds of amino sugar: N-acetylglucosamine (NAG) and N-acetylmuramic acid (NAM). In the length of polysaccharide chain shown here

A, C and E are NAG residues; B, D and F are NAM residues. The inset at left shows the numbering scheme for identifying the principal atoms in each sugar ring. Six rings of the polysaccharide fit into the cleft of the lysozyme molecule, which effects a cleavage between rings D and E (see illustration on pages 58 and 59).

measurements of the changes in amplitude of the diffracted waves, on the assumption that their phase relations have not changed from those determined for the pure protein crystals. The image shows the difference in electron density between crystals that contain the added sugar molecules and those that do not.

In this way the binding to lysozyme of eight different amino sugars was studied at low resolution (that is, through the measurement of changes in the amplitude of 400 diffracted waves). The results showed that the sugars bind to lysozyme at a number of different places in the cleft of the enzyme. The investigation was hurried on to higher resolution in an attempt to discover the exact nature of the binding. Happily these studies at two-angstrom resolution (which required the measurement of 10,000 diffracted waves) have now shown in detail how the trisaccharide made of three NAG units is bound to the enzyme.

The trisaccharide fills the top half of the cleft and is bound to the enzyme by a number of interactions, which can be followed with the help of the illustration on pages 58 and 59. In this illustration six important hydrogen bonds, to be described presently, are identified by number. The most critical of these interactions appear to involve the acetamido group of sugar residue C [*third from top*], whose carbon atom 1 is not linked to another sugar residue. There are hydrogen bonds from the CO group of this side chain to the main-chain NH group of amino acid residue 59 in the enzyme molecule [*bond No. 1*] and from its NH group to the main-chain CO group of residue 107 (alanine) in the enzyme molecule [*bond No. 2*]. Its terminal CH_3 group makes contact with the side chain of residue 108 (tryptophan). Hydrogen bonds [*No. 3 and No. 4*] are also formed between two oxygen atoms adjacent to carbon atoms 6 and 3 of sugar residue C and the side chains of residues 62 and 63 (both tryptophan) respectively. Another hydrogen bond [*No. 5*] is formed between the acetamido side chain of sugar residue A and residue 101 (aspartic acid) in the enzyme molecule. From residue 101 there is a hydrogen bond [*No. 6*] to the oxygen adjacent to carbon atom 6 of sugar residue B. These polar interactions are supplemented by a large number of nonpolar interactions that are more difficult to summarize briefly. Among the more important nonpolar interactions, however, are those between sugar residue B and the ring system of residue

62; these deserve special mention because they are affected by a small change in the conformation of the enzyme molecule that occurs when the trisaccharide is bound to it. The electron-density map showing the change in electron density when tri-NAG is bound in the protein crystal reveals clearly that parts of the enzyme molecule have moved with respect to one another. These changes in conformation are largely restricted to the part of the enzyme structure to the left of the cleft, which appears to tilt more or less as a whole in such a way as to close the cleft slightly. As a result the side chain of residue 62 moves about .75 angstrom toward the position of sugar residue B. Such changes in enzyme conformation have been discussed for some time, notably by Daniel E. Koshland, Jr., of the University of California at Berkeley, whose "induced fit" theory of the enzyme-substrate interaction is supported in some degree by this observation in lysozyme.

The Enzyme-Substrate Complex

At this stage in the investigation excitement grew high. Could we tell how the enzyme works? I believe we can. Unfortunately, however, we cannot see this dynamic process in our X-ray images. We have to work out what must happen from our static pictures. First of all it is clear that the complex formed by tri-NAG and the enzyme is not the enzyme-substrate complex involved in catalysis because it is stable. At low concentrations tri-NAG is known to behave as an inhibitor rather than as a substrate that is broken down; clearly we have been looking at the way in which it binds as an inhibitor. It is noticeable, however, that tri-NAG fills only half of the cleft. The possibility emerges that more sugar residues, filling the remainder of the cleft, are required for the formation of a reactive enzyme-substrate complex. The assumption here is that the observed binding of tri-NAG as an inhibitor involves interactions with the enzyme molecule that also play a part in the formation of the functioning enzyme-substrate complex.

Accordingly we have built a model that shows that another three sugar residues can be added to the tri-NAG in such a way that there are satisfactory interactions of the atoms in the proposed substrate and the enzyme. There is only one difficulty: carbon atom 6 and its adjacent oxygen atom in sugar residue D make uncomfortably close contacts

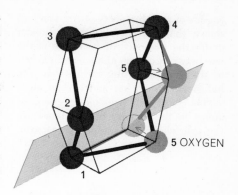

"CHAIR" CONFIGURATION (*gray*) is that normally assumed by the rings of amino sugar in the polysaccharide substrate. When bound against the lysozyme, however, the D ring is distorted (*color*) so that carbon atoms 1, 2 and 5 and oxygen atom 5 lie in a plane. The distortion evidently assists in breaking the substrate below the D ring.

with atoms in the enzyme molecule, unless this sugar residue is distorted a little out of its most stable "chair" conformation into a conformation in which carbon atoms 1, 2 and 5 and oxygen atom 5 all lie in a plane [*see illustration above*]. Otherwise satisfactory interactions immediately suggest themselves, and the model falls into place.

At this point it seemed reasonable to assume that the model shows the structure of the functioning complex between the enzyme and a hexasaccharide. The next problem was to decide which of the five glycosidic linkages would be broken under the influence of the enzyme. Fortunately evidence was at hand to suggest the answer. As we have seen, the cell-wall polysaccharide includes alternate sugar residues of two kinds, NAG and NAM, and the bond broken is between NAM and NAG. It was therefore important to decide which of the six sugar residues in our model could be NAM, which is the same as NAG except for the lactyl side chain appended to carbon atom 3. The answer was clear-cut. Sugar residue C cannot be NAM because there is no room for this additional group of atoms. Therefore the bond broken must be between sugar residues B and C or D and E. We already knew that the glycosidic linkage between residues B and C is stable when tri-NAG is bound. The conclusion was inescapable: the linkage that must be broken is the one between sugar residues D and E.

Now it was possible to search for the origin of the catalytic activity in the neighborhood of this linkage. Our task was made easier by the fact that John A.

Rupley of the University of Arizona had shown that the chemical bond broken under the influence of lysozyme is the one between carbon atom 1 and oxygen in the glycosidic link rather than the link between oxygen and carbon atom 4. The most reactive-looking group of atoms in the vicinity of this bond are the side chains of residue 52 (aspartic acid) and residue 35 (glutamic acid).

One of the oxygen atoms of residue 52 is about three angstroms from carbon atom 1 of sugar residue *D* as well as from the ring oxygen atom 5 of that residue. Residue 35, on the other hand, is about three angstroms from the oxygen in the glycosidic linkage. Furthermore, these two amino acid residues have markedly different environments. Residue 52 has a number of polar neighbors and appears to be involved in a network of hydrogen bonds linking it with residues 46 and 59 (both asparagine) and, through them, with residue 50 (serine). In this environment residue 52 seems likely to give up a terminal hydrogen atom and thus be negatively charged under most conditions, even when it is in a markedly acid solution, whereas residue 35, situated in a nonpolar environment, is likely to retain its terminal hydrogen atom.

A little reflection suggests that the concerted influence of these two amino

acid residues, together with a contribution from the distortion to sugar residue *D* that has already been mentioned, is enough to explain the catalytic activity of lysozyme. The events leading to the rupture of a bacterial cell wall probably take the following course [*see illustration on this page*].

First, a lysozyme molecule attaches itself to the bacterial cell wall by interacting with six exposed amino-sugar residues. In the process sugar residue *D* is somewhat distorted from its usual conformation.

Second, residue 35 transfers its terminal hydrogen atom in the form of a hydrogen ion to the glycosidic oxygen, thus bringing about cleavage of the bond between that oxygen and carbon atom 1 of sugar residue *D*. This creates a positively charged carbonium ion (C^+) where the oxygen has been severed from carbon atom 1.

Third, this carbonium ion is stabilized by its interaction with the negatively charged aspartic acid side chain of residue 52 until it can combine with a hydroxyl ion (OH^-) that happens to diffuse into position from the surrounding water, thereby completing the reaction. The lysozyme molecule then falls away, leaving behind a punctured bacterial cell wall.

It is not clear from this description that the distortion of sugar residue *D* plays any part in the reaction, but in fact it probably does so for a very interesting reason. R. H. Lemieux and G. Huber of the National Research Council of Canada showed in 1955 that when a sugar molecule such as NAG incorporates a carbonium ion at the carbon-1 position, it tends to take up the same conformation that is forced on ring *D* by its interaction with the enzyme molecule. This seems to be an example, therefore, of activation of the substrate by distortion, which has long been a favorite idea of enzymologists. The binding of the substrate to the enzyme itself favors the formation of the carbonium ion in ring *D* that seems to play an important part in the reaction.

It will be clear from this account that although lysozyme has not been seen in action, we have succeeded in building up a detailed picture of how it may work. There is already a great deal of chemical evidence in agreement with this picture, and as the result of all the work now in progress we can be sure that the activity of Fleming's lysozyme will soon be fully understood. Best of all, it is clear that methods now exist for uncovering the secrets of enzyme action.

CARBON
OXYGEN
HYDROGEN

SPLITTING OF SUBSTRATE BY LYSOZYME is believed to involve the proximity and activity of two side chains, residue 35 (glutamic acid) and residue 52 (aspartic acid). It is proposed that a hydrogen ion (H^+) becomes detached from the OH group of residue 35 and attaches itself to the oxygen atom that joins rings *D* and *E*, thus breaking the bond between the two rings. This leaves carbon atom 1 of the *D* ring with a positive charge, in which form it is known as a carbonium ion. It is stabilized in this condition by the negatively charged side chain of residue 52. The surrounding water supplies an OH^- ion to combine with the carbonium ion and an H^+ ion to replace the one lost by residue 35. The two parts of the substrate then fall away, leaving the enzyme free to cleave another polysaccharide chain.

The Structure
6 | of the Hereditary Material

F. H. C. CRICK · October 1954

Viewed under a microscope, the process of mitosis, by which one cell divides and becomes two, is one of the most fascinating spectacles in the whole of biology. No one who watches the event unfold in speeded-up motion pictures can fail to be excited and awed. As a demonstration of the powers of dynamic organization possessed by living matter, the act of division is impressive enough, but even more stirring is the appearance of two identical sets of chromosomes where only one existed before. Here lies biology's greatest challenge: How are these fundamental bodies duplicated? Unhappily the copying process is beyond the resolving power of microscopes, but much is being learned about it in other ways.

One approach is the study of the nature and behavior of whole living cells; another is the investigation of substances extracted from them. This article will discuss only the second approach, but both are indispensable if we are ever to solve the problem; indeed some of the most exciting results are being obtained by what might loosely be described as a combination of the two methods.

Chromosomes consist mainly of three kinds of chemical: protein, desoxyribonucleic acid (DNA) and ribonucleic acid (RNA). (Since RNA is only a minor component, we shall not consider it in detail here.) The nucleic acids and the proteins have several features in common. They are all giant molecules, and each type has the general structure of a main backbone with side groups attached. The proteins have about 20 different kinds of side groups; the nucleic acids usually only four (and of a different type). The smallness of these numbers itself is striking, for there is no obvious chemical reason why many more types of side groups should not occur. Another interesting feature is that no protein or nucleic acid occurs in more than one optical form; there is never an optical isomer, or mirror-image molecule. This shows that the shape of the molecules must be important.

These generalizations (with minor exceptions) hold over the entire range of living organisms, from viruses and bacteria to plants and animals. The impression is inescapable that we are dealing with a very basic aspect of living matter, and one having far more simplicity than we would have dared to hope. It encourages us to look for simple explanations for the formation of these giant molecules.

The most important role of proteins is that of the enzymes—the machine tools of the living cell. An enzyme is specific, often highly specific, for the reaction which it catalyzes. Moreover, chemical and X-ray studies suggest that the structure of each enzyme is itself rigidly determined. The side groups of a given enzyme are probably arranged in a fixed order along the polypeptide backbone. If we could discover how a cell produces the appropriate enzymes, in particular how it assembles the side groups of each enzyme in the correct order, we should have gone a long way toward explaining the simpler forms of life in terms of physics and chemistry.

We believe that this order is controlled by the chromosomes. In recent years suspicion has been growing that the key to the specificity of the chromosomes lies not in their protein but in their DNA. DNA is found in all chromosomes—and only in the chromosomes (with minor exceptions). The amount of DNA per chromosome set is in many cases a fixed quantity for a given species. The sperm, having half the chromosomes of the normal cell, has about half the amount of DNA, and tetraploid cells in the liver, having twice the normal chromosome complement, seem to have twice the amount of DNA. This constancy of the amount of DNA is what one might expect if it is truly the material that determines the hereditary pattern.

Then there is suggestive evidence in two cases that DNA alone, free of protein, may be able to carry genetic information. The first of these is the discovery that the "transforming principles" of bacteria, which can produce an inherited change when added to the cell, appear to consist only of DNA. The second is the fact that during the infection of a bacterium by a bacteriophage the DNA of the phage penetrates into the bacterial cell while most of the protein, perhaps all of it, is left outside.

The Chemical Formula

DNA can be extracted from cells by mild chemical methods, and much experimental work has been carried out to discover its chemical nature. This work has been conspicuously successful. It is now known that DNA consists of a very long chain made up of alternate sugar and phosphate groups [*see diagram below*]. The sugar is always the same sugar, known as desoxyribose. And it is always joined onto the phosphate in the same way, so that the long chain is perfectly regular, repeating the same phosphate-sugar sequence over and over again.

But while the phosphate-sugar chain is perfectly regular, the molecule as a whole is not, because each sugar has a "base" attached to it and the base is not always the same. Four different types of base are commonly found: two of them are purines, called adenine and guanine, and two are pyrimidines, known as thymine and cytosine. So far as is known the order in which they follow one another along the chain is irregular, and

probably varies from one piece of DNA to another. In fact, we suspect that the order of the bases is what confers specificity on a given DNA. Because the sequence of the bases is not known, one can only say that the *general* formula for DNA is established. Nevertheless this formula should be reckoned one of the major achievements of biochemistry, and it is the foundation for all the ideas described in the rest of this article.

At one time it was thought that the four bases occurred in equal amounts, but in recent years this idea has been shown to be incorrect. E. Chargaff and his colleagues at Columbia University, A. E. Mirsky and his group at the Rockefeller Institute for Medical Research and G. R. Wyatt of Canada have accurately measured the amounts of the bases in many instances and have shown that the relative amounts appear to be fixed for any given species, irrespective of the individual or the organ from which the DNA was taken. The proportions usually differ for DNA from different species, but species related to one another may not differ very much.

Although we know from the chemical formula of DNA that it is a chain, this does not in itself tell us the shape of the molecule, for the chain, having many single bonds around which it may rotate, might coil up in all sorts of shapes. However, we know from physical-chemical measurements and electron-microscope pictures that the molecule usually is long, thin and fairly straight,

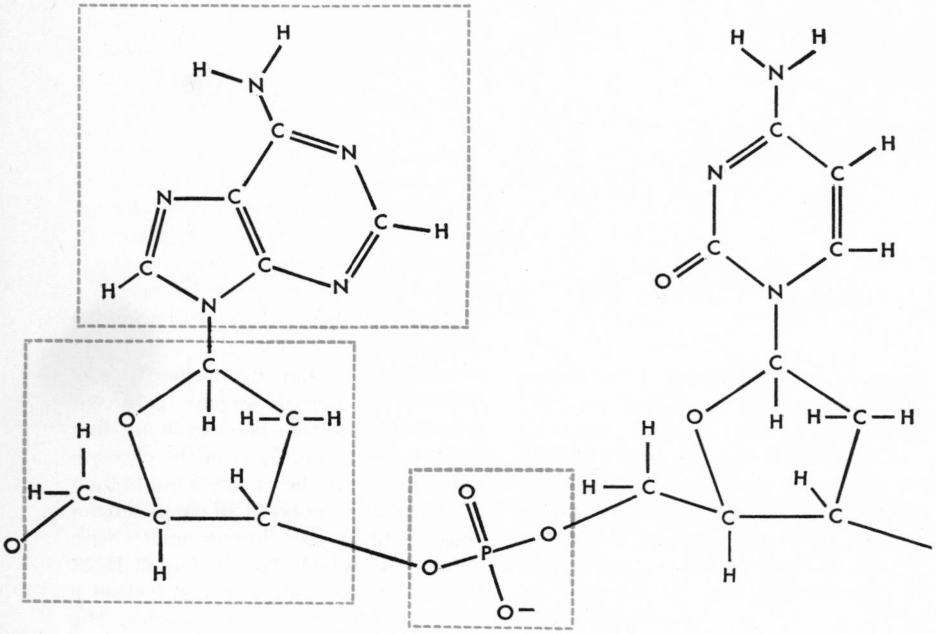

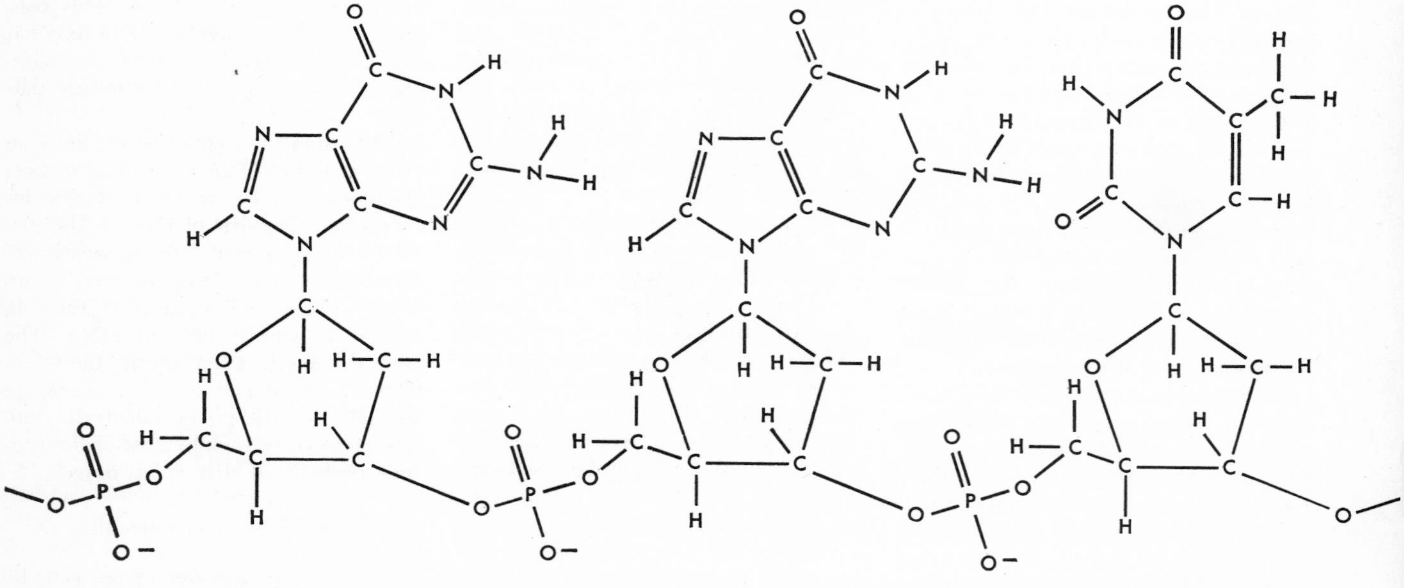

FRAGMENT OF CHAIN of desoxyribonucleic acid shows the three basic units that make up the molecule. Repeated over and over in a long chain, they make it 1,000 times as long

as it is thick. The backbone is made up of pentose sugar molecules (marked by the middle colored square), linked by phosphate groups (bottom square). The bases (top square), adenine, cytosine, guanine and thymine protrude off each sugar in irregular order.

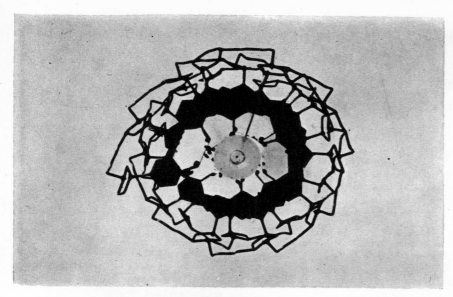

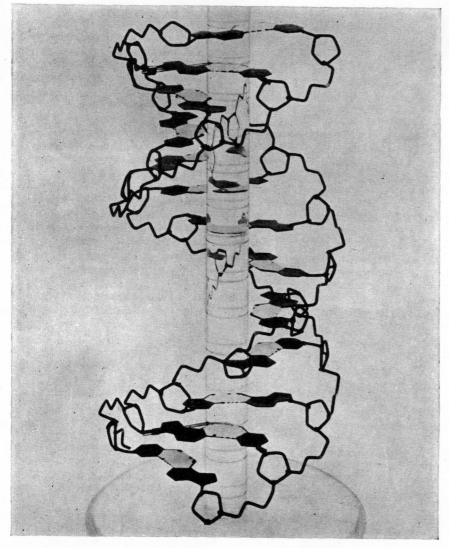

STRUCTURAL MODEL shows a pair of DNA chains wound as a helix about the fiber axis. The pentose sugars can be plainly seen. From every one on each chain protrudes a base, linked to an opposing one at the same level by a hydrogen bond. These base-to-base links act as horizontal supports, holding the chains together. Upper photograph is a top view.

rather like a stiff bit of cord. It is only about 20 Angstroms thick (one Angstrom = one 100-millionth of a centimeter). This is very small indeed, in fact not much more than a dozen atoms thick. The length of the DNA seems to depend somewhat on the method of preparation. A good sample may reach a length of 30,000 Angstroms, so that the structure is more than 1,000 times as long as it is thick. The length inside the cell may be much greater than this, because there is always the chance that the extraction process may break it up somewhat.

Pictures of the Molecule

None of these methods tells us anything about the detailed arrangement in space of the atoms inside the molecule. For this it is necessary to use X-ray diffraction. The average distance between bonded atoms in an organic molecule is about 1½ Angstroms; between unbonded atoms, three to four Angstroms. X-rays have a small enough wavelength (1½ Angstroms) to resolve the atoms, but unfortunately an X-ray diffraction photograph is not a picture in the ordinary sense of the word. We cannot focus X-rays as we can ordinary light; hence a picture can be obtained only by roundabout methods. Moreover, it can show clearly only the periodic, or regularly repeated, parts of the structure.

With patience and skill several English workers have obtained good diffraction pictures of DNA extracted from cells and drawn into long fibers. The first studies, even before details emerged, produced two surprises. First, they revealed that the DNA structure could take two forms. In relatively low humidity, when the water content of the fibers was about 40 per cent, the DNA molecules gave a crystalline pattern, showing that they were aligned regularly in all three dimensions. When the humidity was raised and the fibers took up more water, they increased in length by about 30 per cent and the pattern tended to become "paracrystalline," which means that the molecules were packed side by side in a less regular manner, as if the long molecules could slide over one another somewhat. The second surprising result was that DNA from different species appeared to give identical X-ray patterns, despite the fact that the amounts of the four bases present varied. This was particularly odd because of the existence of the crystalline form just mentioned. How could the structure appear so regular when the bases varied? It seemed that the

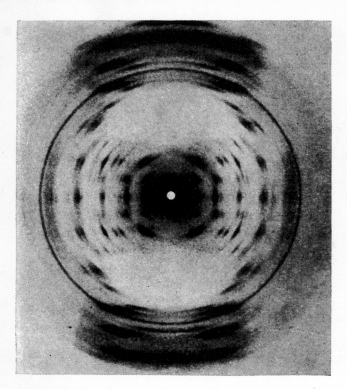

STRUCTURE A is the crystalline form of DNA found at relatively low humidity. This X-ray photograph is by H. R. Wilson.

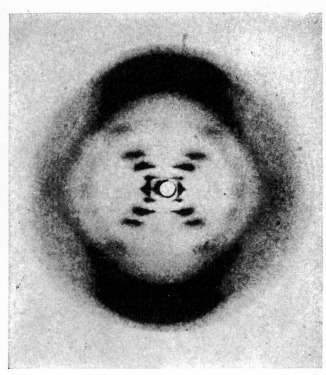

STRUCTURE B is the paracrystalline form of DNA. The molecules are less regularly arranged. Picture is by R. E. Franklin.

broad arrangement of the molecule must be independent of the exact sequence of the bases, and it was therefore thought that the bases play no part in holding the structure together. As we shall see, this turned out to be wrong.

The early X-ray pictures showed a third intriguing fact: namely, that the repeats in the crystallographic pattern came at much longer intervals than the chemical repeat units in the molecule. The distance from one phosphate to the next cannot be more than about seven Angstroms, yet the crystallographic repeat came at intervals of 28 Angstroms in the crystalline form and 34 Angstroms in the paracrystalline form; that is, the chemical unit repeated several times before the structure repeated crystallographically.

J. D. Watson and I, working in the Medical Research Council Unit in the Cavendish Laboratory at Cambridge, were convinced that we could get somewhere near the DNA structure by building scale models based on the X-ray patterns obtained by M. H. F. Wilkins, Rosalind Franklin and their co-workers at Kings' College, London. A great deal is known about the exact distances between bonded atoms in molecules, about the angles between the bonds and about the size of atoms—the so-called van der Waals' distance between adjacent non-bonded atoms. This information is easy

to embody in scale models. The problem is rather like a three-dimensional jig saw puzzle with curious pieces joined together by rotatable joints (single bonds between atoms).

The Helix

To get anywhere at all we had to make some assumptions. The most important one had to do with the fact that the crystallographic repeat did not coincide with the repetition of chemical units in the chain but came at much longer intervals. A possible explanation was that all the links in the chain were the same but the X-rays were seeing every tenth link, say, from the same angle and the others from different angles. What sort of chain might produce this pattern? The answer was easy: the chain might be coiled in a helix. (A helix is often loosely called a spiral; the distinction is that a helix winds not around a cone but around a cylinder, as a winding staircase usually does.) The distance between crystallographic repeats would then correspond to the distance in the chain between one turn of the helix and the next.

We had some difficulty at first because we ignored the bases and tried to work only with the phosphate-sugar backbone. Eventually we realized that we had to take the bases into account,

and this led us quickly to a structure which we now believe to be correct in its broad outlines.

This particular model contains a pair of DNA chains wound around a common axis. The two chains are linked together by their bases. A base on one chain is joined by very weak bonds to a base at the same level on the other chain, and all the bases are paired off in this way right along the structure. In the diagram opposite, the two ribbons represent the phosphate-sugar chains, and the pairs of bases holding them together are symbolized as horizontal rods. Paradoxically, in order to make the structure as symmetrical as possible we had to have the two chains run in opposite directions; that is, the sequence of the atoms goes one way in one chain and the opposite way in the other. Thus the figure looks exactly the same whichever end is turned up.

Now we found that we could not arrange the bases any way we pleased; the four bases would fit into the structure only in certain pairs. In any pair there must always be one big one (purine) and one little one (pyrimidine). A pair of pyrimidines is too short to bridge the gap between the two chains, and a pair of purines is too big to fit into the space.

At this point we made an additional assumption. The bases can theoretically exist in a number of forms depending upon where the hydrogen atoms are attached. We assumed that for each base one form was much more probable than all the others. The hydrogen atoms can be thought of as little knobs attached to the bases, and the way the bases fit together depends crucially upon where these knobs are. With this assumption the only possible pairs that will fit in are: adenine with thymine and guanine with cytosine.

The way these pairs are formed is shown in the diagrams on page 70. The dotted lines show the hydrogen bonds, which hold the two bases of a pair together. They are very weak bonds; their energy is not many times greater than the energy of thermal vibration at room temperature. (Hydrogen bonds are the main forces holding different water molecules together, and it is because of them that water is a liquid at room temperature and not a gas.)

Adenine must always be paired with thymine, and guanine with cytosine; it is impossible to fit the bases together in any other combination in our model. (This pairing is likely to be so fundamental for biology that I cannot help wondering whether some day an enthusiastic scientist will christen his newborn twins Adenine and Thymine!) The model places no restriction, however, on the sequence of pairs along the structure. Any specified pair can follow any other. This is because a pair of bases is flat, and since in this model they are stacked roughly like a pile of coins, it does not matter which pair goes above which.

It is important to realize that the specific pairing of the bases is the direct result of the assumption that both phosphate-sugar chains are helical. This regularity implies that the distance from a sugar group on one chain to that on the other at the same level is always the same, no matter where one is along the chain. It follows that the bases linked to the sugars always have the same amount of space in which to fit. It is the regularity of the phosphate-sugar chains, therefore, that is at the root of the specific pairing.

The Picture Clears

At the moment of writing, detailed interpretation of the X-ray photographs by Wilkins' group at Kings' College has not been completed, and until this has been done no structure can be considered proved. Nevertheless there are certain features of the model which are so strongly supported by the experimental evidence that it is very likely they will be embodied in the final correct structure. For instance, measurements of the density and water content of the DNA fibers, taken with evidence showing that the fibers can be extended in length, strongly suggest that there are two chains in the structural unit of DNA. Again, recent X-ray pictures have shown clearly a most striking general pattern which we can now recognize as the characteristic signature of a helical structure. In particular there are a large number of places where the diffracted intensity is zero or very small, and these occur exactly where one expects from a helix of this sort. Another feature one would expect is that the X-ray intensities should approach cylindrical symmetry, and it is now known that they do this. Recently Wilkins and his co-workers have given a brilliant analysis of the details of the X-ray pattern of the crystalline form, and have shown that they are consistent with a structure of this type, though in the crystalline form the bases are tilted away from the fiber axis instead of perpendicular, as in our model. Our construction was based on the paracrystalline form.

Many of the physical and chemical properties of DNA can now be understood in terms of this model. For example, the comparative stiffness of the structure explains rather naturally why DNA keeps a long, fiber-like shape in solution. The hydrogen bonds of the bases account for the behavior of DNA in response to changes in pH. Most striking of all is the fact that in every kind of DNA so far examined—and over 40 have been analyzed—the amount of adenine is about equal to the amount of thymine and the guanine equal to the cytosine, while the cross-ratios (between, say, adenine and guanine) can vary considerably from species to species. This remarkable fact, first pointed out by Chargaff, is exactly what one would expect according to our model, which requires that every adenine be paired with a thymine and every guanine with a cytosine.

It may legitimately be asked whether the artificially prepared fibers of extracted DNA, on which our model is based, are really representative of intact DNA in the cell. There is every indication that they are. It is difficult to see how the very characteristic features of the model could be produced as artefacts by the extraction process. Moreover, Wilkins has shown that intact biological material, such as sperm heads and bacteriophage, gives X-ray patterns very similar to those of the extracted fibers.

The present position, therefore, is that in all likelihood this statement about DNA can safely be made: its structure consists of two helical chains wound around a common axis and held together by hydrogen bonds between specific pairs of bases.

The Mold

Now the exciting thing about a model of this type is that it immediately suggests how the DNA might produce an exact copy of itself. The model consists of two parts, each of which is the complement of the other. Thus either chain may act as a sort of mold on which a complementary chain can be synthe-

ONE LINKAGE of base to base across the pair of DNA chains is between adenine and thymine. For the structure proposed, the link of a large base with a small one is required to fit chains together.

ANOTHER LINKAGE is comprised of guanine with cytosine. Assuming the existence of hydrogen bonds between the bases, these two pairings, and only these, will explain the actual configuration.

sized. The two chains of a DNA, let us say, unwind and separate. Each begins to build a new complement onto itself. When the process is completed, there are two pairs of chains where we had only one. Moreover, because of the specific pairing of the bases the sequence of the pairs of bases will have been duplicated exactly; in other words, the mold has not only assembled the building blocks but has put them together in just the right order.

Let us imagine that we have a single helical chain of DNA, and that floating around it inside the cell is a supply of precursors of the four sorts of building blocks needed to make a new chain. Unfortunately we do not know the makeup of these precursor units; they may be, but probably are not, nucleotides, consisting of one phosphate, one sugar and one base. In any case, from time to time a loose unit will attach itself by its base to one of the bases of the single DNA chain. Another loose unit may attach itself to an adjoining base on the chain. Now if one or both of the two newly attached units is not the correct mate for the one it has joined on the chain, the two newcomers will be unable to link together, because they are not the right distance apart. One or both will soon drift away, to be replaced by other units. When, however, two adjacent newcomers are the correct partners for their opposite numbers on the chain, they will be in just the right position to be linked together and begin to form a new chain. Thus only the unit with the proper base will gain a permanent hold at any given position, and eventually the right partners will fill in the vacancies all along the forming chain. While this is going on, the other single chain of the original pair also will be forming a new chain complementary to itself.

At the moment this idea must be regarded simply as a working hypothesis. Not only is there little direct evidence for it, but there are a number of obvious difficulties. For example, certain organisms contain small amounts of a fifth base, 5-methyl cytosine. So far as the model is concerned, 5-methyl cytosine fits just as well as cytosine and it may turn out that it does not matter to the organism which is used, but this has yet to be shown.

A more fundamental difficulty is to explain how the two chains of DNA are unwound in the first place. There would have to be a lot of untwisting, for the total length of all the DNA in a single chromosome is something like four centimeters (400 million Angstroms). This

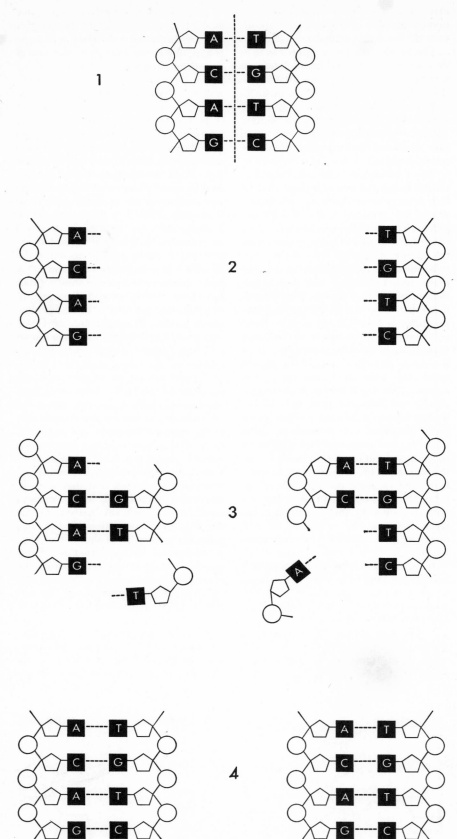

REPLICATION mechanism by which DNA might duplicate itself is shown in diagram. A helix of two DNA chains unwinds and separates (1). Two complementary chains of DNA (2) within the cell begin to attach DNA precursor units floating loosely (3). When the proper bases are joined, two new helixes will build up (4). Letters represent the bases.

means that there must be more than 10 million turns in all, though the DNA may not be all in one piece.

The duplicating process can be made to appear more plausible by assuming that the synthesis of the two new chains begins as soon as the two original chains start to unwind, so that only a short stretch of the chain is ever really single. In fact, we may postulate that it is the growth of the two new chains that unwinds the original pair. This is likely in terms of energy because, for every hydrogen bond that has to be broken, two new ones will be forming. Moreover, plausibility is added to the idea by the fact that the paired chain forms a rather stiff structure, so that the growing chain would tend to unwind the old pair.

The difficulty of untwisting the two chains is a topological one, and is due to the fact that they are intertwined. There would be no difficulty in "unwinding" a single helical chain, because there are so many single bonds in the chain about which rotation is possible. If in the twin structure one chain should break, the other one could easily spin around. This might relieve accumulated strain, and then the two ends of the broken chain, still being in close proximity, might be joined together again. There is even some evidence suggesting that in the process of extraction the chains of DNA may be broken in quite a number of places and that the structure nevertheless holds together by means of the hydrogen bonding, because there is never a break in both chains at the same level. Nevertheless, in spite of these tentative suggestions, the difficulty of untwisting remains a formidable one.

There remains the fundamental puzzle as to how DNA exerts its hereditary influence. A genetic material must carry out two jobs: duplicate itself and control the development of the rest of the cell in a specific way. We have seen how it might do the first of these, but the structure gives no obvious clue concerning how it may carry out the second. We suspect that the sequence of the bases acts as a kind of genetic code. Such an arrangement can carry an enormous amount of information. If we imagine that the pairs of bases correspond to the dots and dashes of the Morse code, there is enough DNA in a single cell of the human body to encode about 1,000 large textbooks. What we want to know, however, is just how this is done in terms of atoms and molecules. In particular, what precisely is it a code for? As we have seen, the three key components of living matter—protein, RNA and DNA—are probably all based on the same general plan. Their backbones are regular, and the variety comes from the sequence of the side groups. It is therefore very natural to suggest that the sequence of the bases of the DNA is in some way a code for the sequence of the amino acids in the polypeptide chains of the proteins which the cell must produce. The physicist George Gamow has recently suggested in a rather abstract way how this information might be transmitted, but there are some difficulties with the actual scheme he has proposed, and so far he has not shown how the idea can be translated into precise molecular configurations.

What then, one may reasonably ask, are the virtues of the proposed model, if any? The prime virtue is that the con-figuration suggested is not vague but can be described in terms acceptable to a chemist. The pairing of the bases can be described rather exactly. The precise positions of the atoms of the backbone is less certain, but they can be fixed within limits, and detailed studies of the X-ray data, now in progress at Kings' College, may narrow these limits considerably. Then the structure brings together two striking pieces of evidence which at first sight seem to be unrelated—the analytical data, showing the one-to-one ratios for adenine-thymine and guanine-cytosine, and the helical nature of the X-ray pattern. These can now be seen to be two facets of the same thing. Finally, is it not perhaps a remarkable coincidence, to say the least, to find in this key material a structure of exactly the type one would need to carry out a specific replication process; namely, one showing both variety and complementarity?

The model is also attractive in its simplicity. While it is obvious that whole chromosomes have a fairly complicated structure, it is not unreasonable to hope that the molecular basis underlying them may be rather simple. If this is so, it may not prove too difficult to devise experiments to unravel it. It would, of course, help enormously if biochemists could discover the immediate precursors of DNA. If we knew the monomers from which nature makes DNA, RNA and protein, we might be able to carry out very spectacular experiments in the test tube. Be that as it may, we now have for the first time a well-defined model for DNA and for a possible replication process, and this in itself should make it easier to devise crucial experiments.

7 | The Nucleotide Sequence of a Nucleic Acid

ROBERT W. HOLLEY · *February 1966*

Two major classes of chainlike molecules underlie the functioning of living organisms: the nucleic acids and the proteins. The former include deoxyribonucleic acid (DNA), which embodies the hereditary message of each organism, and ribonucleic acid (RNA), which helps to translate that message into the thousands of different proteins that activate the living cell. In the past dozen years biochemists have established the complete sequence of amino acid subunits in a number of different proteins. Much less is known about the nucleic acids.

Part of the reason for the slow progress with nucleic acids was the unavailability of pure material for analysis. Another factor was the large size of most nucleic acid molecules, which often contain thousands or even millions of nucleotide subunits. Several years ago, however, a family of small molecules was discovered among the ribonucleic

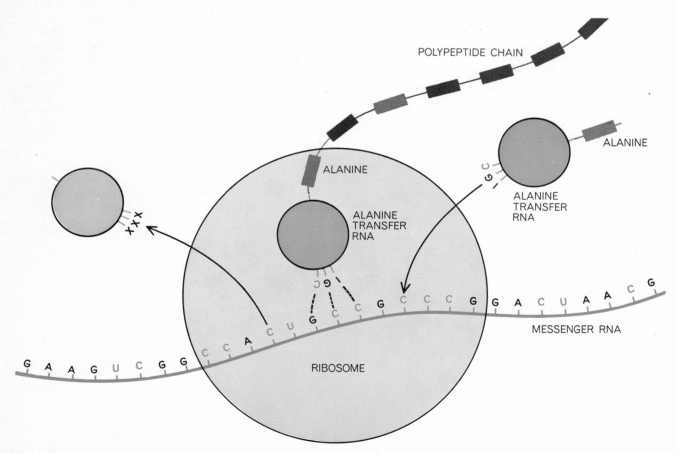

ROLE OF TRANSFER RNA is to deliver a specific amino acid to the site where "messenger" RNA and a ribosome (which also contains RNA) collaborate in the synthesis of a protein. As it is being synthesized a protein chain is usually described as a polypeptide. Each amino acid in the polypeptide chain is specified by a triplet code, or codon, in the molecular chain of messenger RNA.

The diagram shows how an "anticodon" (presumably I—G—C) in alanine transfer RNA may form a temporary bond with the codon for alanine (G—C—C) in the messenger RNA. While so bonded the transfer RNA also holds the polypeptide chain. Each transfer RNA is succeeded by another one, carrying its own amino acid, until the complete message in the messenger RNA has been "read."

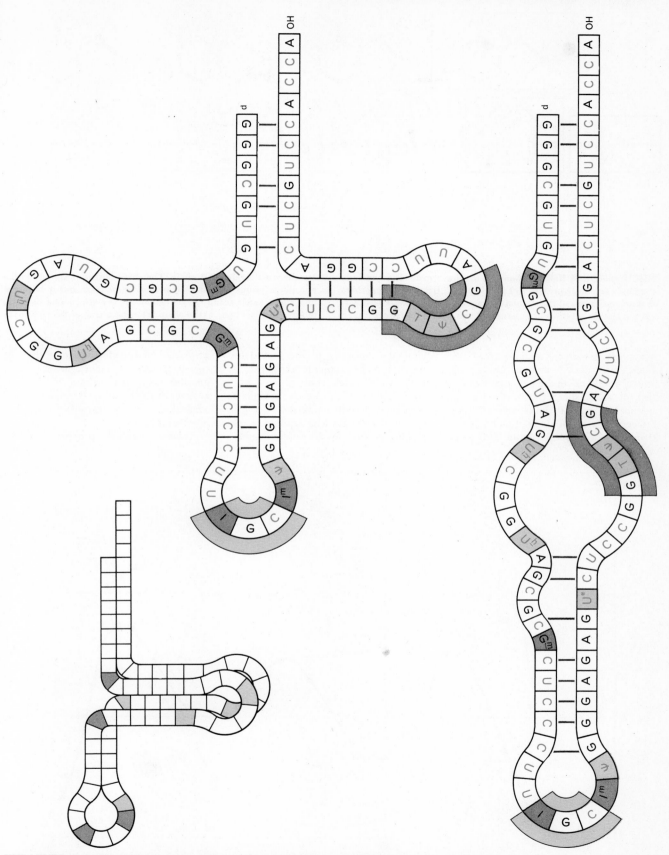

HYPOTHETICAL MODELS of alanine transfer ribonucleic acid (RNA) show three of the many ways in which the molecule's linear chain might be folded. The various letters represent nucleotide subunits; their chemical structure is given at the top of the next two pages. In these models it is assumed that certain nucleotides, such as C—G and A—U, will pair off and tend to form short double-strand regions. Such "base-pairing" is a characteristic feature of nucleic acids. The arrangement at the lower left shows how two of the large "leaves" of the "clover leaf" model may be folded together. The triplet I—G—C is the presumed anticodon shown in the illustration on the opposite page. The region containing the sequence G—T—Ψ—C—G may be common to all transfer RNA's.

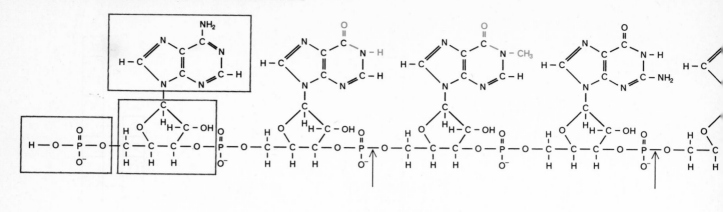

ADENYLIC ACID   INOSINIC ACID   1-METHYLINOSINIC ACID   GUANYLIC ACID   1-METHYLGUA

NUCLEOTIDE SUBUNITS found in alanine transfer RNA include the four commonly present in RNA (A, G, C, U), plus seven others that are variations of the standard structures. Ten of these 11 different nucleotide subunits are assembled above as if they were linked together in a single RNA chain. The chain begins at the left with a phosphate group (*outlined by a small rectangle*) and is followed by a ribose sugar group (*large rectangle*); the two groups alternate to form the backbone of the chain. The chain ends at the right with

acids. My associates and I at the U.S. Plant, Soil and Nutrition Laboratory and Cornell University set ourselves the task of establishing the nucleotide sequence of one of these smaller RNA molecules—a molecule containing fewer than 100 nucleotide subunits. This work culminated recently in the first determination of the complete nucleotide sequence of a nucleic acid.

The object of our study belongs to a family of 20-odd molecules known as transfer RNA's. Each is capable of recognizing one of the 20 different amino acids and of transferring it to the site where it can be incorporated into a growing polypeptide chain. When such a chain assumes its final configuration, sometimes joining with other chains, it is called a protein.

At each step in the process of protein

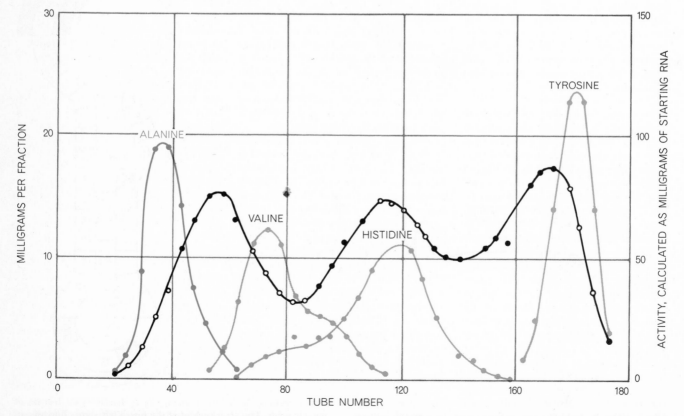

COUNTERCURRENT DISTRIBUTION PATTERN shows two steps in the separation of alanine transfer RNA, as carried out in the author's laboratory. After the first step the RNA content in various collection tubes, measured by ultraviolet absorption, follows the black curve. Biological activity, indicated by the amount of a given amino acid incorporated into polypeptide chains, follows the colored curves. Pure transfer RNA's of four types can be obtained by reprocessing the tubes designated by open circles.

D N²-DIMETHYLGUANYLIC ACID G^m   CYTIDYLIC ACID C   URIDYLIC ACID U   ▲RIBOTHYMIDYLIC ACID T   DIHYDROURIDYLIC ACID U^h   MIXTURE OF URIDYLIC AND DIHYDROURIDYLIC ACIDS U*   PSEUDOURIDYLIC ACID ψ OH

a hydroxyl (OH) group. Each nucleotide subunit consists of a phosphate group, a ribose sugar group and a base. The base portion in the nucleotide at the far left, adenylic acid, is outlined by a large rectangle. In the succeeding bases the atomic variations are shown in color. The base structures without color are those commonly found in RNA. Black arrows show where RNA chains can be cleaved by the enzyme takadiastase ribonuclease T1. Colored arrows show where RNA chains can be cleaved by pancreatic ribonuclease.

synthesis a crucial role is played by the structure of the various RNA's. "Messenger" RNA transcribes the genetic message for each protein from its original storage site in DNA. Another kind of RNA—ribosomal RNA—forms part of the structure of the ribosome, which acts as a jig for holding the messenger RNA while the message is transcribed into a polypeptide chain [see illustration on page 72]. In view of the various roles played by RNA in protein synthesis, the structure of RNA molecules is of considerable interest and significance.

The particular nucleic acid we chose for study is known as alanine transfer RNA—the RNA that transports the amino acid alanine. It was isolated from commercial baker's yeast by methods I shall describe later. Preliminary analyses indicated that the alanine transfer RNA molecule consisted of a single chain of approximately 80 nucleotide subunits. Each nucleotide, in turn, consists of a ribose sugar, a phosphate group and a distinctive appendage termed a nitrogen base. The ribose sugars and phosphate groups link together to form the backbone of the molecule, from which the various bases protrude [see illustration at top of these two pages].

The problem of structural analysis is fundamentally one of identifying each base and determining its place in the sequence. In practice each base is usually isolated in combination with a unit of ribose sugar and a unit of phosphate, which together form a nucleotide. Formally the problem is analogous to de-termining the sequence of letters in a sentence.

It would be convenient if there were a way to snip off the nucleotides one by one, starting at a known end of the chain and identifying each nucleotide as it appeared. Unfortunately procedures of this kind have such a small yield at each step that their use is limited. The alternative is to break the chain at particular chemical sites with the help of enzymes. This gives rise to small fragments whose nucleotide composition is amenable to analysis. If the chain can be broken up in various ways with different enzymes, one can determine how the fragments overlap and ultimately piece together the entire sequence.

One can visualize how this might work by imagining that the preceding sentence has been written out several times, in a continuous line, on different strips of paper. Imagine that each strip has been cut in a different way. In one case, for example, the first three words "If the chain" and the next three words "can be broken" might appear on separate strips of paper. In another case one might find that "chain" and "can" were together on a single strip. One would immediately conclude that the group of three words ending with "chain" and the group beginning with "can" form a continuous sequence of six words. The concept is simple; putting it into execution takes a little time.

For cleaving the RNA chain we used two principal enzymes: pancreatic ribonuclease and an enzyme called taka-diastase ribonuclease T1, which was discovered by the Japanese workers K. Sato-Asano and F. Egami. The first enzyme cleaves the RNA chain immediately to the right of pyrimidine nucleotides, as the molecular structure is conventionally written. Pyrimidine nucleotides are those nucleotides whose bases contain the six-member pyrimidine ring, consisting of four atoms of carbon and two atoms of nitrogen. The two pyrimidines commonly found in RNA are cytosine and uracil. Pancreatic ribonuclease therefore produces fragments that terminate in pyrimidine nucleotides such as cytidylic acid (C) or uridylic acid (U).

The second enzyme, ribonuclease T1, was employed separately to cleave the RNA chain specifically to the right of nucleotides containing a structure of the purine type, such as guanylic acid (G). This provided a set of short fragments distinctively different from those produced by the pancreatic enzyme.

The individual short fragments were isolated by passing them through a thin glass column packed with diethylamino-ethyl cellulose—an adaptation of a chromatographic method devised by R. V. Tomlinson and G. M. Tener of the University of British Columbia. In general the short fragments migrate through the column more rapidly than the long fragments, but there are exceptions [see illustration on next page]. The conditions most favorable for this separation were developed in our laboratories by Mark Marquisee and Jean Apgar.

The nucleotides in each fragment were released by hydrolyzing the fragment with an alkali. The individual nucleotides could then be identified by paper chromatography, paper electrophoresis and spectrophotometric analysis. This procedure was sufficient to establish the sequence of each of the dinucleotides, because the right-hand member of the pair was determined by the particular enzyme that had been used to produce the fragment. To establish the sequence of nucleotides in larger fragments, however, required special techniques.

Methods particularly helpful in the separation and identification of the fragments had been previously described by Vernon M. Ingram of the Massachusetts Institute of Technology, M. Laskowski, Sr., of the Marquette University School of Medicine, K. K. Reddi of Rockefeller University, G. W. Rushizky and Herbert A. Sober of the National Institutes of Health, the Swiss worker M. Staehelin and Tener.

For certain of the largest fragments, methods described in the scientific literature were inadequate and we had to develop new stratagems. One of these involved the use of an enzyme (a phosphodiesterase) obtained from snake venom. This enzyme removes nucleotides one by one from a fragment, leaving a mixture of smaller fragments of all possible intermediate lengths. The mixture can then be separated into fractions of homogeneous length by passing it through a column of diethylaminoethyl cellulose [see illustration on opposite page]. A simple method is available for determining the terminal nucleotide at the right end of each fraction of homogeneous length. With this knowledge, and knowing the length of each fragment, one can establish the sequence of nucleotides in the original large fragment.

A summary of all the nucleotide sequences found in the fragments of transfer RNA produced by pancreatic ribonuclease is shown in Table 1 on page 78. Determination of the structure of the fragments was primarily the work of James T. Madison and Ada Zamir, who were postdoctoral fellows in my laboratory. George A. Everett of the Plant, Soil and Nutrition Laboratory helped us in the identification of the nucleotides.

Much effort was spent in determining the structure of the largest fragments and in identifying unusual nucleotides not heretofore observed in RNA molecules. Two of the most difficult to identify were 1-methylinosinic acid and 5,6-dihydrouridylic acid. (In the illustrations these are symbolized respectively by I^m and U^h.)

Because a free 5'-phosphate group (p) is found at one end of the RNA molecule (the left end as the structure is conventionally written) and a free 3'-hydroxyl group (OH) is found at the other end, it is easy to pick out from Table 1 and Table 2 the two sequences that form the left and right ends of the alanine transfer RNA molecule. The left end has the structure pG—G—G—C— and the right end the structure U—C—C—A—C—COH. (It is known, however, that the active molecule ends in C—C—AOH.)

The presence of unusual nucleotides

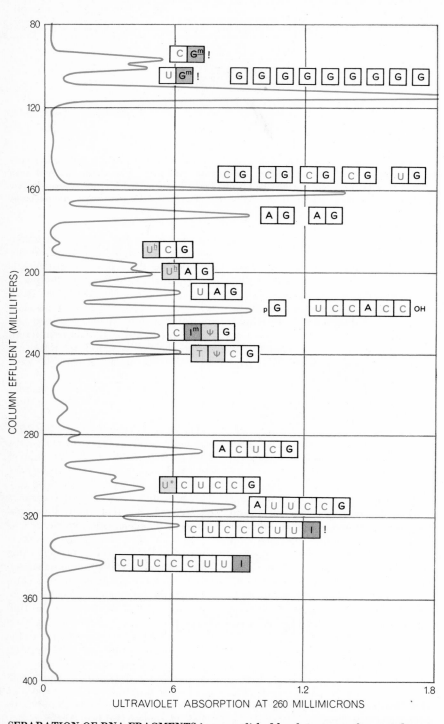

SEPARATION OF RNA FRAGMENTS is accomplished by chromatography carried out in a long glass column packed with diethylaminoethyl cellulose. The curve shows the separation achieved when the column input is a digest of alanine transfer RNA produced by takadiastase ribonuclease T1, an enzyme that cleaves the RNA into 29 fragments. The exclamation point indicates fragments whose terminal phosphate has a cyclical configuration. Such fragments travel faster than similar fragments that end in a noncyclical phosphate.

and unique short sequences made it clear that certain of the fragments found in Table 1 overlapped fragments found in Table 2. For example, there is only one inosinic acid nucleotide (I) in the molecule, and this appears in the sequence I–G–C– in Table 1 and in the sequence C–U–C–C–C–U–U–I– in Table 2. These two sequences must therefore overlap to produce the overall sequence C–U–C–C–C–U–U–I–G–C–. The information in Table 1 and Table 2 was combined in this way to draw up Table 3, which accounts for all 77 nucleotides in 16 sequences [see illustration on page 79].

With the knowledge that two of the 16 sequences were at the two ends, the structural problem became one of determining the positions of the intermediate 14 sequences. This was accomplished by isolating still larger fragments of the RNA.

In a crucial experiment John Robert Penswick, a graduate student at Cornell, found that a very brief treatment of the RNA with ribonuclease T1 at 0 degrees centigrade in the presence of magnesium ions splits the molecule at one position. The two halves of the molecule could be separated by chromatography. Analyses of the halves established that the sequences listed in the first column of Table 3 are in the left half of the molecule and that those in the second column are in the right half.

Using a somewhat more vigorous but still limited treatment of the RNA with ribonuclease T1, we then obtained and analyzed a number of additional large fragments. This work was done in collaboration with Jean Apgar and Everett. To determine the structure of a large fragment, the fragment was degraded completely with ribonuclease T1, which yielded two or more of the fragments previously identified in Table 2. These known sequences could be put together, with the help of various clues, to obtain the complete sequence of the large fragment. The process is similar to putting together a jigsaw puzzle [see illustrations on pages 80 and 81].

As an example of the approach that was used, the logical argument is given in detail for Fragment A. When Fragment A was completely degraded by ribonuclease T1, we obtained seven small fragments: three G–'s, C–G–, U–G–,U–Gm– and pG–. (Gm is used in the illustrations to represent 1-methylguanylic acid, another of the unusual nucleotides in alanine transfer RNA.) The presence of pG– shows that Frag-

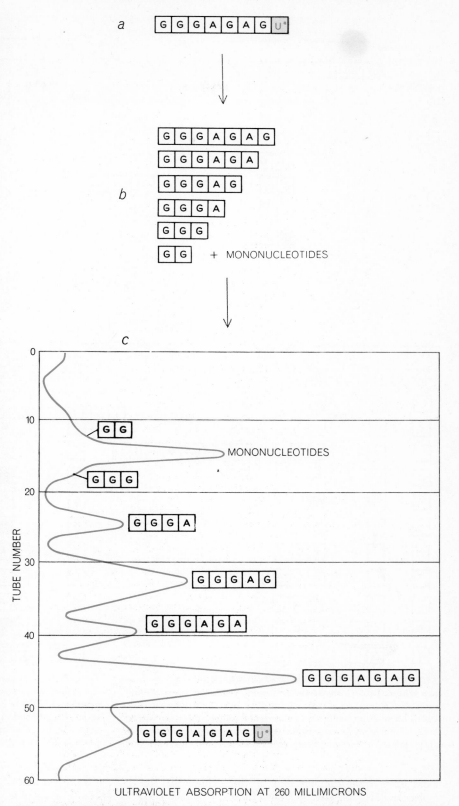

NEW DEGRADATION METHOD was developed in the author's laboratory to determine the sequence of nucleotides in fragments five to eight subunits in length. The example above begins with a fragment of eight subunits from which the terminal phosphate has been removed (a). When the fragment is treated with phosphodiesterase found in snake venom, the result is a mixture containing fragments from one to eight subunits in length (b). These are separated by chromatography (c). When the material from each peak is hydrolyzed, the last nucleoside (a nucleotide minus its phosphate) at the right end of the fragment is released and can be identified. Thus each nucleotide in the original fragment can be determined.

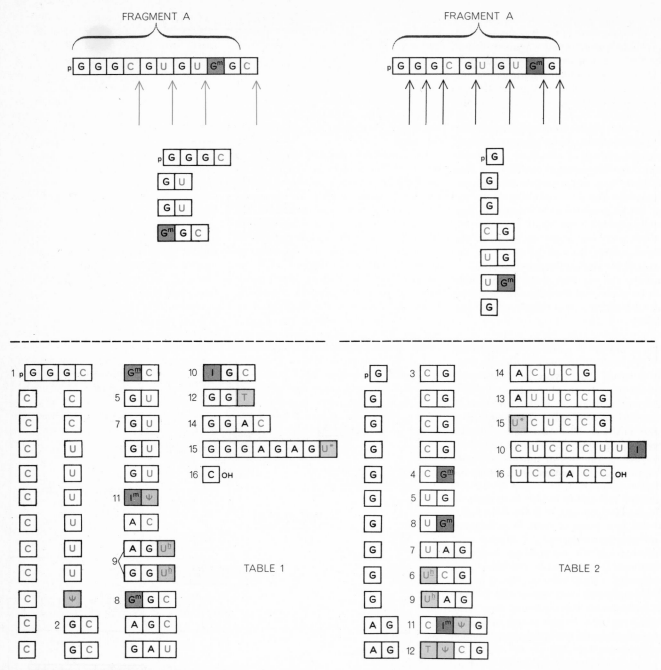

ACTION OF TWO DIFFERENT ENZYMES is reflected in these two tables. Table 1 shows the fragments produced when alanine transfer RNA is completely digested by pancreatic ribonuclease, which cleaves the molecule to the right of nucleotides containing bases with pyrimidine structures (C, U, U^h, ψ and T). The diagram at top left shows how pancreatic ribonuclease would cleave the first 11 nucleotides of alanine transfer RNA. The diagram at top right shows how the same region would be digested by takadiastase ribonuclease T1. Table 2 contains the fragments produced by this enzyme; they all end in nucleotides whose bases contain purine structures (G, G^m, $G\underline{m}$ and I). The numbers indicate which ones appear in the consolidated list in Table 3 on the opposite page.

ment A is from the left end of the molecule. Since it is already known from Table 3 that the left terminal sequence is pG—G—G—C—, the positions of two of the three G—'s and C—G— are known; the terminal five nucleotides must be pG—G—G—C—G—.

The positions of the remaining G—, U—G— and U—G^m— are established by the following information. Table 3 shows that the U—G^m— is present in the sequence U—G^m—G—C—. Since there is only one C in Fragment A, and its position is already known, Fragment A must terminate before the C of the U—G^m—G—C— sequence. Therefore the U—G— must be to the left of the U—G^m—, and the structure of Fragment A can be represented as pG—G—G—C—G—...U—G—...U—G^m—, with one G— remaining to be placed. If the G— is placed to the left or the right of the U—G— in this structure, it would create a G—G—U— sequence. If such a sequence existed in the molecule, it would have appeared as a fragment when the molecule was treated with pancreatic ribonuclease; Table 1 shows that it did not do so. Therefore the remaining G— must be to the right of the G^m—, and the sequence of Fragment A is pG—G—G—C—G—U—G—U—G^m—G—.

Using the same procedure, the entire structure of alanine transfer RNA was worked out. The complete nucleotide sequence of alanine transfer RNA is shown at the top of the next two pages.

The work on the structure of this molecule took us seven years from start to finish. Most of the time was consumed in developing procedures for the isolation of a single species of transfer RNA from the 20 or so different transfer RNA's present in the living cell. We finally selected a fractionation technique known as countercurrent distribution, developed in the 1940's by Lyman C. Craig of the Rockefeller Institute.

This method exploits the fact that similar molecules of different structure will exhibit slightly different solubilities if they are allowed to partition, or distribute themselves, between two nonmiscible liquids. The countercurrent technique can be mechanized so that the mixture of molecules is partitioned hundreds or thousands of times, while the nonmiscible solvents flow past each other in a countercurrent pattern. The solvent system we adopted was composed of formamide, isopropyl alcohol and a phosphate buffer, a modification of a system first described by Robert C. Warner and Paya Vaimberg of New York University. To make the method applicable for fractionating transfer RNA's required four years of work in collaboration with Jean Apgar, B. P. Doctor and Susan H. Merrill of the Plant, Soil and Nutrition Laboratory. Repeated countercurrent extractions of the transfer RNA mixture gave three of the RNA's in a reasonably homogeneous state: the RNA's that transfer the amino acids alanine, tyrosine and valine [see bottom illustration on page 74].

The starting material for the countercurrent distributions was crude transfer RNA extracted from yeast cells using phenol as a solvent. In the course of the structural work we used about 200 grams (slightly less than half a pound) of mixed transfer RNA's isolated from 300 pounds of yeast. The total amount of purified alanine transfer RNA we had to work with over a three-year period was one gram. This represented a practical compromise between the difficulty of scaling up the fractionation procedures and scaling down the techniques for structural analysis.

Once we knew the complete sequence, we could turn to general questions about the structure of transfer

RNA's. Each transfer RNA presumably embodies a sequence of three subunits (an "anticodon") that forms a temporary bond with a complementary sequence of three subunits (the "codon") in messenger RNA. Each codon triplet identifies a specific amino acid [see "The Genetic Code: II," by Marshall W. Nirenberg, beginning on page 206 in this book].

An important question, therefore, is which of the triplets in alanine transfer RNA might serve as the anticodon for the alanine codon in messenger RNA. There is reason to believe the anticodon is the sequence I—G—C, which is found in the middle of the RNA molecule. The codon corresponding to I—G—C could be the triplet G—C—C or perhaps G—C—U, both of which act as code words for alanine in messenger RNA. As shown in the illustration on page 72, the I—G—C in the alanine transfer RNA is upside down when it makes contact with the corresponding codon in messenger RNA. Therefore when alanine transfer RNA is delivering its amino acid cargo and is temporarily held by hydrogen bonds to messenger RNA, the I would pair with C (or U) in the messenger, G would

pair with C, and C would pair with G.

We do not know the three-dimensional structure of the RNA. Presumably there is a specific form that interacts with the messenger RNA and ribosomes. The illustration on page 73 shows three hypothetical structures for alanine transfer RNA that take account of the propensity of certain bases to pair with other bases. Thus adenine pairs with uracil and cytosine with guanine. In the three hypothetical structures the I—G—C sequence is at an exposed position and could pair with messenger RNA.

The small diagram on page 73 indicates a possible three-dimensional folding of the RNA. Studies with atomic models suggest that single-strand regions of the structure are highly flexible. Thus in the "three-leaf-clover" configuration it is possible to fold one side leaf on top of the other, or any of the leaves back over the stem of the molecule.

One would also like to know whether or not the unusual nucleotides are concentrated in some particular region of the molecule. A glance at the sequence shows that they are scattered throughout the structure; in the three-leaf-clo-

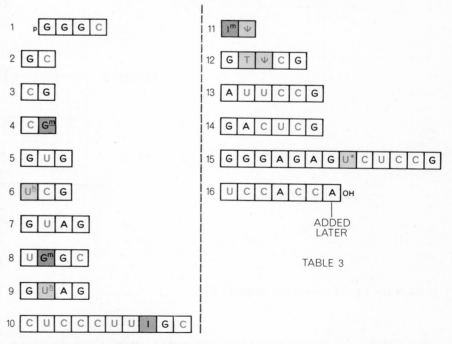

CONSOLIDATED LIST OF SEQUENCES accounts for all 77 nucleotides in alanine transfer RNA. The consolidated list is formed by selecting the largest fragments in Table 1 and Table 2 (opposite page) and by piecing together fragments that obviously overlap. Thus Fragment 15 has been formed by joining two smaller fragments, keyed by the number 15, in Table 1 and Table 2 on the opposite page. Since the entire molecule contains only one U*, the two fragments must overlap at that point. The origin of the other fragments in Table 3 can be traced in similar fashion. A separate experiment in which the molecule was cut into two parts helped to establish that the 10 fragments listed in the first column are in the left half of the molecule and that the six fragments in the second column are in the right half.

FRAGMENT A

FRAGMENT B

FRAGMENT E

COMPLETE MOLECULE of alanine transfer RNA contains 77 nucleotides in the order shown. The final sequence required a care-ful piecing together of many bits of information (*see illustration at bottom of these two pages*). The task was facilitated by degrada-

ver model, however, the unusual nucleotides are seen to be concentrated around the loops and bends.

Another question concerns the presence in the transfer RNA's of binding sites, that is, sites that may interact specifically with ribosomes and with

the enzymes involved in protein synthesis. We now know from the work of Zamir and Marquisee that a particular sequence containing pseudouridylic acid (Ψ), the sequence G—T—Ψ—C—G, is found not only in the alanine transfer RNA but also in the transfer RNA's for

tyrosine and valine. Other studies suggest that it may be present in all the transfer RNA's. One would expect such common sites to serve a common function; binding the transfer RNA's to the ribosome might be one of them.

Work that is being done in many

FRAGMENT A

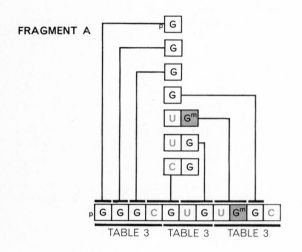

FRAGMENT B

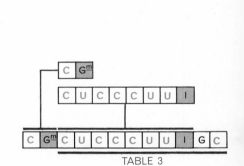

FRAGMENT E

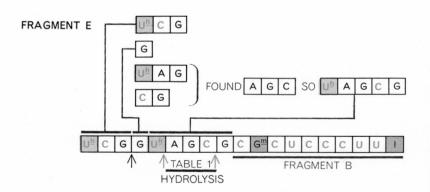

REMAINDER OF LEFT HALF OF MOLECULE

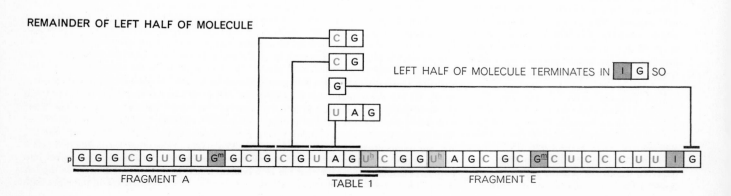

tion experiments that cleaved this molecule into several large fragments (*A, B, C, D, E, F, G*), and by the crucial discovery that

the molecule could be divided almost precisely into two halves. The division point is marked by the "gutter" between these two pages.

laboratories around the world indicates that alanine transfer RNA is only the first of many nucleic acids for which the nucleotide sequences will be known. In the near future it should be possible to identify those structural features that are common to various transfer RNA's,

and this should help greatly in defining the interactions of transfer RNA's with messenger RNA, ribosomes and enzymes involved in protein synthesis. Further in the future will be the description of the nucleotide sequences of the nucleic acids—both DNA and RNA—

that embody the genetic messages of the viruses that infect bacteria, plants and animals. Much further in the future lies the decoding of the genetic messages of higher organisms, including man. The work described in this article is a step toward that distant goal.

FRAGMENT C

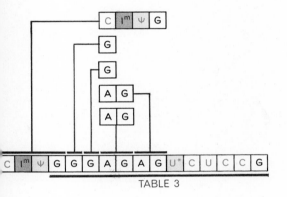

FRAGMENT D

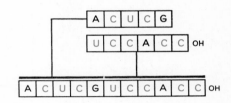

FRAGMENT F

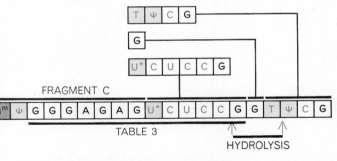

FRAGMENT G

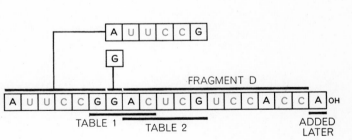

ASSEMBLY OF FRAGMENTS resembled the solving of a jigsaw puzzle. The arguments that established the sequence of nucleotides in Fragment *A* are described in the text. Fragment *B* contains two subfragments. The larger is evidently Fragment 10 in Table 3, which ends in G—C—. This means that the C—G^m— fragment must go to the left. Fragment *E* contains Fragment *B* plus four smaller fragments. It can be shown that *E* ends with I—, therefore the four small pieces are again to the left. A pancreatic digest yielded A—G—C—, thus serving to connect U^h—A—G— and C—G—. A partial digestion with ribonuclease T1 removed U^h—C—G—, showing it to be at the far left. The remaining G— must follow immediately or a pancreatic digest would have yielded a G—G—C— sequence, which it did not. Analyses of Fragments *A* and *E* accounted for everything in the left half of the molecule except for four small pieces. The left half of the molecule was shown to terminate in I—G—, thus the remaining three pieces are between *A* and *E*. Table 1 shows that one U^h is preceded by A—G—, therefore U—

A—G— must be next to *E*. The two remaining C—G—'s must then fall to the left of U—A—G—. Fragment *C* contains five pieces. Table 3 (Fragment 15) shows that the two A—G—'s are next to U* and that the two G—'s are to the left of them. It is also clear that C—I^m—Ψ—G— cannot follow U*, therefore it must be to the left. Fragment *D* contains two pieces; the OH group on one of them shows it to be to the right. Fragment *F* contains Fragment *C* plus three extra pieces. These must all lie to the right since hydrolysis with pancreatic ribonuclease gave G—G—T— and not G—T—, thus establishing that the single G— falls as shown. Fragment *G* gave *D* plus two pieces, which must both lie to the left (because of the terminal C$_{OH}$). Table 1 shows a G—G—A—C— sequence, which must overlap the A—C— in A—C—U—C—G— and the G— at the right end of the A—U—U—C—C—G—. Fragments *F* and *G* can join in only one way to form the right half of the molecule. The molecule is completed by the addition of a final A$_{OH}$, which is missing as the alanine transfer RNA is separated from baker's yeast.

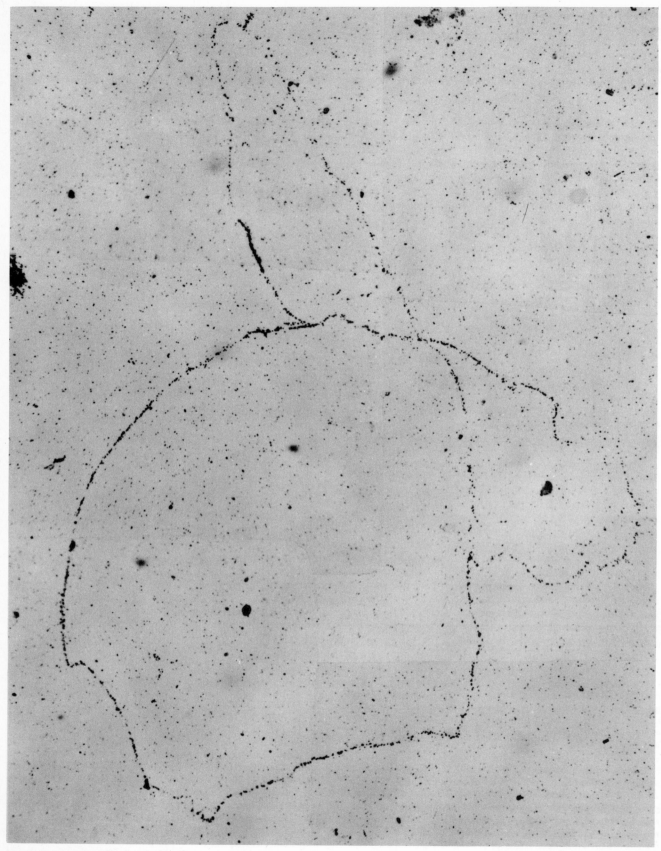

AUTORADIOGRAPH shows a duplicating chromosome from the bacterium *Escherichia coli* enlarged about 480 diameters. The DNA of the chromosome is visible because for two generations it incorporated a radioactive precursor, tritiated thymine. The thy-mine reveals its presence as a line of dark grains in the photographic emulsion. (Scattered grains are from background radiation.) The diagram on the opposite page shows how the picture is interpreted as demonstrating the manner of DNA duplication.

8 | *The Bacterial Chromosome*

JOHN CAIRNS · *January 1966*

The information inherited by living things from their forebears is inscribed in their deoxyribonucleic acid (DNA). It is written there in a decipherable code in which the "letters" are the four subunits of DNA, the nucleotide bases. It is ordered in functional units—the genes—and thence translated by way of ribonucleic acid (RNA) into sequences of amino acids that determine the properties of proteins. The proteins are, in the final analysis, the executors of each organism's inheritance.

The central event in the passage of genetic information from one generation to the next is the duplication of DNA. This cannot be a casual process. The complement of DNA in a single bacterium, for example, amounts to some six million nucleotide bases; this is the bacterium's "inheritance." Clearly life's security of tenure derives in large measure from the precision with which DNA can be duplicated, and the manner of this duplication is therefore a matter of surpassing interest. This article deals with a single set of experiments on the duplication of DNA, the antecedents to them and some of the speculations they have provoked.

When James D. Watson and Francis H. C. Crick developed their two-strand model for the structure of DNA, they saw that it contained within it the seeds of a system for self-duplication. The two strands, or polynucleotide chains, were apparently related physically to each other by a strict system of *complementary* base pairing. Wherever the nucleotide base adenine occurred in one chain, thymine was present in the other; similarly, guanine was always paired with cytosine. These rules meant that the sequence of bases in each chain inexorably stipulated the sequence in the other; each chain, on its own, could generate the entire sequence of base pairs. Watson and Crick therefore suggested that accurate duplication of DNA could occur if the chains separated and each then acted as a template on which a new complementary chain was laid down. This form of duplication was later called "semiconservative" because it supposed that although the individual parental chains were conserved during duplication (in that they were not thrown away), their association ended as part of the act of duplication.

The prediction of semiconservative replication soon received precise experimental support. Matthew S. Meselson and Franklin W. Stahl, working at the California Institute of Technology, were able to show that each molecule of DNA in the bacterium *Escherichia coli* is composed of equal parts of newly synthesized DNA and of old DNA that was present in the previous generation [*see top illustration on next page*]. They realized they had not proved that the two parts of each molecule were in fact two chains of the DNA duplex, because they had not established that the molecules they were working with consisted of only two chains. Later experiments, including some to be described in this article, showed that what they were observing was indeed the separation of the two chains during duplication.

The Meselson-Stahl experiment dealt with the end result of DNA duplication. It gave no hint about the mechanism that separates the chains and then supervises the synthesis of the new chains. Soon, however, Arthur Kornberg and his colleagues at Washington University isolated an enzyme from *E. coli* that, if all the necessary precursors were provided, could synthesize in the test tube chains that were complementary in base sequence to any DNA offered as a template. It was clear, then, that polynucleotide chains could indeed act as templates for the production of complementary chains and that this kind of reaction could be the normal process of duplication, since the enzymes for carrying it out were present in the living cell.

Such, then, was the general background of the experiments I undertook

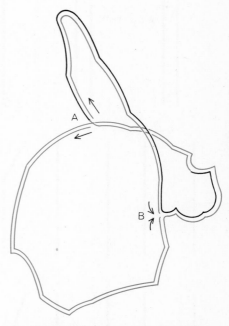

INTERPRETATION of autoradiograph on opposite page is based on the varying density of the line of grains. Excluding artifacts, dense segments represent doubly labeled DNA duplexes (*two colored lines*), faint segments singly labeled DNA (*color and black*). The parent chromosome, labeled in one strand and part of another, began to duplicate at *A*; new labeled strands have been laid down in two loops as far as *B*.

guan + cytosin   aden + thymine

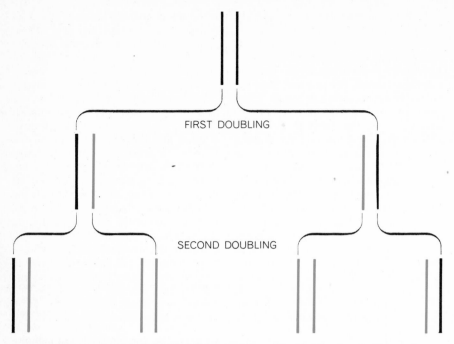

SEMICONSERVATIVE DUPLICATION was confirmed by the Meselson-Stahl experiment, which showed that each DNA molecule is composed of two parts: one that is present in the parent molecule, the other comprising new material synthesized when the parent molecule is duplicated. If radioactive labeling begins with the first doubling, the unlabeled (*black*) and labeled (*colored*) nucleotide chains of DNA form two-chain duplexes as shown here.

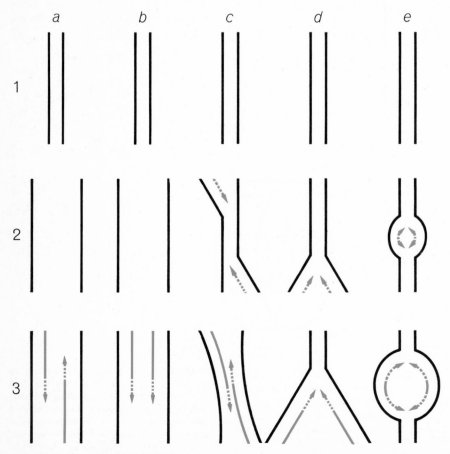

DUPLICATION could proceed in various ways (*a–e*). In these examples parental chains are shown as black lines and new chains as colored lines. The arrows show the direction of growth of the new chains, the newest parts of which are denoted by broken-line segments.

beginning in 1962 at the Australian National University. My object was simply (and literally) to look at molecules of DNA that had been caught in the act of duplication, in order to find out which of the possible forms of semiconservative replication takes place in the living cell: how the chains of parent DNA are arranged and how the new chains are laid down [*see bottom illustration on this page*].

Various factors dictated that the experiments should be conducted with *E. coli.* For one thing, this bacterium was known from genetic studies to have only one chromosome; that is, its DNA is contained in a single functional unit in which all the genetic markers are arrayed in sequence. For another thing, the duplication of its chromosome was known to occupy virtually the entire cycle of cell division, so that one could be sure that every cell in a rapidly multiplying culture would contain replicating DNA.

Although nothing was known about the number of DNA molecules in the *E. coli* chromosome (or in any other complex chromosome, for that matter), the dispersal of the bacterium's DNA among its descendants had been shown to be semiconservative. For this and other reasons it seemed likely that the bacterial chromosome would turn out to be a single very large molecule. All the DNA previously isolated from bacteria had, to be sure, proved to be in molecules much smaller than the total chromosome, but a reason for this was suggested by studies by A. D. Hershey of the Carnegie Institution Department of Genetics at Cold Spring Harbor, N.Y. He had pointed out that the giant molecules of DNA that make up the genetic complement of certain bacterial viruses had been missed by earlier workers simply because they are so large that they are exceedingly fragile. Perhaps the same thing was true of the bacterial chromosome.

If so, the procedure for inspecting the replicating DNA of bacteria would have to be designed to cater for an exceptionally fragile molecule, since the bacterial chromosome contains some 20 times more DNA than the largest bacterial virus. It would have to be a case of looking but not touching. This was not as onerous a restriction as it may sound. The problem was, after all, a topographical one, involving delineation of strands of parent DNA and newly synthesized DNA. There was no need for manipulation, only for visualization. Although electron microscopy is the obvious way to get a look at a large molecule, I chose autoradiography in this instance because it offered certain peculiar advantages (which will become apparent) and because it had already proved to be the easier, albeit less accurate, technique for displaying large DNA molecules. Autoradiography capitalizes on the fact that electrons emitted by the decay of a radioactive isotope produce images on certain kinds of photographic emulsion. It is possible, for example, to locate the destination within a cell of a particular species of molecule by labeling such molecules with a radioactive atom, feeding them to the cell and then placing the cell in contact with an emulsion; a developed grain in the emulsion reveals the presence of a labeled molecule [see "Autobiographies of Cells," by Renato Baserga and Walter E. Kisieleski; SCIENTIFIC AMERICAN Offprint 165].

It happens that the base thymine, which is solely a precursor of DNA, is susceptible to very heavy labeling with tritium, the radioactive isotope of hydrogen. Replicating DNA incorporates the labeled thymine and thus becomes visible in autoradiographs. I had been able to extend the technique to demonstrating the form of individual DNA molecules extracted from bacterial viruses. This was possible because, in spite of the poor resolving power of autoradiography (compared with electron microscopy), molecules of DNA are so extremely long in relation to the resolving power that they appear as a linear array of grains. The method grossly exaggerates the apparent width of the DNA, but this is not a serious fault in the kind of study I was undertaking.

The general design of the experiments called for extracting labeled DNA from bacteria as gently as possible and then

mounting it—without breaking the DNA molecules—for autoradiography. What I did was kill bacteria that had been fed tritiated thymine for various periods and put them, along with the enzyme lysozyme and an excess of unlabeled DNA, into a small capsule closed on one side by a semipermeable membrane. The enzyme, together with a detergent diffused into the chamber, induced the bacteria to break open and discharge their DNA. After the detergent, the enzyme and low-molecular-weight cellular debris had been diffused out of the chamber, the chamber was drained, leaving some of the DNA deposited on the membrane [see illustration below]. Once dry, the membrane was coated with a photographic emulsion sensitive to electrons emitted by the tritium and was left for two months. I hoped by this procedure to avoid subjecting the DNA to appreciable turbulence and so to find

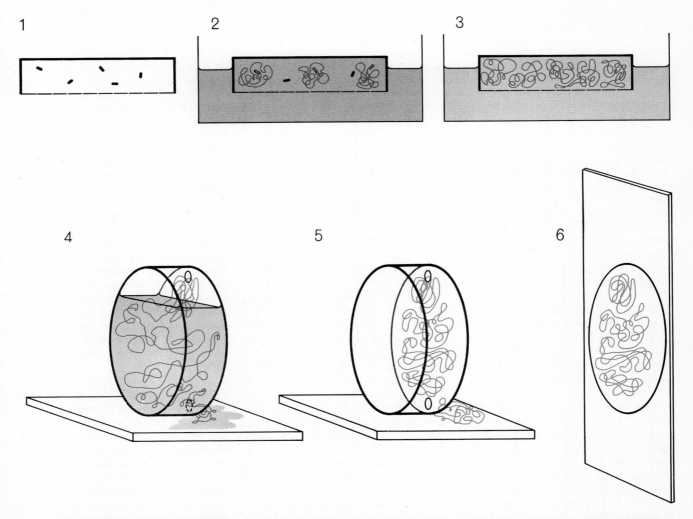

AUTORADIOGRAPHY EXPERIMENT begins with bacteria whose DNA has been labeled with radioactive thymine. The bacteria and an enzyme are placed in a small chamber closed by a semipermeable membrane (1). Detergent diffused into the chamber causes the bacteria to discharge their contents (2). The detergent and cellular debris are washed away by saline solution diffused through the chamber (3). The membrane is then punctured. The saline drains out slowly (4), leaving some unbroken DNA molecules (color) clinging to the membrane (5). The membrane, with DNA, is placed on a microscope slide and coated with emulsion (6).

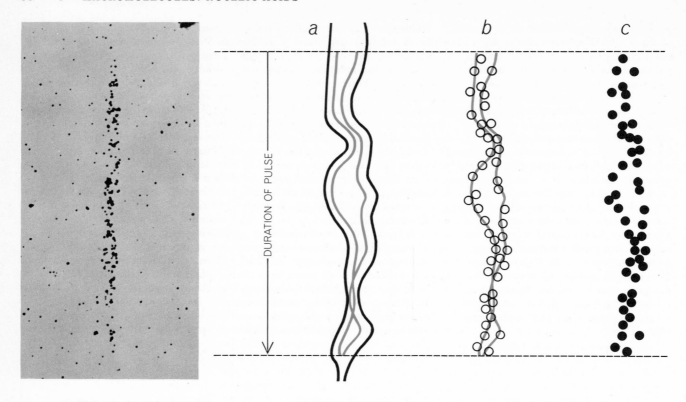

DNA synthesized in *E. coli* fed radioactive thymine for three minutes is visible in an autoradiograph, enlarged 1,200 diameters, as an array of heavy black grains (*left*). The events leading to the autoradiograph are shown at right. The region of the DNA chains synthesized during the "pulse-labeling" is radioactive and is shown in color (*a*). The radioactivity affects silver grains in the photographic emulsion (*b*). The developed grains appear in the autoradiograph (*c*), approximately delineating the new chains of DNA.

some molecules that—however big—had not been broken and see their form. Inasmuch as *E. coli* synthesizes DNA during its entire division cycle, some of the extracted DNA should be caught in the act of replication. (Since there was an excess of unlabeled DNA present, any tendency for DNA to produce artificial aggregates would not produce a spurious increase in the size of the labeled molecules or an alteration in their form.)

It is the peculiar virtue of autoradiography that one sees only what has been labeled; for this reason the technique can yield information on the history as well as the form of a labeled structure. The easiest way to determine which of the schemes of replication was correct was to look at bacterial DNA that had been allowed to duplicate for only a short time in the presence of labeled thymine. Only the most recently made DNA would be visible (corresponding to the broken-line segments in the bottom illustration on page 84), and so it should be possible to determine if the two daughter molecules were being made at the same point or in different regions of the parent molecule. A picture obtained after labeling bacteria for

three minutes, or a tenth of a generation-time [*at left in illustration above*], makes it clear that two labeled structures are being made in the same place. This place is presumably a particular region of a larger (unseen) parent molecule [*see diagrams at right in illustration above*].

The autoradiograph also shows that at least 80 microns (80 thousandths of a millimeter) of the DNA has been duplicated in three minutes. Since duplication occupies the entire generation-time (which was about 30 minutes in these experiments), it follows that the process seen in the autoradiograph could traverse at least 10 × 80 microns, or about a millimeter, of DNA between one cell division and the next. This is roughly the total length of the DNA in the bacterial chromosome. The autoradiograph therefore suggests that the entire chromosome may be duplicated at a single locus that can move fast enough to traverse the total length of the DNA in each generation.

Finally, the autoradiograph gives evidence on the semiconservative aspect of duplication. Two structures are being synthesized. It is possible to estimate how heavily each structure is labeled (in

terms of grains produced per micron of length) by counting the number of exposed grains and dividing by the length. Then the density of labeling can be compared with that of virus DNA labeled similarly but uniformly, that is, in both of its polynucleotide chains. It turns out that each of the two new structures seen in the picture must be a single polynucleotide chain. If, therefore, the picture is showing the synthesis of two daughter molecules from one parent molecule, it follows that each daughter molecule must be made up of one new (labeled) chain and one old (unlabeled) chain—just as Watson and Crick predicted.

The "pulse-labeling" experiment just described yielded information on the isolated regions of bacterial DNA actually engaged in duplication. To learn if the entire chromosome is a single molecule and how the process of duplication proceeds it was necessary to look at DNA that had been labeled with tritiated thymine for several generations. Moreover, it was necessary to find, in the jumble of chromosomes extracted from *E. coli,* autoradiographs of unbroken chromosomes that were disentangled enough to be seen as a whole. Rather than retrace all the steps that led, after many months, to satisfactory pictures of the entire bacterial chromosome in one piece, it is simpler to present two sample autoradiographs and explain how they can be interpreted and what they reveal.

The autoradiographs on page 82 and at the right show bacterial chromosomes in the process of duplication. All that is visible is labeled, or "hot," DNA; any unlabeled, or "cold," chain is unseen. A stretch of DNA duplex labeled in only one chain ("hot-cold") makes a faint trace of black grains. A duplex that is doubly labeled ("hot-hot") shows as a heavier trace. The autoradiographs therefore indicate, as shown in the diagrams that accompany them, the extent to which new, labeled polynucleotide chains have been laid down along labeled or unlabeled parent chains. Such data make it possible to construct a bacterial family history showing the process of duplication over several generations [see illustration on next page].

The significant conclusions are these:

1. The chromosome of E. coli apparently contains a single molecule of DNA roughly a millimeter in length and with a calculated molecular weight of about two billion. This is by far the largest molecule known to occur in a biological system.

2. The molecule contains two polynucleotide chains, which separate at the time of duplication.

3. The molecule is duplicated at a single locus that traverses the entire length of the molecule. At this point both new chains are being made: two chains are becoming four. This locus has come to be called the replicating "fork" because that is what it looks like.

4. Replicating chromosomes are not Y-shaped, as would be the case for a linear structure [see "d" in bottom illustration on page 84]. Instead the three ends of the Y are joined: the ends of the daughter molecules are joined to each other and to the far end of the parent molecule. In other words, the chromosome is circular while it is being duplicated.

It is hard to conceive of the behavior of a molecule that is about 1,000 times larger than the largest protein and that exists, moreover, coiled inside a cell several hundred times shorter than itself. Apart from this general problem of comprehension, there are two special difficulties inherent in the process of DNA duplication outlined here. Both

have their origin in details of the structure of DNA that I have not yet discussed.

The first difficulty arises from the opposite polarities of the two polynucleotide chains [see illustration on page 89]. The deoxyribose-phosphate backbone of one chain of the DNA duplex has the sequence $-O-C_3-C_4-C_5-O-P-O-C_3-C_4-C_5-O-P-\dots$ (The C_3, C_4 and C_5 are the three carbon atoms of the deoxyribose that contribute to the backbone.) The other chain has the sequence $-P-O-C_5-C_4-C_3-O-P-O-C_5-C_4-C_3-O-\dots$

If both chains are having their complements laid down at a single locus moving in one particular direction, it follows that one of these new chains must grow by repeated addition to the C_3 of the preceding nucleotide's deoxyribose and the other must grow by addition to a C_5. One would expect that two different enzymes should be needed for these two quite different kinds of polymerization. As yet, however, only the reaction that adds to chains ending in C_3 has been demonstrated in such experiments as Kornberg's. This fact had seemed to support a mode of replication in which the two strands grew in opposite directions [see "a" and "c" in bottom illustration on page 84]. If the single-locus scheme is correct, the problem of opposite polarities remains to be explained.

The second difficulty, like the first, is related to the structure of DNA. For the sake of simplicity I have been representing the DNA duplex as a pair of chains lying parallel to each other. In actuality the two chains are wound helically around a common axis, with one complete turn for every 10 base pairs, or 34 angstrom units of length (34 ten-millionths of a millimeter). It would seem, therefore, that separation of the chains at the time of duplication, like separation of the strands of an ordinary rope, must involve rotation of the parent molecule with respect to the two daughter molecules. Moreover, this rotation must be very rapid. A fast-multiplying bacterium can divide every 20 minutes;

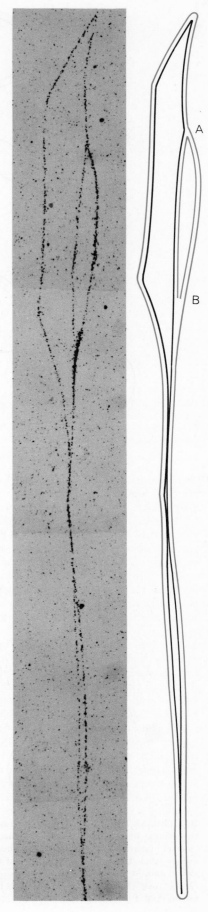

COMPLETE CHROMOSOME is seen in this autoradiograph, enlarged about 370 diameters. Like the chromosome represented on pages 82 and 83, this one is circular, although it happens to have landed on the membrane in a more compressed shape and some segments are tangled. Whereas the first chromosome was more than halfway through the duplication process, this one is only about one-sixth duplicated (from A to B).

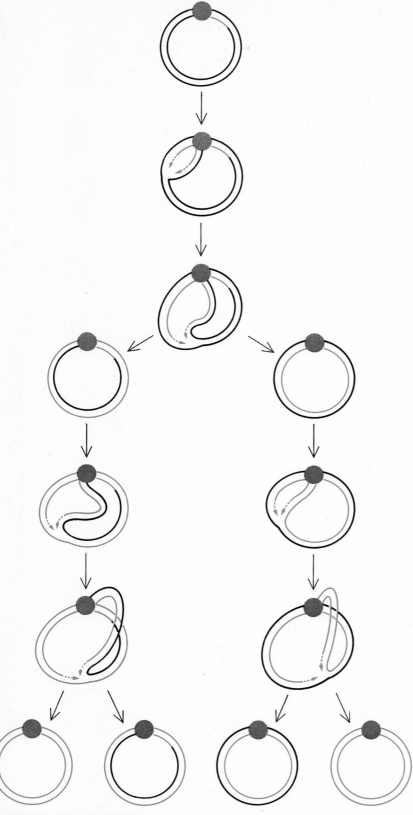

BACTERIAL DNA MOLECULE apparently replicates as in this schematic diagram. The two chains of the circular molecule are represented as concentric circles, joined at a "swivel" (*gray spot*). Labeled DNA is shown in color; part of one chain of the parent molecule is labeled, as are two generations of newly synthesized DNA. Duplication starts at the swivel and, in these drawings, proceeds counterclockwise. The arrowheads mark the replicating "fork": the point at which DNA is being synthesized in each chromosome. The drawing marked *A* is a schematic rendering of the chromosome in the autoradiograph on page 82.

during this time it has to duplicate—and consequently to unwind—about a millimeter of DNA, or some 300,000 turns. This implies an average unwinding rate of 15,000 revolutions per minute.

At first sight it merely adds to the difficulty to find that the chromosome is circular while all of this is going on. Obviously a firmly closed circle—whether a molecule or a rope—cannot be unwound. This complication is worth worrying about because there is increasing evidence that the chromosome of *E. coli* is not exceptional in its circularity. The DNA of numerous viruses has been shown either to be circular or to become circular just before replication begins. For all we know, circularity may therefore be the rule rather than the exception.

There are several possible explanations for this apparent impasse, only one of which strikes me as plausible.

First, one should consider the possibility that there is no impasse—that in the living cell the DNA is two-stranded but not helical, perhaps being kept that way precisely by being in the form of a circle. (If a double helix cannot be unwound when it is firmly linked into a circle, neither can relational coils ever be introduced into a pair of uncoiled circles.) This hypothesis, however, requires a most improbable structure for two-strand DNA, one that has not been observed. And it does not really avoid the unwinding problem because there would still have to be some mechanism for making nonhelical circles out of the helical rods of DNA found in certain virus particles.

Second, one could avoid the unwinding problem by postulating that at least one of the parental chains is repeatedly broken and reunited during replication, so that the two chains can be separated over short sections without rotation of the entire molecule. One rather sentimental objection to this hypothesis (which was proposed some time ago) is that it is hard to imagine such cavalier and hazardous treatment being meted out to such an important molecule, and one so conspicuous for its stability. A second objection is that it does not explain circularity.

The most satisfactory solution to the unwinding problem would be to find some reason why the ends of the chromosome actually *must* be joined together. This is the case if one postulates that there is an active mechanism for unwinding the DNA, distinct from the mechanism that copies the unwound

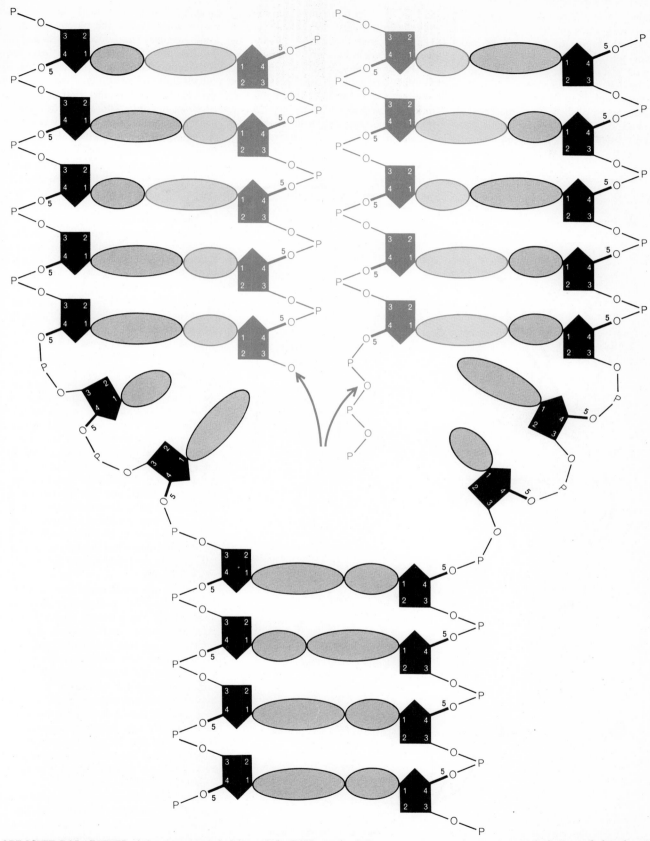

OPPOSITE POLARITIES of the two parental chains of the DNA duplex result in opposite polarities and different directions of growth in the two new chains (*color*) being laid down as complements of the old ones during duplication. Note that the numbered carbon atoms (*1 to 5*) in the deoxyribose rings (*solid black*) are in different positions in the two parental chains and therefore in the two new chains. As the replicating fork moves downward, the new chain that is complementary to the left parental chain must grow by addition to a C_3, the other new chain by addition to a C_5, as shown by the arrows. The elliptical shapes are the four bases.

chains. Now, any active unwinding mechanism must rotate the parent molecule with respect to the two new molecules—must hold the latter fast, in other words, just as the far end of a rope must be held if it is to be unwound. A little thought will show that this can be most surely accomplished by a machine attached, directly or through some common "ground," to the parent molecule and to the two daughters [*see illustration below*]. Every turn taken by such a machine would inevitably unwind the parent molecule one turn.

Although other kinds of unwinding machine can be imagined (one could be situated, for example, at the replicating fork), a practical advantage of this particular hypothesis is that it accounts for circularity. It also makes the surprising —and testable—prediction that any irreparable break in the parent molecule will instantly stop DNA synthesis, no matter how far the break is from the replicating fork. If this prediction is fulfilled, and the unwinding machine acquires the respectability that at present it lacks, we may find ourselves dealing with the first example in nature of something equivalent to a wheel.

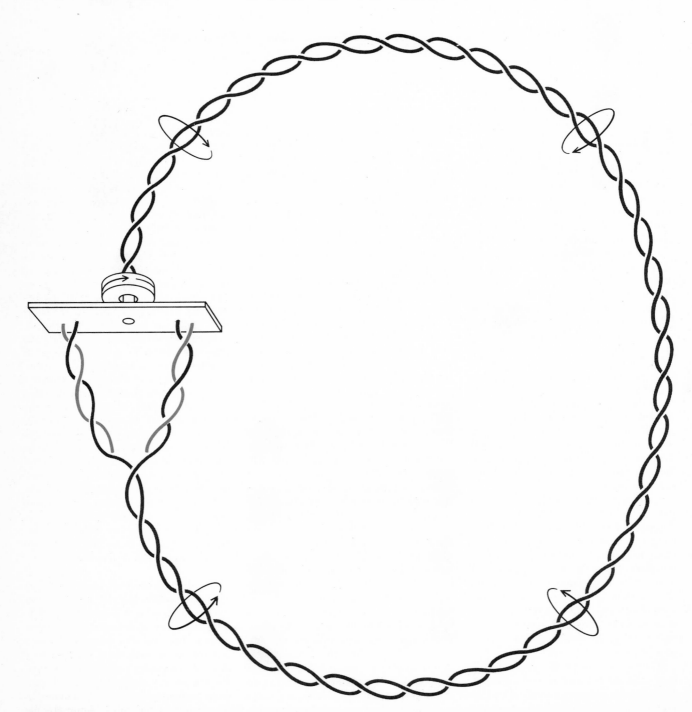

POSSIBLE MECHANISM for unwinding the DNA double helix is a swivel-like machine to which the end of the parent molecule and also the ends of the two daughter molecules are joined. The torque imparted by this machine is considered to be transmitted along the parent molecule, producing unwinding at the replicating fork. If this is correct, chromosome breakage should halt duplication.

9 | The Repair of DNA

PHILIP C. HANAWALT *AND* ROBERT H. HAYNES · February 1967

One of the most impressive achievements of modern industry is its ability to mass-produce units that are virtually identical. This ability is based not solely on the inherent precision of the production facilities. It also involves intensive application of quality-control procedures for the correction of manufacturing errors, since even the best assembly lines can introduce faulty parts at an unacceptable rate. In addition industry provides replacement parts for the repair of a product that is subsequently damaged by exposure to the hazards of its natural environment. Recent studies have demonstrated that living organisms employ analogous processes for repairing defective parts in their genetic material: deoxyribonucleic acid (DNA). This giant molecule must be replicated with extraordinary fidelity if the organism is to survive and make successful copies of itself. Thus the existence of quality-control mechanisms in living cells may account in large part for the fact that "like produces like" over many generations.

Until recently it had been thought that if the DNA in a living cell were damaged or altered, for example by ionizing radiation, the cell might give rise either to mutant "daughter" cells or to no daughter cells at all. Now it appears that many cells are equipped to deal with some of the most serious hazards the environment can present. In this article we shall describe the experimental results that have given rise to this important new concept.

The instructions for the production of new cells are encoded in the sequences of molecular subunits called bases that are strung together along a backbone of phosphate and sugar groups to form the chainlike molecules of DNA. A sequence of a few thousand bases constitutes a

single gene, and each DNA molecule comprises several thousand genes. Before a cell can divide and give rise to two daughter cells, the DNA molecule (or molecules) in the parent cell must be duplicated so that each daughter cell can be supplied with a complete set of genes. On the basis of experiments made with the "chemostat"—a device for maintaining a constant number of bacteria in a steady state of growth—Aaron Novick and the late Leo Szilard estimated that bacterial genes may be duplicated as many as 100 million times before there is a 50 percent chance that even one gene will be altered. This is a remarkable record for any process, and it seems unlikely that it could be achieved without the help of an error-correcting mechanism.

The ability of cells to repair defects in their DNA may well have been a significant factor in biological evolution. On the one hand, repair would be advantageous in enabling a species to maintain its genetic stability in an environment that caused mutations at a high rate. On the other hand, without mutations there would be no evolution, mutations being the changes that allow variation among the individuals of a population. The individuals whose characteristics are best adapted to their environment will leave more offspring than those that are less well adapted. Presumably even the efficiency of genetic repair mechanisms may be subject to selection by evolution. If the repair mechanism were too efficient, it might reduce the natural mutation frequency to such a low level that a population could become trapped in an evolutionary dead end.

Although the error-correcting mechanism cannot yet be described in detail, one can see in the molecular architecture of DNA certain features that should fa-

cilitate both recognition of damage and repair of damage. The genetic material of all cells consists of two complementary strands of DNA linked side by side by hydrogen bonds to form a double helix [see upper illustration on page 93]. Normally DNA contains four chemically distinct bases: two purines (adenine and guanine) and two pyrimidines (thymine and cytosine). The two strands of DNA are complementary because adenine in one strand is always hydrogen-bonded to thymine in the other, and guanine is similarly paired with cytosine [see lower illustration on page 93]. Thus the sequence of bases that constitute the code letters of the cell's genetic message is supplied in redundant form. Redundancy is a familiar stratagem to designers of error-detecting and error-correcting codes. If a portion of one strand of the DNA helix were damaged, the information in that portion could be retrieved from the complementary strand. That is, the cell could use the undamaged strand of DNA as a template for the reconstruction of a damaged segment in the complementary strand. Recent experimental evidence indicates that this is precisely what happens in many species of bacteria, particularly those that are known to be highly resistant to radiation.

The ability to recover from injury is a characteristic feature of living organisms. There is a fundamental difficulty, however, in detecting repair processes in bacteria. For example, when a population of bacteria is exposed to a dose of ultraviolet radiation or X rays, there is no way to determine in advance what proportion of the population will die. How can one tell whether the observed mortality accurately reflects all the damage sustained by the irradiated cells or whether some of the damaged cells have repaired themselves? Fortunately it is possible to turn the repair mechanism on or off at will.

A striking example can be found in the process called photoreactivation [*see bottom illustration on page 95*]. Although hints of its existence can be traced back to 1904, photoreactivation was not adequately appreciated until Albert Kelner rediscovered the effect in 1948 at the Carnegie Institution of Washington's Department of Genetics in Cold Spring Harbor, N.Y. Kelner was puzzled to find that the number of soil organisms (actinomycetes) that survived large doses of ultraviolet radiation could be increased by a factor of several hundred thousand if the irradiated bacteria were subsequently exposed to an intense source of visible light. He concluded that ultraviolet radiation had its principal effect on the nucleic acid of the cell, but he had no inkling what the effect was. In an article published before the genetic significance of DNA was generally appreciated, Kelner wrote: "Per-

haps the real stumbling block [to understanding photoreactivation] is that we do not yet understand at all well the biological role of that omnipresent and important substance—nucleic acid" [see "Revival by Light," by Albert Kelner; SCIENTIFIC AMERICAN, May, 1951].

It is now known that the germicidal action of ultraviolet radiation arises chiefly from the formation of two unwanted chemical bonds between pyrimidine bases that are adjacent to each other on one strand of the DNA molecule. Two molecules bonded in this way are called dimers; of the three possible types of pyrimidine dimer in DNA, the thymine dimer is the one that forms most readily [*see upper illustration on page 94*]. It is therefore not surprising that a given dose of ultraviolet radiation will create more dimers in DNA molecules that contain a high proportion of thymine bases than in DNA molecules with fewer such bases. Consequently bacteria whose DNA is rich in thymine tend to be more sensitive to ultraviolet

radiation than those whose DNA is not.

Richard B. Setlow, his wife Jane K. Setlow and their co-workers at the Oak Ridge National Laboratory have shown that pyrimidine dimers block normal replication of DNA and that bacteria with even a few such defects are unable to divide and form colonies [see "Ultraviolet Radiation and Nucleic Acid," by R. A. Deering; SCIENTIFIC AMERICAN Offprint 143]. In the normal replication of DNA each parental DNA strand serves as a template for the synthesis of a complementary daughter strand. This mode of replication is termed semiconservative because the parental strands separate in the course of DNA synthesis; each daughter cell receives a "hybrid" DNA molecule that consists of one parental strand and one newly synthesized complementary strand. The effect of a pyrimidine dimer on DNA replication may be analogous to the effect on a zipper of fusing two adjacent teeth.

Claud S. Rupert and his associates at

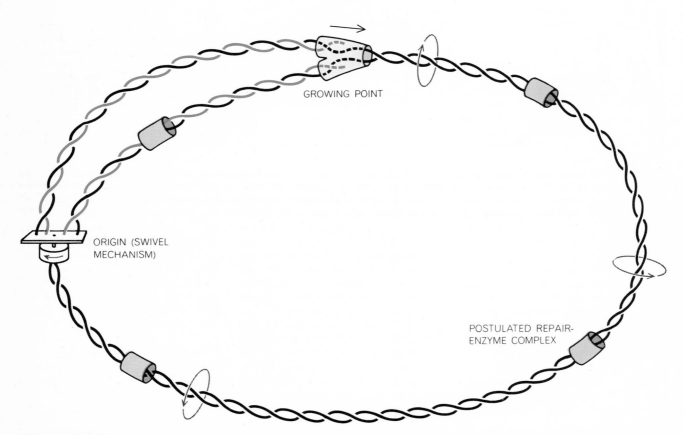

GROWING POINT

ORIGIN (SWIVEL MECHANISM)

POSTULATED REPAIR-ENZYME COMPLEX

REPLICATION OF BACTERIAL CHROMOSOME, a ring-shaped molecule of deoxyribonucleic acid (DNA), has now been shown to take two forms: normal replication and repair replication. In the former process the two strands that constitute the double helix of DNA are unwound and a daughter strand (*color*) is synthesized against each of them. In this way the genetic "message" is transmitted from generation to generation. The pairing of complementary subunits that underlies this process is illustrated on the next page. In repair replication, defects that arise in individual strands of DNA are removed and replaced by good segments. It is hypothesized that "repair complexes," composed of enzymes, are responsible for the quality control of the DNA structure. Although this diagram shows the swivel mechanism for unwinding the parent strands to be at the origin, it may in fact be located at the growing point.

Johns Hopkins University have shown that photoreactivation involves the action of an enzyme that is selectively bound to DNA that has been irradiated with ultraviolet. When this enzyme is activated by visible light (which simply serves as a source of energy), it cleaves the pyrimidine dimers, thereby restoring the two bases to their original form. Photoreactivation is thus a repair process that can be turned on or off merely by flicking a light switch.

Let us now consider another kind of repair mechanism in which light plays no role and that is therefore termed dark reactivation. This type of repair process can be turned off genetically, by finding mutant strains of bacteria that lack the repair capabilities of the original radiation-resistant strain. The "B/r" strain of the bacterium *Escherichia coli,*

first isolated in 1946 by Evelyn Witkin of Columbia University, is an example of a microorganism that is particularly resistant to radiation. The first radiation-sensitive mutants of this strain, known as B_{s-1}, were discovered in 1958 by Ruth Hill, also of Columbia.

Not long after the discovery of the B_{s-1} strain a number of people suggested that its sensitivity to radiation might be due to the malfunction of a particular enzyme system that enabled resistant bacteria such as *B/r* to repair DNA that had been damaged by radiation. This was a reasonable suggestion in view of the steadily accumulating evidence that DNA is the principal target for many kinds of radiobiological damage. Experiments conducted by Howard I. Adler at Oak Ridge and by Paul Howard-Flanders at Yale University lent further support to this hypothesis. It had been

known for some years that bacteria can exchange genes by direct transfer through a primitive form of sexual mating [see "Viruses and Genes," by François Jacob and Elie L. Wollman; SCIENTIFIC AMERICAN Offprint 89]. Howard-Flanders and his co-workers found that bacteria of a certain radiation-resistant strain of *E. coli* (strain *K*-12) have at least three genes that can be transferred by bacterial mating to radiation-sensitive cells, thereby making them radiation-resistant. Since genes direct the synthesis of all enzymes in the living cell, these experiments supported the hypothesis that B_{s-1} and other radiation-sensitive bacteria lack one or more enzymes needed for the repair of radiation-damaged DNA.

The question now arises: Do the enzymes involved in dark reactivation operate in the same way as the enzyme that

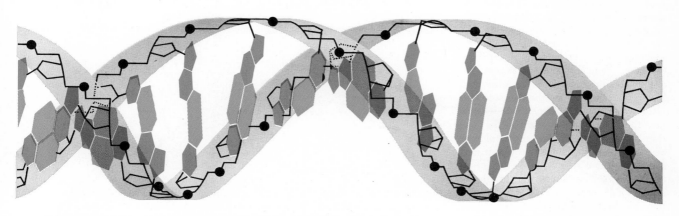

DNA MOLECULE is a double helix that carries the genetic message in redundant form. The backbone of each helix consists of repeating units of deoxyribose sugar (*pentagons*) and phosphate (*black dots*). The backbones are linked by hydrogen bonds between pairs of four kinds of base: adenine, guanine, thymine and cytosine. The bases are the "letters" in which the genetic message is written. Because adenine invariably pairs with thymine and guanine with cytosine, the two strands carry equivalent information.

DNA BASES are held together in pairs by hydrogen bonds. The cytosine-guanine pair (*left*) involve three hydrogen bonds, the thymine-adenine pair (*right*) two bonds. If the CH_3 group in thymine is replaced by an atom of bromine (*Br*), the resulting molecule is called 5-bromouracil. Thymine and 5-bromouracil are so similar that bacteria will incorporate either in synthesizing DNA. Because the bromine compound is so much heavier than thymine its presence can be detected by its effect on the weight of the DNA.

is known to split pyrimidine dimers in the photoreactivation process? Another possibility is that the resistant cells might somehow bypass the dimers during replication of DNA and leave them permanently present, although harmless, in their descendant molecules.

The actual mechanism is even more elegant than either of these possibilities; it exploits the redundancy inherent in the genetic message. The radiation-resistant strains of bacteria possess several enzymes that operate sequentially in removing the dimers and replacing the defective bases with the proper complements of the bases in the adjacent "good" strand. We shall recount the two key observations that substantiate this postulated repair scheme.

The excision of dimers was first demonstrated by Richard Setlow and William L. Carrier at Oak Ridge and was soon confirmed by Richard P. Boyce and Howard-Flanders at Yale. In their studies cultures of ultraviolet-resistant and ultraviolet-sensitive bacteria were grown separately in the presence of radioactive thymine, which was thereupon incorporated into the newly synthesized DNA. The cells were then exposed to ultraviolet radiation. After about 30 minutes they were broken open so that the fate of the labeled thymine could be traced. In the ultraviolet-sensitive strains all the thymine that had been incorporated into DNA was associated with the intact DNA molecules. Therefore any thymine dimers formed by ultraviolet radiation remained within the DNA. In the ultraviolet-resistant strains, however, dimers originally formed in the DNA were found to be associated with small molecular fragments consisting of no more than three bases each. (Thymine dimers can easily be distinguished from the individual bases or combinations of bases by paper chromatography, the technique by which substances are separated by their characteristic rate of travel along a piece of paper that has been wetted with a solvent.) These experiments provided strong evidence that dark repair of ultraviolet-damaged DNA does not involve the splitting of dimers in place, as it does in photoreactivation, but does depend on their actual removal from the DNA molecule.

Direct evidence for the repair step was not long in coming. At Stanford University one of us (Hanawalt), together with a graduate student, David Pettijohn, had been studying the replication of DNA after ultraviolet irradiation of a radiation-resistant strain of E. coli. In

THYMINE   THYMINE DIMER

EFFECT OF ULTRAVIOLET RADIATION on DNA is to fuse adjacent pyrimidine units: thymine or cytosine. The commonest linkage involves two units of thymine, which are coupled by the opening of double bonds. The resulting structure is known as a dimer.

NITROGEN MUSTARD

GUANINE   GUANINE

EFFECT OF NITROGEN MUSTARD, a compound related to mustard gas, is to cross-link units of guanine within the DNA molecule. Unless repaired, the structural defects caused by nitrogen mustard and ultraviolet radiation can prevent the normal replication of DNA.

these experiments we used as a tracer a chemical analogue of thymine called 5-bromouracil. This compound is so similar to the natural base thymine that a bacterium cannot easily tell the two apart [see right half of lower illustration on preceding page]. When 5-bromouracil is substituted for thymine in the growth medium of certain strains of bacteria that are unable to synthesize thymine, it is incorporated into the newly replicated DNA. The fate of 5-bromouracil can be traced because the bromine atom in it is more than five times heavier than the methyl (CH_3) group in normal thymine that it replaces. Therefore DNA fragments containing 5-bromouracil are denser than normal fragments containing thymine. The density difference can be detected by density-gradient centrifugation, a technique introduced in 1957 by Matthew S. Meselson, Franklin W. Stahl and Jerome Vinograd at

the California Institute of Technology.

In density-gradient centrifugation DNA fragments are suspended in a solution of the heavy salt cesium chloride and are spun in a high-speed centrifuge for several days. When equilibrium is reached, the density of the solution varies from 1.5 grams per milliliter at the top of the tube to two grams per milliliter at the bottom. If normal DNA from E. coli is also present, it will eventually concentrate in a band corresponding to a density of 1.71 grams per milliliter. A DNA containing 5-bromouracil instead of thymine has a density of 1.8 and so will form a band closer to the bottom of the tube.

The entire genetic message of E. coli is contained in a single two-strand molecule of DNA whose length is nearly 1,000 times as long as the cell itself. This long molecule must be coiled up like a

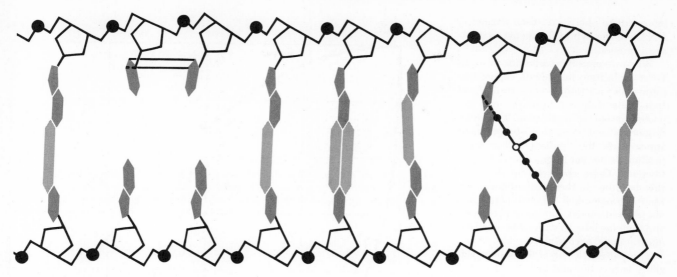

DEFECTS IN DNA probably distort the symmetry of its helical structure. To make the distortions more apparent this diagram shows the DNA in flattened form. A thymine dimer appears in the left half of the structure; a guanine-guanine cross-link is shown in the right half. The authors believe the repair complex recognizes the distortions rather than the actual defects in the bases.

skein of yarn to be accommodated within the cell [see "The Bacterial Chromosome," by John Cairns, beginning on page 83 in this book]. such a molecule is extremely sensitive to fluid shearing forces; in the course of being extracted from the cell it is usually broken into several hundred pieces.

If 5-bromouracil is added to a culture of growing bacteria for a few minutes (a small fraction of one generation), the DNA fragments isolated from the cells fall into several categories of differing density, each of which forms a distinct band in a cesium chloride density gradient. The lightest band will consist of unlabeled fragments: regions of the DNA molecule that were not replicated during the period when 5-bromouracil was present. A distinctly heavier band will contain fragments from regions that have undergone replication during the labeling period. This is the band containing hybrid DNA: molecules made up of one old strand containing thymine and one new strand containing 5-bromouracil in place of thymine. If synthesis proceeds until the chromosome has completed one cycle of replication and has started on the next cycle, some DNA fragments will have 5-bromouracil in both strands and therefore will form a band still heavier than the band containing the hybrid fragments. Finally, one fragment from each chromosome will include the "growing point" where the new strands are being synthesized on the pattern of the old ones, and thus will consist of a mixture of replicated and unreplicated DNA. This fragment, which is presumably shaped like a Y, will show up in the density gradient at a position

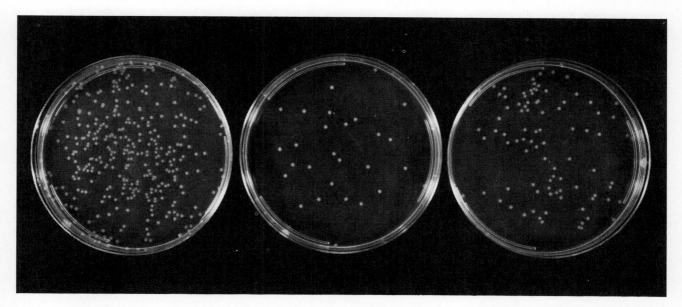

PHOTOREACTIVATION, a type of DNA repair process, is demonstrated in this photograph of three bacterial culture dishes. The dish at the left is a control: it contains 368 colonies of B/r strain of Escherichia coli. The middle dish contains bacteria exposed to ultraviolet radiation; only 35 cells have survived to form colonies. The bacteria in the dish at right were exposed to visible light following ultraviolet irradiation; it contains 93 colonies. Thus exposure to visible light increased the survival rate nearly threefold.

intermediate between the unlabeled DNA and the hybrid fragments containing 5-bromouracil.

When we used this technique to study DNA replication in bacteria exposed to ultraviolet radiation, we observed a pattern quite different from the one expected for normal replication. The DNA fragments containing the 5-bromouracil appeared in the gradient at the same position as normal fragments containing thymine! There could be no doubt of this because in these experiments we used 5-bromouracil labeled with tritium (the radioactive isotope of hydrogen) and thymine labeled with carbon 14 [*see illustration on next page*].

This pattern, which at first seems puzzling, is just the one to be expected if many thymine dimers—created at random throughout the DNA by ultraviolet radiation—had been excised and if 5-bromouracil had been substituted for thymine in the repaired regions. As a result many DNA fragments would contain 5-bromouracil, but no one fragment would contain enough 5-bromouracil to affect its density appreciably.

How can we be sure that the density distribution of 5-bromouracil observed in the foregoing experiment arises from "repair replication" rather than from normal replication? A variety of tests confirmed the repair interpretation. By using enzymes to break down the DNA molecule and separating the bases by paper chromatography we verified that the radioactive label was still in 5-bromouracil and had not been transferred to some other base. Various physical studies showed that the 5-bromouracil had been incorporated into extremely short segments that were distributed randomly throughout both DNA strands. This mode of DNA replication was not observed in the B_{s-1} strain of E. coli, the radiation-sensitive mutant that cannot excise pyrimidine dimers and therefore could not be expected to perform repair replication. Moreover, repair replication was not observed in the radiation-resistant bacteria in which visible light had triggered the splitting of pyrimidine dimers by photoreactivation; this indicates that repair replication is not necessary if the dimers are otherwise repaired *in situ*.

Finally it was shown that DNA repaired by dimer excision and strand reconstruction could ultimately replicate in the normal semiconservative fashion. This is rather compelling evidence for the idea that biologically functional DNA results from repair replication and that the process is not some aberrant

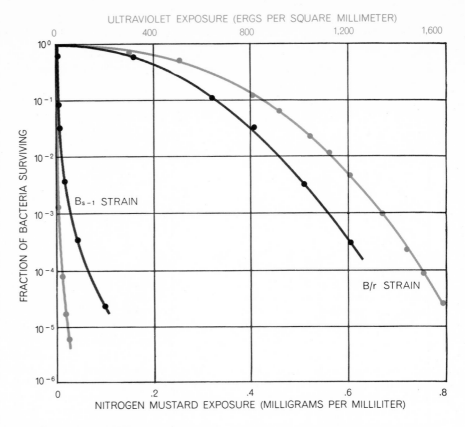

RESISTANCE TO LETHAL AGENTS is demonstrated by certain strains of *E. coli* but not by others. The *B/r* strain, for example, shows a high tolerance to doses of ultraviolet radiation (*colored curves*) and nitrogen mustard (*black curves*) that kill a large percentage of the sensitive B_{s-1} strain. This result suggests that the DNA repair mechanism of the *B/r* strain is effective in removing guanine-guanine cross-links produced by nitrogen mustard as well as in removing thymine dimers formed by exposure to ultraviolet radiation.

form of synthesis with no biological importance.

How can one visualize the detailed sequence of events that must be involved in this type of repair? Two models have been suggested, and the present experimental data seem to be equally compatible with each. The two models are distinguished colloquially by the terms "cut and patch" and "patch and cut" [*see illustrations on page 98*]. The former refers to the model originally proposed by Richard Setlow, Howard-Flanders and others. The latter refers to a model that took form during a discussion at a recent conference on DNA repair mechanisms held in Chicago.

The cut-and-patch scheme postulates an enzyme that excises a short, single-strand segment of the damaged DNA. The resulting gap is enlarged by further enzyme attack and then the missing bases are replaced by repair replication in the genetically correct sequence according to the rules that govern the pairing of bases.

In the patch-and-cut scheme the process is assumed to be initiated by a single

incision that cuts the strand of DNA near the defective bases. Repair replication begins immediately at this point and is accompanied by a "peeling back" of the defective strand as the new bases are inserted. This patch-and-cut scheme is attractive because it could conceivably be carried out by a single enzyme complex or particle that moves in one direction along the DNA molecule, repairing defects as it goes. Furthermore, it does not involve the introduction of long, vulnerable single-strand regions into the DNA molecule while the repair is taking place. Both models are undoubtedly oversimplifications of the actual molecular events inside the living cell, but they have great intuitive appeal and are helpful in planning further studies of the DNA repair process.

Repair replication would be of interest only to radiation specialists if it were not for the evidence that DNA structural defects other than pyrimidine dimers can be repaired and that similar repair phenomena occur in organisms other than *E. coli*. We shall review some of the

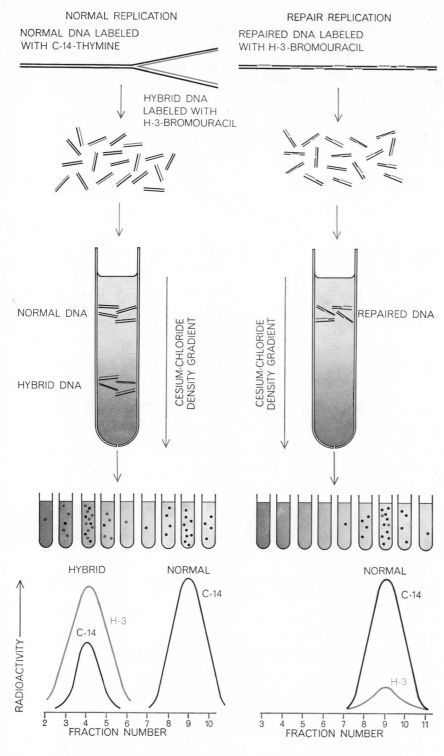

NORMAL REPLICATION

NORMAL DNA LABELED
WITH C-14-THYMINE

HYBRID DNA
LABELED WITH
H-3-BROMOURACIL

NORMAL DNA

HYBRID DNA

CESIUM-CHLORIDE DENSITY GRADIENT

REPAIR REPLICATION

REPAIRED DNA LABELED
WITH H-3-BROMOURACIL

CESIUM-CHLORIDE DENSITY GRADIENT

REPAIRED DNA

HYBRID   NORMAL

H-3

C-14   C-14

RADIOACTIVITY

2 3 4 5 6 7 8 9 10
FRACTION NUMBER

NORMAL

C-14

H-3

3 4 5 6 7 8 9 10 11
FRACTION NUMBER

TWO KINDS OF REPLICATION can be demonstrated by growing bacteria first in a culture containing thymine labeled with radioactive carbon 14 and then in a culture containing 5-bromouracil labeled with radioactive hydrogen 3. In normal replication (*left*), also known as semiconservative replication, daughter strands of "hybrid" DNA incorporate the 5-bromouracil (*color*). Because 5-bromouracil is much heavier than the thymine for which it substitutes, fragments of hybrid DNA form a separate heavier layer when they have been centrifuged and have reached equilibrium in a density gradient of cesium chloride. When the radioactivity in the various fractions is analyzed (*bottom left*), carbon 14 appears in two peaks but hydrogen 3 occurs in only one peak. If the experiment is repeated with DNA fragments that have undergone repair replication (*right*), they all appear to be of normal density. This implies that relatively little 5-bromouracil has been incorporated and also that the repaired segments are randomly scattered throughout the DNA molecule.

evidence indicating that repair replication is of general biological significance.

Just as strains of *E. coli* vary considerably in their sensitivity to ultraviolet radiation, so they vary considerably in their sensitivity to other mutagenic agents. One such agent is nitrogen mustard, so named because it is chemically related to the mustard gas used in World War I. It was the first chemical agent known to be capable of producing mutations and chromosome breaks in fruit flies and other organisms. Its biological action arises primarily from its ability to react with neighboring guanine bases in DNA, thereby producing guanine-guanine cross-links [*see lower illustration on page 94*].

If one compares the survival curves of different strains of bacteria treated with nitrogen mustard with survival curves for bacteria subjected to ultraviolet radiation, one finds that the curves are almost identical [*see illustration on preceding page*]. This similarity led us to suggest that it is not the altered bases themselves that are "recognized" by the repair enzymes but rather the associated distortions, or kinks, that the alteration of the bases produces in the backbone of the DNA molecule. On this hypothesis one would predict that a wide variety of chemically different structural defects in DNA might be repaired by a common mechanism.

A substantial amount of biochemical evidence has now accumulated in support of this idea. We have established, for example, that repair replication of DNA takes place in *E. coli* that have been treated with nitrogen mustard. Others have found evidence that defects produced by agents as diverse as X rays, the chemical mutagen nitrosoguanidine and the antibiotic mitomycin *C* can all be repaired in radiation-resistant strains of *E. coli*. Walter Doerfler and David Hogness of Stanford have even found evidence that simple mispairing of bases between two strands of DNA can be corrected.

Finally, it now seems that certain steps in repair replication may also be involved in such phenomena as genetic recombination and the reading of the DNA code in preparation for protein synthesis. Evidence for these exciting possibilities has begun to appear in the work of Howard-Flanders, Meselson (who is now at Harvard University), Alvin J. Clark, of the University of California at Berkeley, Crellin Pauling of the University of California at Riverside and other investigators.

Repair replication has also been observed in a number of bacterial species other than *E. coli*. For example, Douglas Smith, a graduate student at Stanford, has demonstrated the repair of DNA in the pleuropneumonia-like organisms, which are probably the smallest living cells. These organisms, which are even smaller than some viruses, are thought to possess only the minimum number of structures needed for self-replication and independent existence [see "The Smallest Living Cells," by Harold J. Morowitz and Mark E. Tourtellotte; SCIENTIFIC AMERICAN Offprint 1005]. This suggests that repair replication may be a fundamental requirement for the evolution of free-living organisms.

In view of the impressive versatility of the repair replication process it is natural to ask if there is any type of DNA damage that cannot be mended by the cell. The evidence so far is limited and indirect, but William Rodger Inch, working at the Lawrence Radiation Laboratory of the University of California, has found that the *B/r* strain of *E. coli* is unable to repair all the damage caused when it is exposed to certain energetic beams of atomic nuclei produced by the heavy-ion linear accelerator (HILAC). Considering the extensive damage that must be done to cells by a beam of such intensely ionizing radiation, the result is not too surprising.

The discovery that cells have the facility to repair defects in DNA is a recent one. It is already apparent, however, that the process of repair replication could have broad significance for biology and medicine. Many questions remain to be investigated: What is the structure of the various repair enzymes? Are they organized into particulate units within the cell? What range of DNA defects can be recognized and repaired? Does DNA repair, as we now understand it, take place in the cells of mammals, or do even more complicated processes underlie the recovery phenomena that are observed after these higher types of cells are exposed to radiation? Might it be possible to increase the radiosensitivity of tumors by inhibiting the DNA repair mechanisms that may operate in cancer cells? If so, the idea could be of great practical value in the treatment of cancer.

These and many related questions are now being investigated in many laboratories around the world. Once again it has been demonstrated that the study of what may appear to be rather obscure properties of the simplest forms of life can yield rich dividends of much intellectual and practical value.

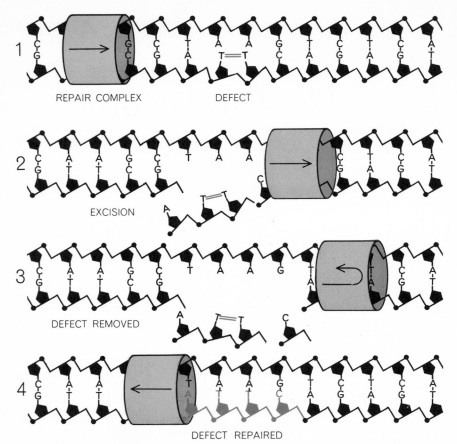

"CUT AND PATCH" repair mechanism was the first one proposed to explain how bacterial cells might remove thymine dimers (*1*) and similar defects from a DNA molecule. The hypothetical repair complex severs the defective strand (*2*) and removes the defective region (*3*). Retracing its path, it inserts new bases according to the rules of base pairing (*4*).

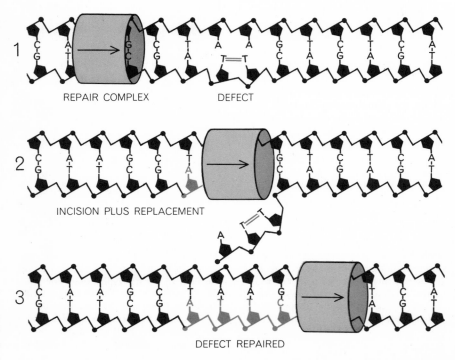

"PATCH AND CUT" mechanism has been proposed as an alternative to the cut-and-patch scheme. On the new model the repair complex inserts new bases as it removes defective ones.

The Duplication of Chromosomes

10

J. HERBERT TAYLOR · June 1958

In the search for the secret of how living things reproduce themselves, geneticists have recently focused on the substance called DNA (deoxyribonucleic acid). DNA seems pretty clearly to be the basic hereditary material—the molecule that carries the blueprints for reproduction. F. H. C. Crick and J. D. Watson have found that the molecule consists of two complementary strands, and they have developed the theory that it duplicates itself by a template process, each strand acting as a mold to form a new partner [see "Nucleic Acids," by F. H. C. Crick; SCIENTIFIC AMERICAN Offprint 54].

The problem now is: How does this model fit into the larger picture of chromosomes? For half a century we have known that chromosomes, the rod-like bodies found in the nucleus of every cell, are the carriers of heredity. They contain the genes that pass on the hereditary traits to offspring. As each cell divides, the chromosomes duplicate themselves, so that every daughter cell has copies of the originals. How is the reproduction of chromosomes related to the reproduction of DNA? The question is being pursued by two approaches: from DNA up toward chromosomes and from chromosomes down toward the molecular level. This article will report some experimental studies of the behavior of chromosomes which have suggested a general model of the mechanism of reproduction.

Chromosomes take their name from the fact that they readily absorb dyes and stand out in strong color when cells are stained [*see photographs on the next page*]. They become visible under the microscope shortly before a cell is ready to divide. At that time each chromosome consists of a pair of rods

side by side. When the cell divides, the two members of the pair (called chromatids) separate, and one chromatid goes to each daughter cell.

In the new cell the chromatid disappears. Then as this cell approaches division, each chromatid reappears, now

twinned with a new partner. It has made a copy of itself for the destined daughter cell. There are two possible ways it may have done this: (1) by staying intact (even though invisible in the microscope) and acting as a template, or (2) by breaking down and generating small

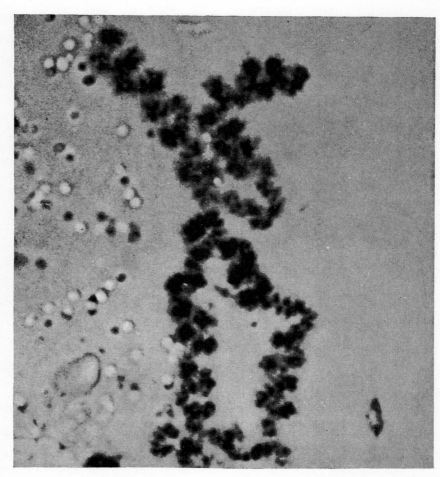

DOUBLE COILED STRUCTURE of a chromosome can be seen in this photomicrograph, the magnification of which is about 4,000 diameters. Chromosome was partly unwound by treatment with dilute potassium cyanide. The chromosome is from a cell of the Easter lily.

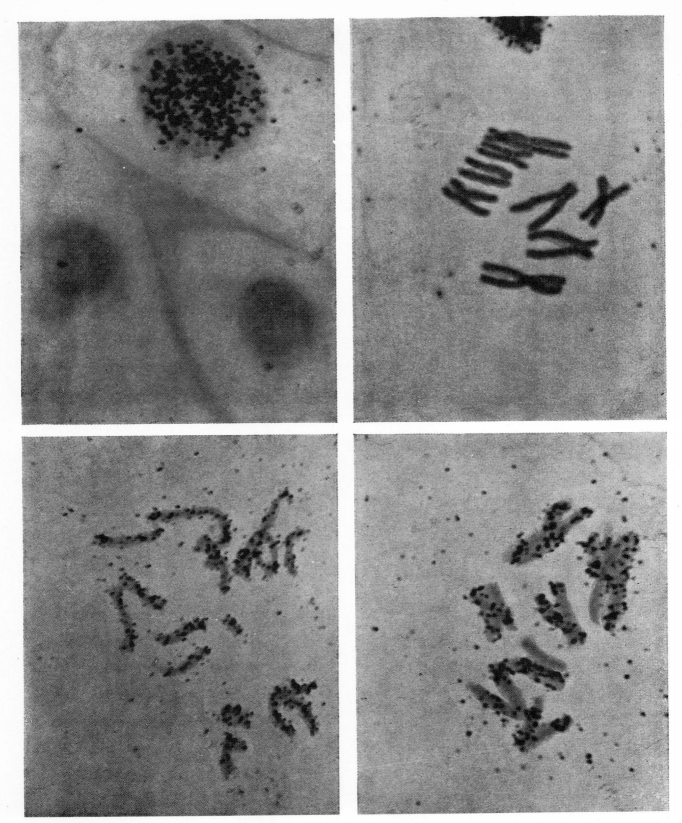

CHROMOSOMES of Bellevalia, a plant of the lily family, are tagged with radioactive thymidine in experiment on duplication. Radiation from the thymidine strikes photographic film placed over the cells, producing black specks. The upper nucleus in the photomicrograph at top left has taken up the tracer material but its chromosomes have not yet become visible. Chromosomes at top right completed their duplication before the cells were placed in radioactive solution and are not tagged. Those at bottom left duplicated once in radioactive solution. Both members of each pair are labeled. The chromosomes at bottom right duplicated once in radioactive solution and once after cells were removed. Only one member of each pair is tagged, except where segments crossed.

units which then reassemble themselves in the form of the original chromatid.

It has recently become possible to resolve this question by means of radioactive tracers. When cells grow in a medium containing thymidine, a component of DNA, all of the thymidine is taken up by the chromosomes; none of it is built into any other part of the cell. Thus if we label thymidine with radioactive atoms (the radioisotopes of hydrogen or carbon), we can follow the transmission of the material through successive replications of the chromosomes. For our own experiments, which I conducted in collaboration with Walter L. Hughes and Philip S. Woods of the Brookhaven National Laboratory, we chose radiohydrogen (tritium) as the tracer. This substance makes it possible to distinguish a radioactive chromatid from a nonradioactive one lying next to it. To localize the radioactivity we use the technique of autoradiography. The cells are squashed flat on a glass slide and covered with a thin sheet of photographic film. Radioactive emanations from the cells produce darkened spots on the film. The emissions from radioactive carbon are fairly penetrating and therefore darken a comparatively wide area of the film; we selected tritium instead because its emissions travel only a short distance—so short that we can narrow down the source to a single chromosome or part of a chromosome.

Our first experiment followed the fate of the thymidine through one duplication of labeled chromosomes. In order to control the situation so that we could identify newly formed chromosomes we treated the cells with colchicine—a drug which prevents cells from dividing but allows chromosomes to go on duplicating themselves. This enabled us to sequester the new chromosomes within the original cells and to tell how many generations had been produced. The cells we studied were those in the growing roots of plants, cultured in a solution containing tritium-labeled thymidine.

We found, to begin with, that in cells that had taken up this thymidine (*i.e.*, produced a new generation of chromosomes preparatory to division), all the chromosomes were labeled, and radioactivity was distributed equally between the two chromatids of each chromosome. This might suggest that the new chromosomes had been formed from a mixture of materials generated by a breakdown of the original chromatids. But when we

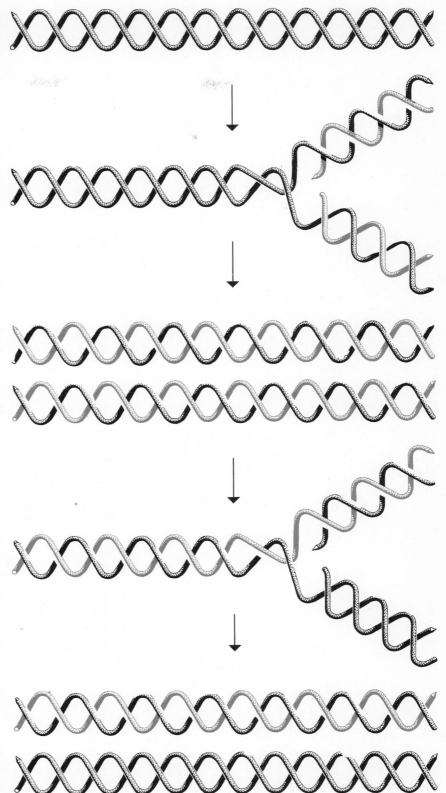

DNA MOLECULES consist of two complementary chains wound around each other in a double helix. When they duplicate, they unwind and each chain builds itself a new partner. Shown here are two cycles of duplication. The first cycle takes place in radioactive solution, producing two labeled chains (*colored helixes*). When a labeled molecule duplicates itself again in nonradioactive solution, only one of its descendants contains a labeled chain.

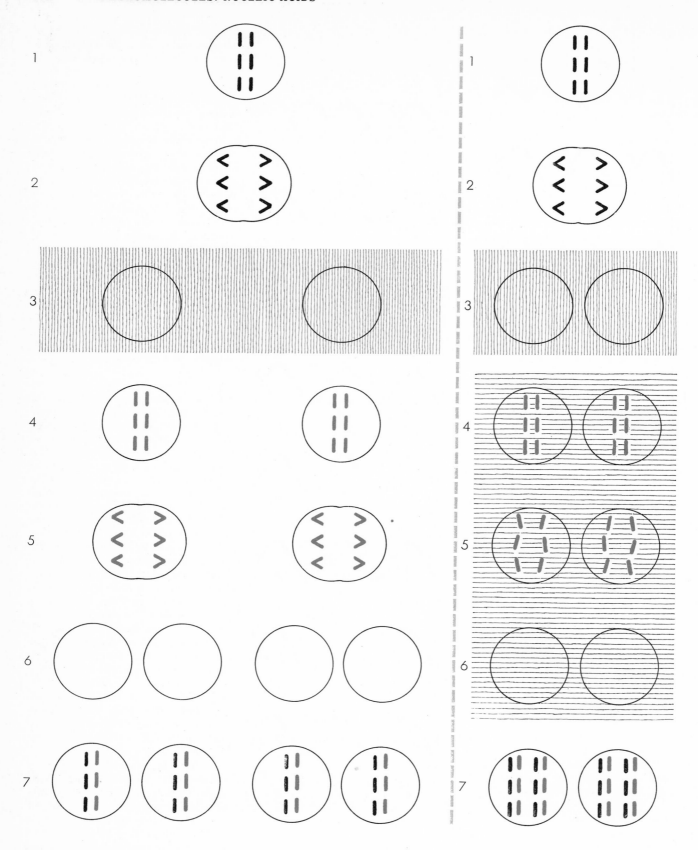

DUPLICATION CYCLES in tracer experiment are diagrammed schematically. Cells to left of the vertical broken line are allowed to divide normally. Those to the right are prevented from dividing when they are placed in colchicine (*black shading*), but their chromosomes continue to duplicate. Black rods represent unlabeled chromatids; colored rods, labeled chromatids. Colored shading indicates radioactive thymidine solution. The empty circles represent stage when chromatids are invisible and duplicating themselves.

followed root cells through a second generation of chromosome reproduction, where the second generation was synthesized in a medium containing non-radioactive thymidine, we found to our delight that in each new doubled chromosome one chromatid was labeled and the other was not!

What might this mean? The simplest and most likely answer was that a chromatid itself consists of two parts, each of which remains intact and acts as a template. In the radioactive medium each of the original chromatids, after splitting in two, builds itself a radioactive partner. Therefore all the new chromosomes are labeled. Now when the labeled chromatids split again to produce a second generation, half of the strands are labeled and half are not. In a nonradioactive medium all of them will build unlabeled partners. As a result, half of the newly formed chromatids will be partly labeled, half will have no label at all [see diagrams on page 102].

Our picture of the chromatid as a two-part structure fits very well with what we know about the DNA molecule and with the Crick-Watson theory. DNA too is a double structure, consisting of two complementary helical chains wound around each other. And some of our recent experiments indicate that the two strands of a chromatid are complementary structures. It is tempting, therefore, to suppose that a chromatid is simply a chain of DNA. But when we consider the question of scale, we realize that the matter cannot be so simple. If all the DNA in a chromatid formed a single linear chain, the chain would be more than a yard long, and its two strands would be twisted around each other more than 300 million times! It seems unthinkable that so long a chain could untwist itself completely, as the chromatid must each time it generates a new chromosome. Furthermore, the chromatid has the wrong dimensions to be a single DNA chain. When fully extended, it is about 100 times thicker and only one 10,000th as long as the linear DNA chain would be.

Under a high-power microscope we can see that the chromatid is a strand of material tightly wound in a helical coil—in fact, so strongly wound that the coil itself often winds up helically, like a coiled telephone cord which is twisted into a series of secondary kinks [see photograph on page 99]. But beyond this the optical microscope cannot resolve details of the chromatid's structure. Assuming that it is made up of pieces of DNA as its basic replicating units, what sort of

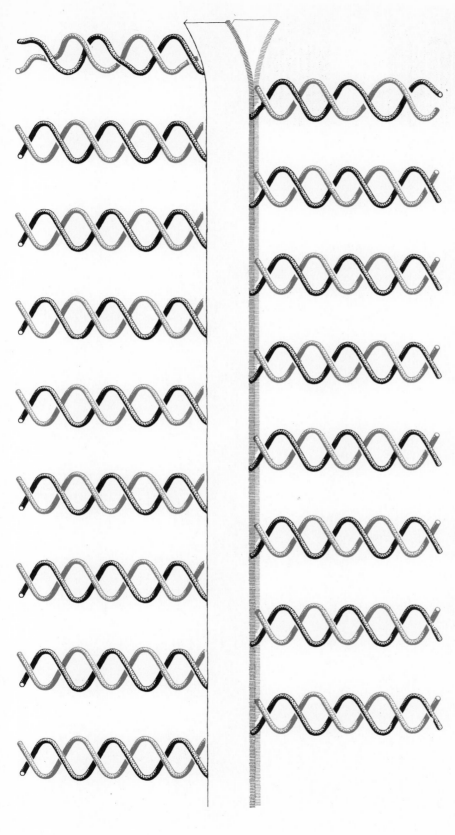

RIBBON MODEL of a chromatid consists of a two-layered central column to which DNA molecules are attached. One chain of each molecule is anchored to the front layer and the other to the back layer. When the chromatid duplicates, the central ribbon peels apart, unwinding the DNA molecules. Each half of the structure then builds itself a new partner.

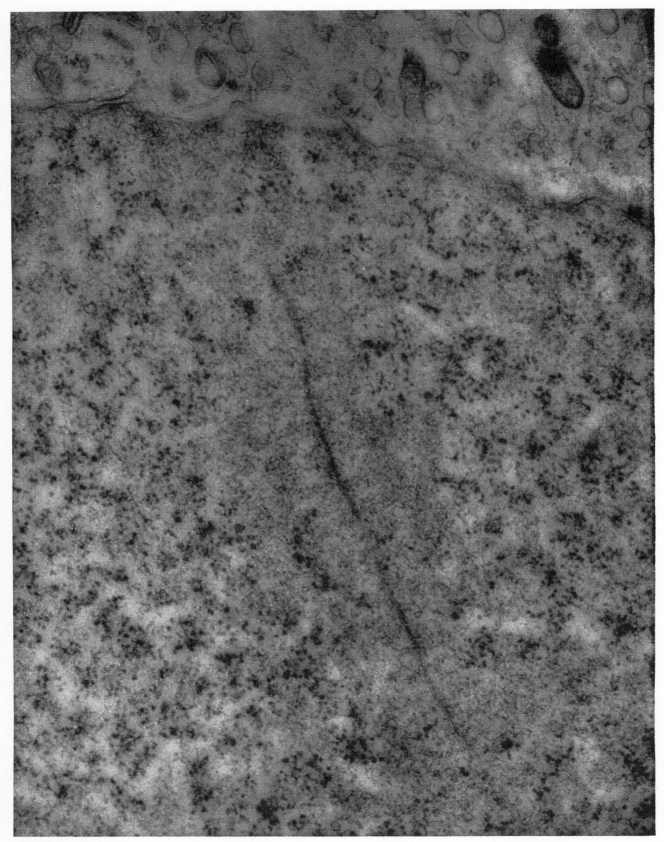

CHROMATID appears as a linear structure running diagonally down the middle of this electron micrograph, made by Montrose J. Moses of the Rockefeller Institute for Medical Research. The magnification is some 50,000 diameters. The line may represent the central column in the author's models and the fuzzy material surrounding the line may be DNA strands running perpendicularly outward.

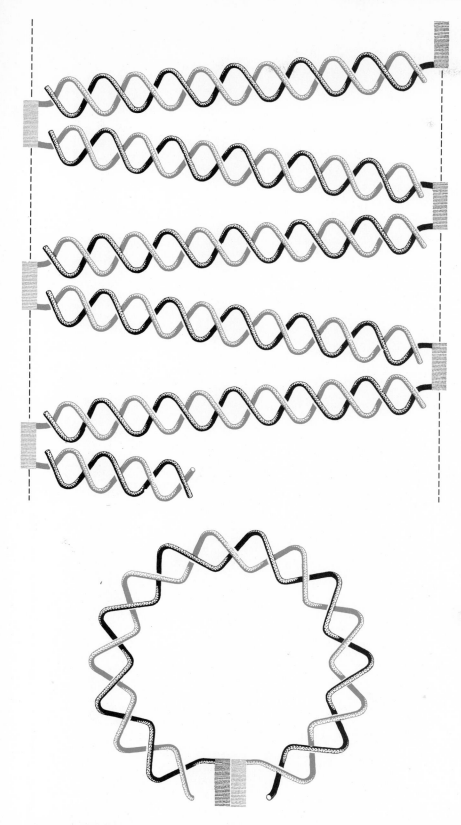

ANOTHER MODEL of the chromatid places its molecules of DNA between two columns, with one chain of each molecule attached to the left-hand column and the other to the right-hand column. Shaded rectangles represent structural material of the columns; broken lines indicate bonds which may include calcium. When the chromatid becomes visible, the columns come together so that the structure appears as in lower drawing when viewed end on.

model can we imagine to explain its construction?

We know that chromosomes contain protein. So as a start we may picture the chromatid as a long protein backbone with DNA molecules branching out to the sides like ribs [*see diagram on page 103*]. Because the chromatid splits in two, we visualize the backbone as a two-layered affair whose layers can separate. The ends of the two strands of a DNA molecule are attached to these layers: one strand to one layer, the complementary strand to the other [*see diagram*]. As the layers peel apart, they unwind the strands. The unwinding strands promptly begin to build matching new strands for themselves. Eventually the new strands also assemble a new backbone, and the original chromatid is thus fully duplicated.

This model seems to have all the necessary mechanical specifications except one. The genes in a chromosome are arranged in a fixed linear order. Here the DNA segments, with one end waving freely about, are not so arranged. To meet this objection Ernst Freese of Harvard University has suggested a slightly different model which joins the free ends of the DNA molecules so that they form a definite sequence. Instead of one spine there are two, with the DNA segments crossing between them somewhat like the rungs of a ladder [*see diagram at the left*]. The spines may consist of blocks of protein joined by flexible bonds involving calcium atoms. The DNA rungs zigzag so that they march up the ladder, and the points on the rungs thus have a sequential order.

Now we can suppose that the calcium bonds give the structure considerable flexibility, allowing it to fold and coil on itself. The two spines may come together and so form a long tube [*see lower drawing at left*]; the tube may then coil into a tight helix. Replication in this model is accomplished by a stretching of the chain and unwinding of the DNA strands, each of which has one free end, as the diagrams show.

Recently Montrose J. Moses of the Rockefeller Institute for Medical Research and Don W. Fawcett of Cornell Medical College, using the electron microscope, have obtained pictures of chromatids which do indeed show a spine structure with DNA branches [*see photograph on page 104*]. It appears that we are beginning to penetrate down to the detailed mechanisms of the duplication of life.

II

THE VIRUS
A Replicating Macromolecular Complex

The simplest macromolecular structure that possesses sufficient genetic information for its own duplication is the virus. This does not mean, however, that a free virus in an appropriate growth medium is able to reproduce itself. The virus may be regarded as a kind of "regressed parasite" that must take advantage of the biochemical machinery of the host cell within which it reproduces. Not only is a virus unable to reproduce outside its host, but, unlike other kinds of parasites, it does not even "metabolize" in the free state; outside its host cell the virus particle is biologically inert. For this reason, some virologists argue that the virus may be properly regarded as a cell component that has become independent enough that it can pass from cell to cell. Viewed in this light, viruses more than fulfill their early promise of being the simplest systems for the study of isolated genetic elements.

Viruses may be divided into three main classes according to the nature of their hosts: animal viruses, plant viruses, and bacterial viruses. In this section, we will restrict our attention primarily to the bacterial viruses, or *bacteriophages* (abbreviated to "phages"), as they are often called. Bacteriophages consist of a nucleic acid core (that may be either DNA or RNA) and a protein coat of regular structure. Even the most complex phages contain no more than about one-sixth as much DNA as the simplest free-living cells. The protein coat is built up of subunits of one, or, at most, a few different protein molecules. The bacteriophage is the simplest replicating structure known to exist, and it has become one of the most important objects of study in molecular genetics.

The success of molecular genetics illustrates the fact that the best way to gain a fundamental understanding of a complex biological phenomenon is to study it first in the simplest system in which it can be found; armed with such basic knowledge, one can then proceed rationally to similar studies on more complex systems. It was this general philosophy that guided Max Delbrück in his efforts to arrive at a detailed understanding of the molecular basis of the phenomenon of replication. The "phage group," started largely by Delbrück and his students at Cal Tech, has been spectacularly successful in reaching its research objectives. The English school of biomolecular structure, some of whose accomplishments are presented in the first section of this volume, and the U.S. phage group gave rise to the two main intellectual currents that have shaped molecular biology. It is therefore appropriate to introduce the reader to the bacteriophage by the article "Bacterial Viruses and Sex," written by Max and Mary Delbrück, for the seventh issue of the newly constituted *Scientific American* in 1948. Many of the important phenomena associated with the life cycle of the bacteriophage are described in this article, and they still form the basis of contemporary phage research. The almost unbelievable advances in phage research that have occurred in a mere twenty-year period are dramatically evident in the comparison of the first article with the final one in this section on "Building a Bacterial Virus," by William B. Wood and R. S. Edgar. In the first article, the bacteriophage designated T4 is dimly seen by electron microscopy, and some of its fundamental biological properties are described; in the last article, not only is this same phage revealed in all of its exquisite structural and functional detail, but even its assembly in the test tube is described.

The life cycle of the bacteriophage T2 that infects the bacterium *Escherichia coli* is described by Gunther S. Stent, in "The Multiplication of Bacterial Viruses." It should be noted that his article was written before the discovery of the Watson-Crick structure of DNA. An important technique described by Stent is the use of radioisotopic tracers to study the fate of parental viral material in the course of its multiplication. This approach led to the conclusion that the nucleic acid core, but not the protein coat, enters the host cell during the process of infection. It has since been shown that the infecting phage does inject a small amount of protein, generally those enzymes needed to initiate the process of taking over the metabolism of the host.

Viruses are found in a comprehensive array of regular geometrical forms. The article by R. W. Horne on "The Structure of Viruses" displays this intricate variety of form that was revealed as the result of a number of important technical improvements in the preparation of samples for electron microscopy. It is worth emphasizing that the simplest biological structures possess a high degree of symmetry—indeed, most of the viruses can be crystallized.

The use of the bacteriophage as a tool for genetic analysis is impressively illustrated in the experiments of Seymour Benzer that are described in "The Fine Structure of the Gene." These studies, which preceded by some years the actual breaking of the genetic code, provided important information on the nature of mutation, as the altering of nucleotides in DNA, and they demonstrated clearly that the ultimate unit of information in DNA is the nucleotide.

The studies of Benzer consisted in the detailed analysis of just one of the many genes in the bacteriophage T4. The next step was to determine the nature and locations of all of the genes in the one DNA molecule that constitutes the T4 genome. This impressive project required the "mapping" of mutations— the basic technique of classical genetics. However, a problem arises when the mutation alters some critical function in the virus life cycle, such as the synthesis of the enzymes responsible for the actual duplication of the viral DNA. Such mutations are normally lethal and would be impossible to study because the virus simply would not be synthesized at all. How can the effects of specific mutations be studied when there are no progeny? The solution to this problem was solved largely through the development of two important classes of "conditional" lethal mutations—the temperature-sensitive mutations and the "ambers." These are described in "The Genetics of a Bacterial Virus" by R. S. Edgar and R. H. Epstein. A temperature-sensitive conditional lethal mutation would be one in which an essential enzyme that is synthesized by the altered gene is active at low temperature but is denatured and rendered inactive at a higher temperature. The expression of such a mutation may be controlled simply by changing the temperature. An important fact that has emerged from the mapping of the bacterial genes is that their arrangement in the DNA molecule is not random: genes that control similar functions are often arranged in clusters. Not only have the positions of genes that specify the various protein components of the T4 bacteriophage been determined, but a large number of genes have been found to function in the assembly of these proteins. This means that certain enzymes must be produced to catalyze the assembly of the viral proteins into the final structure of the bacteriophage. Thus, we begin to see how an understanding of the sequence of nucleotides in a DNA molecule provides the necessary information about the synthesis and assembly of a complex protein structure. At this simple level of organization, what is the distinction between chemical activity and biological activity?

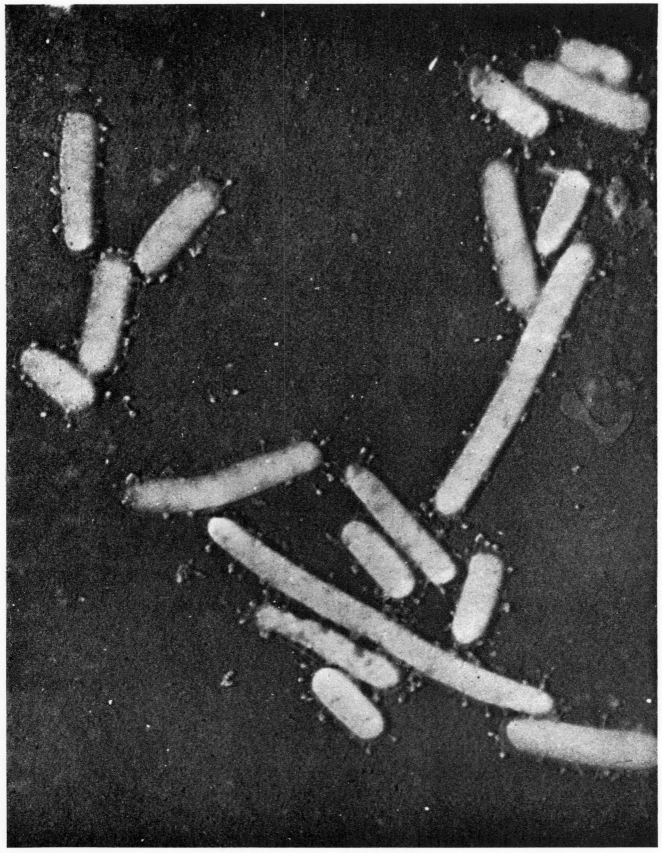

BACTERIA UNDER ATTACK by a swarm of bacterial viruses are shown by the electron microscope. The viruses, which are of the strain T4 described in this article, attach themselves to bacteria and sometimes push inside them. There the viruses reproduce until the bacterium bursts, liberating an entire new generation of viruses.

Bacterial Viruses and Sex

11

MAX AND MARY BRUCE DELBRÜCK · November 1948

TWO YEARS AGO, at a summer symposium in Cold Spring Harbor, N.Y., experiments were presented which showed that bacteria, and even some viruses that live on bacteria, apparently have a method of sexual reproduction. This finding was a considerable surprise. Up to that time it had been generally supposed that the simple one-celled bacteria had no sex and that they multiplied simply by splitting in two; the method of reproduction of the still more rudimentary bacterial viruses was entirely unknown. The simplest organisms previously known to have a sexual mode of reproduction were the molds, yeasts and paramecia. Indeed, the recognition of sex even in those organisms was less than 20 years old.

Sex was once thought to be the exclusive possession of life's higher forms. Yet as biologists have looked more carefully down the line, simpler and simpler forms have been found to be possessed of it. Now, among the viruses, we are searching for it at the lowest known level of life.

Since the Cold Spring Harbor symposium, this research has been pushed further, and some rather remarkable facts have been uncovered. This article will discuss a group of the viruses which are parasites of bacteria, and particularly will go into what has been learned recently concerning their reproduction.

Sexual reproduction is the coming together and exchanging of character factors of two parents in the making of a new individual. Aside from its other aspects, sex has a special interest for biologists as a highly useful and indeed almost necessary device for an organism to survive in the competitive evolutionary scheme of life. Plant and animal species, to avoid extinction in the changing environments of geologic time, evolve by utilizing mutations (changes in the basic hereditary material) which enable them better to adapt themselves to their environment. These mutations turn up spontaneously and spread through the population by the convenient means of sexual reproduction. Mutations are assorted and combined anew in every generation. Thus species that reproduce sexually always have in store a vast array of new types, some of which may be adapted to a changed environment and can become the parents of the next link in the evolutionary chain. This is the evolutionary advantage of sex.

It is logical, therefore, to look for sex in every known form of life. It was with great caution, however, that the discovery of sex in the simplest organisms was reported two years ago. E. L. Tatum and J.

VIRUS T4, shadowed with gold to make a specimen for the electron microscope, has shape of a tadpole.

Lederberg of Yale University told of experiments in which they had found bacteria which seemed to combine certain traits of two parental strains that had been mixed. Similar findings with respect to the viruses that attack bacteria were reported by A. D. Hershey of Washington University, and by W. T. Bailey, Jr. and M. Delbrück at Vanderbilt University.

The bacterial virus is a very small organism which enters a bacterium, reproduces itself and eventually destroys its host. From the latter a generation of new viruses then emerges. The virus thus "infects" a bacterium, even as plant and animal viruses infect plants and animals. Bacterial viruses were first discovered 30 years ago by the French bacteriologist F. D'Herelle, who noticed that the bacteria growing in some of his test tubes mysteriously dissolved. After experimentation D'Herelle concluded that their dissolution was due to some agent much smaller than a bacterium, and that this agent grew at the expense of bacteria. He called the agents that had destroyed the bacteria "bacteriophages" (bacteria-eaters); the same organisms are now often called bacterial viruses.

For many years thereafter bacteriologists and medical men were sure that bacterial viruses existed. The viruses were even measured, isolated and grouped, although they were never actually seen. Bacterial viruses are too small to be seen under the most powerful microscope of the conventional type; they have been made visible only recently by new types of microscopes.

D'Herelle's discovery raised the great expectation that bacterial viruses might be used as "agents of infectious health" to destroy the bacteria that caused human and animal diseases. It was the hope of early research workers that a population infected by a bacterial epidemic could be cured by infecting it with the virus inimical to that bacterium. Their hope has not been realized, but the bacterial viruses remain a subject of keen interest—for good and sufficient reasons.

Viruses seem to lie on that uncertain and perhaps unreal borderline between life and non-life. The uncertainty about this boundary line is both very old and very new. In ancient times all nature was supposed to be animate. Spirits dwelt in stones as well as in animals, and as recently as a few centuries ago the spontaneous generation of complex living organisms from mud was a matter of universal belief. The advance of the scientific method has taught us that there is an enormous difference between the living and

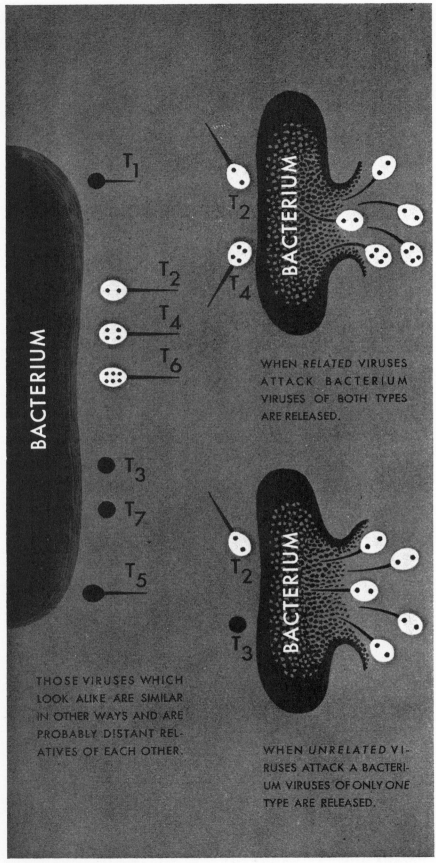

WHEN *RELATED* VIRUSES ATTACK BACTERIUM VIRUSES OF BOTH TYPES ARE RELEASED.

THOSE VIRUSES WHICH LOOK ALIKE ARE SIMILAR IN OTHER WAYS AND ARE PROBABLY DISTANT RELATIVES OF EACH OTHER.

WHEN *UNRELATED* VIRUSES ATTACK A BACTERIUM VIRUSES OF ONLY ONE TYPE ARE RELEASED.

EXPERIMENTAL ORGANISMS of the research discussed in this article are seven bacterial viruses that attack the same species of bacterium.

inorganic worlds. During the development of classical biology in the 19th century, there arose two great generalizations: 1) the theory of evolution, and 2) the cell theory. The theory of evolution proclaims the relatedness of all living things; the cell theory sets forth a universal principle of construction for them. Both of these generalizations unified biology and distinguished it from the study of the inorganic world.

IN our generation, however, the pendulum has begun to swing the other way. The great refinement of scientific technique has pushed the limit of observation beyond the point where it had stood for about 100 years, namely, at the resolving power of the light microscope. With this advance has come the recognition of the existence of many things below cellular size which do not fit into the established categories of life or non-life. Of these the viruses have become the most controversial. To learn all we can about them becomes, then, even more intriguing than the original idea that bacterial viruses might be useful in medicine.

Bacteria-eating viruses are common, and where bacteria exist in the natural state, viruses capable of destroying them almost always can be found. Outside of the bacterium, the virus seems dead. But it does not die; it lies quiescent and functionless until a bacterium presents itself. The virus then attaches itself firmly to the bacterium. Many viruses may cling to a single bacterium, but only one needs to enter the cell to begin a cycle of viral reproduction. Once within the host, the virus quickly comes to life and multiplies prodigiously. How it grows from the one or more particles that are known to enter the cell to the several hundred that burst from the suddenly ruptured host is a secret still closely guarded within the walls of the bacterium.

The guinea pigs of bacterial virus genetics have been seven different viruses which all attack the same bacterium. Some of these viruses, which we shall speak of as T1, T2 and so forth, are surprisingly complex in form and behavior.

The viruses that were first made visible by the electron microscope in 1941 were revealed to be spermlike forms. Some were seen lying free, others were clinging to the exterior of a bacterium. Other pictures revealed the bacterium with new viruses streaming from a hole ripped in its cell wall.

The seven viruses do not all look alike. In appearance they fall into four categories. The members of one family, consisting of T2, T4 and T6, look like tadpoles, with dark forms visible within their bodies. T5 has a round, solid body and a tail. T1 is similar to T5, but smaller. T3 and T7 are the smallest, with spherical bodies and no visible tail.

The viruses which look alike are related in several other respects, and the way they behave as a family is illustrated by a very curious phenomenon. When two viruses which are not related happen to attach themselves to the same bacterium, one successfully enters the bacterium and multiplies, but the other perishes without leaving any offspring. If the two viruses seeking the same bacterial home are related, however, both enter and reproduce. This rule has certain exceptions and certain special modifications, depending on the degree of relatedness between the contending viruses; as among human beings, the restriction of real estate among the viruses has subtle points.

One might wonder how the biologist can learn anything about the behavior of organisms so small that he generally cannot see them. The answer is that bacterial viruses make themselves known by the bacteria they destroy, as a small boy announces his presence when a piece of cake disappears. Much of what we know about the viruses is based on the following experiment, which requires only modest equipment and can be completed in less than a day.

Bacteria first are grown in a test tube of liquid meat broth. Enough viruses of one type are added to the test tube so that at least one virus is attached to each bacterium. After a certain period (between 13 and 40 minutes, depending on the virus, but strictly on the dot for any particular type), the bacterium bursts, liberating large numbers of viruses. At the moment when the bacteria are destroyed, the test tube, which was cloudy while the bacteria were growing, becomes limpid. Observed under the microscope, the bacteria suddenly fade out.

Before the bacteria burst, however, part of the liquid is taken from the test tube and diluted. From this diluted liquid the experimenter takes a small sample expected to contain only a single infected bacterium. When this bacterium has liberated its several hundred viruses into a liquid medium in a test tube, the liquid is poured on a plate covered with a layer of live bacteria. Each virus deposited on the plate will start attacking the bacterium on which it rests. Each of the offspring of the virus, in turn, will attack the nearest bacterium. Successive generations of offspring from the one original virus will spread out in a circle, attacking bacteria until after a few hours a small round clearing becomes visible to the naked eye. The number of such clearings, or "colonies," formed on the plate is a count, therefore, of the number of viruses liberated by the original infected bacterium.

The union of the virus and its bacterium takes place under rather complicated and specific conditions which are not well understood. Of the life of the virus inside the bacterial host, still less can be divined. Does the virus multiply by one individual producing another, by simple splitting, or by some other process? What specific elements of nutrition are necessary for virus

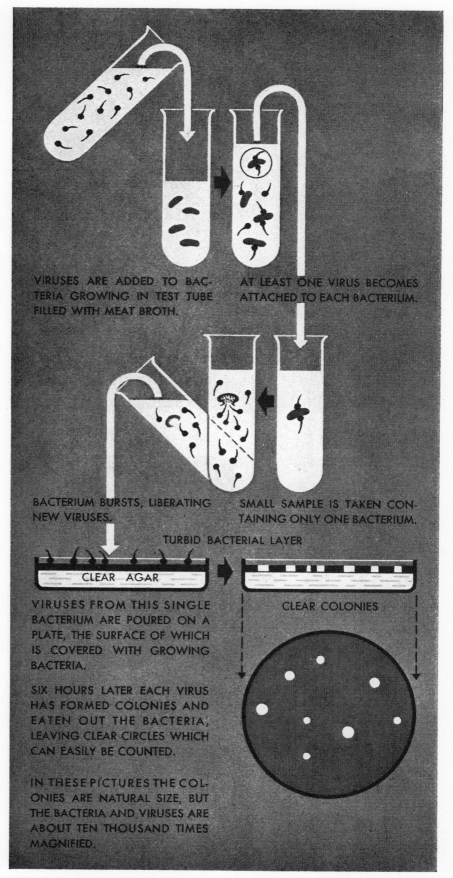

VIRUSES ARE ADDED TO BACTERIA GROWING IN TEST TUBE FILLED WITH MEAT BROTH.

AT LEAST ONE VIRUS BECOMES ATTACHED TO EACH BACTERIUM.

BACTERIUM BURSTS, LIBERATING NEW VIRUSES.

SMALL SAMPLE IS TAKEN CONTAINING ONLY ONE BACTERIUM.

TURBID BACTERIAL LAYER

CLEAR AGAR

VIRUSES FROM THIS SINGLE BACTERIUM ARE POURED ON A PLATE, THE SURFACE OF WHICH IS COVERED WITH GROWING BACTERIA.

SIX HOURS LATER EACH VIRUS HAS FORMED COLONIES AND EATEN OUT THE BACTERIA, LEAVING CLEAR CIRCLES WHICH CAN EASILY BE COUNTED.

IN THESE PICTURES THE COLONIES ARE NATURAL SIZE, BUT THE BACTERIA AND VIRUSES ARE ABOUT TEN THOUSAND TIMES MAGNIFIED.

CLEAR COLONIES

EXPERIMENTAL TECHNIQUE that is used in bacterial virus research is outlined in this drawing. The equipment required is remarkably simple.

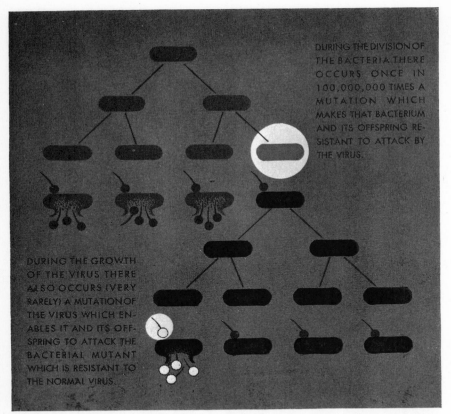

DURING THE DIVISION OF THE BACTERIA THERE OCCURS ONCE IN 100,000,000 TIMES A MUTATION WHICH MAKES THAT BACTERIUM AND ITS OFFSPRING RESISTANT TO ATTACK BY THE VIRUS.

DURING THE GROWTH OF THE VIRUS THERE ALSO OCCURS (VERY RARELY) A MUTATION OF THE VIRUS WHICH ENABLES IT AND ITS OFFSPRING TO ATTACK THE BACTERIAL MUTANT WHICH IS RESISTANT TO THE NORMAL VIRUS.

MUTATION is the mechanism that enables bacteria and viruses and all other living things to adapt themselves to changing environmental conditions.

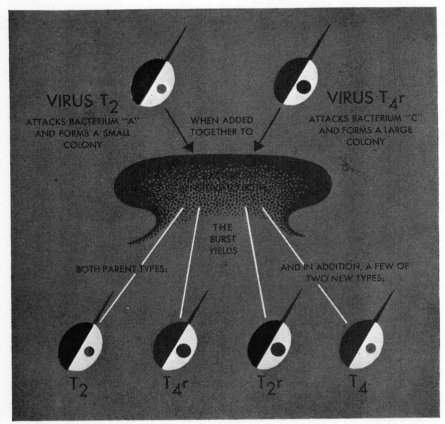

VIRUS T$_2$
ATTACKS BACTERIUM "A" AND FORMS A SMALL COLONY

WHEN ADDED TOGETHER TO

VIRUS T$_4$r
ATTACKS BACTERIUM "C" AND FORMS A LARGE COLONY

THE BURST YIELDS

BOTH PARENT TYPES:

AND IN ADDITION, A FEW OF TWO NEW TYPES:

T$_2$ T$_4$r   T$_2$r   T$_4$

EXCHANGE of virus characteristics is form of sexual reproduction. Here characteristics are type of bacterium attacked and the size of the colony.

reproduction? Is it possible to break open the cell before it would normally burst and from the contents at this intermediate stage learn something of the process of multiplication? What causes the violent disruption and dissolution of a bacterium?

Although we cannot fully answer these questions, it has nevertheless been possible to wrest some remarkable secrets from the viruses. We have learned something about the way in which they transmit characteristics and survive from generation to generation. One method of investigation has been to study the fashion in which viruses are able to meet emergencies in their environment. For example, when viruses are mixed with bacteria, most of the bacteria are destroyed. One in perhaps 100 million bacteria, however, will mutate to a form that is resistant to the virus, thus establishing a line of defense for its species. The virus, on the other hand, is capable of launching a new attack by mutating to a form which can destroy the resistant bacteria.

ALL kinds of mutations, many of them easy to recognize, turn up among the viruses. Some produce variant types of colonies on the bacterial plate; they may create fuzzy clearings instead of sharp-edged ones, or large clearings instead of small round ones. This kind of virus mutation was discovered in 1933 by I. N. Asheshov (who now heads a research project on bacterial viruses at the New York Botanical Garden) during his studies of anti-cholera vibris viruses in India. Other breeds of viruses have been found which need some particular substance, such as a vitamin or calcium, to become capable of attaching themselves to the bacterium. T. F. Anderson, of the Johnson Foundation for Medical Research at the University of Pennsylvania, opened up a totally unexpected new angle in viral research when he discovered that viruses T4 and T6 will not attack a bacterium in a medium lacking a simple organic compound called 1-tryptophane.

The discovery that bacterial viruses have a sexual form of reproduction came about in the following way. M. Delbrück and W. J. Bailey, Jr. were working with viruses T2 and T4r (a mutant of T4), which are relatives that can reproduce in the same bacterium of strain B. Each has two distinguishing characteristics: T2 produces a small colony and can destroy a mutant strain of bacteria called A; T4r produces a large colony and can destroy a mutant strain of bacteria called C. When T2 and T4r were added to a bacterium, viruses of both these parent types were released upon burst, as expected. But in addition two new types of virus came out, with their characteristics switched! One of the new types produced a large colony and destroyed bacterium A; the other produced a small colony and destroyed bacterium C. Obviously the parents had got together and exchanged something. The number of individuals of these new forms coming from a single bacterium varied, but the maximum number found was about 30 per cent of the total yield.

The most surprising discovery of all, however, was made by S. E. Luria of Indiana University. It came about as a sequel to an accidental observation in our laboratory at Vanderbilt University. When a virus that has been "killed" by exposure to ultraviolet light is added to a bacterium, the bacterium is destroyed but no new viruses issue from it. In one such experiment, Bailey irradiated viruses long enough so that most, but not quite all, of them were killed. He then transferred some samples, as usual, to a bacteria-covered plate. He wanted to determine the number of survivors, and expected to find less than 100 virus colonies on the plate. Instead, the next morning he found thousands of colonies! Puzzled, Bailey repeated the experiment, with the same result. The supposedly dead viruses had in some way come to life.

Later, at Indiana, Luria took this problem up seriously. He discovered a curious fact: although a bacterium infected with only one "killed" virus dies and yields nothing, a bacterium infected with two or more "killed" viruses bursts and yields several hundred new viruses. Luria therefore assumed that inside a bacterium two or more "killed" viruses (or perhaps we had now better call them mortally damaged) can pool their undamaged parts to make whole individuals capable of reproducing themselves and of escaping from the bacterium. He estimated that each virus of the T2, T4 or T6 type has about 20 vital units. Assume that each time a virus is shot at, or exposed to ultraviolet light, one vital unit is knocked out. If there are two viruses, each of which has been shot at four times, there is a good chance that the same vital unit has not been hit in both. The remaining units then seem to have a way of combining and forming effective individuals.

This "revival of the dead," as we might call it, which indicates some substitution of vital material, is interrelated with the previously mentioned exchange of character traits in viruses, a phenomenon which has been explored very successfully by A. D. Hershey at Washington University.

Gradually the study of these two phenomena should reveal something more of the way in which one virus produces another and—the most ambitious hope— even something of the simple facts of life. Here, as far as mind and imagination and skill can reach, is a vast region of the very small that is open for exploration.

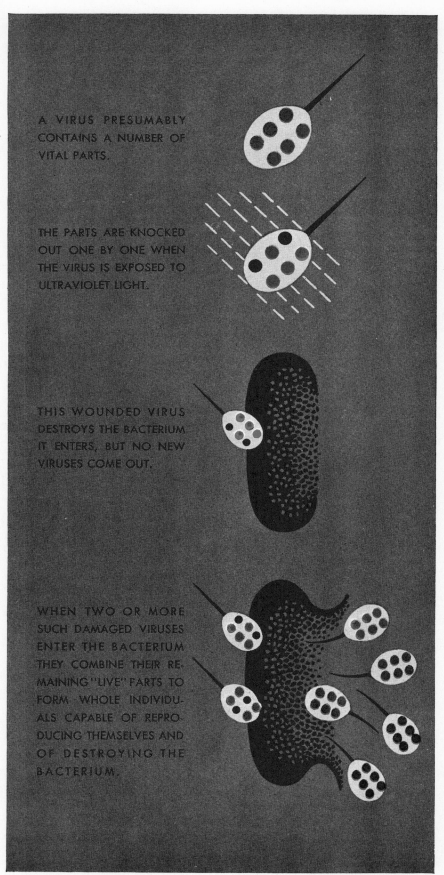

A VIRUS PRESUMABLY CONTAINS A NUMBER OF VITAL PARTS.

THE PARTS ARE KNOCKED OUT ONE BY ONE WHEN THE VIRUS IS EXPOSED TO ULTRAVIOLET LIGHT.

THIS WOUNDED VIRUS DESTROYS THE BACTERIUM IT ENTERS, BUT NO NEW VIRUSES COME OUT.

WHEN TWO OR MORE SUCH DAMAGED VIRUSES ENTER THE BACTERIUM THEY COMBINE THEIR REMAINING "LIVE" PARTS TO FORM WHOLE INDIVIDUALS CAPABLE OF REPRODUCING THEMSELVES AND OF DESTROYING THE BACTERIUM.

DAMAGE to viruses by ultraviolet rays (*second drawing from top*) is added proof that they exchange characteristics. Damaged viruses pool resources.

The Multiplication of Bacterial Viruses

GUNTHER S. STENT · May 1953

THE PROCESS of heredity—how like begets like—is one of the most fascinating mysteries in biology, and all over the world biologists are investigating it with enthusiasm and ingenuity. Of the many angles from which they are attacking the problem, none is more exciting than the experiments on bacterial viruses. Here is an organism that reproduces its own kind in a simple and dramatic way. A virus attaches itself to a bacterium and quickly slips inside. Twenty-four minutes later the bacterium pops open like a burst balloon, and out come about 200 new viruses, each an exact copy of the original invader. What is the trick by which the virus manages to make all these living replicas of itself from the hodgepodge of materials at hand? What happens in the host cell in those critical 24 minutes?

Within the past few years studies with radioactive tracers have made it possible to begin to answer these questions. By labeling with radioactive atoms the substances of the virus or of the medium in which it multiplies, experimenters can follow these materials and trace the events that lead to the construction of a new virus. This article will tell about some of the experiments and the facts learned from them.

The bacterial virus, a tiny organism only seven millionths of an inch long, is a nucleoprotein: that is, a particle made up half of protein and half of nucleic acid. The latter is desoxyribonucleic acid—the well-known DNA which is a basic stuff of all cell nuclei [see "The Chemistry of Heredity," by A. E. Mirsky; SCIENTIFIC AMERICAN Offprint 28]. We are interested in the respective roles of the two parts of the virus molecule: the protein and the DNA. We are also interested in where the various materials come from when a virus synthesizes replicas of itself inside the bacteria growing in a culture medium.

First let us consider the tracer technique. Suppose we wish to label the DNA part of the virus particles. Since an important constituent of DNA is its phosphate links, we shall label the element phosphorus with the radioactive isotope phosphorus 32. We begin with the medium in which we are growing bacteria that are to be infected by the virus. The culture contains inorganic phosphate as the source of phosphorus for the bacteria. To this medium we add a little radiophosphorus, so that there is one radioactive atom for every billion atoms of ordinary, non-radioactive phosphorus. The bacteria will take up the same proportion of radioactive and ordinary phosphorus. We can tell how much phosphate the bacteria contain simply by counting the radiophosphorus atoms with a Geiger counter: the total amount of phosphorus is a billion times that.

Now if we infect the culture of bacteria with viruses, the virus progeny also will have the same proportion of radiophosphorus. But to measure their phosphorus we must isolate them, for the culture contains a great deal of phosphorus not incorporated in them. We can separate the viruses in three ways: (1) by a series of centrifuging operations that remove the other materials through their differences in weight; (2) by adding non-radioactive bacteria, on which the viruses become fixed and which can then be removed by low-speed centrifugation; or (3) by adding a serum (developed in rabbits) which contains antibodies that combine with the viruses and precipitate them from the culture.

Two radioactive isotopes are used in

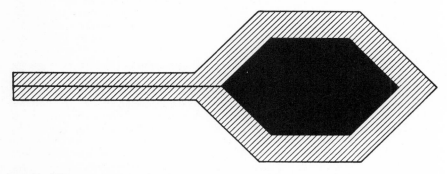

BACTERIAL VIRUS of the T2 strain, which infects the bacterium *Escherichia coli,* has a hexagonal head and a tail and is approximately seven millionths of an inch long. In this schematic drawing the virus is divided into two parts. Its outer layer (*diagonal lines*) is composed of protein which has the ability to attach itself to the surface of a bacterium of the appropriate species and to react with antivirus serum. Its core (*black*) is made up of nucleic acid, which is protected by the layer of protein.

the bacterial virus work: phosphorus 32 to label phosphate and the DNA part of the virus, sulfur 35 to label the protein part of the virus. Now let us look at the experiments.

ALL OF THESE experiments were done on bacterial viruses of the strain called T2, which infects the common bacterium *Escherichia coli*. Some years ago two investigators—Thomas F. Anderson of the University of Pennsylvania and Roger M. Herriott of The Johns Hopkins University—observed that something curious happened to bacterial viruses when they were exposed to "osmotic shock," namely, a sudden change in osmotic pressure effected by adding distilled water to the liquid in which they were suspended. These viruses could still attack and kill bacteria. But they had lost their ability to reproduce. Under the electron microscope they looked like sacs that had been emptied of their contents, and a chemical analysis indicated that they had lost all their DNA.

Recently A. D. Hershey and M. W. Chase, working at the Carnegie Institution of Washington genetics laboratory in Cold Spring Harbor, N. Y., repeated and confirmed these experiments with the help of radioactive tracers. The DNA, labeled with radiophosphorus, was indeed removed from the virus by osmotic shock. It remained as DNA in the solution, but it was easily broken down by an enzyme—an indication that it had lost the protection of the protein "coat" of the virus. As for the protein shell of the virus, when separated from the solution and placed in a culture of bacteria it showed all its old power to seize upon and kill the bacteria. It also retained its ability to react with antivirus serum.

This looked very much as if the two parts of the virus had specialized functions. Apparently the virus' ability to attach itself to and kill a bacterium resided in its protein "coat." Did its power to reproduce and build hereditary images of itself reside in its DNA core? Other investigators had found that DNA did control hereditary continuity in bacteria. Hershey and Chase proceeded to investigate the question in their viruses.

They first put viruses in cultures of bacteria that had been killed by heat. The viruses attached themselves to the dead bacteria and apparently poured out their DNA, for the DNA (labeled with radiophosphorus) was easily broken down by the enzyme desoxyribonuclease, just as when it was spilled out from viruses after osmotic shock. Similarly, when bacteria were killed by heat after viruses had infected them, the enzyme again broke down the DNA. The enzyme had no effect, however, on DNA discharged into *living* bacteria. It seems that the living membrane of a bacterium protects DNA from the enzyme, but

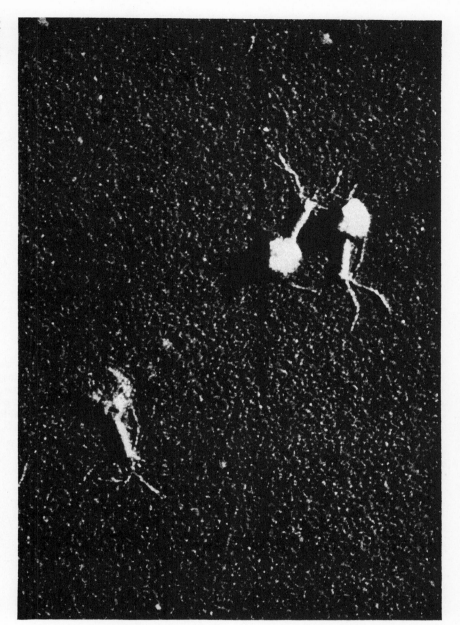

THREE BACTERIAL VIRUSES of the T2 strain are shown in this electron micrograph made by Robley C. Williams and Dean Fraser of the Virus Laboratory at the University of California. At the upper right are two intact viruses; their tails and hexagonal heads are clearly visible. At the lower left is a virus from which the nucleic acid has been removed; as a consequence the head of the virus has collapsed. This reproduction of the micrograph magnifies viruses approximately 100,000 diameters.

when the bacterium is killed, its membrane becomes permeable and lets the enzyme through.

WHAT HAPPENS to the protein coat of the virus after it has emptied its DNA into the bacterium? Hershey and Chase infected living bacteria with virus, this time labeling the protein with radiosulfur. Then they shook up the suspension of infected bacteria in a Waring blender—the device used for stirring laboratory mixtures and for making milk shakes. The shearing force of the mixer

stripped more than 80 per cent of the labeled protein off the bacteria. On the other hand, it did not remove any significant amount of DNA or interfere with the reproduction of viruses within the bacteria. The experiment showed that the virus protein stays outside the bacterium, and its job is finished as soon as it enables the DNA to gain entry into the cell. By the same token, it indicated strongly that the DNA is responsible for reproduction.

Once inside the host, the task of the nucleic acid is to reproduce itself 200-

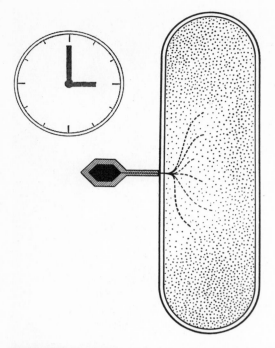

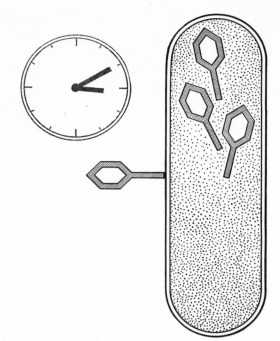

REPRODUCTION of bacterial viruses is shown at four stages in the drawings on these two pages. The large stippled structure is the bacterium. Beside it is a clock which tells the time at which each stage is depicted. The first stage is infection. In it the virus particle attaches itself, probably by the tail, to the surface of the bacterium. The nucleic acid core of the virus empties into the bacterial cell; the protein coat of the virus remains outside. The second stage, called the "dark period," is shown about 10 minutes later. The virus nucleic acid has begun to multiply within the bacterial cell, and has induced the formation of

fold. It must also stimulate the production of 200 protein coats exactly like the one it has just shed. Where do the raw materials come from, and how are they put together?

In 1946 Seymour S. Cohen of the University of Pennsylvania, the first investigator to study bacterial virus reproduction with radioactive tracers, conceived an experiment directed to this question. He wished to find out whether the needed raw materials, particularly the phosphorus, came from the bacterial cell itself or from the medium surrounding it. He grew two cultures of bacteria, one in a medium containing radiophosphorus, the other in a non-radioactive medium. Then he removed the bacterial cells from the liquid in the two test tubes and switched them, putting the non-radioactive bacteria in the radioactive medium and *vice versa*. Now he infected both cultures with viruses. When the bacteria burst and the new viruses emerged, he isolated the viruses and measured their radioactivity. The viruses that came out of the non-radioactive bacteria transferred to the radioactive medium were radioactive: they had two thirds as high a concentration of radiophosphorus as the medium in which the bacteria had been immersed. On the other hand, the viruses that came from the radioactive bacteria in the nonradioactive medium had only one third as much radiophosphorus as the bacteria. Cohen therefore concluded that the new generations of viruses had obtained two thirds of their phosphorus from the growth medium while they were being formed and only one third from their host bacteria. This was a great surprise to those bacteriologists who had long supposed that bacterial viruses were formed from ready-made structures already present in the host cell.

At the University of Chicago Frank W. Putnam and Lloyd M. Kozloff, making similar studies with nitrogen 15 as the tracer, have found that the protein of viruses, like their DNA, is derived mostly from substances assimilated from the growth medium.

COHEN'S EXPERIMENT had covered the state of the system at just one stage: the next step was to follow the whole history of the conversion of inorganic phosphorus into virus DNA, from the moment bacteria began to grow in the medium until the newborn viruses finally emerged. At the State Serum Institute of Denmark Ole Maaloe and I extended Cohen's experiment with radiophosphorus, making the switch of radioactive bacteria to a non-radioactive medium and *vice versa* at many different stages in the development of the culture, both before and after infection of the bacteria with virus. In this way we were able to determine just how much of the phosphorus that the bacteria eventually donated to the new viruses was assimilated by them from the medium during the various periods of development. Before they were infected with virus, the bacteria took up that phosphorus at the rate of their own growth, which means that they were using the phosphorus to make their own DNA. But after infection, their assimilation of phosphorus that they were to donate to the viruses increased sharply. Most of the phosphorus the bacteria were now taking up was going directly into the synthesis of new viruses.

We also observed that it takes at least 12 minutes to convert inorganic phosphorus into virus DNA. Hence any phosphorus that is to go into the making of the new viruses must have been assimilated by the bacteria by the end of the first 12 minutes of the 24-minute period during which the viruses are synthesized in the cell. As a matter of fact, A. H. Doermann has found that the 24-minute latent period divides into two 12-minute phases. In experiments at Cold Spring Harbor he opened infected bacteria at various stages. During the first half of the latent period there were no fully formed viruses with infective power within the bacterial cell; even the original invader had disappeared. Then, after 12 minutes, the first infective particle appeared, and more followed until there were 200 just before the cell burst. The explanation is clear. The original invading virus had shed its protein coat on entering the cell and therefore was no longer an infective unit. No virus could appear in the cell until at least one new protein coat had been manufactured and coupled with a unit of DNA. Apparently

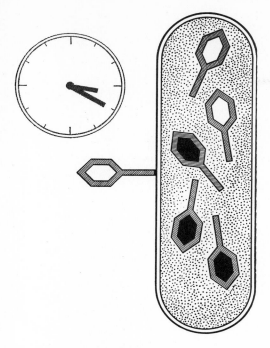
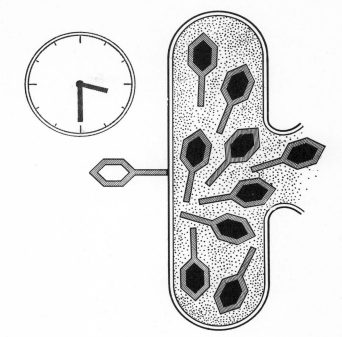

new protein coats. The protein coats contain no nucleic acid; there are no infective particles, not even the particle that caused the infection. The third stage, called the "rise period," is shown about 20 minutes after infection. Now some of the protein coats contain nucleic acid; the first infective particles of the new generation have made their appearance within the bacterial cell. The final stage is shown about 30 minutes after the first. The infected bacterium bursts and releases the new generation of virus particles into the surrounding medium. In the final drawing only a few of the 200 particles in the new generation of bacterial viruses are depicted.

this proceeding takes some 12 minutes.

It seems that the manufacture of protein and of DNA goes on side by side within the cell. In experiments with radiosulfur as the label, Maaloe and Neville Symonds of the California Institute of Technology have recently shown that by the time the first new infective virus appears, there is already enough virus protein in the cell to form about 60 viruses. On the other hand, in similar experiments with radiophosphorus as the label we have found indications that completed units of DNA do not unite with protein units until the last moment; the particle then becomes infective.

THE DNA of the original invading virus is responsible, as we have seen, for reproduction within the cell, both of DNA itself and of protein. How does it go about its job? Putnam and Kozloff labeled viruses with radiophosphorus and followed the radioactivity to see what happened to the phosphorus after the viruses infected bacteria. They found that about 40 per cent of the labeled phosphorus showed up in the viruses' progeny, the rest being discarded in the debris. Experiments with radiocarbon have shown that the same is true of other constituents of the DNA. In other words, about 40 per cent of the DNA of the parent viruses is passed on to the descendants.

How is the old DNA passed on? Is the parent's DNA handed on intact to a single individual virus offspring in each bacterial cell in a random 40 per cent of the cases, or is it distributed generally among the descendants? At Washington University of St. Louis Hershey, Martin D. Kamen, Howard Gest and J. W. Kennedy examined this question. They infected bacteria in a highly radioactive medium (one in every 1,000 phosphorus atoms was radioactive) with non-radioactive viruses. The DNA of the parent viruses was stable; not containing any radiophosphorus, it would not decay by radioactivity. Hence if it was passed on intact, a recognizable number of the viruses' descendants also should have stable DNA. But this was not the case. The descendant population steadily lost its infectivity, due to radioactive decay of its phosphorus atoms, until fewer than one tenth of 1 per cent of the descendants were infective.

Is it possible that the hereditary continuity of the virus resides in a fraction consisting of 40 per cent of the DNA, and that the rest of the DNA does not participate in reproduction at all? To answer this question Maaloe and James D. Watson at the State Serum Institute of Denmark produced three generations of virus. The first had its DNA labeled with radiophosphorus. A single virus of this generation then produced generation II, and passed on to it 40 per cent of its radiophosphorus. Now if the radiophosphorus transmitted from generation I to generation II was carried in a special reproductive fraction of the DNA, all of it should have been passed on to genera-tion III. Actually it was found that generation III received only the usual 40 per cent. One must therefore conclude that the parent DNA material is not handed on in intact fractions but rather is distributed in a general fashion over the structures of the descendants.

SUMMING UP, the tracer studies so far have given us the following picture of how bacterial viruses reproduce themselves. By means of some property residing in its protein coat, a virus is able to attach itself to the surface of a bacterial cell. The contact immediately uncorks the virus, and it pours its DNA into the cell. The emptied protein coat is left outside the cell and thereafter plays no further part. Inside the cell the virus DNA begins to make replicas of itself, using as raw materials the nucleic acids of the bacterium and fresh substances absorbed by the bacterium from the medium surrounding it. About 40 per cent of the parent virus DNA itself is conserved and will reappear in the descendants. The virus DNA also induces the synthesis of new protein in the cell. Finally units of the protein combine with the DNA replicas to form 200 exact copies of the parent virus.

The facts discovered so far give us only an outline of the process, but they seem a good start on the road to solving the mystery of how organisms build structural copies of themselves and pass on their heredity from generation to generation.

13 | The Structure of Viruses

R. W. HORNE · January 1963

When the smaller members of the virus family are enlarged several hundred thousand times in the electron microscope, they are found to possess an extremely high degree of structural symmetry. In such viruses it is probable that the subunits visible in electron micrographs are individual protein molecules, often identical in kind, packed together to form a simple geometric structure. In the larger viruses the geometry is usually more complex, and a certain degree of structural flexibility begins to appear. Viewing the micrographs one has the impression of being shown how the inanimate world of atoms and molecules shades imperceptibly into the world of forms possessing some of the attributes of life.

Viruses are the smallest biological structures that embody all the information needed for their own reproduction. Essentially they consist of a shell of protein enclosing a core of nucleic acid—either ribonucleic acid (RNA) or deoxyribonucleic acid (DNA). The shell serves as a protective jacket and in some instances as a means for breaching the walls of those living cells that the virus is capable of attacking. The nucleic acid core enters the cell and redirects the cell machinery toward the production of scores of complete virus particles. When the job is done, the cell ruptures and the viruses spill out.

Most viruses fall in a size range between 10 and 200 millimicrons; in other terms, between a fortieth of a wavelength and half a wavelength of violet light. Since objects smaller than the wavelength of light cannot be seen in an ordinary microscope, viruses can be observed directly only with the aid of the electron microscope. These instruments employ a beam of electrons whose wavelength is much smaller than the dimensions of a virus. Viruses can also be studied indirectly by placing crystals of a pure virus preparation in an X-ray beam and recording the diffraction patterns produced when the X rays are reflected from the planes of atoms in the crystal. Analysis of such X-ray diffraction patterns suggested that the protein subunits forming the virus shell were arranged symmetrically. The tobacco mosaic virus, for example, showed up in early electron micrographs as a slender rod without visible subunits. When the virus was examined by X-ray diffraction, however, one could see patterns suggesting that the subunits were arranged in a helix. On the other hand, most small viruses, which looked spherical in electron micrographs, gave rise to X-ray patterns indicating that they had a cubic symmetry. This suggested that they were regular polyhedrons and also members of the group of Platonic solids: solids with four, six, eight, 12 and 20 sides.

In the light of the X-ray results, and arguing from general principles, F. H. C. Crick and James D. Watson proposed in 1956 and 1957 that the amount of nucleic acid present in the small viruses was limited, and that the information it carried would be sufficient to code for only a few kinds of protein. They suggested, therefore, that the shells of small "spherical" viruses were probably built from a number of identical protein subunits packed symmetrically. The most likely way for identical units to be packed on the surface of a sphere, Crick and Watson pointed out, would be in some pattern having cubic symmetry.

Some of the predictions of Crick and Watson were subsequently confirmed by electron micrography. There was a period, however, when the design and development of the electron microscope outpaced methods of preparing virus specimens for observation. Dehydrated virus particles are essentially transparent to an electron beam. Various techniques have had to be devised to make the particles visible. One of the earliest and simplest methods was to create "shadows" by allowing a stream of heavy-metal atoms to fall on the virus particles at an angle. This was done by placing the specimen of virus particles in a vacuum chamber and evaporating the metal atoms from a source toward the side of the chamber. The metal atoms that accumulated on the virus particle itself would block the passage of electrons, whereas electrons could pass freely through the shadows where metal atoms had not been deposited. In this way it was possible to discern the overall shape of the virus particle but not all the fine details of its surface structure.

Within the past few years a new and simple method of "staining" isolated particles such as viruses and large protein molecules has been even more successful than shadowing for revealing fine detail at the high magnifications now available in electron microscopes. It consists of surrounding the particles to be examined by an electron-dense material: potassium phosphotungstate. This is achieved by mixing the virus suspension with a solution of the phosphotungstate and spraying the mixture or depositing droplets on the specimen mounts. Since the phosphotungstate method produces images that are reversed compared with those obtained with the normal preparation procedures, it is called "negative staining" or "negative contrast." Application of this method to a large number of viruses has shown that they fall into three main symmetry groups: those with cubic symmetry, those with helical symmetry and those with complex symmetry or combined symmetries.

The class of polyhedrons that have

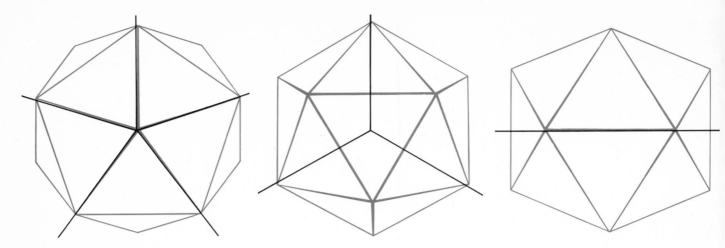

AXES OF SYMMETRY are shown for a regular icosahedron, a figure with 12 corners, 20 faces and 30 edges. Viewed along an axis at any corner, the figure can be rotated in five positions without changing its appearance (*left*). Rotated around any face axis, a regular icosahedron exhibits threefold symmetry (*middle*). Rotated around any edge axis, the figure shows twofold symmetry (*right*).

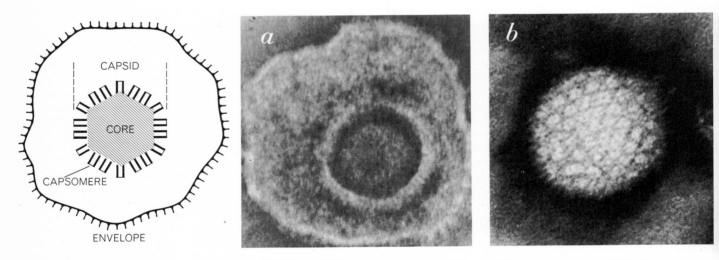

VIRUS NOMENCLATURE covers principal features observed in electron micrographs.

HERPES VIRUS sometimes has an envelope (*a*). The magnification is 310,000 diameters. The capsid (*b*) is composed of 162 capsomeres. Negative staining (*c*) indicates

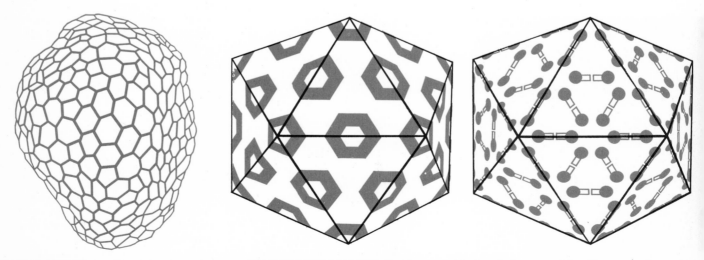

RADIOLARIANS, small marine organisms, have skeletons built of pentagons and hexagons.

ALTERNATIVE SCHEMES show how a regular icosahedron containing 42 pentagonal and hexagonal capsomeres (*left*) could be built up from 120 (or 240) small subunits.

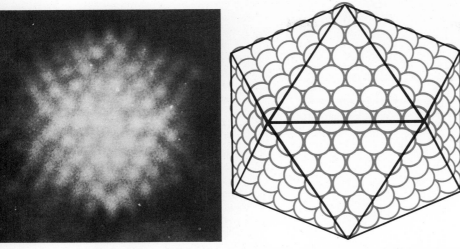

ADENOVIRUS is shown embedded in phosphotungstate, magnified about one million diameters (*left*). The drawing shows how the particle's 252 surface subunits, or capsomeres, are arranged with icosahedral symmetry. There are 12 on corners, 240 on faces or edges.

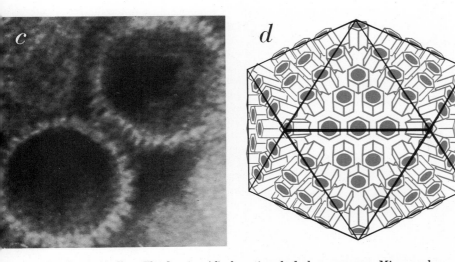

c

d

that they are hollow. The drawing (*d*) shows icosahedral arrangement. Micrographs are by P. Wildy and W. C. Russell of the Institute of Virology in Glasgow and the author.

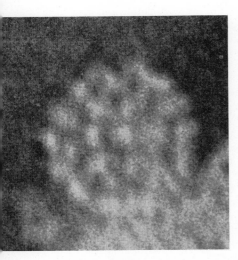

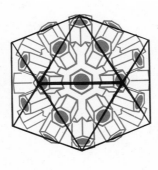

POLYOMA VIRUS is magnified one million diameters in micrograph by Wildy, M. G. P. Stoker and I. A. Macpherson of the Institute of Virology. It has 42 capsomeres (*right*).

cubic symmetry includes the regular tetrahedron (four faces), dodecahedron (12 faces) and icosahedron (20 faces). Shadowed preparations of the tipula iridescent virus, which causes a disease in the larvae of several insects, showed it to have the shape of a regular icosahedron, and the symmetry was self-evident [*see bottom illustration on page 128*]. Smaller viruses, on the other hand, do not reveal symmetry unless they are examined at very high magnification, and this requires the use of negative phosphotungstate staining.

Consider the symmetry properties of a regular icosahedron, in which each face is an equilateral triangle. If spokes are projected from the center of the icosahedron through the corners of the triangles, the spokes will represent one axis of rotational symmetry. Spokes projected from the center of the solid through the center of each face will represent a second axis. And spokes projected from the center through the midpoint of each edge will represent a third axis. (There will be 12 corner spokes, 20 face spokes and 30 edge spokes.) If the icosahedron is viewed along the spoke at any corner, one finds that the body can be rotated in five positions without changing its appearance [*see top illustration on opposite page*]. If the icosahedron is viewed along the spoke at any face, the body can be rotated in three positions without changing its appearance. And if the icosahedron is viewed along an edge spoke, it can be rotated in two positions without change of appearance. The regular icosahedron is thus said to have 5.3.2. symmetry.

Let us see now what implication this symmetry pattern has for a particle of adenovirus, which is associated with respiratory disease in man. The electron microscope shows that the surface of the particle is composed of regularly arranged structural units resembling tiny balls. Moreover, these balls are seen on the vertexes, faces and edges of an icosahedron [*see top illustration on this page*]. One can identify certain balls surrounded by five neighbors, which indicates that they are located on vertexes and therefore on axes of fivefold symmetry. Balls surrounded by six neighbors must lie on faces or edges and thus must occupy axes of either threefold or twofold symmetry. Along each edge there are six balls, including two balls occupying vertexes. To calculate the total number of balls covering the entire icosahedron one applies the simple formula $10(n-1)^2 + 2$, where n is the number of balls along one edge. Substituting 6

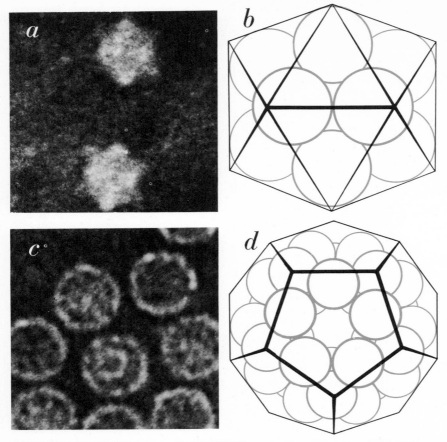

BACTERIOPHAGE ΦX174, magnified 750,000 diameters in *a*, appears to consist of 12 capsomeres arranged in icosahedral symmetry as shown in *b*. In other micrographs (*c*) smaller subunits seem to be arranged in ringlike structures. Each capsomere might actually be formed from five subunits as shown in *d*. Thirty such subunits would form a dodecahedron.

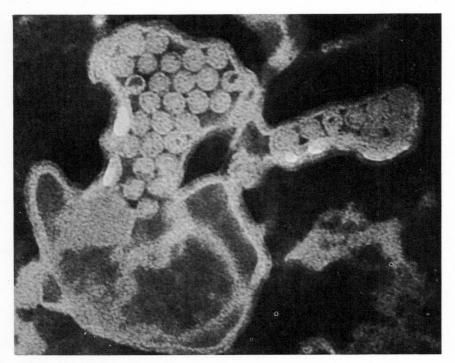

POLIOMYELITIS VIRUS PARTICLES are shown inside a fragment of an infected cell. The particles, magnified 250,000 diameters, appear to be composed of subunits smaller than the typical capsomere. The structural arrangement is not established. Electron micrograph is by Jack Nagington of the Public Health Laboratory in Cambridge and the author.

for *n* yields 252 as the number of morphological units composing the shell of the adenovirus particle.

For purposes of description (and to avoid the term "subunit," which can be applied to morphological, structural or chemical features) I shall adopt the recent terminology suggested for the various viral components [*see illustration at middle left on page 122*]. The morphological units composing the shell have been given the name "capsomeres." The shell itself is the "capsid." The region inside the capsid is the "core." The outer membrane, seen surrounding the capsid of some viruses, is the "envelope."

One merit of the negative-staining technique is that the electron-dense material is capable of penetrating into extremely small regions between, and even within, the capsomeres. A striking instance of such penetration can be seen in the electron micrograph of the herpes virus shown at the middle left on the preceding page. (In man the herpes virus causes, among other things, "cold sores.") Electron micrographs of the shadowed particle had indicated that it had the same external shape and symmetry as the adenovirus. When the two viruses were negatively stained and still further magnified, however, it could be seen on close examination that the capsomeres of the herpes virus, unlike those of the adenovirus, were elongated hollow prisms, some hexagonal in cross section and others pentagonal. In a number of particles the phosphotungstate penetrated into the central region, or core, normally containing the nucleic acid. In these "empty" particles the elongated capsomeres stand out clearly in profile at the periphery of the virus, and one can see their hollow form and the precision of their radial arrangement.

From the micrographs the number of capsomeres located on each edge was estimated to be five, giving a total of 162 capsomeres for the herpes virus. Of the 162 capsomeres, 12 are pentagonal prisms and 150 are hexagonal prisms. To satisfy the packing arrangement in accordance with icosahedral symmetry, the 12 pentagonal prisms would have to be placed at the corners and the 150 hexagonal prisms located on the edges or faces of the particle [*see drawing at middle right on preceding page*].

The need for pentagonal units goes deeper than the simple need to satisfy icosahedral symmetry. As early geometers observed, there is no way to arrange a system of hexagons so that they will enclose space. But if pentagonal units are included with hexagons, it is possible to enclose space in an almost endless variety of ways, with forms both regular and irregular. The radiolarians, a group of marine protozoa, provide a fascinating example of varied structures assembled from pentagonal and hexagonal units [see illustration at bottom left on page 122].

Viruses smaller than the herpes virus usually have fewer capsomeres, but the relation between size and capsomere number is somewhat variable. The polyoma virus, which produces tumors in rodents and has stimulated a search for viruses in human cancer, appears to be almost spherical when examined by the shadowing technique. Nevertheless, negative staining shows that the outer shell is probably composed of 42 elongated angular capsomeres arranged in icosahedral symmetry [see bottom illustration on page 123]. Such a shell can be constructed by placing 12 pentagonal prisms at the corners of an icosahedron and 30 hexagonal prisms on the 30 edges. In this case the 20 faces have no capsomeres of their own, which helps to explain the nearly spherical appearance of the virus.

In the electron microscope the turnip yellow mosaic virus, which causes a disease of the leaves in the turnip and related plants, appears to have 32 capsomeres arranged in accordance with cubic symmetry. Crystals of the same virus studied by X-ray diffraction also show cubic symmetry, but this method indicates that there are 60 subunits instead of 32. Strictly speaking, neither number can be used to construct an icosahedron. But both numbers of subunits can be disposed symmetrically on the surface of an icosahedron. The smaller number can be distributed by placing 12 subunits on corners, 20 on faces and none on edges. (The 32 capsomeres could also be placed on the 32 vertexes of a pentakis dodecahedron or a rhombic triacontahedron.) The larger number can be distributed according to strict icosahedral symmetry by placing two subunits on each of the 30 edges and none on corners or faces. It is evident that if the two figures were transparent, one could be fitted over the other and the subunits of one would fall precisely in between the subunits of the other without overlapping. This suggests that the 60 subunits inferred from X-ray diffraction patterns may combine in some fashion to give the appearance of 32 subunits when the virus particle is observed in the electron microscope.

It has therefore been suggested that in the small spherical viruses the morphological features resolved as pentagons

VIRUS	SYMMETRY	NUMBER OF CAPSOMERES	SIZE OF CAPSID (ANGSTROM UNITS)	NUCLEIC ACID
TIPULA IRIDESCENT	CUBIC	812	1,300	DNA
ADENOVIRUS	CUBIC	252	700–750	?
GAL (GALLUS ADENO-LIKE)	CUBIC	252	950–1,000	?
INFECTIOUS CANINE HEPATITIS	CUBIC	252	820	?
HERPES SIMPLEX	CUBIC	162	1,000	DNA
WOUND TUMOR	CUBIC	92	?	RNA
POLYOMA	CUBIC	42	450	DNA
WARTS	CUBIC	42	500	?
TURNIP YELLOW MOSAIC	CUBIC	32	280–300	RNA
ΦX174	CUBIC	12	230–250	DNA
TOBACCO MOSAIC	HELICAL	2,130	3,000 × 170	RNA
MUMPS	HELICAL	—	170 (DIAMETER)	RNA
NEWCASTLE DISEASE	HELICAL	—	170 (DIAMETER)	RNA
SENDAI	HELICAL	—	170 (DIAMETER)	?
INFLUENZA	HELICAL	—	90–100 (DIAMETER)	RNA
T-EVEN BACTERIOPHAGE	COMPLEX	—	1,000 × 800 (HEAD)	DNA
CONTAGIOUS PUSTULAR DERMATITIS (ORF)	COMPLEX	—	2,600 × 1,600	?
VACCINIA	COMPLEX	—	3,030 × 2,400	DNA

TABLE OF VIRUSES shows the symmetry classification, number of capsomeres and capsid size of some of the principal families. (An angstrom unit is a ten-millionth of a millimeter; the wavelength of violet light is 4,000 angstrom units.) Nucleic acid (column at far right) is the genetic material of the virus. DNA is deoxyribonucleic acid; RNA, ribonucleic acid.

and hexagons may actually be built up from smaller structural subunits. These subunits may not all be identical, but they may be of two or three different molecular species. The diagram at the bottom right on page 122 indicates how such subunits might be assembled to produce pentagonal and hexagonal units, in strict accordance with icosahedral symmetry. The arrangement illustrated, one of several possible combinations, was proposed by A. Klug, D. L. D. Caspar and J. Finch of the University of London. It shows how 42 capsomeres could be formed from 120 (or 240) smaller subunits. Recent evidence suggests that the capsomeres in some of the larger viruses are linked together by small structures that may well correspond to the subunits.

High-resolution electron micrographs have revealed that structures originally identified as capsomeres in one very small virus are indeed composed of still smaller subunits. The virus, known as φX174, has been intensively studied because it contains an unusual single-stranded form of DNA [see "Single-stranded DNA," by Robert L. Sinsheimer; SCIENTIFIC AMERICAN Offprint 128]. When first examined in the electron mi-

croscope, the virus appeared to have a shell composed of 12 spherical capsomeres, the minimum number needed for icosahedral symmetry. More recent electron micrographs indicate that each capsomere is formed from five subunits, but since each capsomere may be shared with a neighbor, the number of subunits is 30 [see top illustration on opposite page]. If they are not shared and each capsomere is composed of five subunits, the total would be 60 and the shape would be that of a dodecahedron. Similar subunits smaller than capsomeres have been observed in electron micrographs of the virus of poliomyelitis, but it has not yet been possible to count them accurately [see bottom illustration on opposite page].

The second broad group of viruses I shall discuss are those that have helical symmetry. Far and away the best known of this group is the virus that causes the mosaic disease of tobacco. Its helical structure was originally inferred from X-ray diffraction data. These data, combined with evidence from other physical and chemical observations, have led to a detailed knowledge of the tobacco mosaic virus' architecture. The

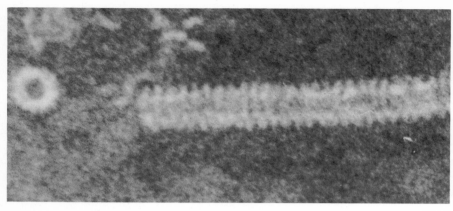

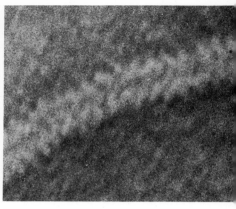

HELICAL SYMMETRY is shown in the electron micrographs of the rodlike tobacco mosaic virus, magnified 800,000 diameters, at left. The second electron micrograph, of the same magnification, shows an internal thread from a disrupted member of the myxovirus group. It too seems to possess helical symmetry. (Intact myxovirus particles are shown directly below.) The tobacco mosaic virus has

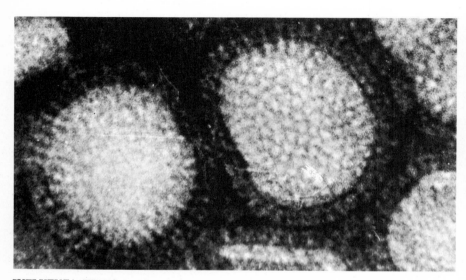

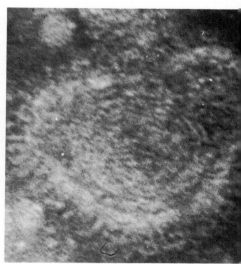

INFLUENZA VIRUS PARTICLES, members of the myxovirus family, are magnified 700,000 diameters in the electron micrograph at left. Although the particles are irregular in both size and shape, they appear to bristle with regularly spaced surface projections. In the second micrograph, which has a magnification of 600,000 diameters, phosphotungstate has penetrated the core of a particle, reveal-

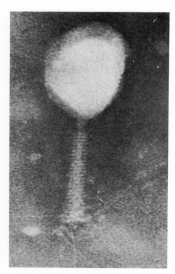

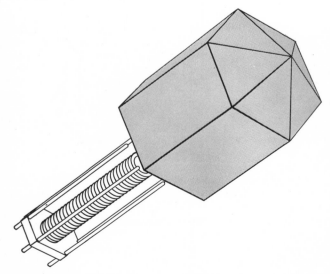

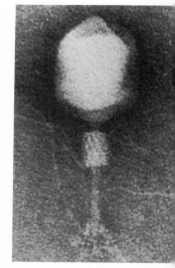

COMPLEX SYMMETRY is displayed by the T2 bacteriophage and other members of the "T even" family. Electron micrographs, in which the particle is magnified 300,000 diameters, clearly show that T2 exists in "untriggered" and "triggered" forms. The untriggered form is shown in the first pair of illustrations. The head of the phage is a bipyramidal hexagonal prism. The tail is a tube-like structure surrounded by a helical sheath. An end plate carries six tail fibers. When triggered, as shown in the second pair of illus-

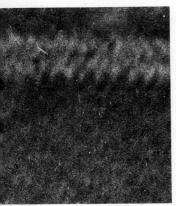

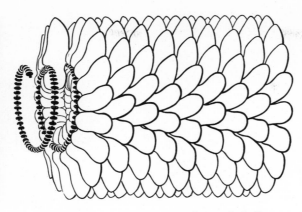

2,130 elongated capsomeres, consisting of protein molecules, arranged around a hollow core, as shown in the diagram at far right. The helical coil embedded in the capsomeres represents viral nucleic acid. The micrographs are by Nagington, A. P. Waterson and the author.

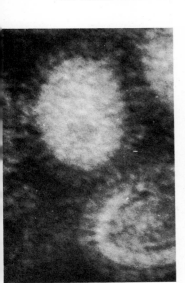

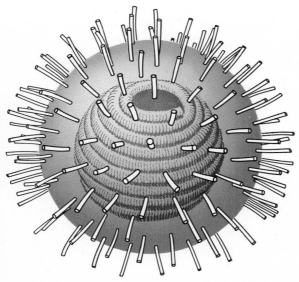

ing a coiled structure inside. The diagram at right shows a possible arrangement of the components in a typical myxovirus. The diagram follows a model built by L. Hoyle, Waterson and the author. The micrographs are by Waterson, Wildy, A. E. Farnham and the author.

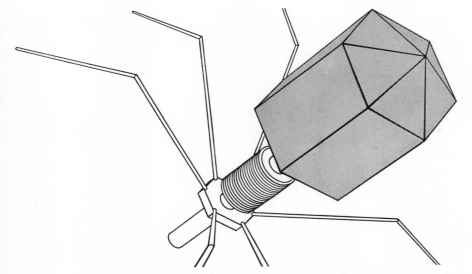

trations, the sheath contracts away from the end of the tail and the tail fibers are released. Presumably this coincides with the ejection of the DNA core (not shown), which previously had been coiled up in the head of the particle. The micrographs are by Sydney Brenner, George Streisinger, S. Champe, Leslie Barnett, Seymour Benzer, M. Rees and the author.

subunits appear to be elongated structures so arranged that about 16 subunits form one turn of a helix. The subunits project from a central axial hole that runs the entire length of the virus. The nucleic acid of the virus does not occupy the hole, as might be expected, but is deeply embedded in the protein subunits and describes a helix of its own. The virus is composed of 2,130 identical protein subunits. Each subunit is a large molecule formed by the joining together of 168 amino acid molecules. The diagram of the virus' structure at the top of this page is based on a model by R. E. Franklin, Klug, Caspar and K. Holmes of the University of London.

Until recently helical symmetry was observed only in plant viruses. Now it has also been found in the complex animal viruses that are members of the influenza, or myxovirus, group. The group includes the viruses of mumps, Newcastle disease (a respiratory ailment of fowl), fowl plague and Sendai disease (a form of influenza). Electron micrographs produced by the shadow-casting technique showed these viruses to be of various shapes and sizes. Some were roughly spherical, some were filaments and others were complex and irregular. Thin sections of purified virus and particles seen at the surface of infected cells suggested the existence of an internal component in the form of ringlike structures surrounded by an outer membrane.

Recent studies using the negative staining method have shown that the internal component, or capsid, has the same dimensions and appearance as the rods of tobacco mosaic virus but is more flexible. This is particularly evident in electron micrographs of mumps virus, which show that the helical capsid forms coils or loops after being released. The particles of influenza and fowl plague are more structurally compact than the mumps virus and, unless subjected to special chemical treatment, are rarely observed releasing their internal components.

The envelopes of influenza virus and fowl plague virus carry surface projections that evidently contain the protein known as hemagglutinin, so named because it causes red blood cells to agglutinate. If these two viruses are treated with ether, the internal helix is released and can be separated from the hemagglutinin in a centrifuge. When this inner component is studied by electron microscopy, it is found to be of smaller diameter than that in the viruses of mumps, Newcastle disease virus and Sendai disease virus. The precise length of the helical components in the various myxo-

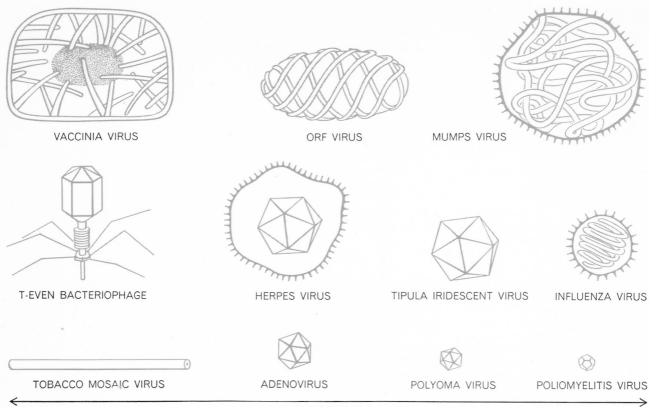

VACCINIA VIRUS

ORF VIRUS

MUMPS VIRUS

T-EVEN BACTERIOPHAGE

HERPES VIRUS

TIPULA IRIDESCENT VIRUS

INFLUENZA VIRUS

TOBACCO MOSAIC VIRUS

ADENOVIRUS

POLYOMA VIRUS

POLIOMYELITIS VIRUS

ONE MICRON

RELATIVE SIZES OF VIRUSES are shown in this chart. A micron, used as a measuring stick, is a thousandth of a millimeter; it is enlarged 175,000 times. The five viruses with polyhedral structures possess cubic symmetry. The tobacco mosaic virus and the internal components of influenza and mumps virus have helical symmetry. The remaining viruses exhibit complex symmetry.

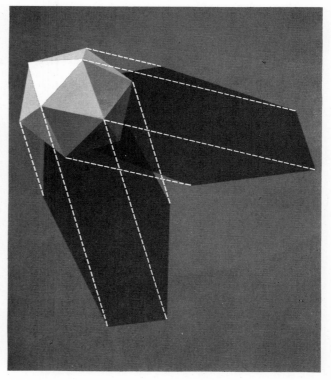

TIPULA IRIDESCENT VIRUS, an insect virus, is so large that its geometrically regular structure shows up clearly when specimens are shadowed with atoms of a heavy metal and enlarged in the electron microscope. In the doubly shadowed micrograph (*left*) the virus particles are enlarged about 58,000 diameters. The shadows indicate that each particle is a regular icosahedron (*right*). The micrograph was made by Kenneth Smith of the University of Cambridge and Robley C. Williams of the University of California.

viruses is not yet known, nor the way they are packed within their envelopes. A possible arrangement for a typical myxovirus is shown in the diagram at the middle on page 127.

The last of the three broad groups of viruses are those whose symmetry is complex. This category includes the large bacterial viruses, such as the T2 virus that infects the bacterium *Escherichia coli*, and the large pox viruses. The T2 virus and several of its "T even" relatives are particularly remarkable because they contain some sort of contractile mechanism, a feature that has not been discerned in any other family of viruses. The electron micrographs at the bottom of page 126 show that the T2 virus has a head shaped in the form of a bipyramidal hexagonal prism. Attached to one end of the prism is a tail sructure consisting of a helical contractile sheath surrounding a central hollow core. At the extreme end of the core there is a curious hexagonal plate carrying six slender tail fibers. The plate structure and tail fibers probably make initial contact with the wall of the bacterium that is being attacked. After contact has been made the helical sheath contracts, allowing the nucleic acid

core of the virus to enter the bacterium.

The contraction of the T2 sheath raises many fascinating questions. The entire T2 virus appears to contain only a few different kinds of protein molecule. If these are allocated to the construction of the different structures— head, sheath, tail plate and tail fibers— one must conclude that the contractile sheath is composed of only two or at most three different kinds of protein. How can so few kinds of building block produce a sheath with contractile ability? What substances trigger the contraction? And how is the contraction related to the ejection of the long DNA molecule that is tightly packed in the T2 core?

Still larger viruses having complex symmetry are several important members of the pox virus family: the viruses of variola, vaccinia, cowpox and ectromelia. They are among the few viruses large enough to be seen in the light microscope. In early shadowed electron micrographs the vaccinia virus appeared to have a three-dimensional bricklike shape with a spherical dense central region. More detailed studies of the virus seen in infected cells after staining and thin sectioning revealed morphological features not observed in

other viruses. The central dense region appeared to be surrounded by a number of layers, or membranes, of varying opacity to the electron beam. In some micrographs tubelike structures could be seen between the outer membranes and the central region. The electron micrographs below illustrate the structural variations that exist between two members of the pox group. In the particles of the virus that causes orf, or contagious pustular dermatitis, the tubular components form a definite crisscross pattern. It is difficult to say whether the tubular structures should be described as capsids or as capsomeres, nor can one say just where the nucleic acid is located in relation to them.

The electron microscope, together with other methods, has greatly contributed to the study of viruses, and it has shown that they come in a surprising variety of mathematically ordered families. It has been understood for many years, of course, that proteins are versatile building blocks and that they account for the tremendous diversity of living forms. But it required the electron microscope to reveal directly what intricate and exquisite structures can be created by putting together only a few kinds of protein molecule.

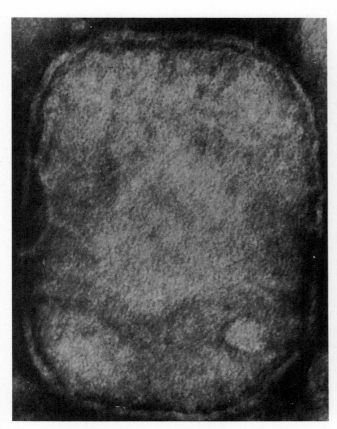

VACCINIA VIRUS, one of the giant pox viruses, is about twice the diameter of the smallest living cells, which are known as pleuropneumonia-like organisms. The magnification is 400,000 diameters.

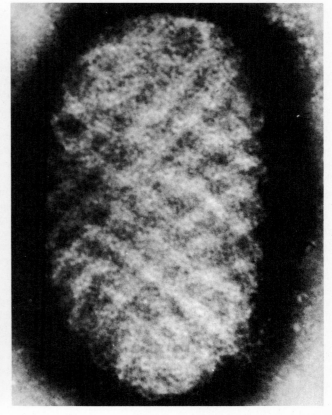

ORF VIRUS, another pox virus, has components wound in a crisscross pattern. The magnification is 450,000 diameters. Micrographs of the orf and vaccinia viruses are by Nagington and the author.

14 | The Fine Structure of the Gene

SEYMOUR BENZER · January 1962

Much of the work of science takes the form of map making. As the tools of exploration become sharper, they reveal finer and finer details of the region under observation. In the December, 1961 issue of *Scientific American* John C. Kendrew of the University of Cambridge described the mapping of the molecule of the protein myoglobin, revealing a fantastically detailed architecture. A living organism manufactures thousands of different proteins, each to precise specifications. The "blueprints" for all this detail are stored in coded form within the genes. In this article we shall see how it is possible to map the internal structure of a single gene, with the revelation of detail comparable to that in a protein.

It has been known since about 1913 that the individual active units of heredity—the genes—are strung together in one-dimensional array along the chromosomes, the threadlike bodies in the nucleus of the cell. By crossing such organisms as the fruit fly *Drosophila,* geneticists were able to draw maps showing the linear order of various genes that had been marked by the occurrence of mutations in the organism. Most geneticists regarded the gene as a more or less indivisible unit. There seemed to be no way to attack the questions "Exactly what is a gene? Does it have an internal structure?"

In recent years it has become apparent that the information-containing part of the chromosomal chain is in most cases a giant molecule of deoxyribonucleic acid, or DNA. (In some viruses the hereditary material is ribonucleic acid, or RNA.) Indeed, the threadlike molecule of DNA can be seen in the electron microscope [*see bottom illustration on opposite page*]. For obtaining information about the fine structure of DNA, however, modern methods of genetic analysis are a more powerful tool than even the electron microscope.

It is important to understand why this fine structure is not revealed by conventional genetic mapping, as is done with fruit flies. Genetic mapping is possible because the chromosomes sometimes undergo a recombination of parts called crossing over. By this process, for example, two mutations that are on different chromosomes in a parent will sometimes emerge on the same chromosome in the progeny. In other cases the progeny will inherit a "standard" chromosome lacking the mutations seen in the parent. It is as if two chromosomes lying side by side could break apart at any point and recombine to form two new chromosomes, each made up of parts derived from the original two. As a matter of chance two points far apart will recombine frequently; two points close together will recombine rarely. By carrying out many crosses in a large population of fruit flies one can measure the frequency—meaning the ease—with which different genes will recombine, and from this one can draw a map showing the parts in correct linear sequence. This technique has been used to map the chromosomes of many organisms. Why not, then, use the technique to map mutations inside the gene? The answer is that points within the same gene are so close together that the chance of detecting recombination between them would be exceedingly small.

In the study of genetics, however, everything hinges on the choice of a suitable organism. When one works with fruit flies, one deals with at most a few thousand individuals, and each generation takes roughly 20 days. If one works with a microorganism, such as a bacterium or, better still, a bacterial virus (bacteriophage), one can deal with billions of individuals, and a generation takes only minutes. One can therefore perform in a test tube in 20 minutes an experiment yielding a quantity of genetic data that would require, if humans were used, the entire population of the earth. Moreover, with microorganisms special tricks enable one to select just those individuals of interest from a population of a billion. By exploiting these advantages it becomes possible not only to split the gene but also to map it in the utmost detail, down to the molecular limits of its structure.

Replication of a Virus

An extremely useful organism for this fine-structure mapping is the T4 bacteriophage, which infects the colon bacillus. T4 is one of a family of viruses that has been most fruitfully exploited by an entire school of molecular biologists founded by Max Delbrück of the California Institute of Technology. The T4 virus and its relatives each consist of a head, which looks hexagonal in electron micrographs, and a complex tail by which the virus attaches itself to the bacillus wall [*see top illustration on opposite page*]. Crammed within the head of the virus is a single long-chain molecule of DNA having a weight about 100 million times that of the hydrogen atom. After a T4 virus has attached itself to a bacillus, the DNA molecule enters the cell and dictates a reorganization of the cell machinery to manufacture 100 or so copies of the complete virus. Each copy consists of the DNA and at least six distinct protein components. To make these components the invading DNA specifies the formation of a series of special enzymes, which themselves are proteins. The entire process is controlled by the battery of genes that constitutes the DNA molecule.

According to the model for DNA de-

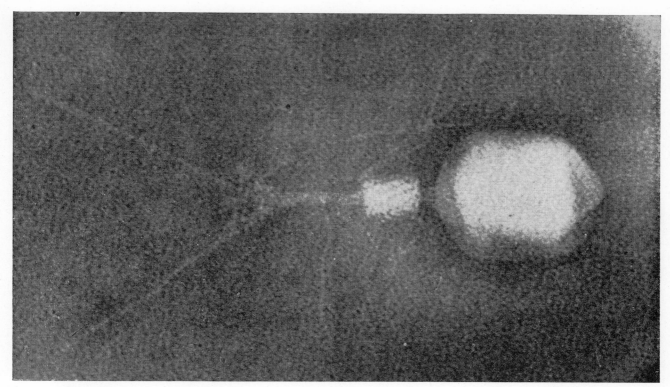

T2 BACTERIOPHAGE, magnified 500,000 diameters, is a virus that contains in its head complete instructions for it own replication. To replicate, however, it must find a cell of the colon bacillus into which it can inject a giant molecule of deoxyribonucleic acid (DNA). This molecule, comprising the genes of the phage, subverts the machinery of the cell to make about 100 copies of the complete phage. The mutations that occasionally arise in the DNA molecule during replication enable the geneticist to map the detailed structure of individual genes. The electron micrograph was made by S. Brenner and R. W. Horne at the University of Cambridge.

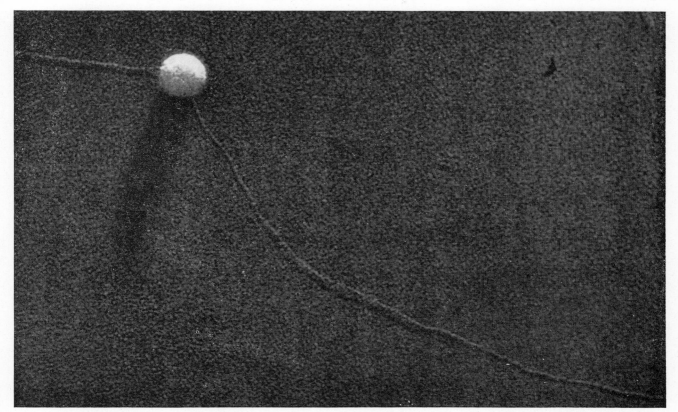

MOLECULE OF DNA is the fundamental carrier of genetic information. This electron micrograph shows a short section of DNA from calf thymus; its length is roughly that of the rII region in the DNA of T4 phage studied by the author. The DNA molecule in the phage would be about 30 feet long at this magnification of 150,-000 diameters. The white sphere, a polystyrene "measuring stick," is 880 angstrom units in diameter. The electron micrograph was made by Cecil E. Hall of the Massachusetts Institute of Technology.

vised by James D. Watson and F. H. C. Crick, the DNA molecule resembles a ladder that has been twisted into a helix. The sides of the ladder are formed by alternating units of deoxyribose sugar groups and phosphate groups. The rungs, which join two sugar units, are composed of pairs of nitrogenous bases: either adenine paired with thymine or guanine paired with cytosine. The particular sequence of bases provides the genetic code of the DNA in a given organism.

The DNA in the T4 virus contains some 200,000 base pairs, which, in amount of information, corresponds to much more than that contained in this article. Each base pair can be regarded as a letter in a word. One word (of the DNA code) may specify which of 20-odd amino acids is to be linked into a polypeptide chain. An entire paragraph might be needed to specify the sequence of amino acids for a polypeptide chain that has functional activity. Several polypeptide

units may be needed to form a complex protein.

One can imagine that "typographical" errors may occur when DNA molecules are being replicated. Letters, words or sentences may be transposed, deleted or even inverted. When this occurs in a daily newspaper, the result is often humorous. In the DNA of living organisms typographical errors are never funny and are often fatal. We shall see how these errors, or mutations, can be used to analyze a small portion of the genetic information carried by the T4 bacteriophage.

Genetic Mapping with Phage

Before examining the interior of a gene let us see how genetic experiments are performed with bacteriophage. One starts with a single phage particle. This provides an important advantage over higher organisms, where two different individuals are required and the male and female may differ in any number of respects besides their sex. Another simplification is that phage is haploid, meaning that it contains only a single copy of its hereditary information, so that none of its genes are hidden by dominance effects. When a population is grown from a single phage particle, using a culture of sensitive bacteria as fodder, almost all the descendants are identical, but an occasional mutant form arises through some error in copying the genetic information. It is precisely these errors in reproduction that provide the key to the genetic analysis of the structure [see upper illustration on pages 134 and 135].

Suppose that two recognizably different kinds of mutant have been picked up; the next step is to grow a large population of each. This can be done in two test tubes in a couple of hours. It is now easy to perform a recombination experiment. A liquid sample of each phage population is added to a culture of bacterial cells in a test tube. It is arranged that the phage particles outnumber the bacterial cells at least three to one, so that each cell stands a good chance of being infected by both mutant forms of phage DNA. Within 20 minutes about 100 new phage particles are formed within each cell and are released when the cell bursts. Most of the progeny will resemble one or the other parent. In a few of them, however, the genetic information from the two parents may have been recombined to form a DNA molecule that is not an exact copy of the molecule possessed by either parent but a combination of the two. This new recombinant phage particle can carry

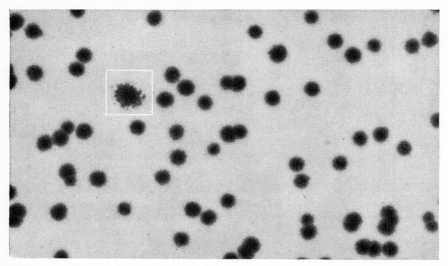

SPONTANEOUS MUTATIONAL EVENT is disclosed by the one mottled plaque (square) among dozens of normal plaques produced when standard T4 phage is "plated" on a layer of colon bacilli of strain B. Each plaque contains some 10 million progeny descended from a single phage particle. The plaque itself represents a region in which cells have been destroyed. Mutants found in abnormal plaques provide the raw material for genetic mapping.

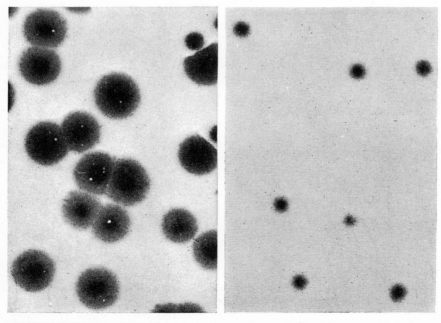

DUPLICATE REPLATINGS of mixed phage population obtained from a mottled plaque, like that shown at top of page, give contrasting results, depending on the host. Replated on colon bacilli of strain B (left), rII mutants produce large plaques. If the same mixed population is plated on strain K (right), only standard type of phage produce plaques.

both mutations or neither of them [*see lower illustration on next two pages*].

When this experiment is done with various kinds of mutant, some of the mutant genes tend to recombine almost independently, whereas others tend to be tightly linked to each other. From such experiments Alfred D. Hershey and Raquel Rotman, working at Washington University in St. Louis, were able to construct a genetic map for phage showing an ordered relationship among the various kinds of mutation, as had been done earlier with the fruit fly *Drosophila* and other higher organisms. It thus appears that the phage has a kind of chromosome —a string of genes that controls its hereditary characteristics.

One would like to do more, however, than just "drosophilize" phage. One would like to study the internal structure of a single gene in the phage chromosome. This too can be done by recombination experiments, but instead of choosing mutants of different kinds one chooses mutants that look alike (that is, have modifications of what is apparently the same characteristic), so that they are likely to contain errors in one or another part of the same gene.

Again the problem is to find an experimental method. When looking for mutations in fruit flies, say a white eye or a bent wing, one has to examine visually every fruit fly produced in the experiment. When working with phage, which reproduce by the billions and are invisible except by electron microscopy, the trick is to find a macroscopic method for identifying just those individuals in which recombination has occurred.

Fortunately in the T4 phage there is a class of mutants called *r*II mutants that can be identified rather easily by the appearance of the plaques they form on a given bacterial culture. A plaque is a clear region produced on the surface of a culture in a glass dish where phage particles have multiplied and destroyed the bacterial cells. This makes it possible to count individual phage particles without ever seeing them. Moreover, the shape and size of the plaques are hereditary characteristics of the phage that can be easily scored. A plaque produced in several hours will contain about 10 million phage particles representing the progeny of a single particle. T4 phage of the standard type can produce plaques on either of two bacterial host strains, B or K. The standard form of T4 occasionally gives rise to *r*II mutants that are easily noticed because they produce a distinctive plaque on B cultures. The key to the whole mapping technique is that

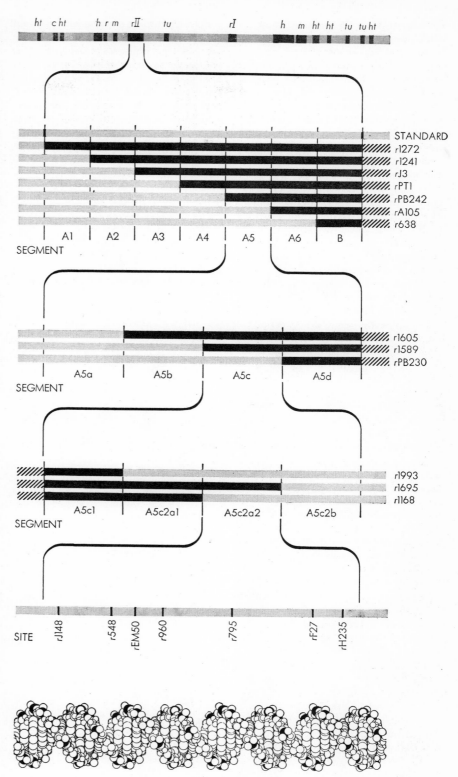

MAPPING TECHNIQUE localizes the position of a given mutation in progressively smaller segments of the DNA molecule contained in the T4 phage. The *r*II region represents to start with only a few per cent of the entire molecule. The mapping is done by crossing an unknown mutant with reference mutants having deletions *(dark gray tone)* of known extent in the *r*II region *(see illustration of method on page 136)*. The order and spacing of the seven mutational sites in the bottom row are still tentative. Each site probably represents the smallest mutable unit in the DNA molecule, a single base pair. The molecular segment *(extreme bottom)*, estimated to be roughly in proper scale, contains a total of about 40 base pairs.

these mutants do not produce plaques on K cultures.

Nevertheless, an rII mutant can grow normally on bacterial strain K if the cell is simultaneously infected with a particle of standard type. Evidently the standard DNA molecule can perform some function required in K that the mutants cannot. This functional structure has been traced to a small portion of the DNA molecule, which in genetic maps of the T4 phage is designated the rII region.

To map this region one isolates a number of independently arising rII mutants (by removing them from mutant plaques visible on B) and crosses them against one another. To perform a cross, the two mutants are added to a liquid culture of B cells, thereby providing an opportunity for the progeny to recombine portions of genetic information from either parent. If the two mutant versions are due to typographical errors in different parts of the DNA molecule, some individuals of standard type may be regenerated. The standards will produce plaques on the K culture, whereas the mutants cannot. In this way one can easily detect a single recombinant among a billion progeny. As a consequence one can "resolve" two rII mutations that are extremely close together. This resolving power is enough to distinguish two mutations that are only one base pair apart in the DNA molecular chain.

What actually happens in the recombination of phage DNA is still a matter of conjecture. Two defective DNA molecules may actually break apart and rejoin to form one nondefective molecule, which is then replicated. Some recent evidence strongly favors this hypothesis. Another possibility is that in the course of replication a new DNA molecule arises from a process that happens to copy only the good portions of the two mutant molecules. The second process is called copy choice. An analogy for the two different processes can be found in the methods available for making a good tape recording of a musical performance from two tapes having defects in different places. One method is to cut the defects out of the two tapes and splice the good sections together. The second method (copy choice) is to play the two tapes and record the good sections on a third tape.

Mapping the rII Mutants

A further analogy with tape recording will help to explain how it has been established that the rII region is a simple linear structure. Given three tapes, each with a blemish or deletion in a different place, labeled *A*, *B* and *C*, one can imagine the deletions so located that deletion *B* overlaps deletion *A* and deletion *C*, but that *A* and *C* do not overlap each other. In such a case a good performance can be re-created only by recombining *A* and *C*. In mutant forms of phage DNA containing comparable deletions the existence of overlapping can be established by recombination experiments of just the same sort.

To obtain such deletions in phage one looks for mutants that show no tendency to revert to the standard type when they reproduce. The class of nonreverting mutants automatically includes those in which large alterations or deletions have occurred. (By contrast, rII mutants that revert spontaneously behave as if their alterations were localized at single points). The result of an exhaustive study covering hundreds of nonreverting rII mutants shows that all can be represented as containing deletions of one size or another in a single linear structure. If the structure were more complex, containing, for example, loops or branches, some mutations would have been expected to overlap in such a way as to make it impossible to represent them in a linear map. Although greater complexity cannot be absolutely excluded, all observations to date are satisfied by the postulate of simple linearity.

Now let us consider the rII mutants that do, on occasion, revert spontaneously when they reproduce. Conceivably they arise when the DNA molecule of the phage undergoes an alteration of a single base pair. Such "point" mutants are those that must be mapped if one is to probe the fine details of genetic structure. However, to test thousands of point mutants against one another for recombination in all possible pairs would

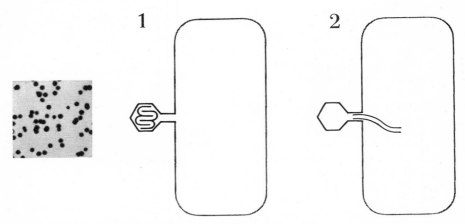

REPLICATION AND MUTATION occur when a phage particle infects a bacillus cell. The experiment begins by isolating a few standard particles from a normal plaque (*photograph at far left*) and growing billions of progeny in a broth culture of strain B colon bacilli. A sample of the broth is then spread on a Petri dish containing the same strain, on which the

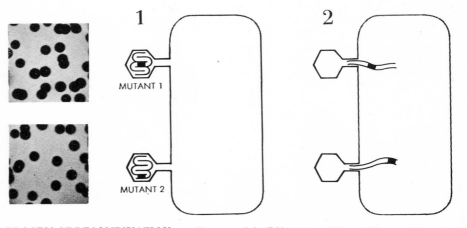

PROCESS OF RECOMBINATION permits parts of the DNA of two different phage mutants to be reassembled in a new DNA molecule that may contain both mutations or neither of them. Mutants obtained from two different cultures (*photographs at far left*) are introduced into a broth of strain B colon bacilli. Crossing occurs (*1*) when DNA from each mutant type

require millions of crosses. Mapping of point mutations by such a procedure would be totally impracticable.

The way out of this difficulty is to make use of mutants of the nonreverting type, whose deletions divide up the *r*II region into segments. Each point mutant is tested against these reference deletions. The recombination test gives a negative result if the deletion overlaps the point mutation and a positive result (over and above the "noise" level due to spontaneous reversion of the point mutant) if it does not overlap. In this way a mutation is quickly located within a particular segment of the map. The point mutation is then tested against a second group of reference mutants that divide this segment into smaller segments, and so on [*see illustration on pages 138 and 139*]. A point mutation can be assigned by this method to any of 80-odd ordered segments.

The final step in mapping is to test against one another only the group of mutants having mutations within each segment. Those that show recombination are concluded to be at different sites, and each site is then named after the mutant indicating it. (The mutants themselves have been assigned numbers according to their origin and order of discovery.) Finally, the order of the sites within a segment can be established by making quantitative measurements of recombination frequencies with respect to one another and neighbors outside the segment.

The Functional Unit

Thus we have found that the hereditary structure needed by the phage to multiply in colon bacilli of strain K consists of many parts distinguishable by mutation and recombination. Is this region to be thought of as one gene (because it controls one characteristic) or as hundreds of genes? Although mutation at any one of the sites leads to the same observed physiological defect, it does not necessarily follow that the entire structure is a single functional unit. For instance, growth in strain K could require a series of biochemical reactions, each controlled by a different portion of the region, and the absence of any one of the steps would suffice to block the final result. It is therefore of interest to see whether or not the *r*II region can be subdivided into parts that function independently.

This can be done by an experiment known as the *cis-trans* comparison. It will be recalled that the needed function can be supplied to a mutant by simultaneous infection of the cell with standard phage; the standard type supplies an intact copy of the genetic structure, so that

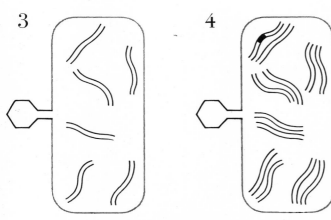
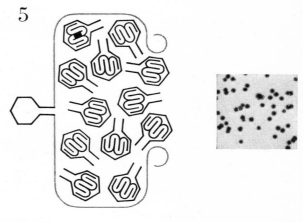
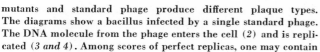

mutants and standard phage produce different plaque types. The diagrams show a bacillus infected by a single standard phage. The DNA molecule from the phage enters the cell (*2*) and is replicated (*3 and 4*). Among scores of perfect replicas, one may contain

a mutation (*dark patch*). Encased in protein jackets, the phage particles finally burst out of the cell (*5*). When a mutant arises during development of a plaque, the mixture of its mutant progeny and standard types makes plaque look mottled (*photograph at right*).

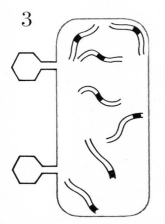
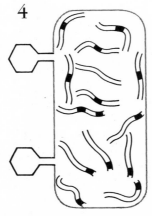
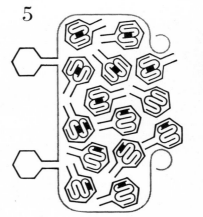
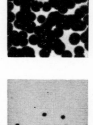

infects a single bacillus. Most of the DNA replicas are of one type or the other, but occasionally recombination will produce either a double mutant or a standard recombinant containing neither mutation. When the progeny of the cross are plated on strain B (*top*

photograph at far right), all grow successfully, producing many plaques. Plated on strain K, only the standard recombinants are able to grow (*bottom photograph at right*). A single standard recombinant can be detected among as many as 100 million progeny.

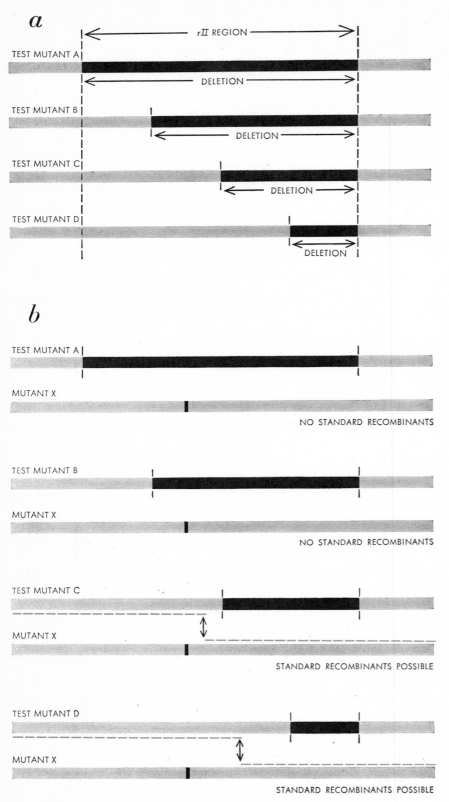

a

TEST MUTANT A

rII REGION

TEST MUTANT B

DELETION

TEST MUTANT C

DELETION

TEST MUTANT D

DELETION

DELETION

b

TEST MUTANT A

MUTANT X

NO STANDARD RECOMBINANTS

TEST MUTANT B

MUTANT X

NO STANDARD RECOMBINANTS

TEST MUTANT C

MUTANT X

STANDARD RECOMBINANTS POSSIBLE

TEST MUTANT D

MUTANT X

STANDARD RECOMBINANTS POSSIBLE

DELETION MAPPING is done by crossing an unknown mutant with a selected group of reference mutants (*four at top*) whose DNA molecules contain deletions—or what appear to be deletions—of known length in the *r*II region. Thus when mutant X is crossed with test mutants *A* and *B*, no standard recombinants are observed because both copies of the DNA molecule are defective at the same place. When X is crossed with *C* and *D*, however, standard recombinants can be formed, as indicated by broken lines and arrows. By using other reference mutants with appropriate deletions the location of X can be further narrowed.

it does not matter what defect the *r*II mutant has and both types are enabled to reproduce. Now suppose the intact structure of the standard type could be split into two parts. If this were to destroy the activity, the two parts could be regarded as belonging to a single functional unit. Although the experiment as such is not feasible, one can do the next best thing. That is to supply piece *A* intact by means of a mutant having a defect in piece *B,* and to use a mutant with a defect in piece *A* to supply an intact piece *B*. If the two pieces *A* and *B* can function independently, the system should be active, since each mutant supplies the function lacking in the other. If, however, both pieces must be together to be functional, the split combination should be inactive.

The actual experimental procedure is as follows. Let us imagine that one has identified two mutational sites in the *r*II region, *X* and *Y*, and that one wishes to know if they lie within the same functional unit. The first step is to infect cells of strain K with the two different mutants, *X* and *Y;* this is called the *trans* test because the mutations are borne by different DNA molecules. Now in K the decision as to whether or not the phage will function occurs very soon after infection and *before* there is any opportunity for recombination to take place. To carry out a control experiment one needs a double mutant (obtainable by recombination) that contains both *X* and *Y* within a single phage particle. When cells of strain K are infected with the double mutant and the standard phage, the experiment is called the *cis* test since one of the infecting particles contains both mutations in a single DNA molecule. In this case, because of the presence of the standard phage, normal replication is expected and provides the control against which to measure the activity observed in the *trans* test. If, in the *trans* test, the phage fails to function or shows only slight activity, one can conclude that *X* and *Y* fall within the same functional unit. If, on the other hand, the phage develops actively, it is probable (but not certain) that the sites lie in different functional units. (Certainty in this experiment is elusive because the products of two defective versions of the same functional unit, tested in a *trans* experiment, will sometimes produce a partial activity, which may be indistinguishable from that produced by a *cis* experiment.)

As applied to *r*II mutants, the test divides the structure into two clear-cut parts, each of which can function independently of the other. The functional units have been called cistrons, and we say that the rII region is composed of an A cistron and a B cistron.

We have, then, genetic units of various sizes: the small units of mutation and recombination, much larger cistrons and finally the rII region, which includes both cistrons. Which one of these shall we call the gene? It is not surprising to find geneticists in disagreement, since in classical genetics the term "gene" could apply to any one of these. The term "gene" is perfectly acceptable so long as one is working at a higher level of integration, at which it makes no difference which unit is being referred to. In describing data on the fine level, however, it becomes essential to state unambiguously which operationally defined unit one is talking about. Thus in describing experiments with rII mutants one can speak of the rII "region," two rII "cistrons" and many rII "sites."

Some workers have proposed using the word "gene" to refer to the genetic unit that provides the information for one enzyme. But this would imply that one should not use the word "gene" at all, short of demonstrating that a specific enzyme is involved. One would be quite hard pressed to provide this evidence in the great majority of cases in which the term has been used, as, for example, in almost all the mutations in *Drosophila*. A genetic unit should be defined by a genetic experiment. The absurdity of doing otherwise can be seen by imagining a biochemist describing an enzyme as that which is made by a gene.

We have seen that the topology of the rII region is simple and linear. What can be said about its topography? Are there local differences in the properties of the various parts? Specifically, are all the subelements equally mutable? If so, mutations should occur at random throughout the structure and the topography would then be trivial. On the other hand, sites or regions of unusually high or low mutability would be interesting topographic features. To answer this question one isolates many independently arising rII mutants and maps each one to see if mutations tend to occur more frequently at certain points than at others. Each mutation is first localized into a main segment, then into a smaller segment, and finally mutants of the same small segment are tested against each other. Any that show recombination are said to define different sites. If two or more reverting mutants are found to show no detectable recombination with each other, they are considered to be

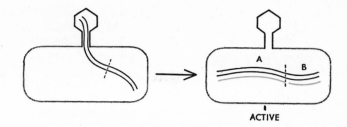

PHAGE ACTIVITY requires that the coded information inside functional units of the DNA molecule be available intact. The rII region consists of two functional units called A cistron and B cistron. When both are present intact (*right*), the phage actively replicates inside colon bacillus of strain K. Colored lines indicate effective removal of coded information.

a

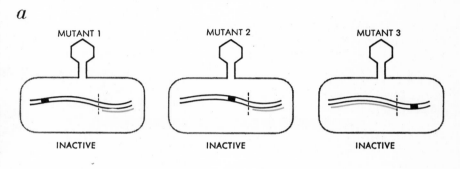

b

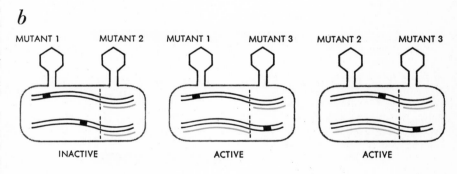

c

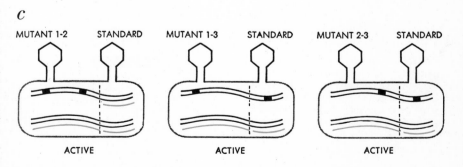

CIS-TRANS TEST determines the size of functional units. In bacillus of strain K, T4 phage is active only if both A and B cistrons are provided intact; hence mutants *1, 2* and *3* are inactive. (The sites of mutation have been previously established.) Tests with the three mutants taken two at a time (*b*) show that sites *1* and *2* must be in the same cistron. A test of each mutant with standard phage (*c*) provides a control; in this case all are active.

repeats, and one of them is chosen to represent the site in further tests. A set of distinct sites is thereby obtained, each with its own group of repeats. The designation of a mutant as a repeat is, of course, tentative, since in principle it remains possible that a more sensitive test could show some recombination.

The illustration on the next two pages shows a map of the rII region with each occurrence of a spontaneous mutation indicated by a square. These mutations, as well as other data from induced mutations, subdivide the map into more than 300 distinct sites, and the distribution of repeats is indeed far from random. The topography for spontaneous mutation is evidently quite complex, the structure consisting of elements with widely different mutation rates.

Spontaneous mutation is a chronic disease; a spontaneous mutant is simply one for which the cause is unknown. By using chemical mutagens such as nitrous acid or hydroxylamine, or physical agents such as ultraviolet light, one can alter the DNA in a more controlled manner and induce mutations specifically. A method of inducing specific mutations has long been the philosophers' stone of genetics. What the genetic alchemist desired, however, was an effect that could be directed at the gene controlling a particular characteristic. Chemical mutagenesis is highly specific but not in this way. When Rose Litman and Arthur B. Pardee at the University of California discovered the mutagenic effect of 5-bromouracil on phage, they regarded it as a nonspecific mutagen because mutations were induced that affected a wide assortment of different phage characteristics. This nonspecificity resulted because each functional gene is a structure with many parts and is bound to contain a number of sites that are responsive to any particular mutagen. Therefore the rate at which mutation is

DELETION MAP shows the reference mutants that divided the rII region into 80 segments. These mutants behave as if various sections of the DNA molecule had been deleted or inactivated, and as a class they do not revert, or back-mutate, spontaneously to produce standard phage. Mutants that do revert usually act as if the mutation is localized at a single point on the DNA molecule. Where this point falls in the rII region is determined by systematically crossing the revertible mutant with these reference deletion mutants, as illustrated on page 136. The net result is to assign the point mutation to smaller and smaller segments of the map.

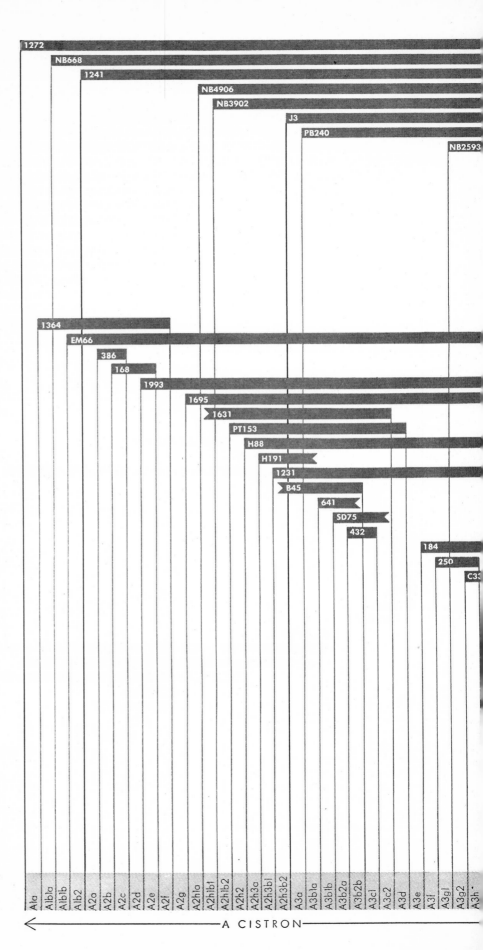

A CISTRON

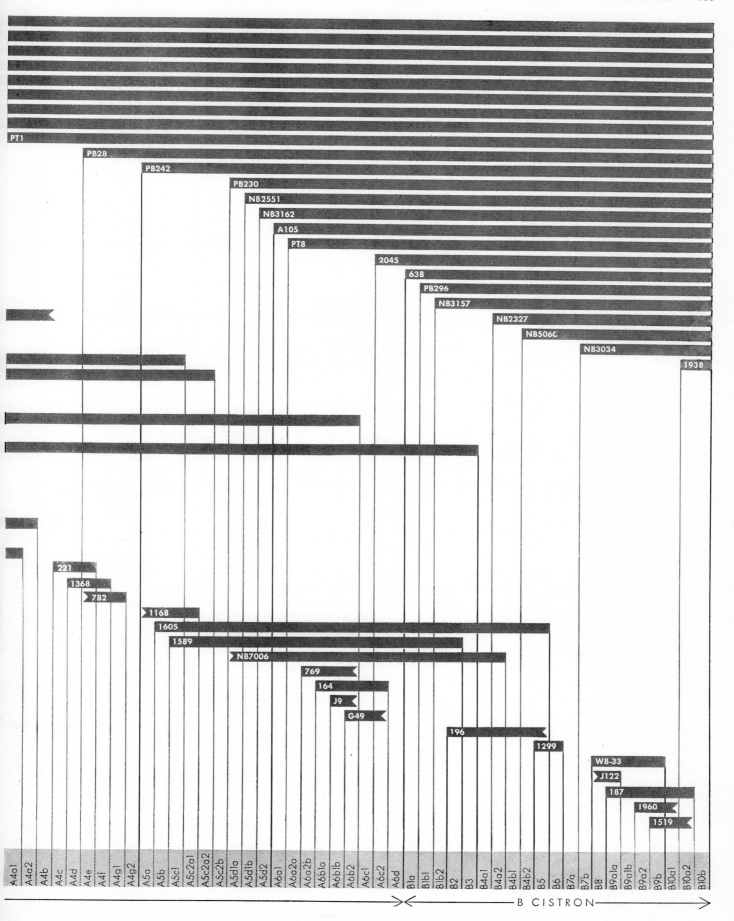

induced in various genes is more or less the same. By fine-structure genetic analysis, however, Ernst Freese and I, working in our laboratory at Purdue University, have found that 5-bromouracil increases the mutation rate at certain sites by a factor of 10,000 or more over the spontaneous rate, while producing no noticeable change at some other sites. This indicates a high degree of specificity indeed, but at the level within the cis-

tron. Furthermore, other mutagens specifically alter other sites. The response of part of the B cistron to a variety of mutagens is shown in the illustration on the following two pages.

Each site in the genetic map can, then, be characterized by its spontaneous mutability and by its response to various mutagens. By this means many different kinds of site have been found. Some response patterns are represented at only

a single site in the entire structure; for example, the prominent spontaneous hot spot in segment B4. This is at first surprising, because according to the Watson-Crick model for DNA the structure should consist of only two types of element, adenine-thymine (AT) pairs and guanine-hydroxymethylcytosine (GC) pairs. One possible explanation for the uneven reactivity among various sites is that the response may depend not

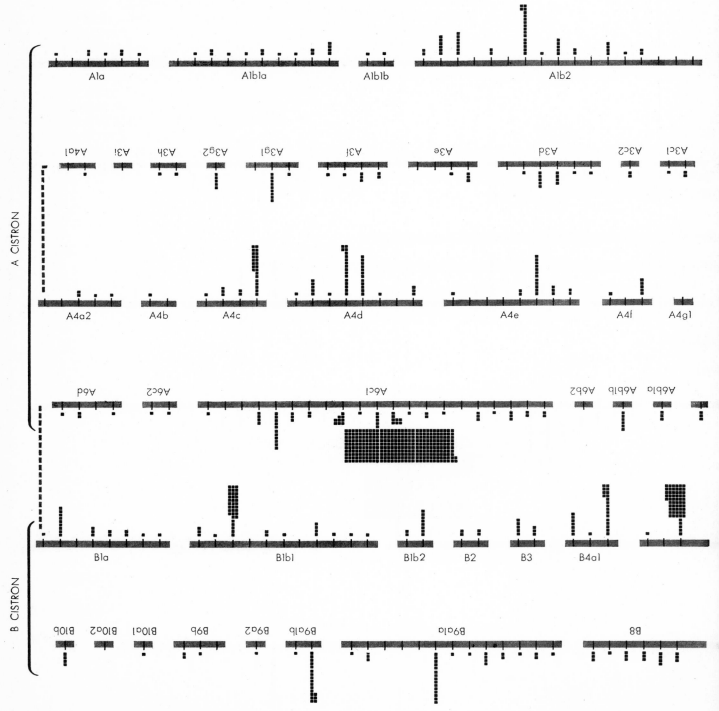

FREQUENCY OF SPONTANEOUS MUTATIONS at various sites is shown in this complete map of the *r*II region. Alternate rows have been deliberately inverted to indicate that the region is a continuous molecular thread. Each spontaneous mutation at a site

only on the particular base pair at a site but also very much on the type and arrangement of neighboring base pairs.

Once a site is identified it can be further characterized by the ease with which a particular mutagen makes reverse mutations produce phage of standard type. Combining such studies with studies of the chemical mechanism of mutagenesis, it may be possible eventually to translate the genetic map, bit by bit, into the actual base sequence.

Saturation of the Map

How far is the map from being run into the ground? Since many of the sites are represented by only one occurrence of a mutation, it is clear that there must still exist some sites with zero occurrences, so that the map as it stands is not saturated. From the statistics of the distribution it can be estimated that there must exist, in addition to some 350 sites now known, at least 100 sites not yet discovered. The calculation provides only a minimum estimate; the true number is probably larger. Therefore the map at the present time cannot be more than 78 per cent saturated.

Everything that we have learned about the genetic fine structure of T4 phage is compatible with the Watson-

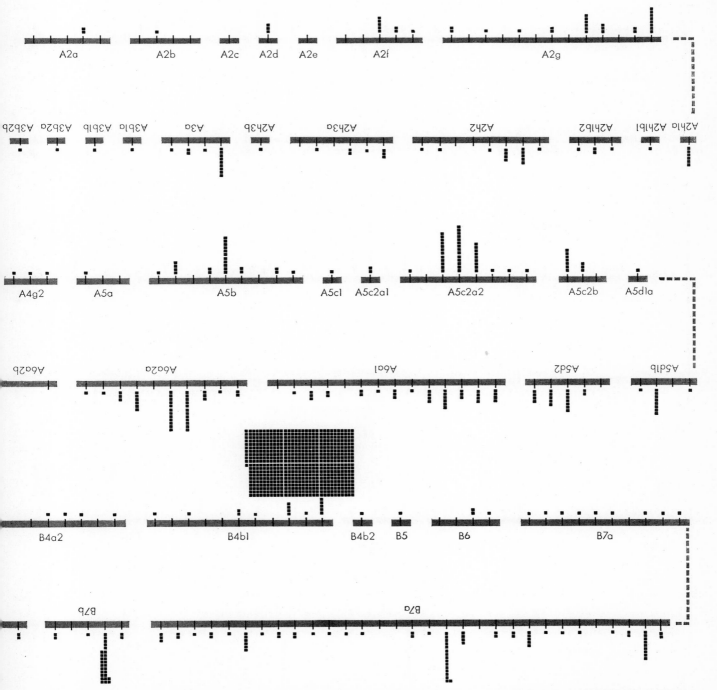

is represented by a small black square. Sites without squares are known to exist because they can be induced to mutate by use of chemical mutagens or ultraviolet light (*see illustration on next two pages*), but they have not been observed to mutate spontaneously.

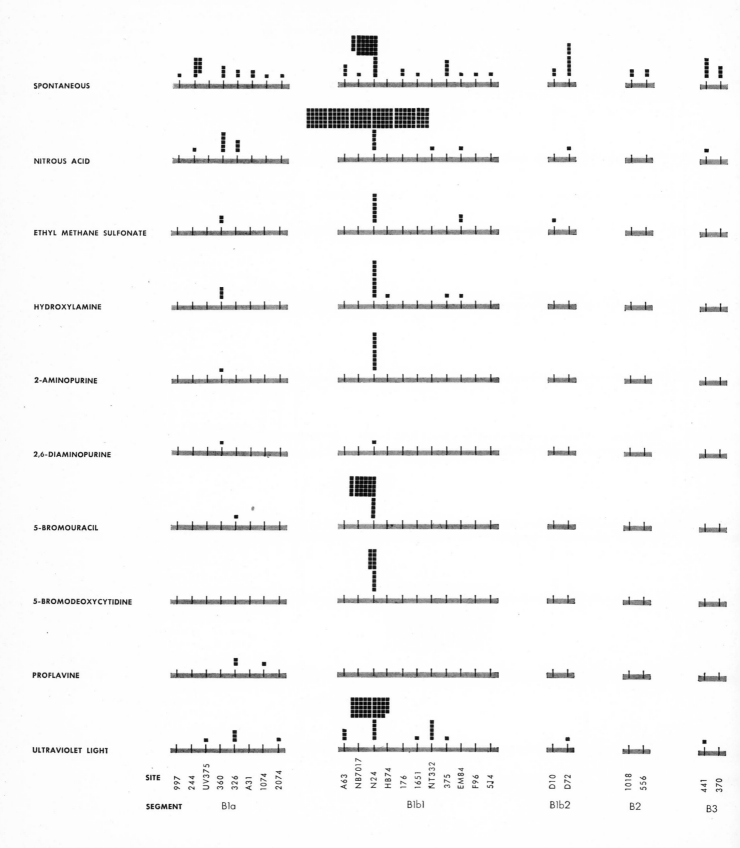

RESPONSE OF PHAGE TO MUTAGENS is shown for a portion of the B cistron. The total number of mutations studied is not the same for each mutagen. It is clear, nevertheless, that mutagenic action is highly specific at certain sites. For example, site EM26,

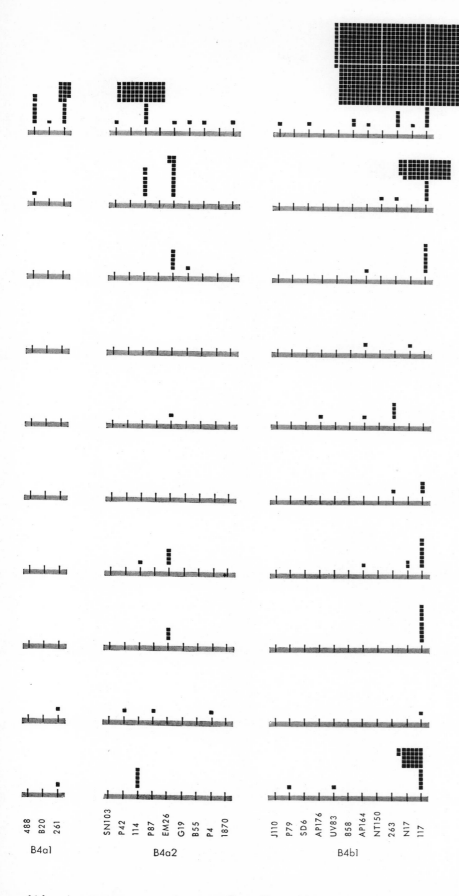

B4a1: 488 B20 261

B4a2: SN103 P42 114 P87 EM26 G19 B55 P4 1870

B4b1: J110 P79 SD6 AP176 UV83 858 AP164 NT150 263 N17 117

Crick model of the DNA molecule. In this model the genetic information is contained in the specific order of bases arranged in a linear sequence. The four-letter language of the bases must somehow be translated into the 20-letter language of the amino acids, so that at least several base pairs must be required to specify one amino acid, and an entire polypeptide chain should be defined by a longer segment of DNA. Since the activity of the resulting enzyme, or other protein, depends on its precise structure, this activity should be impaired by any of a large number of changes in the DNA base sequence leading to amino acid substitutions.

One can also imagine that certain changes in base sequence can lead to a "nonsense" sequence that does not specify any amino acid, and that as a result the polypeptide chain cannot be completed. Thus the genetic unit of function should be vulnerable at many different points within a segment of the DNA structure. Considering the monotonous structure of the molecule, there is no obvious reason why recombination should not be possible at every link in the molecular chain, although not necessarily with the same probability. In short, the Watson-Crick model leads one to expect that the functional units—the genes of traditional genetics—should consist of linear segments that can be finely dissected by mutation and recombination.

Mapping Other Genes

The genetic results fully confirm these expectations. All mutations can in fact be represented in a strictly linear map, the functional units correspond to sharply defined segments, and each functional unit is divisible by mutation and recombination into hundreds of sites. Mutations are induced specifically at certain sites by agents that interact with the DNA bases. Although the data on mutation rates are complex, it is quite probable that they can be explained by interactions between groups of base pairs.

In confining this investigation to rII mutants of T4, attention has been focused on a tiny bit of hereditary material constituting only a few per cent of the genetic structure of a virus, enabling the exploration to be carried almost to the limits of the molecular structure. Similar results are being obtained in many other microorganisms and even in higher organisms such as corn. Given techniques for handling cells in culture in the appropriate way, man too may soon be a subject for genetic fine-structure analysis.

which resists spontaneous mutation, responds readily to certain mutagens. However, site 117 in segment B4b1 is more apt to mutate spontaneously than in response to a mutagen.

ROLE OF INDIVIDUAL GENES of the T4 bacterial virus was investigated by the authors. This electron micrograph made by E. Boy de la Tour of the University of Geneva shows a complete virus particle with its hexagonal head and springlike tail assembly (*upper center*) and a number of "polyheads": cylindrical tubes of hexagonally arranged protein subunits that were not assembled into virus heads. The failure in assembly is due to a mutation in gene No. 20. The enlargement is about 270,000 diameters.

The Genetics of a Bacterial Virus

15

R. S. EDGAR AND R. H. EPSTEIN · February 1965

Viruses, the simplest living things known to man, have two fundamental attributes in common with higher forms of life: a definite architecture and the ability to replicate that architecture according to the genetic instructions encoded in molecules of nucleic acid. Yet in viruses life is trimmed to its bare essentials. A virus particle consists of one large molecule of nucleic acid wrapped in a protective coat of protein. The virus particle can do nothing for itself; it is able to reproduce only by parasitizing, or infecting, a living host cell that can supply the machinery and materials for translating the viral genetic message into the substance and structure of new virus particles. Since a virus is an isolated packet of genetic information unencumbered by the complex supporting systems characteristic of living cells, it is a peculiarly suitable subject for genetic investigation. One can study the molecular basis of life by identifying the individual genes in viral nucleic acid and learning what part each plays in the formation of virus progeny. That is what we have been doing for the past four years, working with the T4 bacteriophage, a virus that infects the colon bacterium *Escherichia coli*.

The T4 virus is one of the most complex viral structures. About .0002 millimeter long, the T4 particle consists of a head in the shape of a bipyramidal hexagonal prism and a tail assembly with several components. The head is a protein membrane stuffed with a long, tightly coiled molecule of deoxyribonucleic acid (DNA). The protein tail plays a role in attaching the virus to the host bacterial cell and injecting the viral DNA through the cell wall. Six tail fibers resembling tentacles bring the virus to the surface of the cell; a flat end plate fitted with prongs anchors the virus

there as the muscle-like sheath of the tail contracts to extrude the viral DNA through a hollow core into the cell.

Within a few minutes after the DNA enters the bacterium the metabolism of the infected bacterial cell undergoes a profound change. The cell's own DNA is degraded and its normal business —the synthesis of bacterial protein— ceases; synthetic activity has come under the control of the viral DNA, which takes over the synthesizing apparatus of the cell to direct the synthesis of new types of protein required for the production of new virus particles. The first proteins to appear include enzymes needed for the replication of the viral DNA, which has components not present in bacterial DNA and for the synthesis of which there are therefore no bacterial enzymes. Once these "early enzymes" are available the replication of viral DNA begins. Soon thereafter a new class of proteins appears in the cell: the proteins that will be required for the head membrane and tail parts.

About 15 minutes after the viral DNA was first injected new viral DNA begins to condense in the form of heads; protein components assemble around these condensates and soon whole virus particles are completed. For perhaps 10 minutes the synthesis and assembly of DNA and protein components continue and mature virus particles accumulate. The lysis, or dissolution, of the infected cell brings this process to an abrupt halt. Some 200 new virus particles are liberated to find new host cells to infect and so repeat the cycle of reproduction.

The remarkable sequence of synthesis, assembly and lysis is directed by the message borne by the genes of the viral DNA. Each gene is a segment of the DNA molecule, a twisted molecular ladder in which the rungs are pairs of nitrogenous bases: either adenine paired with thymine or guanine paired with cytosine. (In T4 DNA the cytosine is hydroxymethyl cytosine.) The sequence of base pairs in the DNA molecule, like

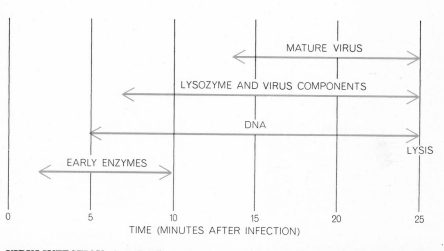

VIRUS INFECTION of a colon bacterium (at 37 degrees centigrade) proceeds on schedule, with the sequence of syntheses leading up to the lysis, or dissolution, of the host cell.

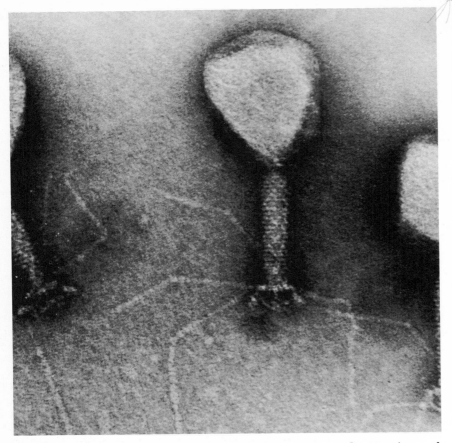

T4 BACTERIOPHAGE is enlarged about 300,000 diameters in an electron micrograph made by Michael Moody of the California Institute of Technology. The preparation was negatively stained with electron-dense uranyl acetate, which makes the background dark.

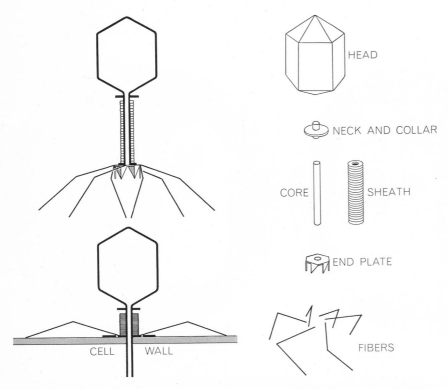

HEAD

NECK AND COLLAR

CORE   SHEATH

END PLATE

CELL   WALL

FIBERS

T4 COMPONENTS are diagrammed. A complete virus particle is shown at top left. Below it is a particle attached to a bacterial cell wall, with its sheath contracted and its hollow core penetrating the cell wall. The various components are shown separately at the right.

the sequence of letters in a word, spells out the information for the assembly of amino acids into protein molecules; a gene is defined as a segment of DNA sufficient to encode a single protein molecule. Since the average protein molecule consists of about 200 amino acid units and the code of DNA requires three base pairs per amino acid, the average length of a gene should be about 600 base pairs. Since there are about 200,000 base pairs in a molecule of T4 DNA, we began by assuming that the molecule contains several hundred genes and initiates the production of several hundred proteins in the host cell. Our task was first to map the location in the T4 DNA molecule of as many genes as possible and then to associate these genes with specific functions.

In order to identify a gene, map its location and learn its function one must find a gene that has undergone mutation: a molecular mistake that occurs like a typographical error in the sequence of base pairs and results either in genetic nonsense, meaning the inability to form protein, or in "missense," meaning the formation of faulty protein. Once a mutation occurs it is copied in successive replications of the DNA and reveals itself by its malfunction in protein synthesis. A mutation therefore serves as a marker for a gene. Moreover, by comparing the growth of a mutant strain of an organism with the growth of a "wild type," or normal, strain one can often infer the normal function of the gene under examination.

The trouble is that most mutations important enough to be recognized and studied are lethal; that is, they result in offspring that cannot survive, or at least cannot reproduce. How, then, can one study lethal mutations? In advanced plants and animals there are two copies of every gene, and it is possible to study "recessive" mutations that are lethal only when they happen to occur in both copies. Less advanced forms of life such as molds, bacteria and viruses, however, have only one copy of each gene, so some other method of studying lethal mutations must be found.

One such method was developed by George W. Beadle and Edward L. Tatum for the study of mutations in the genes of molds and bacteria. The genes that can be investigated by this method are those that direct the synthesis of enzymes required for the formation of nutrients, such as amino acids and vitamins, that are essential to the mold or bacterial cell. In these cases a mutation, although inherently lethal, will not prevent cell growth if the missing nutrient is supplied by the experimenter: it is a "conditional" lethal mutation. Such mutations are restricted to genes whose function can be supplanted by the experimenter. Our aim is to study mutations that affect the synthesis and assembly of virus components, and we had no way of supplying proteins or pieces of virus to infected cells. We needed other kinds of conditional lethal mutations.

One of us (Edgar), working at the California Institute of Technology, has dealt primarily with a class of mutations that are temperature-sensitive: they render the gene inactive at one temperature but not at temperatures a few degrees lower. An example of such a gene in a higher animal is the gene that controls the hair pigment in Siamese cats. The gene is inactive at body temperature, with the result that most of the cat's coat is white. On the cooler parts of the body—the paws, the tip of the tail, the nose and the ears—the gene becomes functional and the hair is pigmented. Of course, this defect is not lethal to the cat, but similar mutations in genes with functions essential to an organism are conditional lethal mutations if one can control the temperature. A strain of T4 bacteriophage with a temperature-sensitive lethal mutation, for example, grows perfectly well if it is incubated on bacteria at 25 degrees cen-

tigrade but not if it is incubated at 42 degrees. Temperature-sensitive mutations can occur in many different genes, since what they do is simply render a protein—regardless of its particular function—more readily inactivated by heat. They apparently do so by substituting one amino acid for another at some sensitive point in the structure of the protein molecule; in other words, they are "missense" mutations.

Epstein has worked with another class of conditional lethal mutations: the "amber" mutations, which he developed at Cal Tech and has studied primarily in the laboratory of Edouard Kellenberger at the University of Geneva. (We call them the amber mutations because they were discovered with the help of a graduate student named Bernstein, and *bernstein* is the German word for "amber"; it is often safer to give a new discovery a silly name than a speculatively descriptive one!) In these mutations the conditional property is not temperature-sensitivity but the ability of a virus to grow in certain host cells. Whereas the wild-type T4 virus grows equally well in colon bacteria of strains B and CR, amber mutants grow only in CR. Apparently only CR bacteria are able to translate the mutant message into protein properly; in strain B the mutant gene is translated into protein only up to the point of mutation and the resulting protein fragment is inactive. In other words, amber mutations are trans-

lated as "nonsense" in strain B but as "sense," or at worst as "missense," in strain CR. Again we could expect the amber mutations to occur in many different genes, since these mutations affect the overall translatability of any affected gene rather than the ability of specific genes to direct the synthesis of specific proteins.

Mutations arise at random in the normal course of virus infection and reproduction; we amplify the process by treating virus particles with one of a variety of chemical mutagens. We then plate the virus on cultures of colon bacteria. Any amber or temperature-sensitive mutant reveals itself by its failure to grow under "restrictive" conditions, that is, on strain B in the case of an amber mutation or at 42 degrees in the case of a temperature-sensitive mutation. In this manner we have isolated more than 1,000 amber and temperature-sensitive mutant strains. The mutations, however, occur at random at various sites in the many genes of the viral DNA. Since we are trying to identify genes, not merely mutations, we need to determine which mutant strains contain mutations affecting the same gene.

We do this by performing complementation tests [*see illustration on next two pages*]. The test consists in infecting bacteria simultaneously with two mutant viruses under restrictive conditions in which each mutant alone would be unable to grow in the bacterial cells.

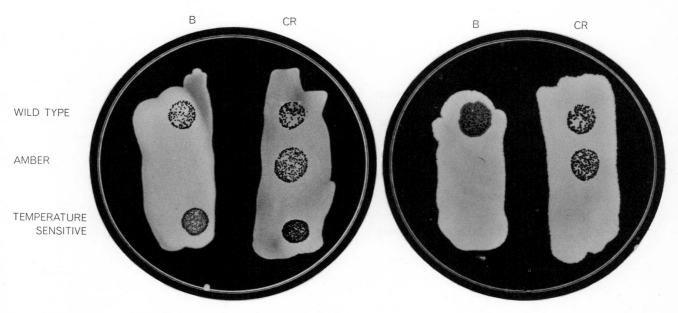

WILD TYPE

AMBER

TEMPERATURE SENSITIVE

INCUBATED AT 25 DEGREES C.   INCUBATED AT 42 DEGREES C.

GROWTH CHARACTERISTICS of "wild type" virus and "amber" and temperature-sensitive mutants are compared. The photographic prints were made by exposing actual Petri dishes in an enlarger. On each dish bacterial strains B and CR had been streaked, with drops of virus suspensions placed on each streak, and the plates had been incubated at two temperatures, as shown. The amber mutants grew only on strain CR, the temperature-sensitive mutants grew only at 25 degrees C. and the wild-type virus grew under all conditions.

Infection of strain *B* bacteria at high temperature is restrictive for both amber and temperature-sensitive mutants. If, under these restrictive conditions, a yield of progeny virus is produced from cells infected by two mutants, the mutations must be complementary defects. Each mutant can perform the function the other mutant is unable to perform, and we can conclude that the two mutations are in different genes. If, on the other hand, the doubly infected bacteria produce no progeny virus, the two mutant strains must be unable to complement each other. Their mutations must affect a common function, and we conclude that they are in the same gene.

When complementation tests are applied to amber mutants, the results are clear-cut. These mutants, when tested against one another, fall into mutually exclusive classes: mutations in different genes result in full complementation no matter how they are paired, whereas mutations within the same gene fail to complement each other no matter how they are paired. In the case of temperature-sensitive mutants, however, the results are equivocal: some of the mutants display "intragenic" complementation and yield virus progeny even under restrictive conditions. Apparently two different "missense" mutations can give rise to "hybrid" proteins that, although

altered, are nevertheless complete and functional. The amber mutants, as we have mentioned, involve "nonsense" mutations and therefore would not be expected to show intragenic complementation. Since both amber and temperature-sensitive mutations occur in many genes, the ambers provide a check on the equivocal temperature-sensitive results.

By means of complementation tests we subdivided our many hundreds of amber and temperature-sensitive mutants into separate groups, each of which identifies one gene of the virus; our mutations turned out to be located in 56 different genes. The next step was

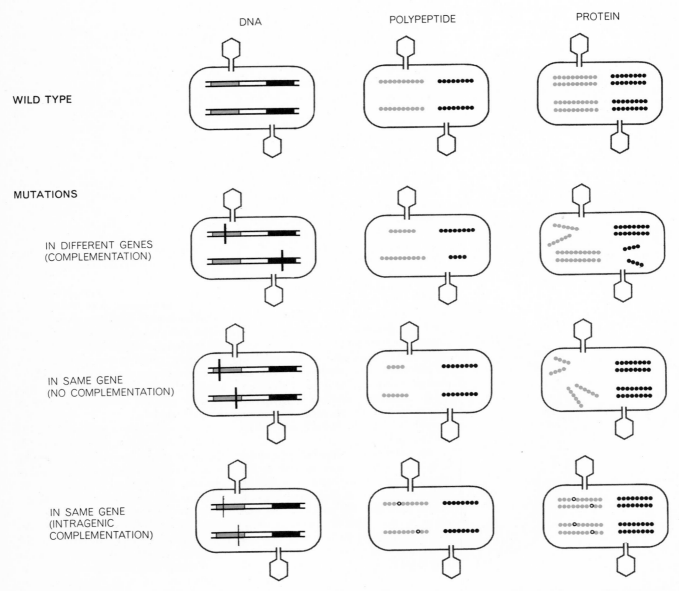

DNA   POLYPEPTIDE   PROTEIN

WILD TYPE

MUTATIONS

IN DIFFERENT GENES
(COMPLEMENTATION)

IN SAME GENE
(NO COMPLEMENTATION)

IN SAME GENE
(INTRAGENIC
COMPLEMENTATION)

COMPLEMENTATION TEST identifies individual genes. The top row shows how, in wild-type virus, two genes of the deoxyribonucleic acid (DNA) molecule (*color and black*) might direct the synthesis of two polypeptide chains that form proteins and end up as virus components. An infection with wild-type virus results in a large number of plaques on a bacterial culture (*right*). If two mutations being tested occur in different genes, one gene makes the protein the other cannot make; they complement each other and virus particles are produced (*second row*). Two mutations in the same gene will ordinarily not complement each other, as

to locate those genes, and four that had been identified earlier by other investigators, on a genetic map—a representation of the position of the genes in relation to one another.

Such a map is constructed on the basis of recombination, the process by which the genetic material from two parents is mixed in the progeny. In viruses recombination can occur when viruses of two different strains infect the same cell. The mechanism of recombination is still poorly understood, but it probably involves the breakage of DNA molecules and the reassociation of pieces derived from both strains to form a new "hybrid" DNA molecule. Recom-

VIRUS PARTICLES   PLAQUES

seen in the third row. In some cases involving the temperature-sensitive mutants, however, "intragenic complementation" occurs: some virus is produced in spite of errors in polypeptide synthesis (*bottom row*).

bination between two different mutants can result in some virus progeny that carry both mutations and in some wild-type viruses with no mutations. The wild-type recombinations can be recognized by their ability to multiply under restrictive conditions. The closer together two genes are on the DNA molecule, the less likely it is that breaks and reunions will occur between them, so the frequency of recombination is a measure of the distance between the two genes. We infect a bacterial culture with two strains that are mutant, say, in genes a and x respectively, and incubate it under "permissive" conditions in which both mutants can grow. Among millions of virus progeny of such a cross there will be some wild-type recombinants. By plating measured amounts of the progeny under permissive and under restrictive conditions we can determine what fraction of the progeny are wild-type. From this we calculate the frequency of recombination between genes a and x and thus the distance between them.

By plotting the results of hundreds of crosses we constructed a genetic map of the T4 DNA molecule [*see illustration on next page*]. A remarkable feature of the map is that it has no "ends" and must be drawn as a linear array that closes on itself—a circle. This is rather surprising, since it has been established by electron microscopy and other means that the actual form of the T4 DNA molecule is that of a strand with two ends. (Just to confuse matters, some other viruses do have circular molecules!) Why the map should be circular is not yet known with certainty. It is probably because different viral DNA molecules have different sequences of genes, all of them circular permutations of the same basic sequence. In alphabetical terms, it is as if one DNA were a, b ... y, z while another were n, o ... z, a ... l, m. In the second case z and a would be "closely linked" and would map close together.

Recombination occurs between mutation sites within genes as well as between genes, so we have been able to make a number of "intragenic" maps. These show that the genes are not uniform in size. Although most of them are quite small, each accounting for about half of 1 percent of the length of the map, gene No. 34 is about 20 times larger, and genes No. 35 and No. 43 are also outsized. Average gene size is therefore not a precise indicator of the number of genes in the virus. It looks as if the mutations discovered to date cover about half of the map, so we con-

clude that roughly half of the genes remain to be discovered. Unfortunately a kind of law of diminishing returns seems to be taking effect: for every 100 new mutants we isolate and test we are lucky to discover one new gene. Apparently amber and temperature-sensitive mutations are rare in the genes that are as yet undiscovered. We are devising new techniques with which to seek them out, but there will probably be a number of genes that are simply not susceptible to the conditional-lethal procedure. This could be because neither amber nor temperature-sensitive mutations occur in them or because, if they do occur, the loss of gene function is not lethal and the mutation therefore goes unnoticed.

While attempting to uncover the remaining genes, we have begun to determine the functions performed by the genes already identified. The mutants were originally detected because of their inability to produce progeny virus under restrictive conditions. In order to investigate the nature of the abortive infections more closely in an attempt to find out just what step in the growth cycle goes awry, we have employed a large number of mutants involving several different defects in each of the 60 genes. We chose just a few aspects of bacteriophage growth to examine, largely because they are easy to observe or measure and because they provide information on the major events of the cycle.

1. Can the infecting mutant virus accomplish the disruption of the bacterial DNA molecule? With the phase microscope one can observe whether or not the bacterial nucleoid, or DNA-containing body, disintegrates. So far every mutant we have tested has been able to disrupt the host DNA, so it is clear that in every case the infective process is at least initiated.

2. Does DNA synthesis occur in the infected cell? After the disruption of the bacterial nucleoid all host functions cease. Any new DNA that is revealed in chemical tests is viral DNA and an indication that the genes responsible for DNA synthesis are operative.

3. Do the infected cells lyse at the normal time? During the last half of the growth cycle an enzyme, lysozyme, is synthesized that is responsible for disrupting the cell wall. Normal lysis indicates that this enzyme is synthesized and does its work.

4. Are complete virus particles or components such as heads and tails produced in the infected cells? Electron

microscopy tells us the extent to which protein virus components have been synthesized and assembled in an infected cell.

Our data indicate that the various genes can be assigned to two groups. There are genes that appear to govern early steps in the infective process, as indicated by the fact that they affect DNA synthesis, and genes that appear to govern later steps, as indicated by their role in the maturation of new phage particles.

The major class of "early" genes includes those that are essential if any DNA synthesis is to occur. Mutations in these genes must cause the loss of some enzyme function necessary for DNA synthesis. Seven genes of this type have been identified, the precise function of one of which has been determined: John M. Buchanan and his co-workers at the Massachusetts Institute of Technology have found that gene No. 42 controls the synthesis of an enzyme necessary for the manufacture of hydroxymethyl cyto-

sine, one of the four bases in the T4 DNA molecule.

The "no DNA" mutants reveal an interesting regulatory feature of gene action. Not only is there no DNA synthesis in cells infected by these mutants, but also the cells do not lyse and no virus components are made. It appears that the decoding of the late-functioning genes depends somehow on the prior synthesis of viral DNA. Buchanan's group has found, moreover, that in these cells any of the early enzymes that are

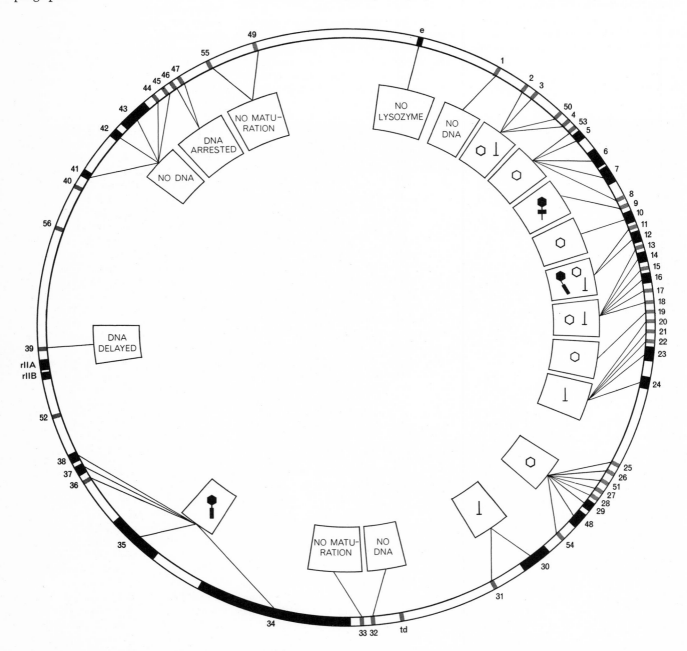

GENE MAP OF T4 shows the relative positions of the 60 genes identified to date and the major physiological properties of mutants defective in various genes. Minimum length is shown for some of the genes (*black segments*) but is not yet known for others (*gray*). The boxes indicate deficiencies in synthesis associated with mutations in some genes or, in the case of other genes, the components that are present in defective lysates of corresponding mutants. There may be no DNA synthesis or it may be delayed or arrested. There may be no virus maturation at all. Synthesis and lysis may proceed normally but, as shown by the symbols, incomplete viruses may be produced, ranging from heads or tails only to complete particles lacking tail fibers (*genes No. 34 through No. 38*).

not eliminated by the particular mutation continue to be synthesized well beyond the normal shutoff time of 10 minutes. It appears, then, that in the absence of normal DNA synthesis some timing mechanism for switching early genes off and turning late ones on fails to function.

Among the early genes some others have been found that appear to delay or modify DNA synthesis or to block the activity of late genes without disturbing DNA synthesis, but the manner in which they function is still obscure.

Most of the genes—about 40 of those we have identified so far—clearly play roles in forming and assembling the virus components. Mutations in these morphogenetic genes seem not to affect the synthesis of DNA or the lysis of the cell. What happens is that no infective progeny virus particles are produced, only bits and pieces of virus. For example, mutations in genes No. 20 through No. 24 result in the production of normal numbers of virus tails but no heads; mutations in the segment from gene No. 25 through No. 54 produce heads but no tails; mutations in genes No. 34 through No. 38 produce particles that are complete except for the tail fibers. Presumably the defective gene in each case is concerned with synthesis or assembly of the missing component.

A glance at the map [opposite page] shows that the arrangement of the genes in the DNA molecule is far from random: genes with like functions tend to fall into clusters. Similar clusters of certain genes in bacteria are called "operons," and all the genes within an operon function together as a unit under the control of separate regulatory genes. There is no indication that the clusters in viral DNA act as operons; the available evidence suggests, indeed, that each gene acts independently. Still, it is difficult to believe the clustering does not reflect in some meaningful way a high degree of coordination in the activities of the genes.

The large number of genes associated with morphogenesis is of particular interest. What do all these genes do? There is evidence that only a few of them are concerned with the actual synthesis of protein components. For example, the head of the virus particle is made up of about 300 identical protein

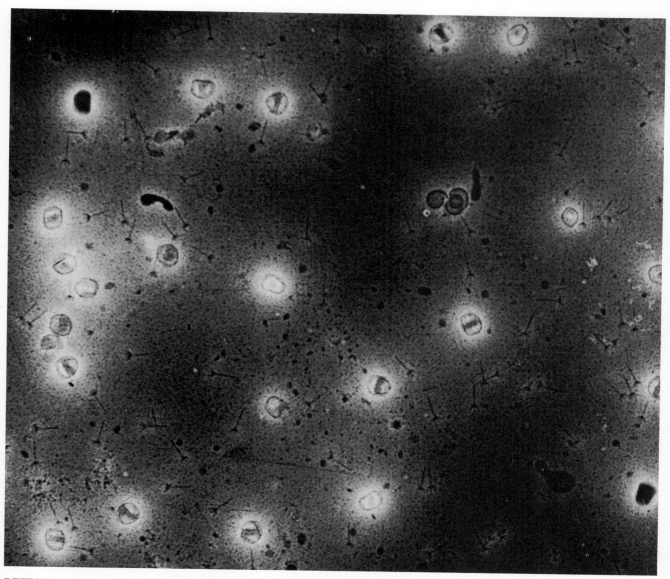

DEFECTIVE LYSATE of a temperature-sensitive strain mutant in gene No. 18 is enlarged about 60,000 diameters in this electron micrograph made by Edgar. Heads and tails have been formed but not assembled, and most of the heads are empty of DNA. The lysate was negatively stained with phosphotungstic acid, which filled the empty virus heads, and the exposed plate was printed as a negative.

subunits aggregated in a precise pattern; if there are any other protein molecules in the head membrane, they must be present in very small amounts. Yet at least seven genes and probably more are involved in the production of virus heads. Sydney Brenner and his associates at the University of Cambridge have found that just one of these genes, No. 23, is responsible for the actual synthesis of the protein subunits; cells infected with mutants defective in any other genes contain normal numbers of the subunits. The other genes must therefore be concerned with the assembly of the units rather than with their synthesis. When gene No. 20 is defective, for instance, the subunits assemble in the form of long cylindrical tubes instead of forming hexagonal heads [*see illustration on page 144*].

At this time we can only speculate as to the precise roles of the many morphogenetic genes. One possibility is that the proteins made by all of them are incorporated into the virus but in minor amounts that have escaped detection. Such minor components might be necessary to serve as the hinges, joints, nuts and bolts of the virus. Another possibility is that the proteins made by some of these late genes do not appear in the completed virus at all but instead play accessory roles in the assembly process —perhaps "gluing" subunits together in the specific configurations necessary for the proper construction of the virus. This notion of accessory morphogenetic genes is somewhat novel to many students of virus structure, who have generally believed that the assembly of viruses comes about through a spontaneous "crystallization" of subunits. In other words, it has been assumed that the form of a virus is inherent in its structural components. Although this may be true of viruses with simple spherical or cylindrical forms, it may not be true of viruses with more complex forms. The study of the effects of mutations on the assembly of viruses should serve as a powerful tool with which to explore this problem.

The relation between genes and form should be of general interest. Life is characterized by the complexity of its architecture. This complexity is manifested at all levels of organization, from molecules to the assemblages of specialized cells that make up higher animals and plants. The building blocks of all living things are, like virus particles, intricate molecular aggregations. Knowing how a bacteriophage such as T4 is put together may help us to understand the origins of form in all living systems.

16 | Building a Bacterial Virus

WILLIAM B. WOOD AND R. S. EDGAR · July 1967

Slice an orange in half, squeeze the juice into a pitcher and then drop in the rind. It comes as no surprise that the orange does not reconstitute itself. If, on the other hand, the components of the virus that causes the mosaic disease of tobacco are gently dissociated and then brought together under the proper conditions, they do reassociate, forming complete, infectious virus particles. The tobacco mosaic virus consists of a single strand of ribonucleic acid with several thousand identical protein subunits assembled around it in a tubular casing. The orange, of course, is a large and complex structure composed of a variety of cell types incorporating many different kinds of proteins and other materials. Yet both orange and virus are examples of biological architecture that must arise as a consequence of the action of genes.

Molecular biologists have now provided a fairly complete picture of how

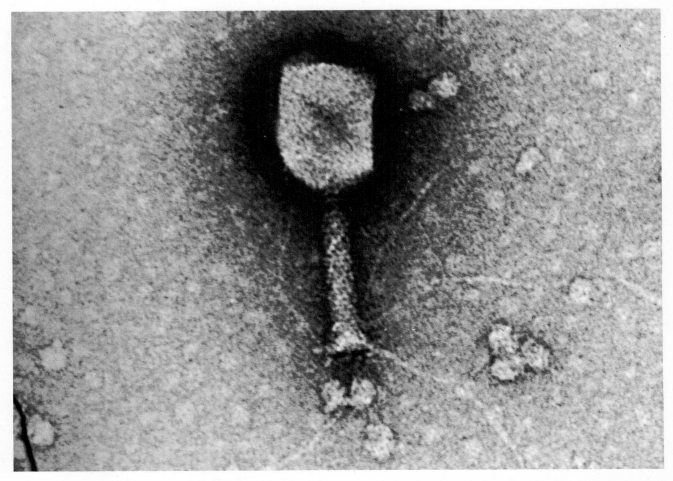

COMPLETE T4 PARTICLE was built by assembling component parts in the test tube. The virus is enlarged about 300,000 diameters in this electron micrograph made, like the ones on the next page, by Jonathan King of the California Institute of Technology.

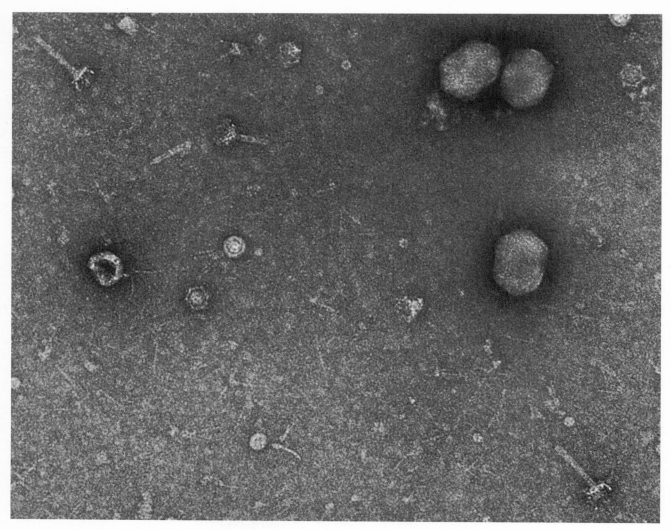

UNASSEMBLED PARTS of the T4 virus are present in this extract. It was prepared by infecting colon bacilli with a mutant virus defective in gene No. 18, which specifies the synthesis of the sheath *(see upper illustration on page 155)*. The result is the accumulation of all major components except the sheath: heads, free tail fibers and "naked" tails consisting of cores and end plates.

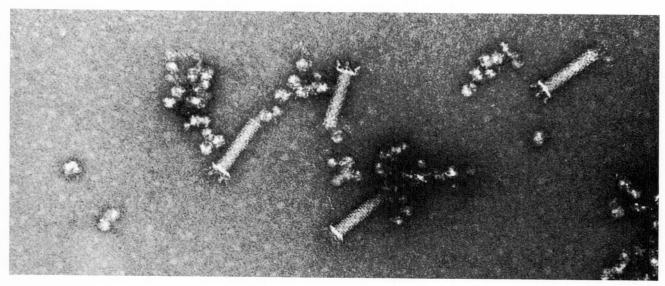

COMPLETE TAILS, enclosed in sheaths, were produced by a different mutant, defective in a gene involved in head formation. The tails were separated from the resulting extract (along with some spherical bacterial ribosomes) by being spun in a centrifuge. If the tails are added to the extract (*top photograph*), they combine with the heads and free fibers in it to form infectious virus.

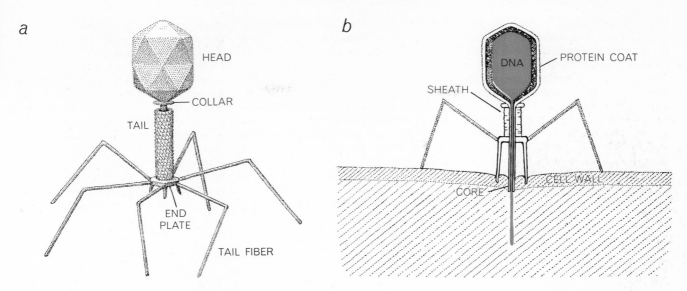

a

HEAD

COLLAR

TAIL

END
PLATE

TAIL FIBER

b

DNA

PROTEIN COAT

SHEATH

CELL WALL

CORE

T4 BACTERIAL VIRUS is an assembly of protein components (*a*). The head is a protein membrane, shaped like a kind of prolate icosahedron with 30 facets and filled with deoxyribonucleic acid (DNA). It is attached by a neck to a tail consisting of a hol-low core surrounded by a contractile sheath and based on a spiked end plate to which six fibers are attached. The spikes and fibers affix the virus to a bacterial cell wall (*b*). The sheath contracts, driving the core through the wall, and viral DNA enters the cell.

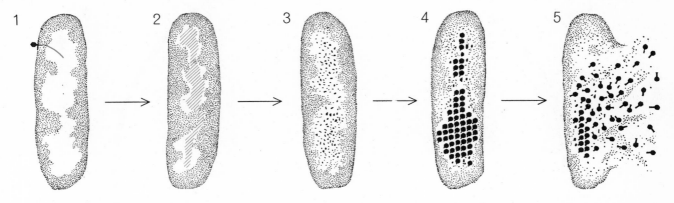

1   2   3   4   5

VIRAL INFECTION begins when viral DNA (*color*) enters a bacterium (*1*). Bacterial DNA is disrupted and viral DNA replicated (*2*). Synthesis of viral structural proteins (*3*) and their assembly into virus (*4*) continues until the cell bursts, releasing particles (*5*).

genes carry out their primary function: the specification of protein structure. The segment of nucleic acid (DNA or RNA) that constitutes a single gene specifies the chain of amino acids that comprises a protein molecule. Interactions among the amino acids cause the chain to fold into a unique configuration appropriate to the enzymatic or structural role for which it is destined. In this way the information in one gene determines the three-dimensional structure of a single protein molecule.

Where does the information come from to direct the next step: the assembly of many kinds of protein molecules into more complex structures? To build the relatively simple tobacco mosaic virus no further information is required; the inherent properties of the strand of RNA and the protein subunits cause them to interact in a unique way that results in the formation of virus particles. Clearly such a self-assembly process cannot explain the morphogenesis of an orange. At some intermediate stage on the scale of biological complexity there must be a point at which self-assembly becomes inadequate to the task of directing the building process. Working with a virus that may be just beyond that point, the T4 virus that infects the colon bacillus, we have been trying to learn how genes supply the required additional information.

Although the T4 virus is only a few rungs up the biological ladder from the tobacco mosaic virus, it is considerably more complex. Its DNA, which comprises more than 100 genes (compared with five or six in the tobacco mosaic virus), is coiled tightly inside a protein membrane to form a polyhedral head. Connected to the head by a short neck is a springlike tail consisting of a contractile sheath surrounding a central core and attached to an end plate, or base, from which protrude six short spikes and six long, slender fibers.

The life cycle of the T4 virus begins with its attachment to the surface of a colon bacillus by the tail fibers and spikes on its end plate. The sheath then contracts, driving the tubular core of the tail through the wall of the bacterial cell and providing an entry through which the DNA in the head of the virus can pass into the bacterium. Once inside, the genetic material of the virus quickly takes over the machinery of the cell. The bacterial DNA is broken down, production of bacterial protein stops and within less than a minute the cell has begun to manufacture viral proteins under the control of the injected virus genes. Among the first proteins to be made are the enzymes needed for viral DNA replication, which begins five minutes after infection. Three minutes later a second set of genes starts to direct the synthesis of the structural proteins that will form the head components and the tail components, and the process of viral morpho-

genesis begins. The first completed virus particle materializes 13 minutes after infection. Synthesis of both the DNA and the protein components continues for 12 more minutes until about 200 virus particles have accumulated within the cell. At this point a viral enzyme, lysozyme, attacks the cell wall from the inside to break open the bacterium and liberate the new viruses for a subsequent round of infection.

Additional insight into this process has come from studying strains of T4

carrying mutations—molecular defects that arise randomly and infrequently in the viral DNA during the course of its replication [see "The Genetics of a Bacterial Virus," by R. S. Edgar and R. H. Epstein, beginning on page 145 in this book]. When a mutation is present, the protein specified by the mutant gene is synthesized in an altered form. This new protein is often nonfunctional, in which case the development of the virus stops at the point where the protein is required. Normally such a mutation has little experimental use, since the virus in

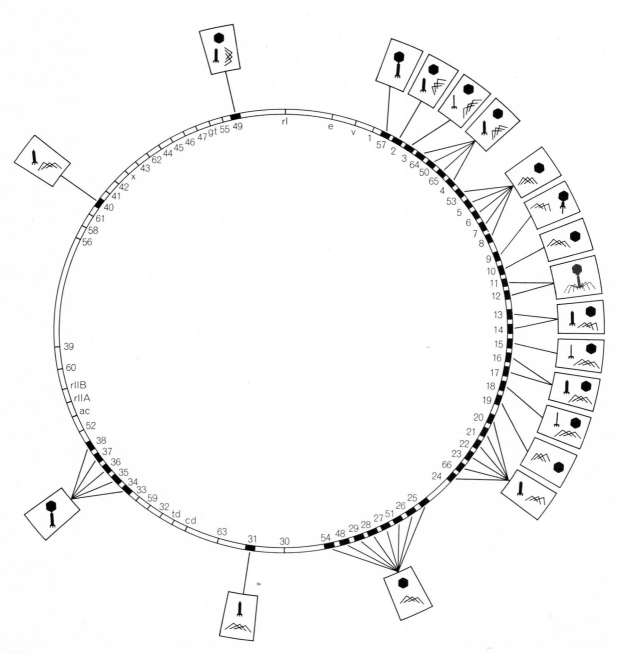

GENETIC MAP of the T4 virus shows the relative positions of more than 75 genes so far identified on the basis of mutations. The solid black segments of the circle indicate genes with morphogenetic functions. The boxed diagrams show which viral components are seen in micrographs of extracts of cells infected by mutants defective in each morphogenetic gene. A defect in gene No. 11 or 12 produces a complete but fragile particle. Heads, all tail parts, sheaths or fibers are the missing components in other extracts.

which it arises is dead and hence cannot be recovered for study. Edgar and Epstein, however, found mutations that are only "conditionally lethal": the mutant protein is produced in either a functional or a nonfunctional form, depending on the conditions of growth chosen by the experimenter. Under "permissive" conditions reproduction is normal, so that the mutants can be cultured and crossed for genetic studies. Under "restrictive" conditions, however, viral development comes to a halt at the step where the protein is needed, and by determining the point at which development is blocked the investigator can infer the normal function of the mutated gene. In this way a number of conditionally lethal mutations have been assigned to different genes, have been genetically mapped and have been tested for their effects on viral development under restrictive conditions [see illustration on page 156].

In the case of genes that control the later stages of the life cycle, involving the assembly of virus particles, mutations lead to the accumulation of unassembled viral components. These can be identified with the electron microscope. By noting which structures are absent as a result of mutation in a particular gene, we learn about that morphogenetic gene's normal function. For example, genes designated No. 23, No. 27 and No. 34 respectively appear to control steps in the formation of the head, the tail and the tail fibers; these are the structures that are missing from the corresponding mutant-infected cells.

A blockage in the formation of one of these components does not seem to affect the assembly of the other two, which accumulate in the cell as seemingly normal and complete structures. This information alone provides some insight into the assembly process. The virus is apparently not built up the way a sock is knitted—by a process starting at one end and adding subunits sequentially until the other end is reached. Instead, construction seems to follow an assembly-line process, with three major branches that lead independently to the formation of heads, tails and tail fibers. The finished components are combined in subsequent steps to form the virus particle.

A second striking aspect of the genetic map is the large number of genes controlling the morphogenetic process. More than 40 have already been discovered, and a number probably remain to be identified. If all these genes specify proteins that are component parts of the virus, then the virus is considerably more complex than it appears to be. Alternatively, however, some gene products

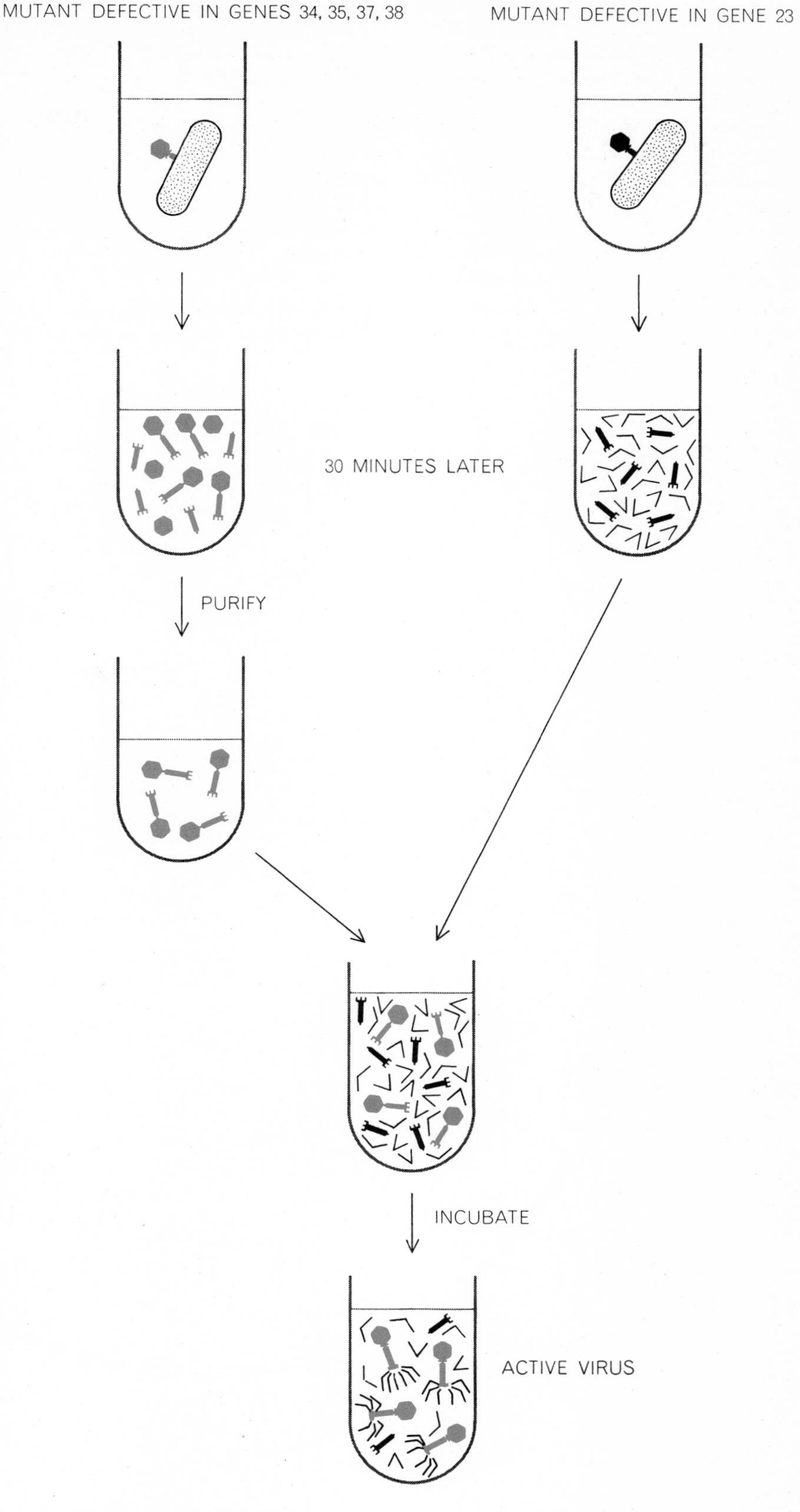

MUTANT DEFECTIVE IN GENES 34, 35, 37, 38   MUTANT DEFECTIVE IN GENE 23

30 MINUTES LATER

PURIFY

INCUBATE

ACTIVE VIRUS

TAIL FIBERS are attached to fiberless particles in the experiment diagrammed here. Cells are infected with a virus (color) bearing defective tail-fiber genes. The progeny particles, lacking fibers, are isolated with a centrifuge. A virus with a head-gene mutation (black) infects a second bacterial culture, providing an extract containing free tails and fibers. When the two preparations are mixed and incubated at 30 degrees centigrade, the fiberless particles are converted to infectious virus particles by the attachment of the free fibers.

may play directive roles in the assembly process without contributing materially to the virus itself. Studies of seven genes controlling formation of the virus's head support this possibility [see "The Genetic Control of the Shape of a Virus," by Edouard Kellenberger; SCIENTIFIC AMERICAN Offprint 1058].

In order to determine the specific functions of the many gene products in-

volved in morphogenesis, it seemed necessary to seek a way to study individual assembly steps under controlled conditions outside the cell. One of us (Edgar) is a geneticist by training, the other (Wood) a biochemist. The geneticist is inclined to let reproductive processes take their normal course and then, by analyzing the progeny, to deduce the molecular events that must have occurred within the organism. The bio-

chemist is eager to break the organism open and search among the remains for more direct clues to what is going on inside. For our current task a synthesis of these two approaches has proved to be most fruitful. Since it seemed inconceivable that the T4 virus could be built from scratch like the tobacco mosaic virus, starting with nucleic acid and individual protein molecules, we decided to let cells infected with mutants serve as sources of preformed viral components. Then we would break open the cells and, by determining how the free parts could be assembled into complete infectious virus, learn the sequence of steps in assembly, the role of each gene product and perhaps its precise mode of action.

Our first experiment was an attempt to attach tail fibers to the otherwise complete virus particle—a reaction we suspected was the terminal step in morphogenesis. Cells infected with a virus bearing mutations in several tail fiber genes (No. 34, 35, 37 and 38) were broken open, and the resulting particles —complete except for fibers and noninfectious—were isolated by being spun in a high-speed centrifuge. Other cells, infected with a gene No. 23 mutant that was defective in head formation, were similarly disrupted to make an extract containing free fibers and tails but no heads. When a sample of the particles was incubated with the extract, the level of infectious virus in the mixture increased rapidly to 1,000 times its initial value. Electron micrographs of samples taken from the mixture at various times showed that the particles were indeed acquiring tail fibers as the reaction proceeded.

In that first experiment the production of infectious virus required only one kind of assembly reaction—the attachment of completed fibers to completed particles. We went on to test more demanding mixtures of defective cell extracts. For example, with a mutant blocked in head formation and another one blocked in tail formation we prepared two extracts, one containing tails and free tail fibers but no heads and another containing heads and free tail fibers but no tails. When a mixture of these two extracts also gave rise to a large number of infectious viruses, we concluded that at least two reactions must have occurred: the attachment of heads to tails and the attachment of fibers to the resulting particles.

MUTANT DEFECTIVE IN GENE 27   MUTANT DEFECTIVE IN GENE 23

30 MINUTES LATER

INCUBATE

ACTIVE VIRUS

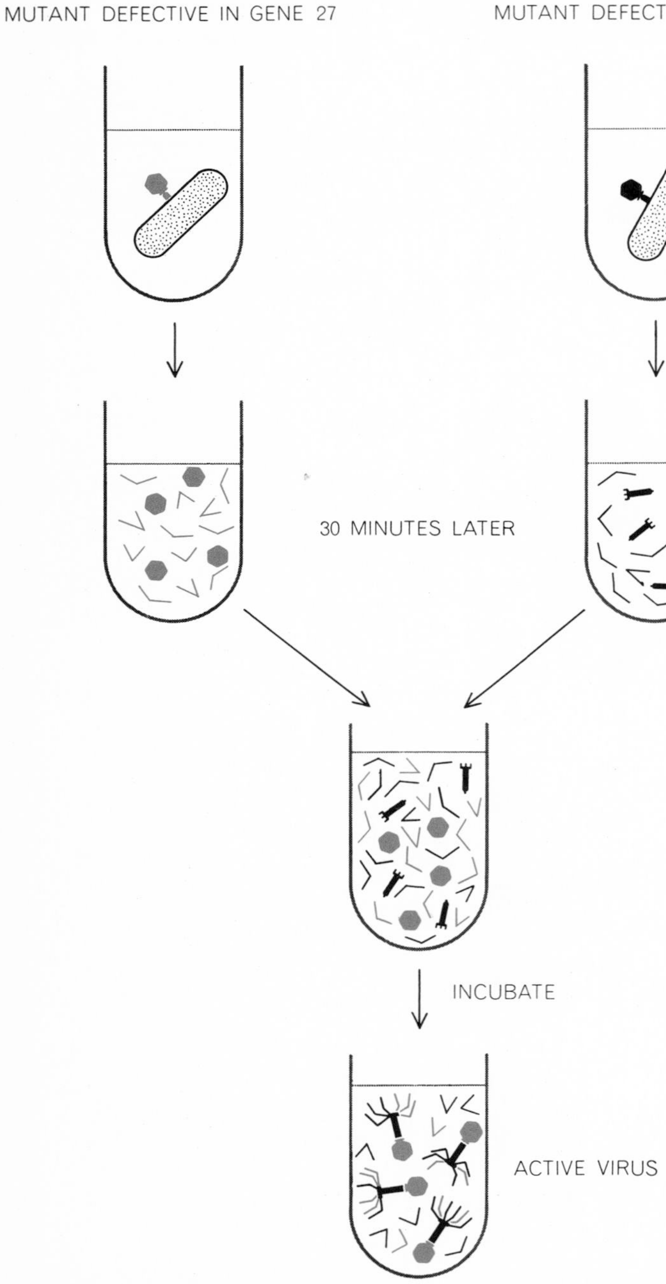

TWO ASSEMBLY REACTIONS occur in this experiment: union of heads and tails and attachment of fibers. One virus (*color*), with a defective tail gene, produces heads and fibers. Another (*black*), with a mutation in a head gene, produces tails and fibers. When the two extracts are mixed and incubated, the parts assemble to produce infectious virus.

By infecting bacilli with mutants bearing defects in different genes concerned with assembly, we prepared 40 different extracts containing viral components but no infectious virus. When we tested the extracts by mixing pairs of them in many of the appropriate combinations, some mixtures produced active virus and others showed no detectable activity. The production of infective virus implied that the two extracts were complementing each other in the test tube, that each was supplying a component that was missing or defective in the other and that could be assembled into complete, active virus under our experimental conditions. Lack of activity, on the other hand, suggested that both extracts were deficient in the same viral component—a component being defined as a subassembly unit that functions in our experimental system. By analyzing the pattern of positive and negative results we could find out how many functional components we were dealing with.

It developed that there are at least 13 such components. That is, analysis of our pair combinations produced 13 complementation groups, the members of which did not complement one another but did complement any member of any other group. Two of these groups were quite large [see illustration below]. Since one gene produces one protein and since each extract has a different defective gene product, a mixture of any two extracts should include all the proteins required for building the virus. The fact that members of these large groups do not complement one another must mean that our experimental system is not as efficient as an infected cell; whatever the gene products that are missing in each of these extracts do, they cannot do it in the test tube.

The idea that a complementation group consisted of extracts deficient in

EXTRACT GROUP	MUTANT GENES	COMPONENTS PRESENT	INFERRED DEFECT
I	5, 6, 7, 8, 10, 25, 26, 27, 28, 29, 48, 51, 53		TAIL
II	20, 21, 22, 23, 24, 31	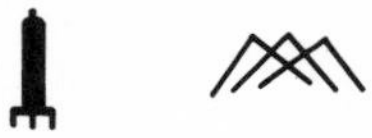	HEAD (FORMATION)
II	2, 4, 16, 17, 49, 50, 64, 65		HEAD (COMPLETION)
III	54		TAIL CORE
IV	13, 14		?
V	15		?
VI	18		?
VII	9		?
VIII	11	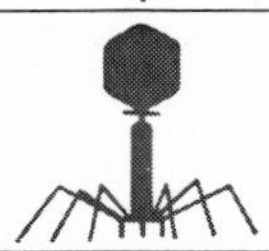	?
IX	12		?
X	37, 38		TAIL FIBERS
XI	36		TAIL FIBERS
XII	35		TAIL FIBERS
XIII	34		TAIL FIBERS

COMPLEMENTATION TESTS defined 13 groups of defective extracts, as described in the text. Mixing any two extracts in a single group fails to produce infectious virus in the test tube, but mixing any two members of different groups yields infectious virus. Apparently each group represents the genes concerned with the synthesis of a component that is functional under experimental conditions. The precise nature of the defect in some extracts, and hence the function of the missing gene product, could not be identified on the basis of the structures recognized in electron micrographs and remained to be determined by additional experiments.

the same functional component could be checked against the earlier electron micrograph results. Micrographs of the 12 defective extracts of Group I, for example, all show virus heads and tail fibers but no tails. Each of these extracts must therefore be deficient in a gene product that has to do with a stage of tail formation that cannot be carried out in our extracts. The second large complementation group appeared at first to be anomalous in terms of electron micrography: some extracts contained only tails and tail fibers, whereas others contained heads as well. Tests against extracts known to contain active tails revealed, however, that these heads—although they looked whole—could not combine to produce active virus in the test tube. In other words, heads, like tails, must be nearly completed within an infected cell before they become active for comple-

mentation. The early stages of head formation are still inaccessible to study in mixed extracts.

The remaining defective extracts gave rise to active virus in almost all possible pair combinations, segregating into another 11 complementation groups. With a total of 13 groups, there must be at least 12 assembly steps that can occur in mixtures of extracts. The defects recognizable in micrographs suggest what some of these steps must be: the completion and union of heads and tails, the assembly of tail fibers and the attachment of fibers to head-tail particles. These, then, are the steps that can be studied further in our present experimental system. We have in effect a virus-building kit, some of whose more intricate parts have been preassembled at the cellular factory.

Our next experiments were designed

to determine the normal sequence of assembly reactions and further characterize those whose nature remained ambiguous. Examples of the latter were the steps controlled by genes No. 13, 14, 15 and 18. Defects in the corresponding gene products resulted in the accumulation of free heads and tails, suggesting that they are somehow involved in head-tail union. It was unclear, however, whether these gene products are required for the attachment process itself or for completion of the head or the tail before attachment. We could distinguish the alternatives by complementation tests using complete heads and tails. These we isolated from the appropriate extracts in the centrifuge, taking advantage of their large size in relation to the other materials present. On the basis of the evidence for the independent assembly of heads and tails, we assumed that

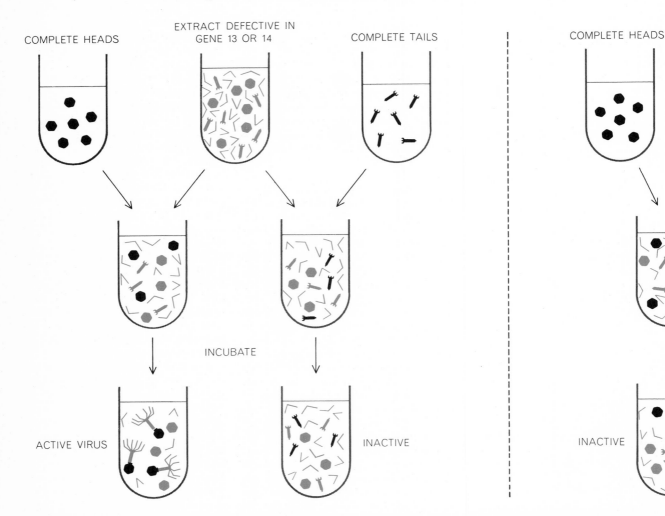

ASSEMBLY DEFECTS of mutants (*color*) that seem to produce complete heads, tails and fibers are identified, using isolated complete heads and tails (*black*) as test reagents. When complete heads are added to some extracts to be tested (*left*), infectious virus is produced, but the addition of complete tails is ineffective. This indicates that the tails made by these mutants must be functional,

the heads we isolated from a tail-defective extract would be complete, as would tails isolated from a head-defective extract.

The results of the tests were unambiguous. The addition of isolated heads to extracts lacking the products of gene No. 13 or 14 resulted in virus production, whereas the addition of tails did not. We could therefore conclude that the components missing from these extracts normally affect the head structure, and that genes No. 13 and 14 control head completion rather than tail completion or head-tail union. The remaining two of the four extracts gave the opposite result; these were active with added tails but not with added heads, indicating that genes No. 15 and 18 are involved in the completion of the tail. All four of these steps must precede the attachment of heads to tails, since defects in any of

XTRACT DEFECTIVE IN
GENE 15 OR 18   COMPLETE TAILS

INCUBATE

ACTIVE VIRUS

implying that the heads must be defective. In the case of other mutants (*right*), such tests indicate that the tails must be defective.

the corresponding genes block head-tail union.

By manipulating extracts blocked at other stages we worked out the remaining steps in the assembly process with the help of Jonathan King and Jeffrey Flatgaard. The various reactions were characterized and their sequence determined by many experiments similar to those described above. In addition, more detailed electron micrographs of defective components helped to clarify the nature of some individual steps. For example, knowing that genes No. 15 and 18 were concerned with tail completion, we went on to find just what each one did. Electron micrographs showed that in the absence of the No. 18 product no contractile sheaths were made. If No. 18 was functional but No. 15 was defective, the sheath units were assembled on the core but were unstable and could fall away. The addition of the product of gene No. 15 (and of No. 3 also, as it turned out) supplied a kind of "button" at the upper end of the core and thus apparently stabilized the sheath.

The results to date of this line of investigation can be summarized in the form of a morphogenetic pathway [*see illustration on page 162*]. As we had thought, it consists of three principal independent branches that lead respectively to the formation of the head, the tail and the tail fibers.

The earliest stages of head morphogenesis are controlled by six genes. These genes direct the formation of a precursor that is identifiable as a head in electron micrographs but is not yet functional in extract-complementation experiments. Eight more gene products must act on this precursor to produce a head structure that is active in complementation experiments. This active structure undergoes the terminal step in head formation (the only one so far demonstrated in the test tube): conversion to the complete head that is able to unite with the tail. The nature of this conversion, which is controlled by genes No. 13 and 14, remains unclear. A likely possibility would be that these genes control the formation of the upper neck and collar, but evidence on this point is lacking. The attachment of head structures to tails has never been observed in extracts prepared with mutants defective in gene No. 13 or 14, or with any of the preceding class of eight genes. It therefore appears that completion of the head is a

prerequisite for the union of heads and tails.

The earliest structure so far identified in the morphogenesis of the tail is the end plate. It is apparently an intricate bit of machinery, since 15 different gene products participate in its formation. All the subsequent steps in tail formation can be demonstrated in the test tube. The core is assembled on the end plate under the control of the products of gene No. 54 and probably No. 19; the resulting structure appears as a tail without a sheath. The product of gene No. 18 is the principal structural component of the sheath, which is somehow stabilized by the products of genes No. 3 and 15. Tails without sheaths do not attach themselves to head structures, indicating that the tail as well as the head must be completed before head-tail union can occur. Moreover, unattached tail structures are never fitted with fibers, suggesting that these can be added only at a later stage of assembly.

Completed heads and tails unite spontaneously, in the absence of any additional factors, to produce a precursor particle that interacts in a still undetermined manner with the product of gene No. 9, resulting in the complete head-plus-tail particle. It is only at this point that tail fibers can become attached to the end plate.

At least five gene products participate in the formation of the tail fiber. In the first step, which has not yet been demonstrated in extracts, the products of genes No. 37 and 38 combine to form a precursor corresponding in dimensions to one segment of the finished fiber. This precursor then interacts sequentially with the products of genes No. 36, 35 and 34 to produce the complete structure. Again the completion of a major component—in this case the tail fiber—appears to be a prerequisite for its attachment, since we have never seen the short segments linked to particles.

The final step in building the virus is the attachment of completed tail fibers to the otherwise finished particle. We have studied this process in reaction mixtures consisting of purified particles and a defective extract containing complete tail fibers but no heads or tails. When we divided the extract into various fractions, we found that it supplies two components, both of which are necessary for the production of active virus. One of these of course is the tail fiber. The other is a factor whose properties suggest that

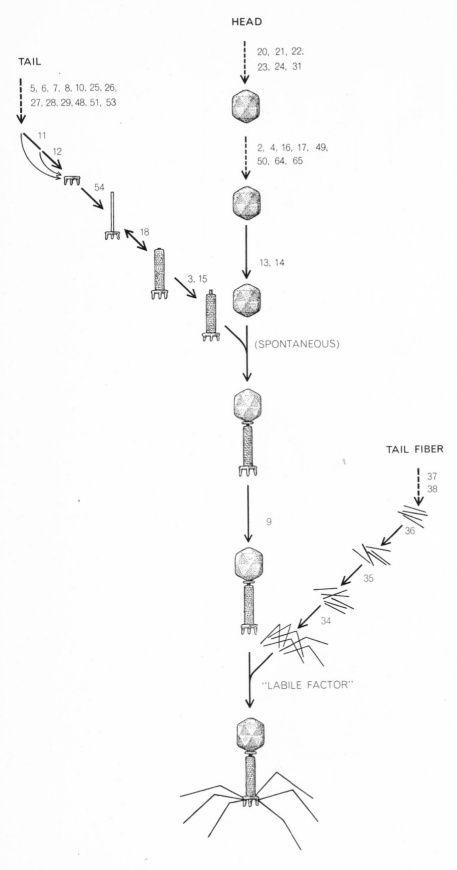

TAIL

5, 6, 7, 8, 10, 25, 26,
27, 28, 29, 48, 51, 53

11

12

54

18

3, 15

HEAD

20, 21, 22,
23, 24, 31

2, 4, 16, 17, 49,
50, 64, 65

13, 14

(SPONTANEOUS)

TAIL FIBER

37
38

36

35

9

34

"LABILE FACTOR"

MORPHOGENETIC PATHWAY has three principal branches leading independently to the formation of heads, tails and tail fibers, which then combine to form complete virus particles. The numbers refer to the gene product or products involved at each step. The solid portions of the arrows indicate the steps that have been shown to occur in extracts.

it might be an enzyme. For one thing, the rate at which fibers are attached depends on the level of this factor present in the reaction mixture, and yet the factor does not appear to be used up in the process. Moreover, the rate of attachment depends on the temperature of incubation—increasing by a factor of about two with every rise in temperature of 10 degrees centigrade. These characteristics suggest that the factor could be catalyzing the formation of bonds between the fibers and the tail end plate. At the moment we can only speculate on its possible mechanism of action, since the chemical nature of these bonds is not yet known; we call it simply a "labile factor," not an enzyme. Although no gene controlling the factor has yet been discovered, we assume that its synthesis must be directed by the virus, since it is not found in extracts of uninfected bacteria.

The T4 assembly steps so far accomplished and studied in the test tube represent only a fraction of the total number. Already, however, it is apparent that there is a high degree of sequential order in the assembly process; restrictions are somehow imposed at each step that prevent its occurrence until the preceding step has been completed. Only two exceptions to this rule have been discovered. The steps controlled by genes No. 11 and 12, which normally occur early in the tail pathway, can be bypassed when these gene products are lacking. In that case the tail is completed, attaches itself to a head and acquires tail fibers, but the result is a fragile, defective particle. The particle can, however, be converted to a normal active virus by exposure to an extract containing the missing gene products. These are the only components whose point of action in the pathway appears to be unimportant.

The problem has now reached a tantalizing stage. A partial sequence of gene-controlled assembly steps can be written, but the manner in which the corresponding gene products contribute to the process remains unclear, and the questions posed at the beginning of this article cannot yet be answered definitively. There is the suggestion that the attachment of tail fibers is catalyzed by a virus-induced enzyme. If this finding is substantiated, it would overthrow the notion that T4 morphogenesis is entirely a self-assembly process. Continued investigation of this reaction and the assembly steps that precede it can be expected to provide further insight into how genes control the building of biological structures.

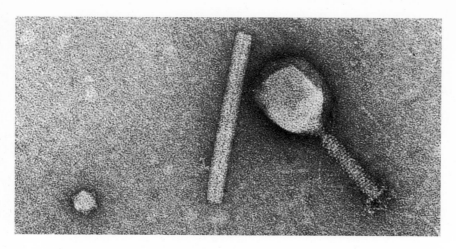

TWO SIMPLER VIRUSES are shown with the T4 in an electron micrograph made by Fred Eiserling of the University of California at Los Angeles. The icosahedral ΦX174 virus (*left*) infects the colon bacillus, as does the T4. The rod-shaped tobacco mosaic virus reassembles itself in the test tube after dissociation. The enlargement is 200,000 diameters.

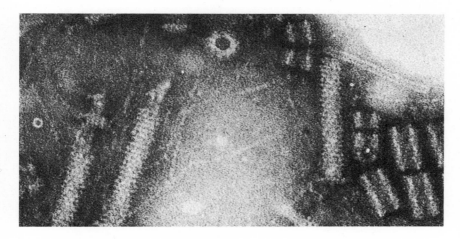

COMPLEX STRUCTURE of the T4 tail is shown in an electron micrograph made by E. Boy de la Tour of the University of Geneva. The parts were obtained by breaking down virus particles, not by synthesis, which is why fibers are attached to tails. The hollow interiors of the free core (*top right*) and pieces of sheath are delineated by dark stain that has flowed into them. There are end-on views of pieces of core (*left*) and sheath (*top center*).

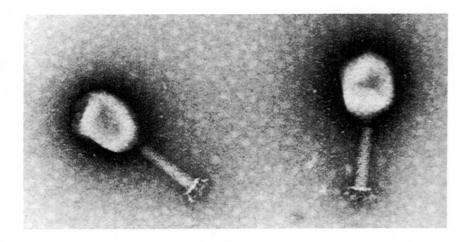

FIBERLESS PARTICLES, otherwise complete, are the products of infection by a mutant defective in one of the fiber-forming genes. Heads, tails and fibers are each formed by a subassembly line (*see illustration on page 162*). The electron micrograph was made by King.

III

GENE ACTION IN PROTEIN SYNTHESIS

The Expression
of Genetic Information

GENE ACTION
IN PROTEIN
SYNTHESIS
*The Expression
of Genetic Information*

INTRODUCTION

One of the most exciting phases of the development of molecular biology was the step-by-step elucidation of the detailed mechanism by which the genetic information in DNA is translated into functioning proteins. In the articles of this section, the story of the confirmation of the "central dogma" of molecular biology is unfolded. At the time of the rediscovery of Mendel's work, the gene was a hypothetical construct and its only significant property was its particulate nature. During the years since 1945 both the chemical identity and the mode of action of the gene have been worked out in detail. The first article in this section, "The Genes of Men and Molds," was written by George W. Beadle five years before the Watson-Crick structure of DNA was presented. Beadle writes, "...it now seems clear that genes are the basic units of all living things. They are the master molecules that guide the development and direct the vital activities of men and amoebas." George Beadle and Edward Tatum were among the first to realize the advantage of a biochemical approach to genetics and to choose one of the most appropriate organisms, the fungus *Neurospora crassa*, for this study. Following this account of the beginnings of biochemical genetics, Beadle suggests that the genes are probably nucleoproteins that act as templates for the synthesis of the *"non-genic"* proteins. It is now known that certain inborn errors of metabolism in man, such as phenylketonuria, as well as the more easily studied biosynthetic deficiencies in *Neurospora* and other microorganisms, are due to slight chemical alterations in DNA called mutations.

The function of nucleic acids as templates is now well understood and, in fact, the complementarity of the nucleotide sequences of two nucleic acid strands can be tested by the formation of a double-stranded "hybrid" molecule. In "Hybrid Nucleic Acids," Sol Spiegelman describes the methods by which these hybrid duplex molecules were first prepared. It was subsequently shown by Spiegelman and others that the RNA that was synthesized in a bacterial cell after infection by a bacteriophage was complementary to the phage DNA rather than to the bacterial DNA. This gave credence to the idea that a messenger RNA molecule is transcribed from the master DNA template. This messenger RNA is then taken up by ribosomes, where the message is translated into the amino acid sequences of newly synthesized protein. The hybridization technique has also been used to demonstrate the origin of the unique RNA molecules that are built into the ribosome structure itself as well as the origin of the various transfer RNA molecules that are required for the translation of the code. Since both of these classes of RNA were found to hybridize with specific regions of the DNA genome, it was realized that they too were formed by transcription from the master template. Refinements in the hybridization technique have recently led to its use in determining the degree of genetic homology that exists between the DNA from different organisms. Such studies provide a powerful method for mapping evolutionary relationships among the many species of plants and animals. Returning to the problem of the transcription of messenger RNA from the DNA template, it is natural to wonder whether one or both of the DNA strands are transcribed. It is clear that only one strand (the "sense" strand) of the DNA is read, but it is not yet understood why the other ("antisense") strand is not read.

As soon as a sufficient length of messenger RNA has been synthesized it may be engaged by a ribosome, thereby initiating the process of translation of the genetic message into protein; alternatively, a complete messenger RNA molecule might have to be synthesized before attachment to ribosomes occurs. In

"Polyribosomes" Alexander Rich describes the experiments that demonstrated that not one but many ribosomes may read the same messenger RNA at the same time. In the preceding article Spiegelman has discussed the technique of cesium chloride density-gradient equilibrium sedimentation, by which macromolecules can be separated on the basis of their different bouyant densities in a given solvent. Rich describes another important use of density gradients. Zone sedimentation may be carried out in the ultracentrifuge in preformed sucrose gradients, in order that particle sizes may be measured by their *rates* of sedimentation. The gradient in this technique serves only to stabilize the system against convective disturbances so that the sedimented zones may be collected at the end of the run. This method has now been refined to the point at which polyribosomes containing four ribosomes can be resolved clearly from those containing only three.

The fine-structure mapping experiments of Benzer, described in Part II, illustrated the utility of mutation and genetic recombination for the resolution of the genetic message to the limit of a single nucleotide. A single nucleotide change is adequate to cause a mutation. In "The Genetic Code," Francis H. C. Crick discusses the nature of mutagenesis in more detail. The discovery of a new class of mutations that have been described as "reading-frame shifts" resulted in the identification of a nonoverlapping, nonpunctuated genetic code composed of triplets of nucleotides. Thus, a triplet composed of three nucleotides is the unit piece of information needed to specify a single amino acid in any given protein. In the course of this study, certain triplets were found to be inactive by virtue of the fact that they did not code for any amino acid. The code was also found to be "degenerate" in that each amino acid is coded for by more than one triplet of nucleotides.

The final identification of the specific triplets that correspond to specific amino acids was obtained in two types of experiments. The first approach, as described in "The Genetic Code: II" by Marshall Nirenberg, involved the "feeding" of ribosomes with synthetic polynucleotides of known composition and then the examination of the nature of the polypeptide that was produced *in vitro*. The current version of the genetic code is provided by Crick in "The Genetic Code: III." The second approach to the breaking of the genetic code is illustrated in the elegant experiments of Charles Yanofsky and his associates. In "Gene Structure and Protein Structure" Yanofsky outlines his studies on the tryptophan synthetase enzyme of *E. coli* and his demonstration of the linear correspondance between the sequence of amino acids in the protein and the sequence of codons in the DNA that specifies the protein. This completes the proof of the central dogma of molecular biology.

At present, attention is being focused more and more on the details of the process by which the actual assembly of the protein occurs at the ribosome. The ribosome is still largely a "black box," although at least 30 different protein molecules and three different RNA molecules are known to make up its structure. The ribosome can be separated into a number of subunits and these subunits can be reassembled into functional units *in vitro*. It may be predicted that the detailed operation of the ribosome will be understood within the next few years. The last article in this section, "How Proteins Start" by Brian F. C. Clark and Kjeld A. Marcker, describes the important first step in the elucidation of the detailed biochemistry of protein biosynthesis.

17 | *The Genes of Men and Molds*

GEORGE W. BEADLE · *September 1948*

EIGHTY-FIVE years ago, in the garden of a monastery near the village of Brünn in what is now Czechoslovakia, Gregor Johann Mendel was spending his spare moments studying hybrids between varieties of the edible garden pea. Out of his penetrating analysis of the results of his studies there grew the modern theory of the gene. But like many a pioneer in science, Mendel was a generation ahead of his time; the full significance of his findings was not appreciated until 1900.

In the period following the "rediscovery" of Mendel's work biologists have developed and extended the gene theory to the point where it now seems clear that genes are the basic units of all living things. They are the master molecules that guide the development and direct the vital activities of men and amoebas.

Today the specific functions of genes in plants and animals are being isolated and studied in detail. One of the most useful genetic guinea pigs is the red bread mold *Neurospora crassa*. Its genes can conveniently be changed artificially and the part that they play in the chemical alteration and metabolism of cells can be analyzed with considerable precision. We are learning what sort of material the genes are made of, how they affect living organisms and how the genes themselves, and thereby heredity, are affected by forces in their environment. Indeed, in their study of genes biologists are coming closer to an understanding of the ultimate basis of life itself.

It seems likely that life first appeared on earth in the form of units much like the genes of present-day organisms. Through the processes of mutation in such primitive genes, and through Darwinian natural selection, higher forms of life evolved—first as simple systems with a few

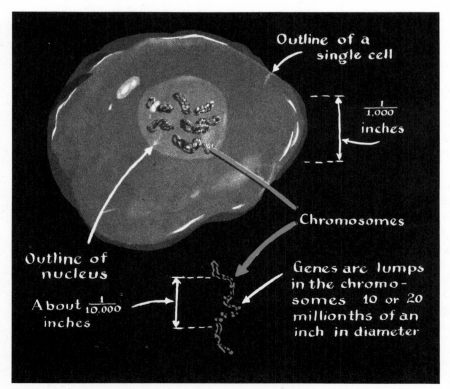

THE CELL is the site of nearly all the interactions between the gene and its environment. The genes themselves are located in the chromosomes, shown above in the stage before cell divides, duplicating each gene in the process.

THE MOLD *Neurospora* is an admirable organism for the study of genes, mainly because of its unusually simple reproductive apparatus. This may be neatly dissected to isolate a single complete set of genes. The sequence of steps in the drawing at the right shows how the tiny fruiting body of the mold is taken apart in the laboratory. With the aid of a microscope, the laboratory worker is able to spread out a set of spore sacs, each containing eight spores. One spore sac may then be separated from the others, and its spores carefully removed. The individual spores are lined up on a block of agar and finally planted in a test tube which contains all the substances that are normally required for the mold to grow.

genes, then as single-celled forms with many genes, and finally as multicellular plants and animals.

What do we know about these genes that are so all-important in the process of evolution, in the development of complex organisms, and in the direction of those vital processes which distinguish the living from the non-living worlds?

In the first place, genes are characterized by students of heredity as the units of inheritance. What is meant by this may be illustrated by examples of some inherited traits in man.

Blue-eyed people may differ by a single gene from those with brown eyes. This eye-color gene exists in two forms, which for convenience may be designated *B* and *b*.

Every person begins as a single cell a few thousandths of an inch in diameter— a cell that comes into being through the fusion of an egg cell from the mother and a sperm cell from the father. This fertilized egg carries two representatives of the eye-color gene, one from each parent. Depending on the parents, there are therefore three types of individuals possible so far as this particular gene is concerned. They start from fertilized eggs represented by the genetic formulas *BB*, *Bb* and *bb*. The first two types, *BB* and *Bb*, will develop into individuals with brown eyes. The third one, *bb*, will have blue eyes. You will note that when both forms of the gene are present the individual is brown-eyed. This is because the form of the gene for brown eyes is *dominant* over its alternative form for blue eyes. Conversely, the form for blue eyes is said to be *recessive*.

During the division of the fertilized egg cell into many daughter cells, which through growth, division and specialization give rise to a fully developed person, the genes multiply regularly with each cell division. As a result each of the millions of cells of a fully developed individual carries exact copies of the two representatives of the eye-color gene

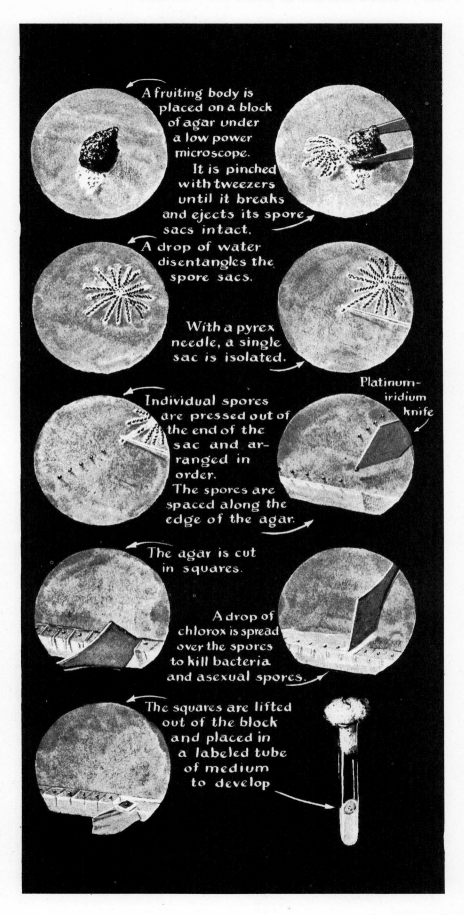

A fruiting body is placed on a block of agar under a low power microscope. It is pinched with tweezers until it breaks and ejects its spore sacs intact.

A drop of water disentangles the spore sacs.

With a pyrex needle, a single sac is isolated.

Platinum-iridium knife

Individual spores are pressed out of the end of the sac and arranged in order. The spores are spaced along the edge of the agar.

The agar is cut in squares.

A drop of chlorox is spread over the spores to kill bacteria and asexual spores.

The squares are lifted out of the block and placed in a labeled tube of medium to develop

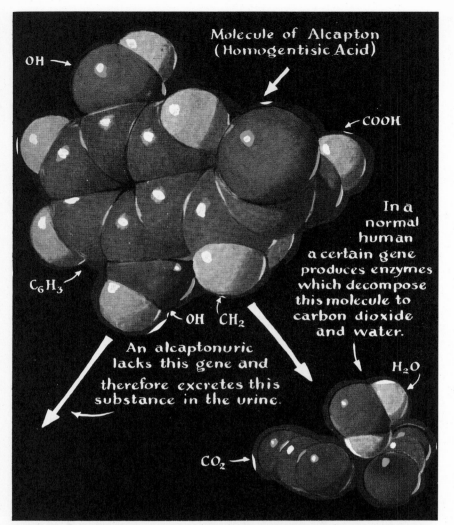

Molecule of Alcapton
(Homogentisic Acid)

OH →

↙ COOH

In a
normal
human
a certain gene
produces enzymes
which decompose
this molecule to
carbon dioxide
and water.

C_6H_3 →

← OH CH_2

An alcaptonuric
lacks this gene and
therefore excretes this
substance in the urine.

H_2O

CO_2 →

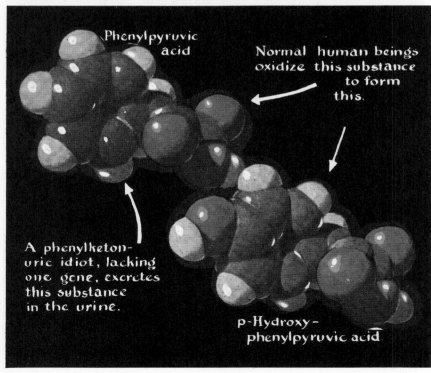

Phenylpyruvic
acid

Normal human beings
oxidize this substance
to form
this.

A phenylketon-
uric idiot, lacking
one gene, excretes
this substance
in the urine.

p-Hydroxy-
phenylpyruvic acid

DEFECTIVE GENES in man can cause serious hereditary disorders. The chemical basis of two such disorders is shown in the drawings on this page. The large molecule in the drawing at the left is homogentisic acid, or alcapton. In most human beings a single gene produces an enzyme which is capable of breaking alcapton down to carbon dioxide and water. When the gene that produces the enzyme is faulty, however, alcapton is not decomposed. It must be eliminated in the urine, to which it gives a dark color. This excretion of alcapton in the urine is called alcaptonuria. The drawing at the bottom of this page shows the basis of a much more serious genetic disorder. The biochemical apparatus of most human beings, again, is able to transform phenylpyruvic acid into p-hydroxy phenylpyruvic acid. Those who cannot transform it are called phenylketonurics. Phenylketonuria is characterized by extreme feeble-mindedness. Most phenylketonurics are imbeciles or idiots; a few are low-grade morons. The faulty genes that are responsible for both are recessive. This means that they are expressed only when two such genes are paired in the union of an egg and sperm cell. Thus most of the genes responsible for these disorders are carried by normal people without being expressed.

which has been contributed by the parents.

In the formation of egg and sperm cells, the genes are again reduced from two to one per cell. Therefore a mother of the type *BB* forms egg cells carrying only the *B* form of the gene. A type *bb* mother produces only *b* egg cells. A *Bb* mother, on the other hand, produces both *B* and *b* egg cells, in equal numbers on the average. Exactly corresponding relations hold for the formation of sperm cells.

With these facts in mind it is a simple matter to determine the types of children expected to result from various unions. Some of these are indicated in the following list:

Mother	Father	Children
BB (brown)	*BB* (brown)	All *BB* (brown)
Bb (brown)	*Bb* (brown)	¼ *BB* (brown)
		½ *Bb* (brown)
		¼ *bb* (blue)
BB (brown)	*bb* (blue)	All *Bb* (brown)
Bb (brown)	*bb* (blue)	½ *Bb* (brown)
		½ *bb* (blue)
bb (blue)	*bb* (blue)	All *bb* (blue)

This table shows that while it is expected that some families in which both parents have brown eyes will include blue-eyed children, parents who are both blue-eyed are not expected to have brown-eyed children.

LIFE CYCLE of the mold *Neurospora* is illustrated in the drawing at the right. The hyphal fusion of Sex A and Sex a at the bottom of the page is taken as a starting point. *Neurospora* enters a sexual stage rather similar to the union of sperm and egg cells in higher organisms. The union produces a fertile egg, in which two complete sets of genes are paired. The fertile egg cell then divides (*center of drawing*), and divides again. This produces four nuclei, each of which has only a single set of genes. Lined up in a spore sac, the four nuclei divide once more to produce four pairs of nuclei that are genetically identical. A group of spore sacs is gathered in a fruiting body. The sacs and the spores may then be dissected by the technique outlined on page 169. Following this, the germinating spores (*top of page*) may be planted in test tubes containing the necessary nutrients. It is at this point that genetic defects can be exposed by changing the constitution of the medium. Here also *Neurospora* may be allowed to multiply by asexual means. This makes it possible to grow large quantities of the mold without genetic change for convenient chemical analysis. The entire life cycle of the mold takes only 10 days, another reason why *Neurospora* is an exceptionally useful experimental organism.

It is important to emphasize conditions that may account for apparent exceptions to the last rule. The first is that eye-color inheritance in man is not completely worked out genetically. Probably other genes besides the one used as an example here are concerned with eye color. It may therefore be possible, when these other genes are taken into account, for parents with true blue eyes to have brown-eyed children. A second factor which accounts for some apparent exceptions is that brown-eyed persons of the *Bb* type may have eyes so light brown that an inexperienced observer may classify them as blue. Two parents of this type may, of course, have a *BB* child with dark brown eyes.

Another example of an inherited trait in man is curly hair. Ordinary curly hair, such as is found frequently in people of European descent, is dominant to straight hair. Therefore parents with curly hair may have straight-haired children but straight-haired parents do not often have children with curly hair. Again there are other genes concerned, and the simple rules based on a one-gene interpretation do not always hold.

Defective Genes

Eye-color and hair-form genes have relatively trivial effects in human beings. Other known genes are concerned with

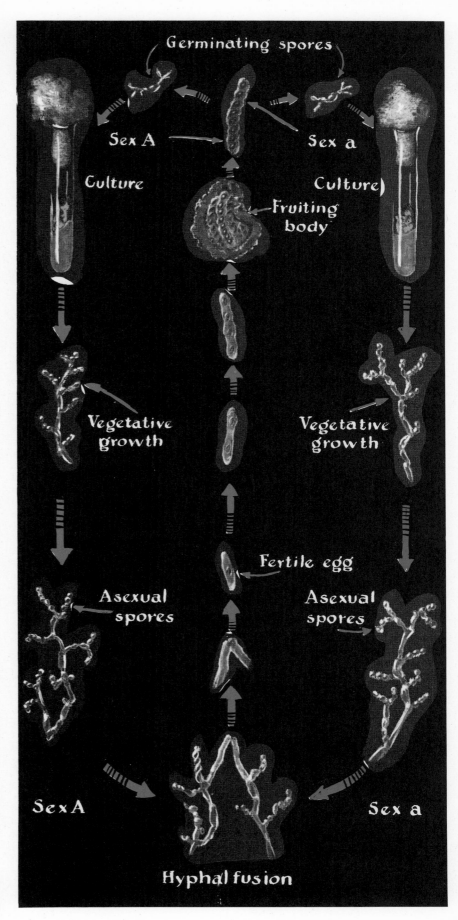

Germinating spores

Sex A   Sex a

Culture   Culture

Fruiting body

Vegetative growth   Vegetative growth

Fertile egg

Asexual spores   Asexual spores

Sex A   Sex a

Hyphal fusion

traits of deeper significance. One of these involves a rare hereditary disease in which the principal symptom is urine that turns black on exposure to air. This "inborn error of metabolism," as the English physician and biochemist Sir Archibald Garrod referred to it, has been known to medical men for probably 300 years. Its biochemical basis was established in 1859 by the German biochemist C. Bödeker, who showed that darkening of urine is due to a specific chemical substance called alcapton, later identified chemically as 2,5-dihydroxyphenylacetic acid. The disease is known as alcaptonuria, meaning "alcapton in the urine."

Alcaptonuria is known to result from a gene defect. It shows typical Mendelian inheritance, like blue eyes, but the defective form of the gene is much less frequent in the population than is the recessive form of the eye-color gene.

The excretion of alcapton is a result of the body's inability to break it down by oxidation. Normal individuals possess an enzyme (a protein-containing catalyst, often called a biocatalyst) which makes possible a reaction by which alcapton is further oxidized. This enzyme is absent in alcaptonurics. As a result alcaptonurics cannot degrade alcapton to carbon dioxide and water as normal individuals do.

Alcaptonuria is of special interest genetically and biochemically because it gives us a clue as to what genes do and how they do it. It is clear that the normal kind of gene is essential for the production of the enzyme necessary for the breakdown of alcapton. If the cells of an individual contain only the recessive or inactive form of the gene, no enzyme is formed, alcapton accumulates and is excreted in the urine. The relations between gene and chemical reaction are shown in the diagram at the top of page 170.

A hereditary error of metabolism related biochemically to alcaptonuria is phenylketonuria, a rare disease in which phenylpyruvic acid is excreted in the urine. Like alcaptonuria, this metabolic defect is inherited as a simple Mendelian recessive. It is more serious in its consequences, however, because it is invariably associated with feeble-mindedness of an extreme kind. Most phenylketonurics are imbeciles or idiots; a few are low-grade morons. It should be made clear, however, that only a small fraction of feeble-minded persons are of this particular genetic type.

Phenylketonurics excrete phenylpyruvic acid because they cannot oxidize it, as normal individuals can, to a closely related derivative differing from phenylpyruvic acid by having one more oxygen atom per molecule (see diagram at the bottom of page 170). Again it is evident that the normal form of a gene is essential for the carrying out of a specific chemical reaction.

Man, however, is far from an ideal organism in which to study genes. His life cycle is too long, his offspring are too few, his choice of a mate is not often based on a desire to contribute to the knowledge of heredity, and it is inconvenient to subject him to a complete chemical analysis. As a result, most of what we have learned about genes has come from studies of such organisms as garden peas, Indian corn plants and the fruit fly *Drosophila*.

In these and other plants and animals there are many instances in which genes seem to be responsible for specific chemical reactions. It is believed that in most or all of these cases they act as pattern molecules from which enzymes are copied.

Many enzymes have been isolated in a pure crystalline state. All of them have proved to be proteins or to contain proteins as essential parts. Gene-enzyme relations such as those considered above suggest that the primary function of genes may be to serve as models from which specific kinds of enzyme proteins are copied. This hypothesis is strengthened by evidence that some genes control the presence of proteins that are not parts of enzymes.

For example, normal persons have a specific blood protein that is important in blood clotting. Bleeders, known as hemophiliacs, differ from non-bleeders by a single gene. Its normal form is presumed to be essential for the synthesis of the specific blood-clotting protein. Hemophilia, incidentally, is almost completely limited to the male because it is sex-linked; that is, it is carried in the so-called X chromosome, which is concerned with the determination of sex. As is well known, this hereditary disorder has been carried for generations by some of the royal families of Europe.

The genes that determine blood types in man and other animals direct the production of so-called antigens. These are giant molecules which apparently derive their specificity from gene models, and which are capable of inducing the formation of specific antibodies.

Neurospora

The hypothesis that genes are concerned with the elaboration of giant protein molecules has been tested by experiments with the red mold *Neurospora*. This fungus has many advantages in the study of what genes do. It has a short life cycle—only 10 days from one sexual spore generation to the next. It multiplies profusely by asexual spores. The result is that any strain can be multiplied a millionfold in a few days without any genetic change. Each of the cell nuclei that carry the genes of the bread mold has only a single set of genes instead of the two sets found in the cells of man and other higher organisms. This means that recessive genes are not hidden by their dominant counterparts.

During the sexual stage, in which

EXPERIMENT to determine the role of a single *Neurospora* gene essentially consists in disabling a gene and tracking down its missing biochemical function. Spores of the mold are first exposed to radiation that will cause mutation, *i.e.*, change in a gene. This culture is then crossed with another. The spores resulting from this union are then planted in a medium that contains all the substances that normal *Neurospora* needs for growth, plus a few that the mold normally manufactures for itself. All the spores, including those which may carry a defective gene, germinate on this medium. Spores from these same cultures are then planted in a medium that contains only the bare minimum of substances required by *Neurospora*. Four of the cultures fail to grow, indicating that they have lost the power to manufacture one substance that *Neurospora* normally synthesizes. In test tubes at the bottom of opposite page, the detailed identification of exactly what synthetic power has been lost is begun by planting the defective culture in media that contain (1) all substances required by the normal mold plus vitamins, and (2) all substances plus amino acids. When mold grows on first medium, it appears it has lost the power to synthesize vitamin.

molds of opposite sex reactions come together, there is a fusion comparable to that between egg and sperm in man. The fusion nucleus then immediately undergoes two divisions in which genes are reduced again to one per cell. The four products formed from a single fusion nucleus by these divisions are lined up in a spore sac. Each divides again so as to produce pairs of nuclei that are genetically identical. The eight resulting nuclei are included in eight sexual spores, each one-thousandth of an inch long. This life cycle of *Neurospora* is shown in the illustration on page 171.

Using a microscope, a skilled laboratory worker can dissect the sexual spores from the spore sac in orderly sequence. Each of them can be planted separately in a culture tube (*see illustration on page 169*). If the two parental strains differ by a single gene, four spores always carry descendants of one form of the gene and four carry descendants of the other. Thus if a yellow and a white strain are crossed, there occur in each spore sac four spores that will give white molds and four that will give yellow.

The red bread mold is almost ideally suited for chemical studies. It can be grown in pure culture on a chemically known medium containing only nitrate, sulfate, phosphate, various other inorganic substances, sugar and biotin, a vitamin of the B group. From these relatively

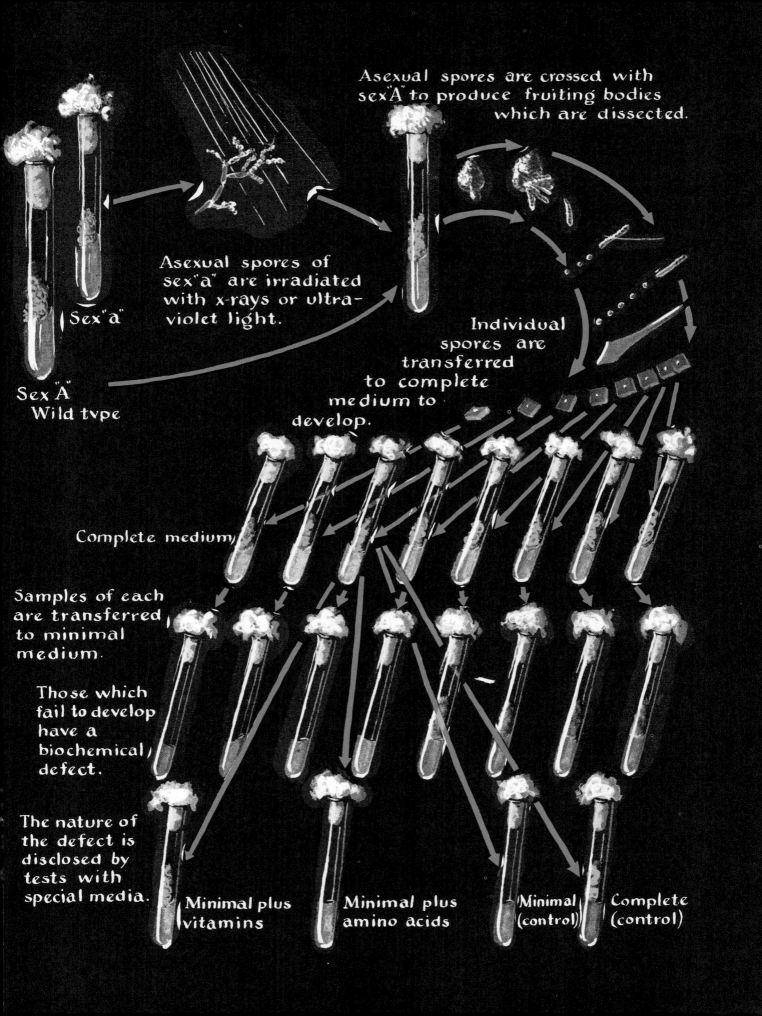

Sex"a"

Sex"A"
Wild type

Asexual spores of
sex"a" are irradiated
with x-rays or ultra-
violet light.

Asexual spores are crossed with
sex"A" to produce fruiting bodies
which are dissected.

Individual
spores are
transferred
to complete
medium to
develop.

Complete medium

Samples of each
are transferred
to minimal
medium.

Those which
fail to develop
have a
biochemical
defect.

The nature of
the defect is
disclosed by
tests with
special media.

Minimal plus
vitamins

Minimal plus
amino acids

Minimal
(control)

Complete
(control)

simple starting materials, the mold produces all the constituent parts of its protoplasm. These include some 20 amino acid building blocks of proteins, nine water-soluble vitamins of the B group, and many other organic molecules of vital biological significance.

To one interested in what genes do in a human being, it might at first thought seem a very large jump from a man to a mold. Actually it is not. For in its basic metabolic processes, protoplasm—Thomas Huxley's physical stuff of life—is very much the same wherever it is found.

If the many chemical reactions by which a bread mold builds its protoplasm out of the raw materials at its disposal are catalyzed by enzymes, and if the proteins of these enzymes are copied from genes, it should be possible to produce

It is known that changes in genes—mutations—occur spontaneously with a low frequency. The probability that a given gene will mutate to a defective form can be increased a hundredfold or more by so-called mutagenic (mutation producing) agents. These include X-radiation, neutrons and other ionizing radiations, ultraviolet radiation, and mustard gas. Radiations are believed to cause mutations by literally "hitting" genes in a way to cause ionization within them or by otherwise causing internal rearrangements of the chemical bonds.

A bread-mold experiment to test the hypothesis that genes control enzymes and metabolism can be set up in the manner shown in the diagrams on pages 173 and 175. Asexual spores are X-rayed or otherwise treated with mutagenic agents.

IN CONTINUATION of the experiment begun on page 173, the strain of *Neurospora* that carries a defective gene is put through another series of steps. On page 173 it had been determined that the strain in question did not grow in the absence of vitamins. This indicated that the defective gene was involved in the synthesis of a vitamin. Now the question is: exactly what vitamin? This may be found by planting the strain carrying the defective gene on a group of minimal media, each of which is supplemented by a single vitamin. The mold will then grow on the medium which contains the vitamin that it has lost the power to synthesize. In the experiment outlined on the opposite page, the missing vitamin turns out to be pantothenic acid, a vitamin of the B group. When this has been established, further experiments must be run to determine whether the deficiency of the strain involves a single gene. This is done by crossing the strain bearing the defective gene with a normal strain. All the spores from the union flourish in a medium supplemented with pantothenic acid. When they are planted in a medium that does not contain pantothenic acid, however, only four cultures grow. This is proof that one gene is involved.

PHOTOMICROGRAPH of *Neurospora* shows the structure of its fine red tendrils. This photograph, supplied through the courtesy of Life Magazine, was made by Herbert Gehr in the genetics laboratory of E. L. Tatum at Yale.

molds with specific metabolic errors by causing genes to mutate. Or to state the problem somewhat differently, one ought to be able to discover what genes do by making them defective.

The simplicity of this approach can be illustrated by an analogy. The manufacture of an automobile in a factory is in some respects like the development of an organism. The workmen in the factory are like genes—each has a specific job to do. If one observed the factory only from the outside and in terms of the cars that come out, it would not be easy to determine what each worker does. But if one could replace able workers with defective ones, and then observe what happened to the product, it would be a simple matter to conclude that Jones puts on the radiator grill, Smith adds the carburetor, and so forth. Deducing what genes do by making them defective is analogous and equally simple in principle.

Following a sexual phase of the life cycle, descendants of mutated genes are recovered in sexual spores. These are grown separately, and the molds that grow from them are tested for ability to produce the molecules out of which they are built.

If a gene essential for the production of vitamin B-1 by the mold is made defective, then B-1 must be supplied in the medium if a mold is to develop from a spore carrying the defective gene. But in the present state of our knowledge it is not possible to produce mutations in specific genes at will. By X-raying, for example, any one or more of several thousand genes may be mutated, or in many cases none at all will be changed. There is no known method of predicting which of the genes, if any, will be hit. It is therefore necessary to grow presumptive mutant spores on a medium supplemented with protoplasmic building blocks of which the formation could be

blocked if defective genes were present.

Molds grown on such supplemented medium may grow normally either (1) by making a particular essential part themselves or (2) by taking it ready-made from the culture medium, as they must do if the gene involved in making it is defective. The two possibilities can be distinguished by trying to grow the mold on an unsupplemented medium and on media to which single supplements are added.

Following heavy ultraviolet treatment, about two sexual spores out of every hundred tested carry defective forms of those genes which are necessary for the production of essential substances supplied in the supplemented medium. For example, strain number 5531 of the mold cannot manufacture the B-vitamin pantothenic acid. For normal growth it requires an external supply of this vitamin just as human beings do.

How do we know that the inability of the mold to produce its own pantothenic acid involves a gene defect? The only way this question can be answered at present is by seeing if inability to make pantothenic acid behaves in crosses as a single unit of inheritance.

The answer is that it does. If the mold that cannot make pantothenic acid is crossed with a normal strain of the other sex, the resulting spore sacs invariably contain four spores that produce molds like one parent and four that produce

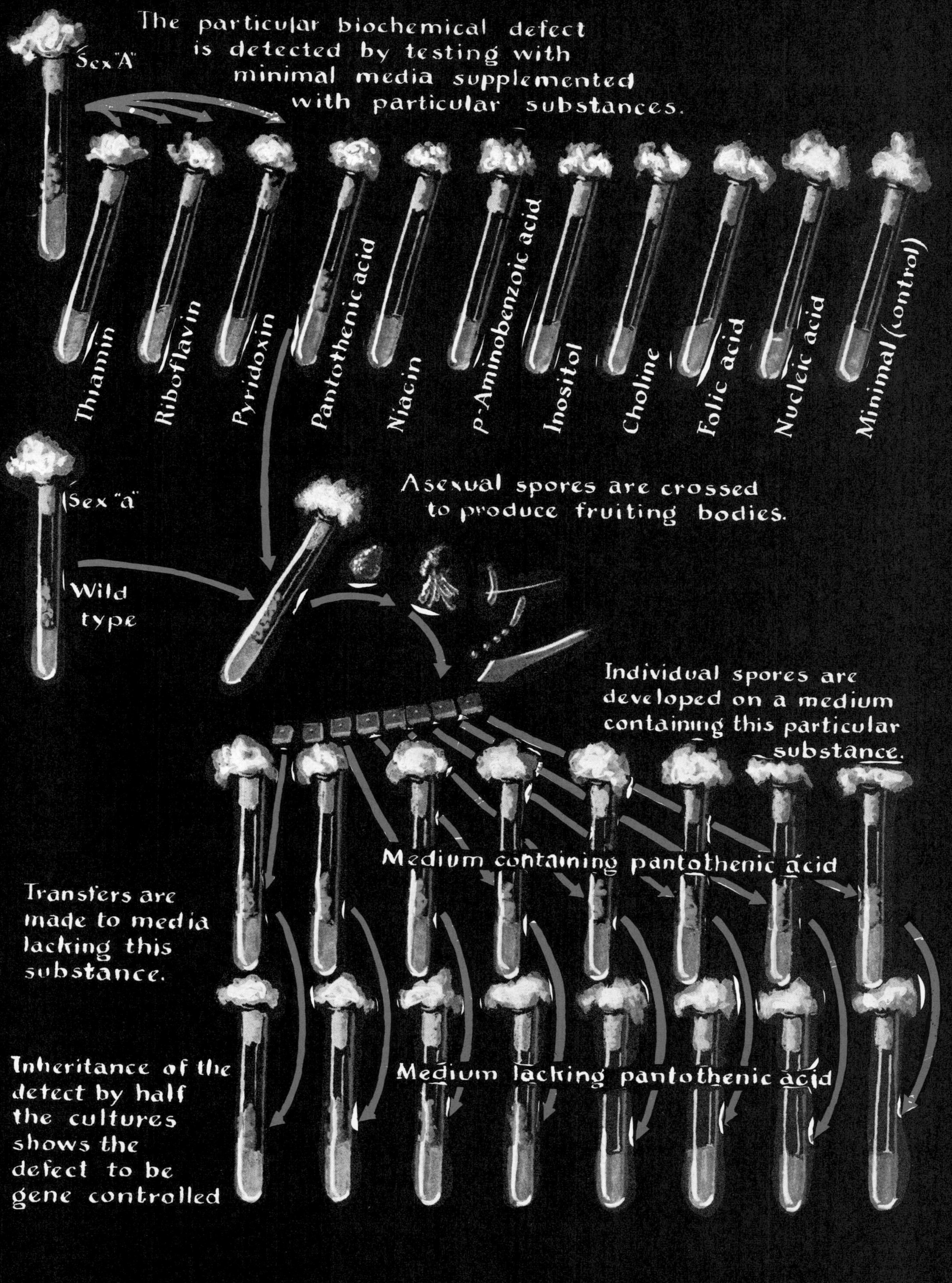

The particular biochemical defect is detected by testing with minimal media supplemented with particular substances.

Sex "A"

Thiamin
Riboflavin
Pyridoxin
Pantothenic acid
Niacin
P-Aminobenzoic acid
Inositol
Choline
Folic acid
Nucleic acid
Minimal (control)

Sex "a"

Wild type

Asexual spores are crossed to produce fruiting bodies.

Individual spores are developed on a medium containing this particular substance.

Transfers are made to media lacking this substance.

Medium containing pantothenic acid

Inheritance of the defect by half the cultures shows the defect to be gene controlled

Medium lacking pantothenic acid

strains like the other parent. Four daughter molds out of each set of eight from a spore sac are able to make pantothenic acid, and four are not (*see page 175*).

In a similar way, genes concerned with many other specific bread-mold chemical reactions have been mutated. In each case that has been studied in sufficient detail to be sure of the relation, it has been found that single genes are directly concerned with single chemical reactions.

An example that illustrates not only that genes are concerned with specific chemical reactions but also how mutant types can be used as tools for the study of metabolic processes involves the production of the amino acid tryptophane and the vitamin niacin (also known as nicotinic acid) by bread mold. Several steps in the synthesis of tryptophane, an indispensable component of the protoplasm of all organisms, have been shown to be gene-controlled. These have been used to show that bread mold forms this component by combining indole and the amino acid serine.

It has been found that indole, in turn, is made from anthranilic acid. If the second gene in the series in the accompanying diagram is made defective, anthranilic acid cannot be converted to indole, and if the mold carrying this gene in defective form is grown on a small amount of tryptophane it accumulates anthranilic acid in much the same way as an alcaptonuric accumulates alcapton. The accumulated anthranilic acid has been chemically identified in the culture medium of such a defective strain.

A recent report that rats fed on diets rich in tryptophane did not need niacin suggested to animal biochemists that possibly niacin is made from tryptophane. Following this lead, studies were made of the strains of bread mold which require ready-made tryptophane and niacin. They gave clear evidence that the bread mold does indeed derive its niacin from tryptophane. Intermediates in the chain of reactions by which the conversion is made were then identified (*see drawing on the opposite page*).

Men and Molds

The tryptophane-niacin relation so clearly disclosed by bread mold mutants has an interesting relation to the dietary deficiency disease pellagra in man. In the past this disease has been variously attributed to poor quality of dietary proteins, to a toxic factor in Indian corn, and to lack of a vitamin. When, in 1937, C. A. Elvehjem of Wisconsin demonstrated that niacin would bring about spectacular cures of black tongue, a disease of dogs like pellagra in man, the problem seemed to be solved. It was very soon found that pellagra in man, too, is cured by small amounts of niacin in the diet. The alternative hypotheses were promptly forgotten, even though the facts that led to

them were not explained by niacin alone.

The tryptophane-niacin relation now makes it clear that the protein quality theory also is correct. Good quality proteins contain plenty of tryptophane. If this is present in sufficient amounts in the diet, niacin appears not to be needed. The corn toxin theory also has a reasonable basis. There appear to be chemical substances in this grain that interfere with the body's utilization of tryptophane and niacin in such a way as to increase the requirements of those two materials.

Another point of interest in connection with the tryptophane-niacin story is that it illustrates again that, in terms of basic protoplasmic reactions, pretty much the same things go on in men and molds. It is supposed that in much the same way as a single gene is in control of the enzyme by which alcaptonuria is broken down in man, genes of the bread mold guide chemical reactions indirectly through their control of enzyme proteins. In most instances the enzymes involved have not yet been studied directly.

Bread-mold studies have contributed strong support to the hypothesis that each gene controls a single protein. But they have not proved it to the satisfaction of all biologists. There remains a possibility that some genes possess several distinct functions and that such genes were automatically excluded by the experimental procedure followed.

What is the process by which genes direct the formation of specific proteins? This is a question to which the answer is not yet known. There is evidence that genes themselves contain proteins combined with nucleic acids to form giant nucleoprotein molecules hundreds of times larger than the relatively simple molecules pictured on the opposite page. And it has been suggested that genes direct the building of non-genic proteins in essentially the same way in which they form copies of themselves.

The general question of how proteins are synthesized by living organisms is one of the great unsolved problems of biology. Until we have made headway toward its solution, it will not be possible to understand growth, normal or abnormal, in anything but superficial terms.

Do all organisms have genes? All sexually reproducing organisms that have been investigated by geneticists demonstrably possess them. Until recently there was no simple way of determining whether bacteria and viruses also have them. As a result of very recent investigations it has been found that some bacteria and some bacterial viruses perform a kind of sexual reproduction in which hereditary units like genes can be quite clearly demonstrated.

By treatment of bacteria with mutagenic agents, mutant types can be produced that parallel in a striking manner those found in the bread mold. These

GENES DIRECT a sequence of vital chemical reactions in *Neurospora*. Each of the molecules shown in the models on the opposite page is made up of the atoms hydrogen (*white spheres*), oxygen (*red*), carbon (*black*) and nitrogen (*brown*). Reactions involving the genes switch these atoms around to manufacture one molecule out of another. Beginning at the upper left, a single gene is known to be involved in the synthesis of anthranilic acid. Two genes are then involved in making anthranilic acid into indole, with an unknown intermediate indicated by a question mark. Indole is combined with serine to make the amino acid tryptophane, with water left over. Tryptophane is made into kynurenine. Two genes transform kynurenine into 3-hydroxy-anthranilic acid, again with an unknown intermediate molecule. Two genes finally synthesize the last product of the chain: niacin, the B vitamin that is an essential of both plant and animal life. This sequence of events is also involved in the human nutritional disease pellagra. A diet poor in the amino acid tryptophane obviously will lead to a deficiency of niacin, which causes the symptoms of pellagra. Therefore supplying either tryptophane or niacin to patient will alleviate disease.

make it almost certain that bacterial genes are functionally like the genes of molds.

So we can sum up by asserting that genes are irreducible units of inheritance in viruses, single-celled organisms and in many-celled plants and animals. They are organized in threadlike chromosomes which in higher plants and animals are carried in organized nuclei. Genes are probably nucleoproteins that serve as patterns in a model-copy process by which new genes are copied from old ones and by which non-genic proteins are produced with configurations that correspond to those of the gene templates.

Through their control of enzyme proteins many genes show a simple one-to-one relation with chemical reactions. Other genes appear to be concerned primarily with the elaboration of antigens—giant molecules which have the property of inducing antibody formation in rabbits or other animals.

It is likely that life first arose on earth as a genelike unit capable of multiplication and mutation. Through natural selection of the fittest of these units and combinations of them, more complex forms of life gradually evolved.

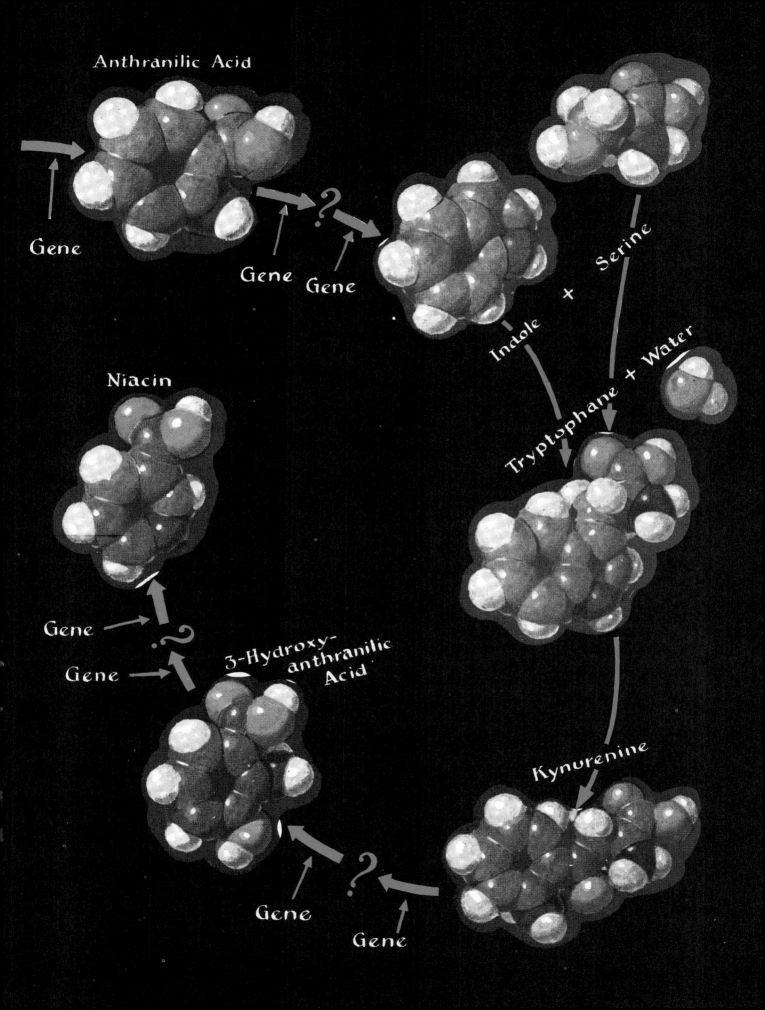

18 | Hybrid Nucleic Acids

S. SPIEGELMAN · *May 1964*

One of the most useful techniques for studying how genes work depends on the remarkable fact that certain chainlike molecules found in the living cell can "recognize" other chains whose molecular composition is complementary to their own. If one molecule is composed of subunits that can be symbolized by the sequence CATCATCAT..., it will recognize the complementary sequence GTAGTA-GTA... in a second molecule. As we shall see, these particular letters represent the chemical subunits that transmit the genetic information. When two such complementary chains are brought together under suitable conditions, they will "hybridize," or combine, to form a double-strand molecule in which the subunits C and G and A and T are linked by the weak chemical bond known as the hydrogen bond. This article will describe how hybridization has been exploited to study the cell's mechanism for manufacturing proteins.

A typical living cell synthesizes hundreds of different proteins, most of which serve as the enzymes, or biological catalysts, that mediate the myriad chemical reactions involved in growth and reproduction. Proteins are large chainlike molecules made out of some 20 different kinds of amino acids. According to current theory the sequence of amino acid units in a protein is specified by a single gene, and the genes are strung together in the chainlike molecules of deoxyribonucleic acid (DNA). The subunits of DNA that constitute the genetic code are four "bases": adenine (A), thymine (T), guanine (G) and cytosine (C). Normally DNA consists of two complementary chains linked by hydrogen bonds to form a double helix. Wherever A occurs in one chain, T occurs in the other; similarly,

G pairs with C. It is evident that each chain contains all the information needed to specify the complementary chain.

The flow of information in a cell begins with the base-pairing found in the double helix of DNA. Three principal modes of information transfer are distinguished by the end purposes they serve [*see illustrations on the next page*]. The first is a duplication, which provides exact copies of the DNA molecule for transmission from one generation of cells to the next. The copying process utilizes the same "language" and the same "alphabet" that are present in the original material.

The second mode of transfer is a "transcription," which uses the same language but a slightly different alphabet. In this step DNA is transcribed into ribonucleic acid (RNA), a chainlike molecule that, like DNA, has four code units. Three are the same as those found in DNA: A, G and C. The fourth is uracil (U), which takes the place of thymine (T). One particular variety of RNA carries the actual program for protein synthesis. Although this variety of RNA is frequently called "messenger RNA," I prefer to speak of "translatable RNA" or "RNA messages." A "messenger" cannot be translated, but a message can.

The third mode of information transfer converts the information from the four-element language of translatable RNA to the 20-element language of the proteins. This step is properly regarded as a translation. Since every translation calls for a dictionary, it is not surprising that the cell uses one also. The cellular dictionary is made up of a collection of comparatively small RNA molecules known as transfer RNA (or soluble

RNA), which have the task of delivering specific amino acids to the site of protein synthesis. Each amino acid is attached to a transfer-RNA molecule by a specific activating enzyme.

The actual synthesis of protein molecules is accomplished with the help of ribosomes, which evidently serve to hold the translatable RNA "tape" in position while the message is being "read." Ribosomes are small spherical particles composed of protein and two kinds of RNA. One kind is about a million times heavier than a hydrogen atom; the other is about 600,000 times heavier. They are respectively called 23S RNA and 16S RNA, designations that refer to how fast they settle out of solution when they are spun at high speed in an ultracentrifuge.

Thus we see that cellular RNA is divided into two major categories: translatable and nontranslatable. The translatable variety (messenger RNA) constitutes only about 5 per cent of all the RNA in a cell; it is usually unstable and must be continuously resynthesized. The nontranslatable varieties of RNA (transfer RNA and the two kinds of ribosomal RNA) make up about 95 per cent of the RNA found in a cell and are extremely stable.

This picture of the genetic mechanism has arisen from the contributions of a large number of investigators using a wide variety of methods of analyzing gene function. I shall focus attention on some of the things that have been learned about the translatable and nontranslatable forms of RNA by exploiting the ability of RNA to hybridize with DNA of complementary composition. In effect this technique enables one to return an RNA molecule to the site of its synthesis on a particular stretch of DNA.

Early in 1958 my colleagues Masayasu Nomura and Benjamin D. Hall and I at the University of Illinois undertook to re-examine a remarkable experiment described in 1955 by Elliot Volkin and Lazarus Astrachan of the Oak Ridge National Laboratory. These workers had used radioactive isotopes to identify and study the RNA produced when the colon bacillus is infected with the bacterial virus designated T2. Infection occurs when T2 injects into the cell of the bacterium a double helix of DNA bearing all the information needed for the synthesis of new virus particles. Volkin and Astrachan had concluded that the RNA synthesized in the infected cells mimicked the composition of the T2 DNA.

At the time neither the experimenters nor anyone else thought that the RNA might represent a genetic message formed on a DNA template. It was suggested, rather, that this new kind of

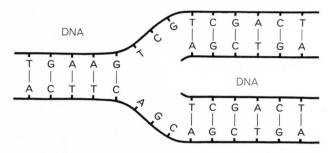

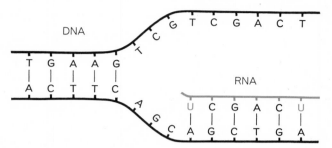

FLOW OF GENETIC INFORMATION involves duplication (*left*), transcription (*right*) and translation (*below*). Genetic information resides in giant chainlike molecules of deoxyribonucleic acid (DNA), in which the code "letters" are four bases: adenine (A), thymine (T), guanine (G) and cytosine (C). DNA normally consists of two complementary strands in which A pairs with T and G with C. During duplication, by an unknown mechanism, a new complementary strand is synthesized on each of the parent strands. In transcription only one strand of the DNA serves as a template and the new molecule formed is ribonucleic acid (RNA). In RNA the base uracil (U) takes the place of thymine as the partner of adenine. RNA molecules can be translatable or nontranslatable.

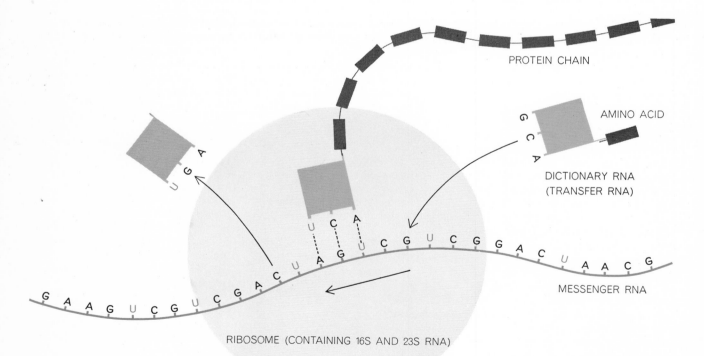

TRANSLATION PROCESS converts genetic information from the four-letter "language" of nucleic acids (DNA and RNA) into the 20-letter language of proteins. The letters of the protein language are the 20 amino acids that link together to form protein chains. If the DNA code is transcribed into translatable, or messenger, RNA, the RNA message becomes associated with one or more particles called ribosomes, which mediate the actual synthesis of protein. Ribosomes are made up of protein and two kinds of nontranslatable RNA, identified as 16S and 23S. Still another form of RNA called dictionary, or transfer, RNA delivers amino acids to the site of protein synthesis. It appears that a group of three bases in messenger RNA identifies each particular amino acid. According to one hypothesis the code group is "recognized" by a complementary set of bases in dictionary RNA. Evidently the ribosome serves as a "jig" for positioning amino acid subunits on the growing protein chain as the messenger RNA "tape" travels by.

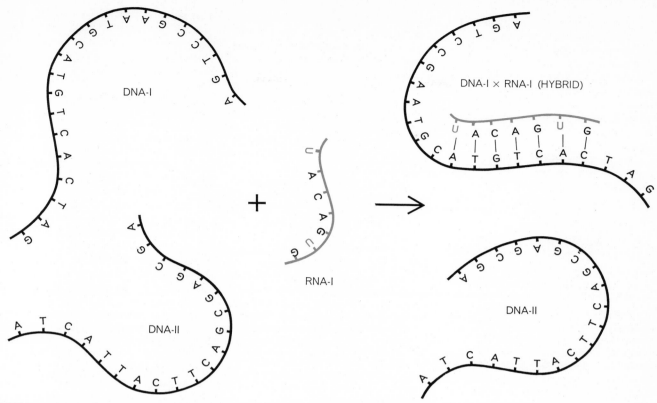

HYBRIDIZATION can occur when the base sequence in a strand of RNA matches up with that in single-strand ("denatured") DNA.

Here RNA-I is "challenged" with genetically related DNA-I and unrelated DNA-II. Only the genetically related strands hybridize.

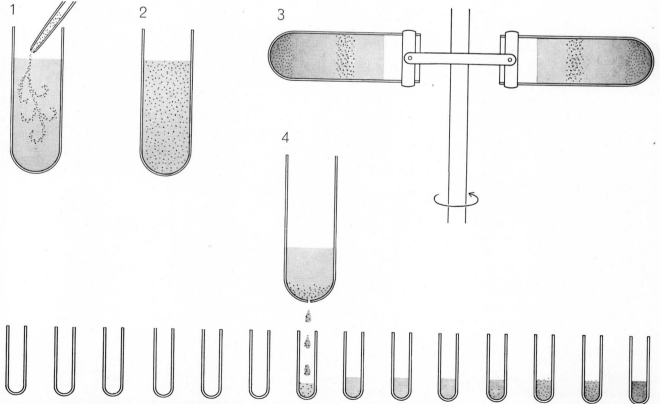

DENSITY-GRADIENT TECHNIQUE reveals if hybridization has taken place between RNA and DNA. The sample in question is added to a solution of cesium chloride (*1 and 2*). After centrifuga-

tion (*3*) the salt solution attains a smooth gradation in density. RNA (*color*), DNA (*black*) and RNA-DNA hybrids form layers according to their density. Fractions (*4*) can then be analyzed.

RNA was a precursor of the DNA needed to complete new virus particles. No doubt the experiment was misinterpreted and then neglected because it came so early in the modern history of DNA investigation. The helical model of DNA had been proposed only two years before by James D. Watson and F. H. C. Crick. Moreover, the experiment involved rather complex calculations and assumptions to support the view that the infected cells contained a distinctive new kind of RNA. It is clear in retrospect that this was the first experiment suggesting the existence of RNA copies of DNA.

It seemed to us that the Volkin-Astrachan observations were potentially so important that the design of an unequivocal experiment was well worth the effort. We set out, therefore, to see if bacterial cells infected with the T2 virus contained an RNA that could be specifically related to the T2 DNA. In our first experiments we sought evidence for this new type of RNA by physically isolating it from other RNA's. Two different procedures were successful. One (electrophoresis) measures the rate at which molecules migrate in an electric field; the other (sucrose-gradient centrifugation) measures their rate of migration when they are spun in a solution of smoothly varying density. Both of these methods showed that the RNA synthesized after virus infection was indeed a physically separable entity, differing in mobility and size from the bulk cellular RNA.

We found further that the ratio of the quantities of the bases (A, U, G and C) in the T2-specific RNA mimicked the ratio of the quantities of their counterparts (A, T, G and C) in the DNA of the virus. This suggested the possibility that the similarity might extend to a detailed correspondence of base sequence. A direct attack on this question by the complete determination of the sequences of bases was, and still is, too difficult.

Just at the right time, however, two groups of workers independently published experiments showing that if double-strand DNA was separated into single strands by heat (a process called denaturing), the two strands would re-form into a double-strand structure if the mixture was reheated and slowly cooled. This work was done by Julius Marmur and Dorothy Lane of Brandeis University and by Paul Doty and his colleagues at Harvard University. These investigators showed further that reconstitution of the double-strand molecule occurs only between strands that originate from the same or closely related organisms. This suggested that double-strand hybrid structures could be formed from mixtures of single-strand DNA and RNA, and that the appearance of such hybrids could be accepted as evidence for a perfect, or near perfect, complementarity of their base sequences. It had already been shown by Alexander Rich of the Massachusetts Institute of Technology and by Doty that synthetic RNA molecules containing adenine as the only base would form hybrid structures with synthetic DNA molecules containing thymine as the only base.

With this work as background, we undertook to determine if T2 RNA would hybridize with T2 DNA. It was first necessary to solve certain technical problems. We had already devised methods for obtaining T2 RNA in a reasonable state of purity. The question was how to design the experiment so that if a hybrid structure formed, we could be certain of detecting it and identifying it as such.

All previous work on the reconstitution of two-strand DNA had involved sizable amounts of material that could form optically observable layers when it was spun in an ultracentrifuge. In our experiments the amount of hybrid material formed would probably be so small that it would escape detection by this method.

The detection method finally evolved combined several techniques. One depended on the fact that RNA has a slightly higher density than DNA; consequently RNA-DNA hybrids should have an intermediate density. Molecules of different densities can be readily separated by the density-gradient method developed by M. S. Meselson, Franklin W. Stahl and Jerome R. Vinograd at the California Institute of Technology. In this method the sample to be analyzed is added to a solution of a heavy salt, cesium chloride, and the mixture is centrifuged for about three days at more than 30,000 revolutions per minute. Under centrifugation the salt solution attains a smooth gradation in density, being most dense at the bottom of the sample tube and least dense at the top. The components of the sample migrate to layers at which their density

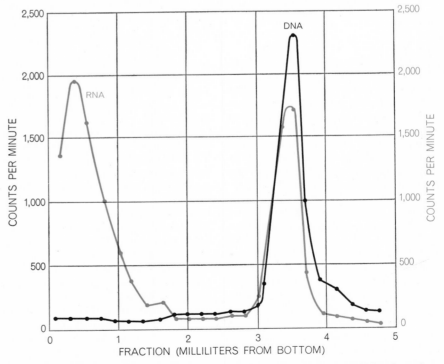

HYBRIDIZATION EXPERIMENT shows that RNA produced after a cell has been infected with the T2 virus is genetically related to the DNA of the virus. The RNA is labeled with radioactive phosphorus and the T2 DNA with radioactive hydrogen (tritium). The sample is subjected to density-gradient centrifugation (see bottom illustration on preceding page) and the radioactivity of the various fractions is determined. Although some of the RNA is driven to the bottom of the sample tube, much of it has hybridized with the lighter DNA fraction and thus appears between three and four milliliters above the bottom.

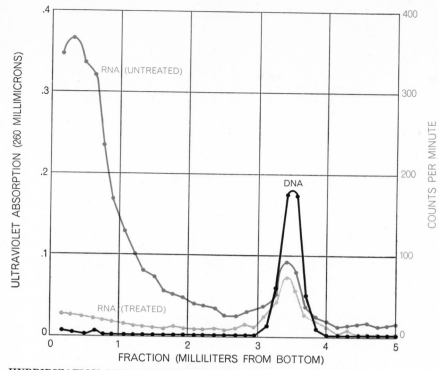

HYBRIDIZATION OF BACTERIAL RNA AND DNA is demonstrated for the bacterium *Pseudomonas aeruginosa*. Untreated RNA chiefly represents messenger RNA obtained by a special "step-down" procedure described in the text. In this experiment the presence of DNA in centrifuged fractions is determined by ultraviolet absorption. The coincident peaks in the two RNA curves represent RNA bound in RNA-DNA hybrids. "Treated RNA" refers to a portion of the sample that was treated before centrifugation with ribonuclease, an enzyme that normally destroys RNA. Although the enzyme has little or no effect on the hybridized RNA, it largely eliminates unhybridized RNA from the centrifuged sample.

If precautions are taken to ensure that all the cells in a given sample are infected with the DNA virus, one finds that none of the RNA synthesized later can hybridize with the host DNA. This suggests that one of the first steps taken by a virulent virus in establishing infection is turning off production of the host's messenger RNA. Evidently RNA transcribed from the viral DNA provides the genetic messages needed for the formation of various proteins required to manufacture complete virus particles. Subsequent studies at the University of Cambridge by Sydney Brenner, François Jacob and Meselson have shown that the T2 messenger RNA is able to make use of ribosomes preexisting in the host cell for the synthesis of proteins.

We wondered next whether the transcription of the DNA code into RNA messages was a universal mechanism or whether it might be restricted to the simple mode of replication followed by viruses. The study of the flow of genetic information in normal cells is a problem of considerable difficulty. As noted above, about 95 per cent of the RNA present at any given moment is of the nontranslatable variety, consisting of ribosomal RNA and transfer, or dictionary, RNA. It is precisely because the translatable RNA molecules are so few—only about 5 per cent of the total amount of RNA—that they were overlooked for so long in normal cells. The detection of the RNA messages of T2 was made easy because the synthesis of ribosomal and transfer RNA is turned off in virus-infected cells.

We decided to look for a situation in normal cells that would imitate the advantages provided by infected ones. It had been known that the total RNA content of cells is positively correlated with rate of growth, and since most of the RNA is ribosomal RNA, a high growth rate implies a high content of ribosomes. What happens if cells are subjected to a "step-down" transfer, that is, a transfer from a rich nutrient medium to a poor one? The growth rate declines, usually by about half. More important, for a generation after they have been placed in a poorer medium the cells contain more ribosomes than they can usefully employ. We reasoned that in this period the synthesis of ribosomal RNA might stop. Since protein production continues at a low rate, however, some synthesis of RNA messages, which must be continuously replaced, should persist.

exactly matches that of the salt solution. In place of the analytical ultracentrifuge we employed a centrifuge with swinging-bucket rotors, which permits actual isolation and analysis of various fractions. For this purpose the plastic sample tube is punctured at the bottom and the fractionated sample is withdrawn drop by drop for analysis [*see bottom illustration on page 181*].

To ensure a sensitive and unambiguous detection of the hybrid we labeled RNA with one radioactive isotope and DNA with another. The T2 RNA was labeled with radioactive phosphorus (P-32) and the T2 DNA with radioactive hydrogen (H-3). The beta particles emitted by P-32 have a characteristic energy different from those emitted by H-3; thus the isotopes can be assayed in each other's presence. The existence of hybrids in the centrifuged fractions would be signaled by the appearance of a layer containing the P-32 label of the RNA and the H-3 label of the DNA. Subsequently we observed that the layer of the hybrid fraction coincided closely with the layer of the unhybridized DNA. We could

therefore dispense with the radioactive label on DNA and establish its presence simply by its strong absorption of ultraviolet radiation at a wavelength of 260 millimicrons.

With these techniques we soon found that T2 RNA indeed hybridizes with T2 DNA. Furthermore, analysis of the hybrid confirmed that it was similar in overall base composition to T2 DNA. It was then necessary to show that hybrid formation occurs only between RNA and DNA that are genetically related. We exposed T2 RNA to a variety of unrelated DNA's from both bacteria and viruses. No hybrid formation could be detected, even with unrelated DNA's having an overall base composition indistinguishable from that of T2 DNA.

From these experiments one can conclude that T2 RNA has a base sequence complementary to that of at least one of the two strands in T2 DNA. Thus the similarity in base composition first noted by Volkin and Astrachan is a reflection of a more profound relatedness.

These experiments also tell us something about the events that take place when a virus invades a bacterial cell.

My colleague Masaki Hayashi undertook experiments to determine if this was the case. If it was, any RNA synthesized after step-down transition would be different from the ribosomal RNA. Hayashi selected three species of bacteria with DNA's of widely different base composition. In all three species the RNA synthesized after step-down transition possessed all the features that had characterized the RNA produced in virus-infected cells. These included instability, a base composition similar to that of the organisms' DNA's and a range of molecular sizes different from that of the ribosomal RNA.

Hybridization tests were carried out between the message-RNA fraction and genetically related DNA as well as with genetically unrelated DNA. The results were clear-cut. Hybrid structures were formed only when the mixture contained RNA and DNA of the same genetic origin. An experiment in hybrid formation that involved RNA and DNA from the bacterium *Pseudomonas aeruginosa* is summarized in the illustration on the preceding page.

This particular experiment illustrates an interesting and useful property of RNA-DNA hybrids. A portion of each sample of hybrid material was treated with the enzyme ribonuclease, which normally destroys RNA. One of the curves shows the amount of RNA in each fraction that was resistant to the enzyme. It can be seen that the RNA bound in the hybrid is quite resistant, whereas the free RNA is almost completely destroyed. This phenomenon turned out to be very useful for distinguishing between free and hybridized RNA. We can conclude from Hayashi's studies, and from those of others, that the flow of information from DNA to translatable RNA occurs normally in bacteria and is probably a universal mechanism in protein synthesis.

By the time these investigations were completed we were convinced that the RNA-DNA hybridization technique could be developed into an extremely powerful and versatile tool. Accordingly we decided to put it to a severe test. The problem we wanted to solve was this: Where do the nontranslatable molecules of RNA—ribosomal RNA and transfer RNA—come from?

Let us consider first the ribosomal variety. Two principal alternatives can be suggested for its mode of origin. Either it is formed on a DNA template or it is not. If it is formed on DNA, it should be complementary to some seg-

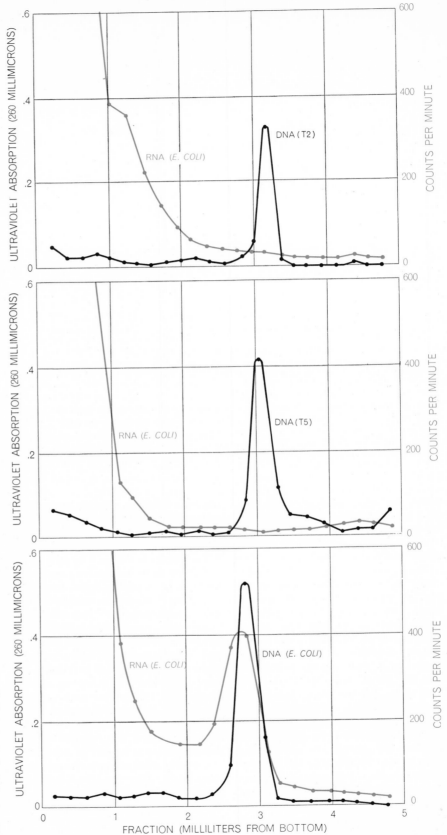

HYBRIDIZATION OF RIBOSOMAL RNA provides evidence that, like messenger RNA, it too is formed on a DNA template. In this experiment ribosomal RNA of the 23S variety was obtained from the colon bacillus (*Escherichia coli*). The top and middle curves show that no hybridization occurs when the RNA is challenged with single-strand DNA from the T2 and T5 viruses. When challenged with DNA from *E. coli*, however, hybridization is seen.

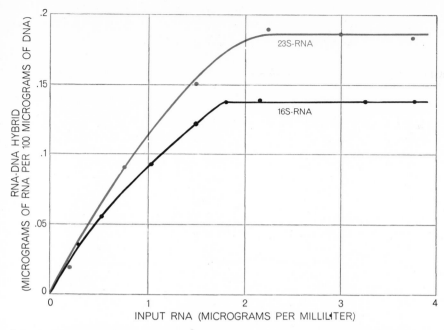

SATURATION CURVES indicate what fraction of the DNA molecule is set aside for producing the two forms of ribosomal RNA designated as 16S and 23S. The RNA and DNA samples were obtained from *Bacillus megaterium*. The results show that about .14 per cent of the DNA molecule is complementary to 16S and about .18 per cent to the 23S form.

ment of DNA and hence subject to hybridization.

It has been known for some time that the base composition of ribosomal RNA is not correlated with that of DNA found in the same cell. This, however, tells us nothing about the origin of the RNA; the DNA segment needed to serve as a template for ribosomal RNA might be so small as to constitute a nonrepresentative sample of the DNA's overall base composition.

Some three years ago one of my students, Saul A. Yankofsky, undertook the job of determining if hybridization could shed any light on this problem. The major complication was that a ribosomal RNA molecule appeared to be only about a ten-thousandth as long as the entire DNA molecule in a typical bacterial cell. We were faced, therefore, with the task of designing experiments that would detect hybridizations involving only a minute segment of DNA.

Theoretically the required sensitivity can be attained simply by labeling RNA so that it has a suitably high level of radioactivity. If no radioactivity was found in association with DNA, one could conclude that no hybrid had been formed. Experiments of this sort would require RNA labeled at a level of about one million counts per minute per microgram. The trouble with such high levels of radioactivity is that irrelevant "noise" can spoil the experiment. It is easy to detect 100 counts per minute

above the background level of radiation. Thus if as little as .0001 microgram of unhybridized RNA accidentally got into the DNA fraction, it would be detected and give a false reading. Such accidental contamination could occur in a number of ways. For example, the ribosomal RNA preparation might contain traces of radioactive translatable RNA that would hybridize with DNA. Small amounts of ribosomal RNA might be mechanically trapped by strands of DNA. Or there might be partial hybridization resulting from accidental coincidences of base complementarity over small regions.

By a variety of biological and technical stratagems it was possible to design a satisfactory experiment. Organisms were chosen with a DNA base composition far removed from that of ribosomal RNA, thereby making it possible to show that hybridized material actually contained ribosomal RNA. Contamination of the radioactive ribosomal RNA preparation by radioactive translatable RNA was eliminated by a simple trick. After the RNA in the cells was labeled with a suitable isotope the cells were transferred to a nonradioactive medium for a period long enough for the labeled RNA messages to disappear. Ribosomal RNA, being stable, retains its radioactive label. Finally, to avoid false readings from RNA that was either mechanically trapped or accidentally paired over short regions, all

suspected hybrids were treated with ribonuclease. The RNA in a genuine hybrid is resistant to this treatment.

It was noted earlier in this article that ribosomes contain two types of RNA, designated 23S RNA and 16S RNA. The outcome of a series of hybridizations between 23S RNA obtained from the colon bacillus and three different DNA preparations is presented in the illustration on the preceding page. A ribonuclease-resistant structure appears in the DNA-density region only when the DNA and the ribosomal RNA are from the same organism. These results clearly imply that ribosomal RNA is produced on a DNA template.

An extension of these studies gave us an answer to the following question: How much of the DNA molecule is set aside for turning out ribosomal RNA? To get the answer we simply add increasing amounts of ribosomal RNA to a fixed amount of DNA and determine the ratio of RNA to DNA in the hybrid at saturation. The illustration at the left shows the outcome of this experiment with the ribosomal RNA of *Bacillus megaterium*. The results indicate that approximately .18 per cent of the total DNA molecule is complementary to 23S RNA and .14 per cent to 16S RNA.

The difference in these two saturation values suggests that 23S RNA and 16S RNA are distinctly different molecules, but the evidence is not unequivocal. Although different in size, the two ribosomal RNA molecules have essentially the same base composition. There is still no direct way of telling whether they have the same or different base sequences. The similarity in base composition and the fact that the 23S RNA has about twice the weight of the 16S RNA had led, however, to the concept that the 23S-RNA molecule is a union of two 16S-RNA molecules.

To probe the matter further we designed an experiment to find out if the two kinds of ribosomal RNA compete for the same sites when they are hybridized with DNA. Hybridization mixtures were prepared that contained fixed amounts of DNA and saturating concentrations of 23S RNA labeled with P-32. To these we added increasing amounts of 16S RNA labeled with H-3, after which we determined the relative amounts of P-32 and H-3 in the hybrid structures. If the two kinds of RNA have an identical sequence, the entry of the H-3-labeled 16S RNA into the hybrid should displace an equivalent amount of P-32-labeled 23S RNA. If the sequences are different, the 16S RNA should hybridize as though the 23S material were not present. The experiment decisively supported the second alternative [*see illustration on this page*].

Following these experiments, there seemed little doubt that the third variety of RNA, transfer RNA, would also be found to originate on segments of DNA. The small size of transfer-RNA molecules made hybridization experiments even more difficult than the earlier ones. Nevertheless, the experiments were successfully carried out by Dario Giacomoni in our laboratory and by Howard M. Goodman in Rich's laboratory at M.I.T. Both workers obtained virtually identical results. They demonstrated by specific hybridization that the DNA of a cell contains sequences complementary to its molecules of transfer RNA. The amount of DNA set aside for the cell's genetic dictionary was found by both groups to be about .025 per cent, or less than a tenth of the combined space allotted to the two types of ribosomal RNA.

These experiments also ruled out an interesting possibility. The molecules of transfer RNA contain only about 80 bases (compared with about 2,000 for 16S RNA) and it was conceivable that the sequence of bases in transfer RNA's might be the same, or much the same, in the cells of different organisms. This possibility seemed more likely when Günter von Ehrenstein of Johns Hopkins University and Fritz A. Lipmann of the Rockefeller Institute showed, in a joint experiment, that transfer RNA's from the colon bacillus can serve as a dictionary in translating the RNA message for the synthesis of the protein hemoglobin from materials present in the red blood cells of the rabbit.

Giacomoni was able to show, however, that the base sequence in transfer-RNA molecules differs from organism to organism. In one such experiment a mixture of transfer-RNA molecules from two different organisms was challenged with DNA molecules obtained from one of them. For identification the genetically related transfer RNA was labeled with P-32 and the unrelated variety with H-3. Only the related RNA formed a hybrid; the genetically unrelated RNA did not [*see chart at left in illustration on next page*].

Instead of using one kind of DNA and two kinds of transfer RNA, one can reverse matters and also demonstrate specificity. For this purpose it is helpful to choose DNA preparations that migrate to different layers when they are subjected to density-gradient centrifuga-

tion. In such a mixture a hybrid will form only with radioactively labeled transfer RNA that is genetically related to one of the DNA's. In the experiment performed in our laboratory the DNA was obtained from two bacteria, *Pseudomonas aeruginosa* and *Bacillus megaterium,* and the transfer RNA was obtained only from the latter [*see chart at right in illustration on next page*].

These experiments reveal an interesting feature of the biological universe. It is assumed that only three of the 80-odd bases in a transfer-RNA molecule provide the means for "reading" the three-base code "words" in the RNA message. Although evidence is lacking on this point, it is possible that a temporary association between three bases in transfer RNA and three bases in the RNA message guarantees that the correct amino acid is deposited where it belongs in a growing protein chain [*see lower illustration on page 180*].

If this picture is accepted, what is the role of the other 70-odd bases in transfer RNA? The function of the non-coding portion is unknown, but its presence provides an opportunity for biological individuality, from species to species, without disturbing the dictionary function of the molecule. The fact that the base sequences are different in the transfer RNA's of different organisms shows that this opportunity has not been neglected in the course of biological evolution.

We have now seen that all forms of RNA can be traced back to their point of origin on the DNA template. But the double-strand helix of DNA represents two templates, one the complement of the other. When any given segment of DNA is transcribed, two entirely different RNA molecules can be produced, depending on which strand of the DNA molecule serves as a template. Assuming that the entire length of the DNA molecule contains genetic

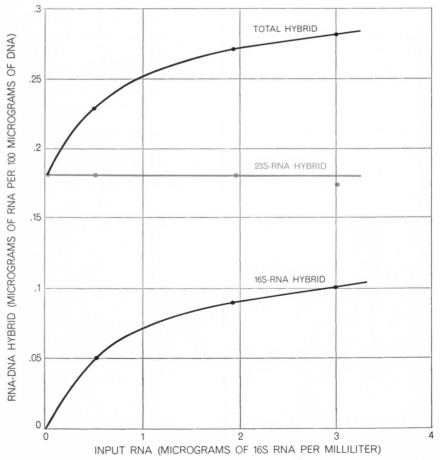

COMPETITION TEST shows that 16S and 23S ribosomal RNA form hybrids with different segments of the DNA molecule. The 16S RNA was labeled with tritium, the 23S RNA with radioactive phosphorus. Increasing amounts of 16S RNA were added to hybridization mixtures containing a saturating concentration of 23S RNA. Subsequently the relative amounts of tritium and radioactive phosphorus in the hybrids were determined. Since the two kinds of RNA hybridize without interference they must have different base sequences.

information that must be transcribed into RNA, there are three possibilities: (1) All of both strands are transcribed into complementary RNA; (2) both strands serve as templates, but in any given segment only one strand or the other is transcribed; (3) only one strand is transcribed.

Here again the hybridization test has supplied evidence to decide among the alternatives. Ideally what is required is a method of separating the two strands of the DNA molecule. If this could be done, one could test the various forms of RNA against each strand and determine if hybridization occurs.

Although the two strands of normal DNA can be separated, no way has yet been found to obtain a pure preparation containing strands of only one type. Fortunately nature provides a solution to the problem in the form of an organism that contains a single strand of DNA. The organism is the small DNA virus ϕX174, discovered in Parisian sewage about 30 years ago by French investigators. It is fairly easy to purify the virus particle and remove its DNA. Nature also provides a source of the complementary strand. When the virus infects a bacterial cell, the single strand of DNA serves as a template for the synthesis of a complementary strand, resulting in a normal double-strand DNA molecule. This molecule, known as the replicating form, can also be isolated for experimental purposes.

In order to run a hybridization test my co-workers Marie and Masaki Hayashi grew ϕX174 in infected cells in the presence of P-32 and extracted labeled molecules of translatable RNA. These molecules were then brought together with the single-strand DNA of ϕX174 and with a denatured sample of the double-strand form. The results obtained were satisfyingly clear. No hybrids were formed with the single-strand DNA, but excellent hybrids were produced with the DNA from the double-strand form. This implied that the RNA messages are complementary to the *other* strand in the two-strand DNA molecule, that is, the one not normally present in the ϕX174 particle. As a final confirmation we analyzed the base composition of the RNA that was hybridized. The results agreed with the expectation that it was complementary to only one of the two strands of the replicating form of ϕX174 DNA.

Using similar methods with other viruses, identical conclusions have now been drawn by two other groups: Glauco P. Tocchini-Valentini and his co-workers at the University of Chicago and Carol Greenspan and Marmur at Brandeis University. There seems little doubt that in all organisms only one strand of the DNA molecule serves as a template for RNA synthesis.

The original procedures of detecting hybrids involved lengthy high-speed centrifugations. Ekkehard K. F. Bautz of Rutgers University and Benjamin D. Hall of the University of Illinois have introduced the use of cellulose-acetate columns for hybridization experiments. Ellis T. Bolton and Brian J. McCarthy of the Carnegie Institution of Washington's Department of Terrestrial Magnetism have developed a convenient and rapid method using an agar column. Here the DNA is trapped on the agar gel and the RNA is hybridized with it. The RNA can then be removed by raising the temperature of the column and lowering the ionic strength of an eluting, or rinsing, solution.

The exploitation of the hybridization technique is still at an early stage, but it has already proved of great value in the analysis of gene function. It seems likely to play an increasingly important role in helping to illuminate many problems of molecular biology, including those pertinent to an understanding of the specialization of cells and biological evolution in general.

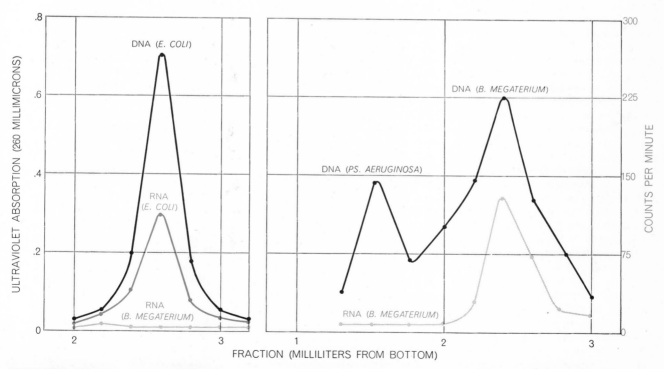

TESTS FOR GENETIC RELATIONSHIP can be carried out by challenging the RNA from two different organisms with the DNA from one of them. In one experiment (*left*) transfer RNA from *E. coli* was labeled with radioactive phosphorus; transfer RNA from *B. megaterium* was labeled with tritium. Only the former hybridizes with *E. coli* DNA. Conversely, in a second experiment (*right*), transfer RNA from *B. megaterium* hybridizes with genetically related DNA but not with DNA from *Ps. aeruginosa*.

19 | *Polyribosomes*

ALEXANDER RICH · *December 1963*

A typical mammalian cell contains instructions for making many thousands of different proteins and has the capacity to turn out thousands of protein molecules every minute. To a very large extent the living cell is an expression of the particular kinds of proteins it manufactures. It has been known for several years that the site of protein synthesis within the cell is the particle called the ribosome. Visible only in the electron microscope, ribosomes are approximately spherical and can be seen throughout the substance of all living cells. Although the internal structure of these particles is obscure, it has been established that they are composed of protein and ribonucleic acid (RNA) in about equal amounts.

Within the past 18 months experiments in our laboratory at the Massachusetts Institute of Technology and elsewhere have led to the hypothesis that the protein "factories" of the cell are not single ribosomes working in isolation but collections of ribosomes working together in orderly fashion as if they were machines on an assembly line. We have called such collections polyribosomes, or simply polysomes. As we shall see, the polyribosome is not the usual kind of assembly line. In such an assembly line the product moves down the line and component parts are added to it. In the polyribosome assembly line the ribosomes move down the line and each one makes a complete product. There is much evidence that the ribosomes are all alike, or at least interchangeable. They can move from one assembly line to another, making whatever protein a given line happens to call for.

How this specification of a protein takes place has been fully described in these pages, most recently in "The Genetic Code," by F. H. C. Crick, beginning on page 198 in this book,

and "The Genetic Code: II," by Marshall W. Nirenberg, which begins on page 206. The genetic code of the cell, which constitutes the instructions for the synthesis of the cell's proteins, is embodied in a double-chain molecular helix of deoxyribonucleic acid (DNA). The code itself consists of sequences of four different kinds of subunit called bases. The DNA of a bacterium may contain some five million pairs of bases, which are needed to specify several thousand different proteins. The DNA of a mammalian cell may contain nearly 100 times as many base pairs, which specify many more proteins.

Proteins consist of linear chains of amino acid subunits. Short chains or chains that lack full protein activity are called polypeptides. Polypeptide chains can be folded into a specific three-dimensional configuration, and they often combine to form complex proteins. For example, the protein hemoglobin, which carries oxygen in the blood, is composed of four polypeptide chains, each of which contains about 150 amino acid subunits. Protein chains are built up from about 20 different kinds of amino acid. Each chain must have the right sequence of amino acid subunits to make sense, just as a sentence must consist of the right sequence of letters, spaces and punctuation. It is evident that an enormous number of different polypeptide chains can be constructed from 20 different amino acids, just as an enormous number of different sentences can be composed from the 26 letters of our alphabet.

The kernel of the genetic coding problem was to discover how a sequence of four different bases in DNA could specify a sequence of 20 different amino acids in a protein. It now appears that a triplet code is employed: a sequence of three bases is needed to specify each

amino acid. It has also been shown that DNA does not take part directly in protein synthesis. Instead the genetic code in the long double-chain molecule of DNA is transcribed into shorter single chains of RNA, which carry away the information needed to construct one kind of polypeptide chain, or perhaps in some cases several chains. Because these molecules of RNA bear the genetic code to the site of protein synthesis they are called messenger RNA.

How do the amino acid molecules get to the site of synthesis and find their proper place in the polypeptide chain? As a first step they must be "activated," a task performed by the energy-rich substance adenosine triphosphate (ATP). So activated, they can be "recognized" by still smaller RNA molecules, containing about 70 base subunits, called transfer, or soluble, RNA. There is a different kind of transfer RNA for each amino acid. The transfer RNA and amino acid are joined by a specific enzyme, a protein with catalytic activity. The transfer RNA then acts as an adapter for depositing a given amino acid at a position in the polypeptide chain specified by messenger RNA. Presumably the ultimate selection of an amino acid is determined by weak chemical bonds between a sequence of bases in messenger RNA and a complementary sequence in transfer RNA. By this mechanism, through the agency of the ribosome, the information coded in messenger RNA is translated into a polypeptide chain.

About a year and a half ago my colleagues and I began puzzling about one geometrical aspect of this system. Consider for a moment the problem of synthesizing one of the polypeptide chains of hemoglobin, which contains about 150 amino acid subunits. If each subunit is specified by a triplet code, the messenger RNA must contain 450 bases merely to specify the sequence of subunits in one chain. In most RNA molecules the bases are stacked on top of one another more or less like a pile of pennies. Since the bases have a thickness of 3.4 angstrom units, the messenger RNA strand for the hemoglobin polypeptide chains should have a molecular length of at least 1,500 angstroms. In other possible arrangements of the RNA molecule the length might be almost twice as great. By comparison, the individual ribosome has a diameter of only about 230 angstroms, and so we wondered how the long messenger molecule interacted with such a small particle to manufacture a polypeptide chain. Some investigators thought that the RNA chain might be wrapped around the outside of the ribosome, but it was hard to visualize how intimate contact between the two could be maintained. The wrapping problem would be still more difficult for RNA chains 20,000 angstroms long, which are found in many viruses. Alternative suggestions that the messenger RNA might somehow be coiled inside the ribosome seemed to present even more formidable topological problems.

It occurred to us that proteins might actually be made on groups of ribosomes, linked together somehow by messenger RNA. There was already a little evidence pointing in this direction. Walter Gilbert of Harvard University, as well as other investigators, had found that when a synthetic RNA was added to a cell-free system of bacterial ribosomes, the ribosomes would tend to clump together. (In such experiments, initiated by Marshall Nirenberg at the National Institutes of Health, the ribosomes make synthetic polypeptides in accordance with instructions coded in the synthetic RNA. By comparing the base composition of the RNA with the amino acid composition of the polypeptide it is possible to compile a genetic code "dictionary.")

In some of the initial experiments in our laboratory Jonathan R. Warner, then a graduate student, tried to find in bacterial cells structures larger than single ribosomes. He was initially unsuccessful because, as we later realized, the vigorous grinding needed to break open the bacteria also destroys the delicate polyribosome structure.

At the same time Paul M. Knopf, a post-doctoral fellow in our group, was working with reticulocytes—the cells that make hemoglobin—from rabbits. Since the cells were readily available, we began looking for multiple ribosomal structure in them. The reticulocyte is a cell that has lost its nucleus but retains

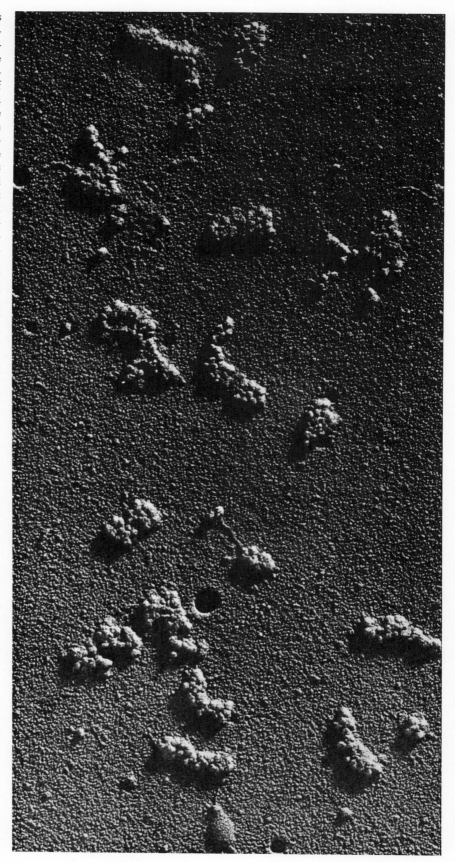

LARGE POLYRIBOSOMES obtained from a culture of human tumor cells are enlarged 100,000 diameters in this electron micrograph made by the author and his colleagues. Individual globular units in the clusters are ribosomes, believed to be held together by strands of messenger RNA (ribonucleic acid). Polyribosomes are the site of protein synthesis.

CELL COMPONENT	STRUCTURE	FUNCTION
DNA (DEOXYRIBONUCLEIC ACID)	A polymer molecule in the form of a double-strand helix containing many thousands of subunits.	Contains genetic information coded in sequences of subunits called bases.
MESSENGER RNA (A FORM OF RIBONUCLEIC ACID)	A single-strand polymer molecule containing hundreds of subunits.	Transcribes from DNA the information needed to make a protein molecule and carries it to site of protein synthesis.
TRANSFER, OR SOLUBLE, RNA (A FORM OF RIBONUCLEIC ACID)	A single-strand polymer molecule containing about 70 subunits. May be folded into a double helix in some regions.	Conveys specific amino acids to site of protein synthesis. Each amino acid has its own type of transfer RNA.
RIBOSOME	A globular structure consisting of 40 per cent protein and 60 per cent RNA.	Collaborates with messenger RNA to link together amino acids delivered by transfer RNA, thereby creating proteins.
POLYRIBOSOME OR POLYSOME	Strings of ribosomes temporarily held together by messenger RNA.	Provides actual mechanism of protein synthesis.

GLOSSARY OF CELL COMPONENTS required for protein synthesis describes their structure, function and size. The end result of the collaboration among these components is to produce protein molecules whose composition has been specified by the genetic code

the molecular apparatus for producing hemoglobin molecules. It is also a highly specialized cell: hemoglobin is virtually the only protein it manufactures. For this reason the reticulocyte offers many advantages for studying protein synthesis. Using this cell, for example, Howard M. Dintzis was able to show at M.I.T. that the polypeptides in hemoglobin are assembled by the sequential addition of amino acids, starting at one end of the polypeptide chain and proceeding to the other.

The choice of reticulocytes for our search proved fortunate because they can be broken open by gentle methods. The cells are suspended in a medium whose salt concentration is lower than that within the cells. Water flows into the cell, making it swell until it bursts. A series of experiments demonstrated that protein synthesis is carried out not on individual ribosomes but on ribosome clusters. At about the same time Alfred Gierer, working independently at the Max Planck Institute in Tübingen, made similar observations with rabbit reticulocytes. A short time later F. O. Wettstein, Theophil Staehelin and Hans Noll of the University of Pittsburgh found ribosome clusters in liver tissues.

The basic technique we used in our work was sucrose-gradient centrifuga-

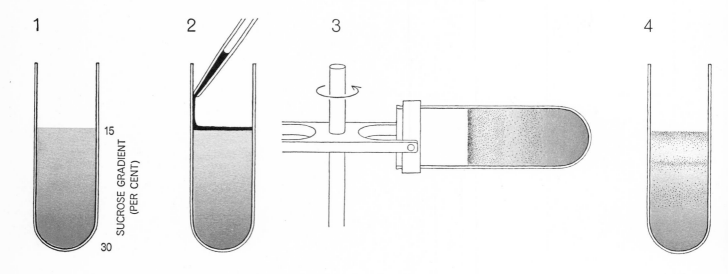

1   2   3   4

SUCROSE GRADIENT (PER CENT)

15

30

SUCROSE-GRADIENT TECHNIQUE provides a simple way to separate cell components that sediment at different rates when centrifuged. The gradient consists of ordinary sugar dissolved in a test tube (1). In a typical experiment rabbit reticulocytes (red-blood cells) are incubated 45 seconds with amino acids containing radioactive carbon 14. Ribosomes from the cells are layered on the sucrose gradient (2) and spun in a centrifuge (3). Separated fractions are removed in sequence (5) and analyzed. Ribosomes reveal their presence by strongly absorbing ultraviolet radiation at 2,600 angstrom units (6). A radiation counter determines the presence of newly synthesized polypeptide chains containing carbon 14 (7). These chains turn out to be in the faster sedimenting fractions.

SIZE

Diameter: 20 angstrom units
  Length: several thousand angstroms
          up to several millimeters

Diameter: 10 to 15 angstroms
  Length: 1,000 to several thousand angstroms

Length: 250 angstroms unfolded

Diameter: about 230 angstroms

Length: varies with length of messenger
        RNA holding ribosomes together

contained in DNA. Proteins are built up from about 20 varieties of amino acid.

tion, which enables one to separate materials that sediment at different speeds in a strong gravitational field. In this technique a plastic centrifuge tube is filled with a sugar solution that varies smoothly from a concentration of 30 per cent at the bottom of the tube to 15 per cent at the top. The gradient is obtained simply by slowly filling the tube from two reservoirs containing 15 and 30 per cent sucrose. The sample material, con-taining molecules of different sizes, is carefully deposited in a layer on top of the sugar solution; the tube is then placed in a centrifuge with a swinging-bucket rotor. The sucrose gradient is preserved during the centrifugation and is still maintained after the run by gravity. During the run molecules that sediment at different speeds travel different distances and remain separated when the run is ended. The plastic tube is removed from the centrifuge and its bottom is punctured to allow the collection of a sequence of fractions from bottom to top. These fractions can now be analyzed in various ways.

We designed the following simple experiment. A suspension of rabbit reticulocytes was incubated in a nutrient medium and then fed for 45 seconds with amino acids containing the radioactive isotope carbon 14. The time was kept short because we were interested in looking at the early stages of protein synthesis. After 45 seconds the cells were chilled to stop further metabolic activity, gently broken open and placed on a sucrose gradient. After centrifugation the fractions collected from the sucrose gradient were treated in two ways. The optical density, or amount of absorption, was read in the ultraviolet region at a wavelength of 2,600 angstroms, where nucleic acids strongly absorb radiation. Because ribosomes contain large amounts of ribonucleic acid, this is a sensitive method for determining their presence. In addition the radioactivity of the various fractions was measured. This measurement, by indicating the presence of amino acids containing carbon 14, told us which fractions contained polypeptide chains that were still growing.

The results are shown in the top illustration on the next page. It can be seen that two ultraviolet-absorbing peaks have migrated from the top of the tube. The first, or slow-moving, peak is typical of the peak for single ribosomes. Its speed of movement is represented by the sedimentation constant 74. The fast-moving peak has traveled about two and a half times farther and is much broader. Furthermore, the radioactivity in the growing hemoglobin chains was associated with the fast-moving peak and not with the peak containing single ribosomes. This clearly suggested that the fast-moving peak rather than the single-ribosome peak was the site of protein synthesis.

We then set about analyzing the fast-moving peak. It seemed plausible that it might contain clusters of ribosomes held together by one or more strands of messenger RNA. If this were so, it should be possible to free the ribosomes by subjecting the cell-free medium to ribonuclease, an enzyme that specifically

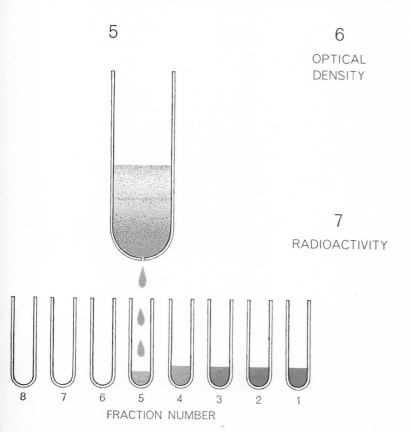

5

7   RADIOACTIVITY

FRACTION NUMBER

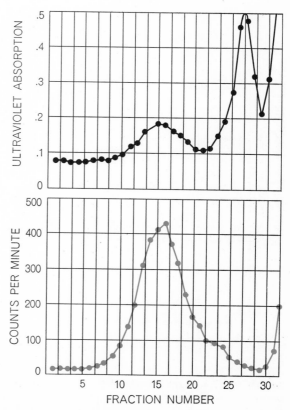

6   OPTICAL
    DENSITY

FRACTION NUMBER

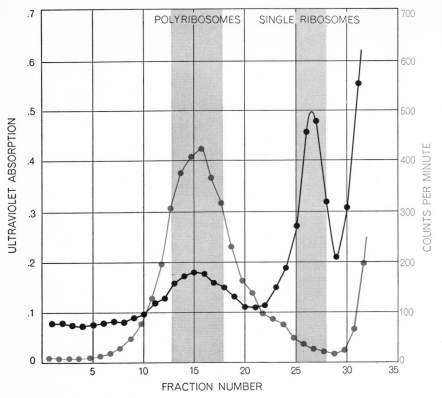

NORMAL RIBOSOME DISTRIBUTION in rabbit reticulocytes consists of a fast-sediment-ing fraction of polyribosomes and a slow-sedimenting fraction of single ribosomes. High radioactivity (*color*) indicates that polyribosomes contain newly synthesized polypeptides.

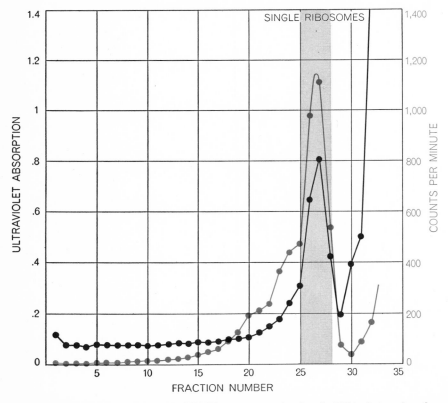

AFTER ADDITION OF RIBONUCLEASE, an enzyme that breaks RNA chains, the ribo-somes from reticulocytes no longer exhibit a fast-sedimenting fraction. This implies that polyribosomes are held together by RNA, which, on breaking, releases single ribosomes.

breaks RNA chains. In fact, when a very small amount of ribonuclease was added to the medium before centrifugation, the fast-moving peak did not appear. Both its optical density and its radioactivity were transferred to the peak containing single ribosomes [*see bottom illustration on this page*]. This confirmed the hypothesis that the fast-moving peak represented ribosomes held together by RNA.

Further experiments told us more about this fast-moving component. We learned, for example, that it is fairly fragile. When we subjected the gently opened cells to a modest amount of shearing in a homogenizer, the sucrose-gradient pattern changed dramatically [*see illustration on opposite page*]. The broad peak containing the fast-moving component disappeared and was re-placed by a series of peaks. The sedimen-tation pattern again told us the slow-moving first peak contained single ribo-somes. We speculated that the second peak might contain pairs of ribosomes, the third peak clusters of three and so on. This tentative hypothesis was readily confirmed by an electron-microscope examination conducted in the laboratory of Cecil E. Hall at M.I.T. A sample taken from the first peak showed single ribo-somes. A sample from the third peak showed mainly clusters of three ribo-somes, and the fifth peak showed mainly clusters of five. These initial observations showed us that hemoglobin synthesis is actually carried out on a group of ribo-somes, which we named the polyribo-some, or polysome.

Further analysis showed that hemo-globin synthesis takes place primarily in a polysome containing five units, as shown clearly in electron micrographs. The micrographs also show, however, a fair number of four-unit and six-unit polysomes [*see top illustration on page 194*]. We were quite sure that these were not artifacts and that they must reflect the mechanism of protein synthesis.

The fragility of the polysome when subjected to mechanical forces, as well as its sensitivity to small amounts of ribonuclease, suggested that the ribo-somes are held together by a single strand of RNA. This impression was strongly reinforced by more specialized electron micrographs made by Henry S. Slayter of M.I.T. The technique called negative staining shows that the ribo-somes in a polysome are separated by gaps of 50 to 150 angstroms. Positive staining with uranyl acetate reveals that the ribosomes are connected by a thin thread 10 to 15 angstroms in diameter, which is about the thickness of a single strand of RNA. From the size of the gap between ribosomes one can compute that the over-all length of a five-unit polysome is near 1,500 angstroms. (The five ribosomes hav a total diameter of 5×230, or about 1,150 angstroms, and there are five inter-ribosomal gaps of 50 to 150 angstroms each.) These measurements of total polysome length are thus near the length that we concluded must be needed to specify the information in a hemoglobin polypeptide chain of 150 amino acid subunits. In other words, the messenger RNA for a hemoglobin polypeptide chain is about the right length to hold together a five-unit polysome.

These various observations led us to the following picture of how the polysome functions. The fact that the ribosomes are separated by a considerable distance makes it seem unlikely that they cooperate in synthesizing a single polypeptide chain. Furthermore, if a ribosome is to have access to all the information coded in messenger RNA, it must "read" the strand from one end to the other. As it travels it must build up a polypeptide chain, adding one amino acid after another according to instructions. A similar conclusion was reached by Gilbert after he studied how transfer RNA is bound to the ribosome. The conclusion is also consistent with Dintzis' observation that hemoglobin synthesis proceeds in sequence.

Let us now imagine that the messenger RNA for hemoglobin contains not just one ribosome but five, all moving, say, from left to right [*see bottom illustration on next two pages*]. The ribosome at the extreme left has just attached itself to the strand and has started synthesizing a polypeptide chain. The other four ribosomes are proportionately further along in the synthesis process and the one at the extreme right has almost completed a polypeptide chain. Presumably the ribosomes are carried along by a ratchet-like mechanism that does not allow them to go backward. At each station along the way the appropriate amino acid, borne by transfer RNA, is selected from the cellular milieu and

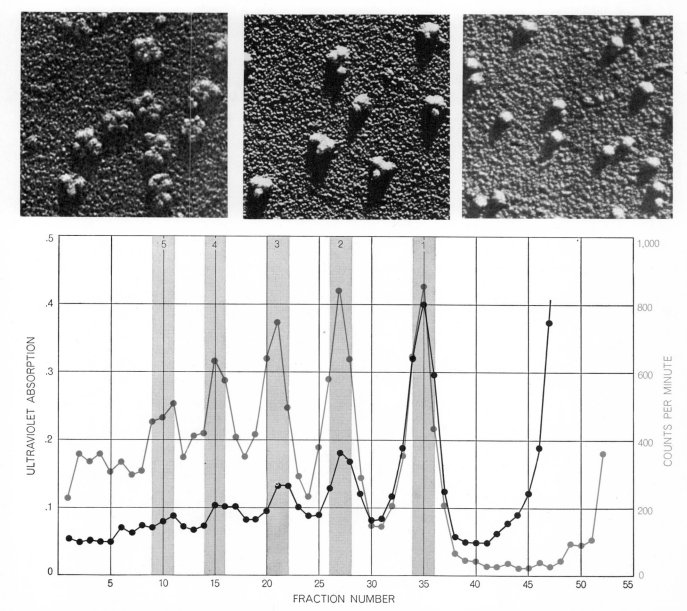

EFFECT OF GENTLE GRINDING is to produce a series of sedimentation peaks, indicating that the polyribosomes from reticulocytes have been broken up into smaller units. Electron micrographs (*top*) were made of samples obtained from the first, third and fifth peaks from the left. They contained respectively five-unit polyribosomes, three-unit polyribosomes and single ribosomes.

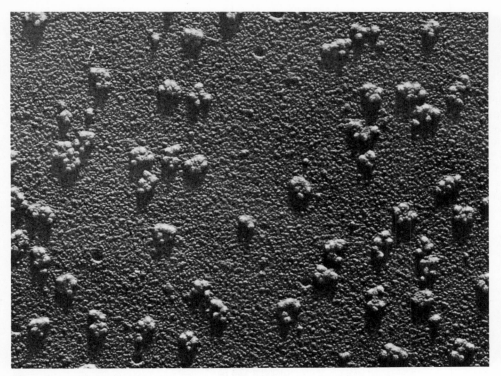

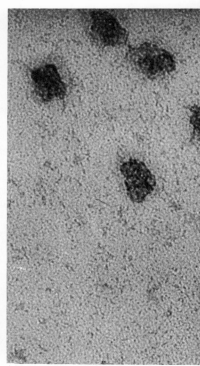

RETICULOCYTE POLYRIBOSOMES are shown at left shadowed with platinum and magnified 100,000 diameters in the electron microscope. Reticulyte polyribosomes at right have been positively stained with uranyl acetate and magnified 400,000 diameters by Henry

added to the growing polypeptide chain. When the synthesis is complete, the ribosome liberates the polypeptide chain and itself drops off the messenger strand. At about the same time another ribosome has found its way onto the messenger at the other end. The time needed for a single ribosome to traverse the messenger strand and produce a hemoglobin polypeptide chain has been estimated at one minute. In a bacterial cell the pro-

tein-synthesis time may be as little as 10 seconds.

In the reticulocyte the five-unit polysome is the most common species. The gaps between ribosomes vary somewhat, however, suggesting that the movement of ribosomes along the messenger strand has a statistical character. In some cases a ribosome will detach at one end before a new ribosome is attached at the other; this could account for the four-unit poly-

somes we see in some pictures. In other cases a ribosome may attach at one end before the fifth is released at the other end, thereby giving rise to a six-unit polysome. Such a statistical mode of operation would account for the distribution of polysome sizes observed in the reticulocyte.

Detroit might well envy the efficiency of the cell's protein factories. It is evident that protein synthesis is not really an

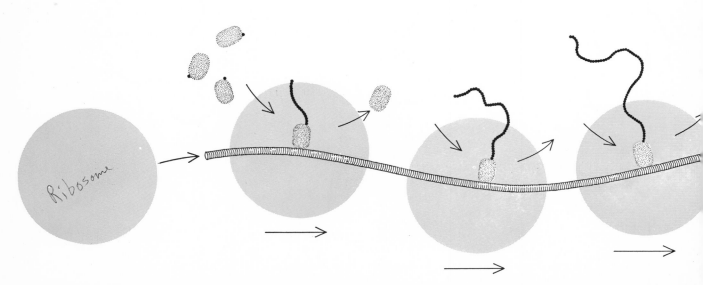

POLYRIBOSOME MECHANISM, as now visualized, consists of a long strand of messenger RNA to which single ribosomes attach themselves temporarily. As each ribosome travels along the strand it "reads" the information needed to synthesize a complete polypep-

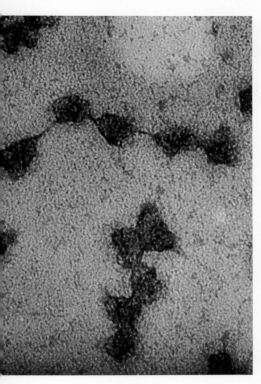

S. Slayter of the Massachusetts Institute of Technology. **Note the connecting threads.**

easily be fed through a battery of identical tools. The living cell evidently makes one tape serve for many tools because this is an efficient way to do the job.

As the concept of the polysome became clearer we were naturally anxious to look for polysomes in other cells. It seemed likely that a variety of messenger lengths and polysome sizes would be found. This has turned out to be the case.

A human tumor cell known as the HeLa cell is widely grown in tissue culture and provides a convenient example of a mammalian cell that produces many kinds of protein. Polysomes from the HeLa cell were prepared at M.I.T. by Sheldon Penman, Yachiel Becker and James E. Darnell. When we subjected these polysomes to sucrose-gradient centrifugation, we obtained the curves plotted in the illustration at the top of the next page. The electron microscope shows that the most common polysome species is one containing five or six ribosomes, but the distribution is much broader than that in the reticulocyte. Some of the HeLa polysomes contain 30 or 40 ribosomes.

It is not surprising that the distribution of polysomes from another kind of mammalian cell is much broader than that found in the reticulocyte. The reticulocyte is highly specialized and predominantly makes a single protein. Other mammalian cells make a great variety of protein molecules to conduct a variety of metabolic activities. A broad distribution of polysome sizes implies that a cell contains messenger RNA of many different lengths. Presumably their length is proportional to the lengths of the poly-

peptide chains being synthesized, but this may not be the only interpretation. Some of the long messenger RNA strands associated with polysomes that contain 20 or more ribosomes may contain information for making more than one kind of polypeptide chain.

This is almost certainly true of polysomes consisting of 50 to .70 ribosomes, which are found in cells infected by the virus of poliomyelitis. The long chain of RNA that bears the genetic code of this virus evidently serves as a strand of messenger RNA when it enters a mammalian host cell. Experiments by Penman, Darnell, Becker and Klaus Scherrer have shown that the polysomes that occur normally in a mammalian cell in tissue culture decrease sharply when the cell has been infected by polio virus. The rate of disappearance of the polysomes can be hastened by feeding the cells actinomycin D, an antibiotic that prevents the manufacture of messenger RNA. Thus about three hours after poliovirus infection and treatment with actinomycin D few polysomes can be found in the cell. Half an hour later, however, a new class of polysomes appears. The proteins synthesized on these polysomes are characteristic of the polio virus rather than of the mammalian cell. These virus-induced polysomes are among the largest we have seen in the electron microscope. They undoubtedly manufacture more than one kind of protein molecule; hence some additional features may have to be added to the simple polysome model I have described.

I shall mention briefly a few of the experiments we have designed to test our polysome model. The model as-

assembly line process as it is normally understood. It would be more appropriate to compare protein synthesis with the operation of a tape-controlled machine tool. The tool will turn out an object of any shape within its range of capabilities, in response to information coded on the input tape. In factories where such tools are used each tool is provided with its own tape, but if it served any purpose a single tape could

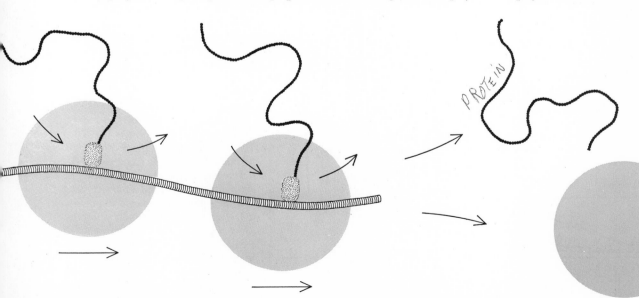

tide chain. The amino acids (*black dots*) for the chain are delivered by transfer RNA (*oblong shapes*). The polypeptide shown here contains 150 amino acid subunits, the number found in one chain of hemoglobin. The complete protein contains four chains.

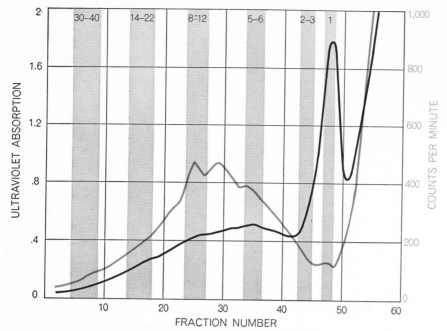

MAMMALIAN POLYRIBOSOMES appear as a very broad peak of fast-sedimenting material when analyzed by sucrose-gradient centrifugation. Electron micrographs show that one peak of the ultraviolet absorption coincides with polyribosomes containing five or six units.

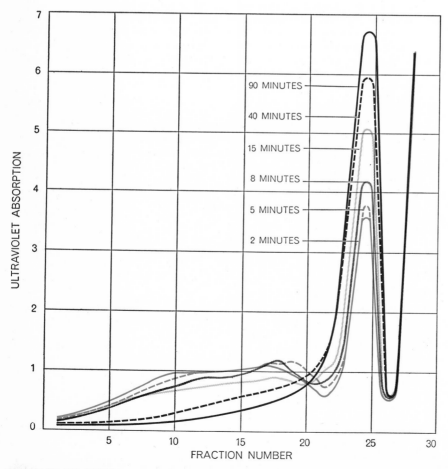

RELEASE OF SINGLE RIBOSOMES is demonstrated by incubating cell extracts with amino acids and an energy supply. Sucrose-gradient experiments show that the broad initial peak of polyribosomes gradually disappears and that the single-ribosome peak rises steadily.

sumes, for example, that an individual ribosome should be able to synthesize a polypeptide chain even though it normally works side by side with other ribosomes. This can be tested by saturating a reticulocyte extract with large amounts of external messenger RNA, such as the synthetic messenger RNA polyuridylic acid. This substance, which contains only one of the four bases normally found in messenger RNA, produces a synthetic polypeptide containing only one kind of amino acid: phenylalanine. By adding enough of the synthetic messenger to a reticulocyte extract one can obtain an extract in which there are as many messenger molecules as ribosomes. In this case most of the ribosomes should pair off with a messenger, leaving few ribosomes to form polysomes. The polysomes already in solution should be unaffected by the introduction of new messengers. Experiments of this type performed in our laboratory, as well as by Gierer in Tübingen, have shown that single ribosomes actively make the synthetic polypeptide polyphenylalanine when polyuridylic acid is added but that the polysomes themselves are inactive. Hence it is clear that individual ribosomes attached to single messenger strands can produce a polypeptide.

Our model also suggests that it should be possible to attach an additional ribosome to a polysome. We have postulated that a ribosome can attach itself to only one end of a messenger strand. If a ribosome could attach itself anywhere, chaos would result. In our simple model there should be only one attachment site on a polysome, whether it contains five ribosomes or 10. In two fractions containing equal numbers of ribosomes, however, there should be twice as many attachment sites in a fraction composed of five-unit polysomes as in a fraction composed of 10-unit polysomes.

Experiments to test this assumption were performed in our laboratory by Howard M. Goodman, a graduate student. Using a culture of HeLa cells, he produced single ribosomes labeled with the radioactive isotope hydrogen 3, or tritium. These single ribosomes were extracted and added to an unlabeled HeLa extract that contained a normal distribution of single ribosomes and polysomes. After a short period of incubation the extract was subjected to sucrose-gradient centrifugation. A test for radioactivity showed that some of the tritium-labeled single ribosomes had indeed become attached to polysomes. Moreover, in accordance with the prediction, twice as many single ribosomes were attached to five-unit polysomes as to 10-unit polysomes when the total number of ribosomes in each fraction was equal.

Our model also makes predictions about events at the terminal end of the messenger strand. It indicates that both ribosomes and polypeptide chains should be released from polysomes that are incubated under protein-synthesizing conditions. This can readily be tested in cell-free extracts because the extracts do not fully reproduce the functions of the intact cell. In particular, the messenger RNA is not replaced and other substances are destroyed, so that in the course of 90 minutes to two hours the cell extract gradually loses its ability to initiate the synthesis of protein. We are still, however, able to test for the release of ribosomes and polypeptide chains from polysomes.

To determine if single ribosomes are released from polysomes as protein synthesis proceeds we incubated cell extracts for varying periods before subjecting them to sucrose-gradient centrifugation. The results are plotted in the bottom illustration on the opposite page. At the beginning there is a large polysomal peak and a modest peak of single ribosomes, representing the normal distribution in the mammalian HeLa cell. As incubation proceeds there is a gradual decrease in the number of polysomes and a decrease in their size. At the same time there is an increase in the number of single ribosomes. At the end of 90 minutes of incubation most of the polysomes have disappeared, having been converted into single ribosomes. We have established that this release of single ribosomes takes place only if the energy necessary for protein synthesis is added to the reaction mixture. In other words, the system is not degraded simply by the passage of time.

To determine if polypeptides are released as incubation proceeds we devised the following experiment. A suspension of living mammalian cells was incubated for a minute and a half with carbon-14-labeled amino acids and then the cells were chilled to halt protein synthesis. This process loaded the polysomes with labeled amino acids that were linked into still unfinished polypeptide chains. Now the cells were broken open and the ribosomes and polysomes were isolated by centrifuging them into a pellet. The liquid on top of the pellet was poured off in order to get rid of the labeled amino acids floating around in the cell extract. The ribosomes and polysomes were then resuspended in a fresh cell extract identical with that removed except that it contained normal rather than radioactive amino acids.

This suspension was incubated under protein-synthesizing conditions, and radioactivity was measured as a function of time in the polysome fraction as well as in the soluble-protein fraction floating at the top of the sucrose gradient. As incubation proceeded, the radioactivity decreased in the former fraction and rose in the latter, showing that most of the labeled amino acids, originally held in the polysomes, were ultimately released as soluble protein. In sum, these three groups of experiments show that it is possible to attach ribosomes to polysomes, to detach ribosomes from polysomes and to liberate polypeptide chains under the conditions of protein synthesis.

I shall mention just one more experiment that supports our polysome model. This experiment, performed in our laboratory by Warner, established the average length of the incomplete polypeptide chains in the polysomes of the reticulocyte. In a complete polypeptide chain found in hemoglobin there are 17 subunits of the amino acid leucine. Warner incubated intact reticulocytes with carbon-14-labeled leucine and determined the number of leucine subunits in the polysome fraction. Knowing the number of ribosomes per polysome, he could easily calculate the number of leucine subunits per ribosome. He found the average number was 7.4. This implies that on the average there is almost half of a complete polypeptide chain on each ribosome in the polysome region. This is consistent with our proposed mechanism, which suggests that there is one growing polypeptide chain for each ribosome in the polysome.

Whether or not polysomes exist in all living cells is still to be determined. To date polysomes have been isolated from several species of bacteria, from the primitive plantlike organisms known as slime molds, from unicellular protozoa and from much more complex cells, including those of man. Therefore I believe that polyribosomes may be the general method used by nature for assembling amino acids into most proteins, and that protein synthesis does not usually occur on single ribosomes.

The discovery of polysomes represents the latest addition to the rapidly growing body of knowledge that describes at the molecular level how genetic information coded in DNA is eventually expressed in terms of active proteins that govern the metabolism and structure of the cell. One of the key problems still to be explained is how complicated globular proteins are put together to form a biologically active molecule. Some of these proteins have more than one polypeptide chain, and it may be that the polysomes play an active role in this next step of protein synthesis.

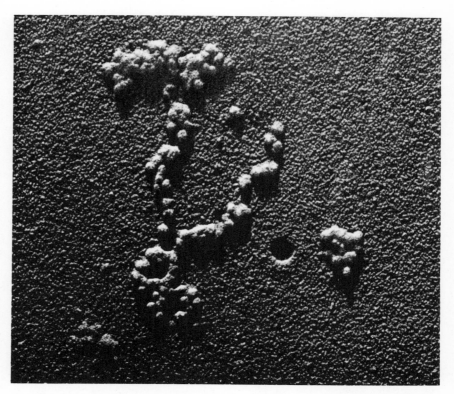

POLIO VIRUS POLYRIBOSOMES, the largest yet observed in the electron microscope, contain at least 50 individual ribosomes. These have been enlarged 115,000 diameters.

20 | The Genetic Code

F. H. C. CRICK · October 1962

Within the past year important progress has been made in solving the "coding problem." To the biologist this is the problem of how the information carried in the genes of an organism determines the structure of proteins.

Proteins are made from 20 different kinds of small molecule—the amino acids—strung together into long polypeptide chains. Proteins often contain several hundred amino acid units linked together, and in each protein the links are arranged in a specific order that is genetically determined. A protein is therefore like a long sentence in a written language that has 20 letters.

Genes are made of quite different long-chain molecules: the nucleic acids DNA (deoxyribonucleic acid) and, in some small viruses, the closely related RNA (ribonucleic acid). It has recently been found that a special form of RNA, called messenger RNA, carries the genetic message from the gene, which is located in the nucleus of the cell, to the surrounding cytoplasm, where many of the proteins are synthesized [see "Messenger RNA," by Jerard Hurwitz and J. J. Furth; SCIENTIFIC AMERICAN Offprint 119].

The nucleic acids are made by joining up four kinds of nucleotide to form a polynucleotide chain. The chain provides a backbone from which four kinds of side group, known as bases, jut at regular intervals. The order of the bases, however, is not regular, and it is their precise sequence that is believed to carry the genetic message. The coding problem can thus be stated more explicitly as the problem of how the sequence of the four bases in the nucleic acid determines the sequence of the 20 amino acids in the protein.

The problem has two major aspects, one general and one specific. Specifically one would like to know just what sequence of bases codes for each amino acid. Remarkable progress toward this goal was reported early in 1962 by Marshall W. Nirenberg and J. Heinrich Matthaei of the National Institutes of Health and by Severo Ochoa and his colleagues at the New York University School of Medicine. [Editor's note: Brief accounts of this work appeared in "Science and the Citizen" for February and March, 1962. This article was planned as a companion to the one by Nirenberg which deals with the biochemical aspects of the genetic code.]

The more general aspect of the coding problem, which will be my subject, has to do with the length of the genetic coding units, the way they are arranged in the DNA molecule and the way in which the message is read out. The experiments I shall report were performed at the Medical Research Council Laboratory of Molecular Biology in Cambridge, England. My colleagues were Mrs. Leslie Barnett, Sydney Brenner, Richard J. Watts-Tobin and, more recently, Robert Shulman.

The organism used in our work is the bacteriophage T4, a virus that infects the colon bacillus and subverts the biochemical machinery of the bacillus to make multiple copies of itself. The infective process starts when T4 injects its genetic core, consisting of a long strand of DNA, into the bacillus. In less than 20 minutes the virus DNA causes the manufacture of 100 or so copies of the complete virus particle, consisting of a DNA core and a shell containing at least six distinct protein components. In the process the bacillus is killed and the virus particles spill out. The great value of the T4 virus for genetic experiments is that many generations and billions of individuals can be produced in a short time. Colonies containing mutant individuals can be detected by the appearance of the small circular "plaques" they form on culture plates. Moreover, by the use of suitable cultures it is possible to select a single individual of interest from a population of a billion.

Using the same general technique, Seymour Benzer of Purdue University was able to explore the fine structure of the A and B genes (or cistrons, as he prefers to call them) found at the "rII" locus of the DNA molecule of T4 [see "The Fine Structure of the Gene," by Seymour Benzer, beginning on page 130 in this book]. He showed that the A and B genes, which are next to each other on the virus chromosome, each consist of some hundreds of distinct sites arranged in linear order. This is exactly what one would expect if each gene is a segment, say 500 or 1,000 bases long, of the very long DNA molecule that forms the virus chromosome [see illustration on following page]. The entire DNA molecule in T4 contains about 200,000 base pairs.

The Usefulness of Mutations

From the work of Benzer and others we know that certain mutations in the A and B region made one or both genes inactive, whereas other mutations were only partially inactivating. It had also been observed that certain mutations were able to suppress the effect of harmful mutations, thereby restoring the function of one or both genes. We suspected that the various—and often puzzling—consequences of different kinds of mutation might provide a key to the nature of the genetic code.

We therefore set out to re-examine the effects of crossing T4 viruses bearing mutations at various sites. By growing two different viruses together in a common culture one can obtain "recombinants" that have some of the properties

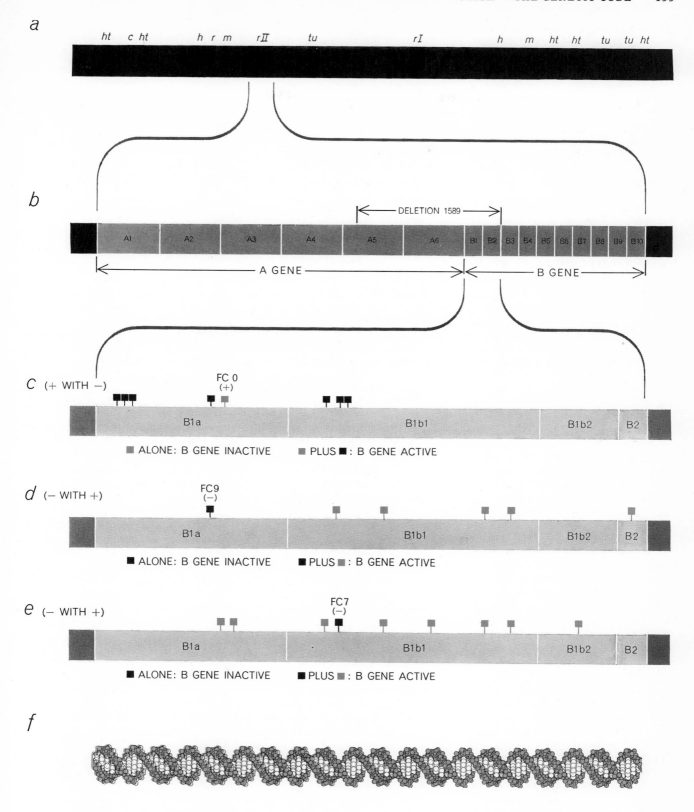

a

ht c ht   h r m   rII   tu   rI   h m ht ht tu tu ht

b

| A1 | A2 | A3 | A4 | A5 | A6 | B1 | B2 | B3 | B4 | B5 | B6 | B7 | B8 | B9 | B10 |

DELETION 1589

←——————————— A GENE ———————————→ ←————— B GENE —————→

c (+ WITH −)

FC 0
(+)

B1a   B1b1   B1b2   B2

■ ALONE: B GENE INACTIVE   ■ PLUS ■: B GENE ACTIVE

d (− WITH +)

FC9
(−)

B1a   B1b1   B1b2   B2

■ ALONE: B GENE INACTIVE   ■ PLUS ■: B GENE ACTIVE

e (− WITH +)

FC7
(−)

B1a   B1b1   B1b2   B2

■ ALONE: B GENE INACTIVE   ■ PLUS ■: B GENE ACTIVE

f

*r*II REGION OF THE T4 VIRUS represents only a few per cent of the DNA (deoxyribonucleic acid) molecule that carries full instructions for creating the virus. The region consists of two genes, here called A and B. The A gene has been mapped into six major segments, the B gene into 10 (*b*). The experiments reported in this article involve mutations in the first and second segments of the B gene. The B gene is inactivated by any mutation that adds a molecular subunit called a base (*colored square*) or removes one (*black square*). But activity is restored by simultaneous addition and removal of a base, as shown in *c, d* and *e*. An explanation for this recovery of activity is illustrated on page 202. The molecular representation of DNA (*f*) is estimated to be approximately in scale with the length of the B1 and B2 segments of the B gene. The two segments contain about 100 base pairs.

of one parent and some of the other. Thus one defect, such as the alteration of a base at a particular point, can be combined with a defect at another point to produce a phage with both defects [*see upper illustration below*]. Alternatively, if a phage has several defects, they can be separated by being crossed with the "wild" type, which by definition has none. In short, by genetic methods one can either combine or separate different mutations, provided that they do not overlap.

Most of the defects we shall be considering are evidently the result of adding or deleting one base or a small group of bases in the DNA molecule and not merely the result of altering one of the bases [*see lower illustration on this page*]. Such additions and deletions can be produced in a random manner with the compounds called acridines, by a process that is not clearly understood. We think they are very small additions or deletions, because the altered gene seems to have lost its function completely; mutations produced by reagents capable of changing one base into another are often partly functional. Moreover, the acridine mutations cannot be reversed by such reagents (and vice versa). But our strongest reason for believing they are additions or deletions is that they can be combined in a way that suggests they have this character.

To understand this we shall have to go back to the genetic code. The simplest sort of code would be one in which a small group of bases stands for one particular acid. This group can scarcely be a pair, since this would yield only 4×4, or 16, possibilities, and at least 20 are needed. More likely the shortest code group is a triplet, which would provide $4 \times 4 \times 4$, or 64, possibilities. A small group of bases that codes one amino acid has recently been named a codon.

The first definite coding scheme to be proposed was put forward eight years ago by the physicist George Gamow, now at the University of Colorado. In this code adjacent codons overlap as illustrated on the following page. One consequence of such a code is that only certain amino acids can follow others. Another consequence is that a change in a single base leads to a change in three adjacent amino acids. Evidence gathered since Gamow advanced his ideas makes an overlapping code appear unlikely. In the first place there seems to be no restriction of amino acid sequence in any of the proteins so far examined. It has also been shown that typical mutations change only a single amino acid in the

polypeptide chain of a protein. Although it is theoretically possible that the genetic code may be partly overlapping, it is more likely that adjacent codons do not overlap at all.

Since the backbone of the DNA molecule is completely regular, there is nothing to mark the code off into groups of

three bases, or into groups of any other size. To solve this difficulty various ingenious solutions have been proposed. It was thought, for example, that the code might be designed in such a way that if the wrong set of triplets were chosen, the message would always be complete nonsense and no protein would

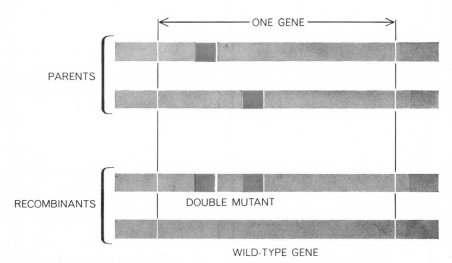

GENETIC RECOMBINATION provides the means for studying mutations. Colored squares represent mutations in the chromosome (DNA molecule) of the T4 virus. Through genetic recombination, the progeny can inherit the defects of both parents or of neither.

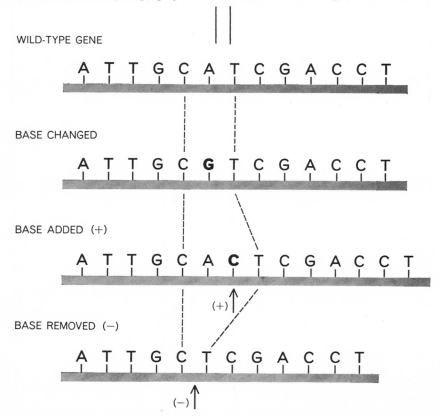

TWO CLASSES OF MUTATION result from introducing defects in the sequence of bases (A, T, G, C) that are attached to the backbone of the DNA molecule. In one class a base is simply changed from one into another, as A into G. In the second class a base is added or removed. Four bases are adenine (A), thymine (T), guanine (G) and cytosine (C).

be produced. But it now looks as if the most obvious solution is the correct one. That is, the message begins at a fixed starting point, probably one end of the gene, and is simply read three bases at a time. Notice that if the reading started at the wrong point, the message would fall into the wrong sets of three and would then be hopelessly incorrect. In fact, it is easy to see that while there is only one correct reading for a triplet code, there are two incorrect ones.

If this idea were right, it would immediately explain why the addition or the deletion of a base in most parts of the gene would make the gene completely nonfunctional, since the reading of the genetic message from that point onward would be totally wrong. Now, although our single mutations were always without function, we found that if we put certain pairs of them together, the gene would work. (In point of fact we picked up many of our functioning double mutations by starting with a nonfunctioning mutation and selecting for the rare second mutation that restored gene activity, but this does not affect our argument.) This enabled us to classify all our mutations as being either plus or minus. We found that by using the following rules we could always predict the

behavior of any pair we put together in the same gene. First, if plus is combined with plus, the combination is nonfunctional. Second, if minus is combined with minus, the result is nonfunctional. Third, if plus is combined with minus, the combination is nonfunctional if the pair is too widely separated and functional if the pair is close together.

The interesting case is the last one. We could produce a gene that functioned, at least to some extent, if we combined a plus mutation with a minus mutation, provided that they were not too far apart.

To make it easier to follow, let us assume that the mutations we called plus really had an extra base at some point and that those we called minus had lost a base. (Proving this to be the case is rather difficult.) One can see that, starting from one end, the message would be read correctly until the extra base was reached; then the reading would get out of phase and the message would be wrong until the missing base was reached, after which the message would come back into phase again. Thus the genetic message would not be wrong over a long stretch but only over the short distance between the plus and the minus. By the same sort of argument one

can see that for a triplet code the combination plus with plus or minus with minus should never work [see illustration on the next page].

We were fortunate to do most of our work with mutations at the left-hand end of the B gene of the rII region. It appears that the function of this part of the gene may not be too important, so that it may not matter if part of the genetic message in the region is incorrect. Even so, if the plus and minus are too far apart, the combination will not work.

Nonsense Triplets

To understand this we must go back once again to the code. There are 64 possible triplets but only 20 amino acids to be coded. Conceivably two or more triplets may stand for each amino acid. On the other hand, it is reasonable to expect that at least one or two triplets may not represent an amino acid at all but have some other meaning, such as "Begin here" or "End here." Although such hypothetical triplets may have a meaning of some sort, they have been named nonsense triplets. We surmised that sometimes the misreading produced in the region lying between a plus and a minus mutation might by chance give rise to a nonsense triplet, in which case the gene might not work.

We investigated a number of plus-with-minus combinations in which the distance between plus and minus was relatively short and found that certain combinations were indeed inactive when we might have expected them to function. Presumably an intervening nonsense triplet was to blame. We also found cases in which a plus followed by a minus worked but a minus followed by a plus did not, even though the two mutations appeared to be at the same sites, although in reverse sequence. As I have indicated, there are two wrong ways to read a message; one arises if the plus is to the left of the minus, the other if the plus is to the right of the minus. In cases where plus with minus gave rise to an active gene but minus with plus did not, even when the mutations evidently occupied the same pairs of sites, we concluded that the intervening misreading produced a nonsense triplet in one case but not in the other. In confirmation of this hypothesis we have been able to modify such nonsense triplets by mutagens that turn one base into another, and we have thereby restored the gene's activity. At the same time we have been able to locate the position of the nonsense triplet.

Recently we have undertaken one

PROPOSED CODING SCHEMES show how the sequence of bases in DNA can be read. In a nonoverlapping code, which is favored by the author, code groups are read in simple sequence. In one type of overlapping code each base appears in three successive groups.

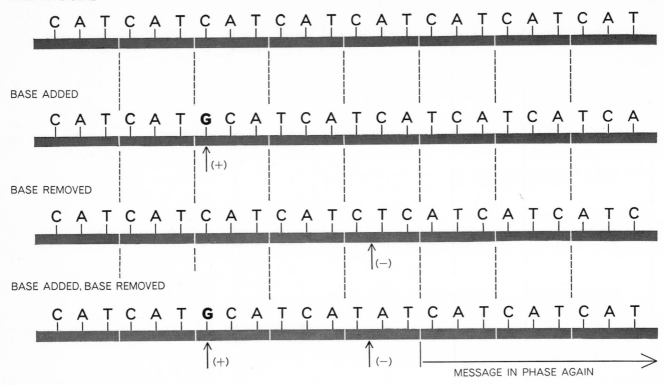

WILD-TYPE GENE

C A T C A T C A T C A T C A T C A T C A T C A T C A T

BASE ADDED

C A T C A T **G** C A T C A T C A T C A T C A T C A

(+)

BASE REMOVED

C A T C A T C A T C A T C T C A T C A T C A T C

(−)

BASE ADDED, BASE REMOVED

C A T C A T **G** C A T C A T A T C A T C A T C A T

(+)   (−) |⟶
                                   MESSAGE IN PHASE AGAIN

EFFECT OF MUTATIONS that add or remove a base is to shift the reading of the genetic message, assuming that the reading begins at the left-hand end of the gene. The hypothetical message in the wild-type gene is CAT, CAT... Adding a base shifts the reading to TCA, TCA... Removing a base makes it ATC, ATC... Addition and removal of a base puts the message in phase again.

other rather amusing experiment. If a single base were changed in the left-hand end of the B gene, we would expect the gene to remain active, both because this end of the gene seems to be unessential and because the reading of the rest of the message is not shifted. In fact, if the B gene remained active, we would have no way of knowing that a base had been changed. In a few cases, however, we have been able to destroy the activity of the B gene by a base change traceable to the left-hand end of the gene. Presumably the change creates a nonsense triplet. We reasoned that if we could shift the reading so that the message was read in different groups of three, the new reading might not yield a nonsense triplet. We therefore selected a minus and a plus that together allowed the B gene to function, and that were on each side of the presumed nonsense mutation. Sure enough, this combination of three mutants allowed the gene to function [see top illustration on page 204]. In other words, we could abolish the effect of a nonsense triplet by shifting its reading.

All this suggests that the message is read from a fixed point, probably from one end. Here the question arises of how one gene ends and another begins,

since in our picture there is nothing on the backbone of the long DNA molecule to separate them. Yet the two genes A and B are quite distinct. It is possible to measure their function separately, and Benzer has shown that no matter what mutation is put into the A gene, the B function is not affected, provided that the mutation is wholly within the A gene. In the same way changes in the B gene do not affect the function of the A gene.

The Space between the Genes

It therefore seems reasonable to imagine that there is something about the DNA between the two genes that isolates them from each other. This idea can be tested by experiments with a mutant T4 in which part of the rII region is deleted. The mutant, known as T4 1589, has lost a large part of the right end of the A gene and a smaller part of the left end of the B gene. Surprisingly the B gene still shows some function; in fact this is why we believe this part of the B gene is not too important.

Although we describe this mutation as a deletion, since genetic mapping shows that a large piece of the genetic

information in the region is missing, it does not mean that physically there is a gap. It seems more likely that DNA is all one piece but that a stretch of it has been left out. It is only by comparing it with the complete version—the wild type —that one can see a piece of the message is missing.

We have argued that there must be a small region between the genes that separates them. Consequently one would predict that if this segment of the DNA were missing, the two genes would necessarily be joined. It turns out that it is quite easy to test this prediction, since by genetic methods one can construct double mutants. We therefore combined one of our acridine mutations, which in this case was near the beginning of the A gene, with the deletion 1589. Without the deletion present the acridine mutation had no effect on the B function, which showed that the genes were indeed separate. But when 1589 was there as well, the B function was completely destroyed [see top illustration on page 203]. When the genes were joined, a change far away in the A gene knocked out the B gene completely. This strongly suggests that the reading proceeds from one end.

We tried other mutations in the A

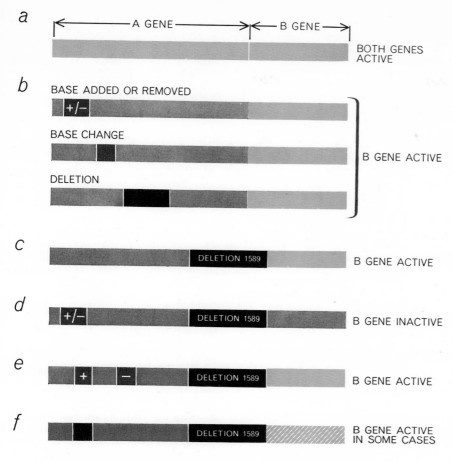

a A GENE — B GENE
BOTH GENES ACTIVE

b BASE ADDED OR REMOVED
+/−
BASE CHANGE
DELETION
B GENE ACTIVE

c DELETION 1589
B GENE ACTIVE

d +/− DELETION 1589
B GENE INACTIVE

e + − DELETION 1589
B GENE ACTIVE

f DELETION 1589
B GENE ACTIVE IN SOME CASES

DELETION JOINING TWO GENES makes the B gene vulnerable to mutations in the A gene. The messages in two wild-type genes (*a*) are read independently, beginning at the left end of each gene. Regardless of the kind of mutation in A, the B gene remains active (*b*). The deletion known as 1589 inactivates the A gene but leaves the B gene active (*c*). But now alterations in the A gene will often inactivate the B gene, showing that the two genes have been joined in some way and are read as if they were a single gene (*d, e, f*).

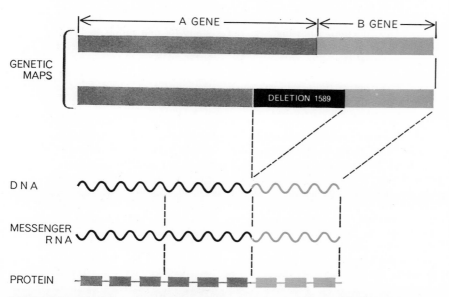

A GENE — B GENE
GENETIC MAPS
DELETION 1589
DNA
MESSENGER RNA
PROTEIN

PROBABLE EFFECT OF DELETION 1589 is to produce a mixed protein with little or no A-gene activity but substantial B activity. Although the conventional genetic map shows the deletion as a gap, the DNA molecule itself is presumably continuous but shortened. In virus replication the genetic message in DNA is transcribed into a molecule of ribonucleic acid, called messenger RNA. This molecule carries the message to cellular particles known as ribosomes, where protein is synthesized, following instructions coded in the DNA.

gene combined with 1589. All the acridine mutations we tried knocked out the B function, whether they were plus or minus, but a pair of them (plus with minus) still allowed the B gene to work. On the other hand, in the case of the other type of mutation (which we believe is due to the change of a base and not to one being added or subtracted) about half of the mutations allowed the B gene to work and the other half did not. We surmise that the latter are nonsense mutations, and in fact Benzer has recently been using this test as a definition of nonsense.

Of course, we do not know exactly what is happening in biochemical terms. What we suspect is that the two genes, instead of producing two separate pieces of messenger RNA, produce a single piece, and that this in turn produces a protein with a long polypeptide chain, one end of which has the amino acid sequence of part of the presumed A protein and the other end of which has most of the B protein sequence—enough to give some B function to the combined molecule although the A function has been lost. The concept is illustrated schematically at the bottom of this page. Eventually it should be possible to check the prediction experimentally.

How the Message Is Read

So far all the evidence has fitted very well into the general idea that the message is read off in groups of three, starting at one end. We should have got the same results, however, if the message had been read off in groups of four, or indeed in groups of any larger size. To test this we put not just two of our acridine mutations into one gene but three of them. In particular we put in three with the same sign, such as plus with plus with plus, and we put them fairly close together. Taken either singly or in pairs, these mutations will destroy the function of the B gene. But when all three are placed in the same gene, the B function reappears. This is clearly a remarkable result: two blacks will not make a white but three will. Moreover, we have obtained the same result with several different combinations of this type and with several of the type minus with minus with minus.

The explanation, in terms of the ideas described here, is obvious. One plus will put the reading out of phase. A second plus will give the other wrong reading. But if the code is a triplet code, a third plus will bring the message back into phase again, and from then on to the end it will be read correctly. Only between the pluses will the message be wrong [see illustration below].

Notice that it does not matter if plus is really one extra base and minus is one fewer; the conclusions would be the same if they were the other way around. In fact, even if some of the plus mutations were indeed a single extra base, others might be two fewer bases; in other words, a plus might really be minus minus. Similarly, some of the minus mutations might actually be plus plus. Even so they would still fit into our scheme.

Although the most likely explanation is that the message is read three bases at a time, this is not completely certain. The reading could be in multiples of three. Suppose, for example, that the message is actually read six bases at a time. In that case the only change needed in our interpretation of the facts is to assume that all our mutants have been changed by an even number of bases. We have some weak experimental evidence that this is unlikely. For instance, we can combine the mutant 1589 (which joins the genes) with medium-sized deletions in the A cistron. Now, if deletions were random in length, we should expect about a third of them to allow the B function to be expressed if the message is indeed read three bases at a time, since those deletions that had lost an exact multiple of three bases should allow the B gene to function. By the same reasoning only a sixth of them should work (when combined with 1589) if the reading proceeds six at a time. Actually we find that the B gene is active in a little more than a third. Taking all the evidence together, however, we find that although three is the most likely coding unit, we cannot completely rule out multiples of three.

There is one other general conclusion we can draw about the genetic code. If we make a rough guess as to the actual

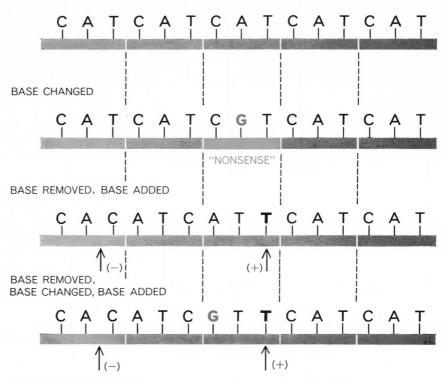

NONSENSE MUTATION is one creating a code group that evidently does not represent any of the 20 amino acids found in proteins. Thus it makes the gene inactive. In this hypothetical case a nonsense triplet, CGT, results when an A in the wild-type gene is changed to G. The nonsense triplet can be eliminated if the reading is shifted to put the G in a different triplet. This is done by recombining the inactive gene with one containing a minus-with-plus combination. In spite of three mutations, the resulting gene is active.

size of the B gene (by comparing it with another gene whose size is known approximately), we can estimate how many bases can lie between a plus with minus combination and still allow the B gene to function. Knowing also the frequency with which nonsense triplets are created in the misread region between the plus and minus, we can get some idea whether there are many such triplets or only a few. Our calculation suggests that nonsense triplets are not

too common. It seems, in other words, that most of the 64 possible triplets, or codons, are not nonsense, and therefore they stand for amino acids. This implies that probably more than one codon can stand for one amino acid. In the jargon of the trade, a code in which this is true is "degenerate."

In summary, then, we have arrived at three general conclusions about the genetic code:

1. The message is read in nonover-

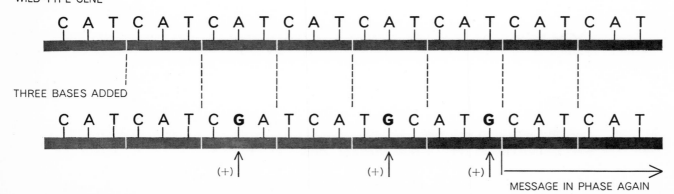

TRIPLE MUTATION in which three bases are added fairly close together spoils the genetic message over a short stretch of the gene but leaves the rest of the message unaffected. The same result can be achieved by the deletion of three neighboring bases.

lapping groups from a fixed point, probably from one end. The starting point determines that the message is read correctly into groups.

2. The message is read in groups of a fixed size that is probably three, although multiples of three are not completely ruled out.

3. There is very little nonsense in the code. Most triplets appear to allow the gene to function and therefore probably represent an amino acid. Thus in general more than one triplet will stand for each amino acid.

It is difficult to see how to get around our first conclusion, provided that the B gene really does code a polypeptide chain, as we have assumed. The second conclusion is also difficult to avoid. The third conclusion, however, is much more indirect and could be wrong.

Finally, we must ask what further evidence would really clinch the theory we have presented here. We are continuing to collect genetic data, but I doubt that this will make the story much more convincing. What we need is to obtain a protein, for example one produced by a double mutation of the form plus with minus, and then examine its amino acid sequence. According to conventional theory, because the gene is altered in only two places the amino acid sequences also should differ only in the two corresponding places. According to our theory it should be altered not only at these two places but also at all places in between. In other words, a whole string of amino acids should be changed. There is one protein, the lysozyme of the T4 phage, that is favorable for such an approach, and we hope that before long workers in the U.S. who have been studying phage lysozyme will confirm our theory in this way.

The same experiment should also be useful for checking the particular code schemes worked out by Nirenberg and Matthaei and by Ochoa and his colleagues. The phage lysozyme made by the wild-type gene should differ over only a short stretch from that made by the plus-with-minus mutant. Over this stretch the amino acid sequence of the two lysozyme variants should correspond to the same sequence of bases on the DNA but should be read in different groups of three.

If this part of the amino acid sequence of both the wild-type and the altered lysozyme could be established, one could check whether or not the codons assigned to the various amino acids did indeed predict similar sequences for that part of the DNA between the base added and the base removed.

21 | *The Genetic Code: II*

MARSHALL W. NIRENBERG · *March 1963*

J ust 10 years ago James D. Watson and Francis H. C. Crick proposed the now familiar model for the structure of DNA (deoxyribonucleic acid), for which they, together with Maurice H. F. Wilkins, received a Nobel prize last year. DNA is the giant helical molecule that embodies the genetic code of all living organisms. In the October 1962 issue of *Scientific American* F. H. C. Crick described this code (Offprint #123).

By ingenious experiments with bacterial viruses he and his colleagues established that the "letters" in the code are read off in simple sequence and that "words" in the code most probably consist of groups of three letters. The code letters in the DNA molecule are the four bases, or chemical subunits, adenine, guanine, cytosine and thymine, respectively denoted A, G, C and T.

This article describes how various combinations of these bases, or code letters, provide the specific biochemical information used by the cell in the construction of proteins: giant molecules assembled from 20 common kinds of amino acids. Each amino acid subunit is directed to its proper site in the protein chain by a sequence of code letters in the DNA molecule (or molecules) that each organism inherits from its ancestors. It is this DNA that is shaped by evolution. Organisms compete with each other for survival; occasional random changes in their information content, carried by DNA, are sometimes advantageous in this competition. In this way organisms slowly become enriched with instructions facilitating their survival.

The exact number of proteins required for the functioning of a typical living cell is not known, but it runs to many hundreds. The great majority, if not all, of the proteins act as enzymes, or biological catalysts, which direct the hundreds of different chemical reactions that go on simultaneously within each cell. A typical protein is a molecular chain containing about 200 amino acid subunits linked together in a specific sequence. Each protein usually contains all or most of the 20 different kinds of amino acids. The code for each protein is carried by a single gene, which in turn is a particular region on the linear DNA molecule. To describe a protein containing 200 amino acid subunits a gene must contain at least 200 code words, represented by a sequence of perhaps 600 bases. No one yet knows the complete base sequence for a single gene. Viruses, the smallest structures containing the blueprints for their own replication, may contain from a few to several hundred genes. Bacteria may contain 1,000 genes; a human cell may contain a million. The human genes are not strung together in

EXPERIMENT BEGINS when cells of the colon bacillus are ground in a mortar with finely divided aluminum oxide. "Sap" released from ruptured cells still synthesizes protein.

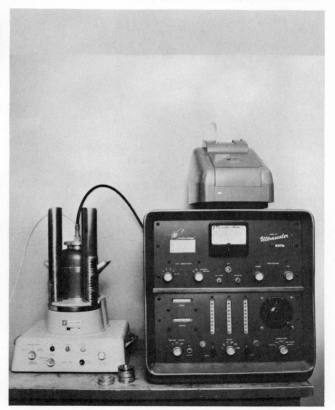

STEPS IN CODE BREAKING are shown in this sequence of photographs taken in the author's laboratory at the National Institutes of Health in Bethesda, Md. The open test tubes at upper left contain samples of the cell-free bacterial system capable of synthesizing protein when properly stimulated. The photograph shows stimulants being added. They include synthetic "messenger RNA" (ribonucleic acid) and amino acids, one of which is radioactive. The protein is produced when the samples are incubated 10 to 90 minutes. At upper right the protein is precipitated by the addition of trichloroacetic acid (TCA). At lower left the precipitate is transferred to filter-paper disks, which will be placed in carriers called planchettes. At lower right the planchettes are stacked in a radiation counting unit. Radiation measurement indicates how well a given sample of messenger RNA has directed amino acids into protein.

BASES

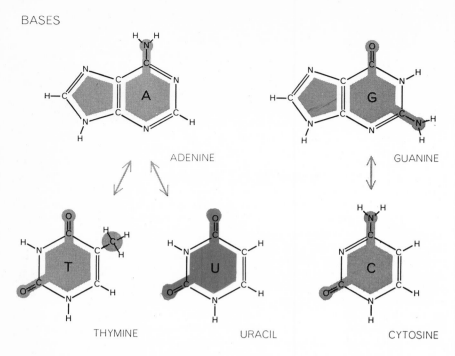

CHAIN COMPONENTS

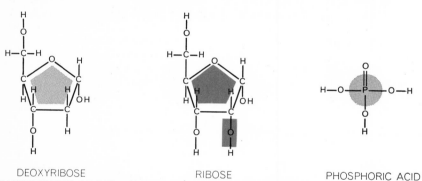

DEOXYRIBOSE   RIBOSE   PHOSPHORIC ACID

COMPONENTS OF DNA (deoxyribonucleic acid) are four bases adenine, guanine, thymine and cytosine (symbolized A, G, T, C), which act as code letters. Other components, deoxyribose and phosphoric acid, form chains to which bases attach (*see below*). In closely related RNA, uracil (U) replaces thymine and ribose replaces deoxyribose.

DNA STRUCTURE

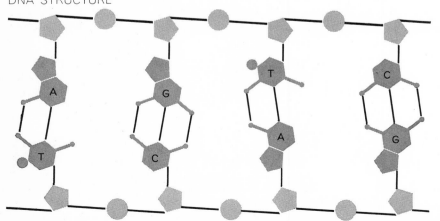

DNA MOLECULE resembles a chain ladder (actually twisted into a helix) in which pairs of bases join two linear chains constructed from deoxyribose and phosphate subunits. The bases invariably pair so that A links to T and G to C. The genetic code is the sequence of bases as read down one side of the ladder. The deoxyribose-phosphate linkages in the two linear chains run in opposite directions. DNA molecules contain thousands of base pairs.

one long chain but must be divided among at least 46 DNA molecules. The minimum number is set by the number of human chromosomes (46), which collectively carry the hereditary material. In fact, each chromosome apparently carries not one or two but several copies of the same genetic message. If it were possible to assemble the DNA in a single human cell into one continuous thread, it would be about a yard long. This three-foot set of instructions for each individual is produced by the fusion of egg and sperm at conception and must be precisely replicated billions of times as the embryo develops.

The bottom illustration at left shows how the bases in DNA form the cross links connecting two helical strands composed of alternating units of deoxyribose (a simple sugar) and phosphate. The bases are attached to the sugar units and always occur in complementary pairs: A joined to T, and G joined to C. As a result one strand of the DNA molecule, with its associated bases, can serve as the template for creating a second strand that has a complementary set of bases. The faithful replication of genes during cell division evidently depends on such a copying mechanism.

The coding problem centers around the question: How can a four-letter alphabet (the bases A, G, C and T) specify a 20-word dictionary corresponding to the 20 amino acids? In 1954 the theoretical physicist George Gamow, now at the University of Colorado, pointed out that the code words in such a dictionary would have to contain at least three bases. It is obvious that only four code words can be formed if the words are only one letter in length. With two letters 4 × 4, or 16, code words can be formed. And with three letters 4 × 4 × 4, or 64, code words become available—more than enough to handle the 20-word amino acid dictionary [*see top illustration on page 214*]. Subsequently many suggestions were made as to the nature of the genetic code, but extensive experimental knowledge of the code has been obtained only within the past 18 months.

The Genetic Messenger

It was recognized soon after the formulation of the Watson-Crick model of DNA that DNA itself might not be directly involved in the synthesis of protein, and that a template of RNA (ribonucleic acid) might be an intermediate in the process. Protein synthesis is conducted by cellular particles called ribosomes, which are about half protein and half RNA (ribosomal RNA). Several years ago Jacques Monod and François Jacob of the Pasteur Institute in Paris coined the term "messenger RNA" to describe the template RNA that carried genetic messages from DNA to the ribosomes.

A few years ago evidence for the enzymatic synthesis of RNA complementary to DNA was found by Jerard Hurwitz of the New York University School of Medicine, by Samuel Weiss of the University of Chicago, by Audrey Stevens of St. Louis University and their respective collaborators [see "Messenger RNA," by Jerard Hurwitz and J. J. Furth; SCIENTIFIC AMERICAN Offprint 119]. These groups, and others, showed that an enzyme, RNA polymerase, catalyzes the synthesis of strands of RNA on the pattern of strands of DNA.

RNA is similar to DNA except that RNA contains the sugar ribose instead of deoxyribose and the base uracil instead of thymine. When RNA is being formed on a DNA template, uracil appears in the RNA chain wherever adenine appears at the complementary site on the DNA chain. One fraction of the RNA formed by this process is messenger RNA; it directs the synthesis of protein. Messenger RNA leaves the nucleus of the cell and attaches to the ribosomes. The sequence of bases in the messenger

RNA specifies the amino acid sequence in the protein to be synthesized.

The amino acids are transported to the proper sites on the messenger RNA by still another form of RNA called transfer RNA. Each cell contains a specific activating enzyme that attaches a specific amino acid to its particular transfer RNA. Moreover, cells evidently contain more than one kind of transfer RNA capable of recognizing a given amino acid. The significance of this fact will become apparent later. Although direct recognition of messenger RNA code words by transfer RNA molecules has not been demonstrated, it is clear that these molecules perform at least part of the job of placing amino acids in the proper position in the protein chain. When the amino acids arrive at the proper site in the chain, they are linked to each other by enzymic processes that are only partly understood. The linking is accomplished by the formation of a peptide bond: a chemical bond created when a molecule of water is removed from two adjacent molecules of amino acid. The process requires a transfer enzyme, at least one other enzyme and a cofactor: guanosine triphosphate. It appears that amino acid subunits are bonded into the growing protein chain one at a time, starting at the end of the chain carrying an amino group (NH_2)

and proceeding toward the end that terminates with a carboxyl group (COOH).

The process of protein synthesis can be studied conveniently in cell-free extracts of the colon bacillus (*Escherichia coli*). The bacteria grow rapidly in suitable nutrients and are harvested by sedimenting them out of suspension with a centrifuge. The cells are gently broken open by grinding them with finely powdered alumina [*see illustration on page 206*]; this releases the cell sap, containing DNA, messenger RNA, ribosomes, enzymes and other components. Such extracts are called cell-free systems, and when they are fortified with energy-rich substances (chiefly adenosine triphosphate), they readily incorporate amino acids into protein. The incorporation process can be followed by using amino acids containing carbon 14, a radioactive isotope of carbon.

Optimal conditions for protein synthesis in bacterial cell-free systems were determined by workers in many laboratories, notably Alfred Tissières of Harvard University, Marvin Lamborg and Paul C. Zamecnik of the Massachusetts General Hospital, G. David Novelli of the Oak Ridge National Laboratory and Sol Spiegelman of the University of Illinois. When we began our work at the National Institutes of Health, our

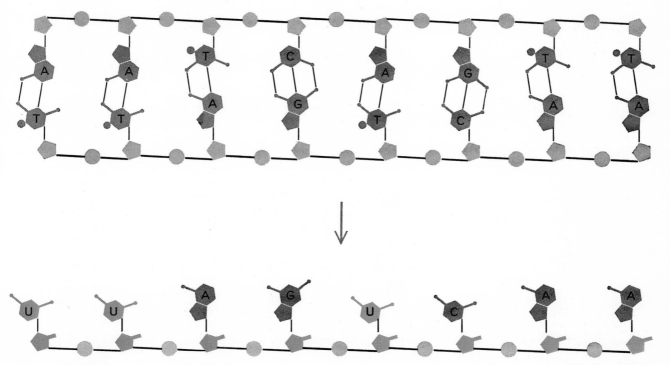

MESSENGER RNA is the molecular agent that transcribes the genetic code from DNA and carries it to the sites in the cell (the ribosomes) where protein synthesis takes place. The letters in messenger RNA are complementary to those in one strand of the DNA molecule. In this example UUAGUCAA is complementary to AATCAGTT. The exact mechanism of transcription is not known.

progress was slow because we had to prepare fresh enzyme extracts for each experiment. Later my colleague J. Heinrich Matthaei and I found a way to stabilize the extracts so that they could be stored for many weeks without appreciable loss of activity.

Normally the proteins produced in such extracts are those specified by the cell's own DNA. If one could establish the base sequence in one of the cell's genes—or part of a gene—and correlate it with the amino acid sequence in the protein coded by that gene, one would

be able to translate the genetic code. Although the amino acid sequence is known for a number of proteins, no one has yet determined the base sequence of a gene, hence the correlation cannot be performed.

The study of cell-free protein syn-

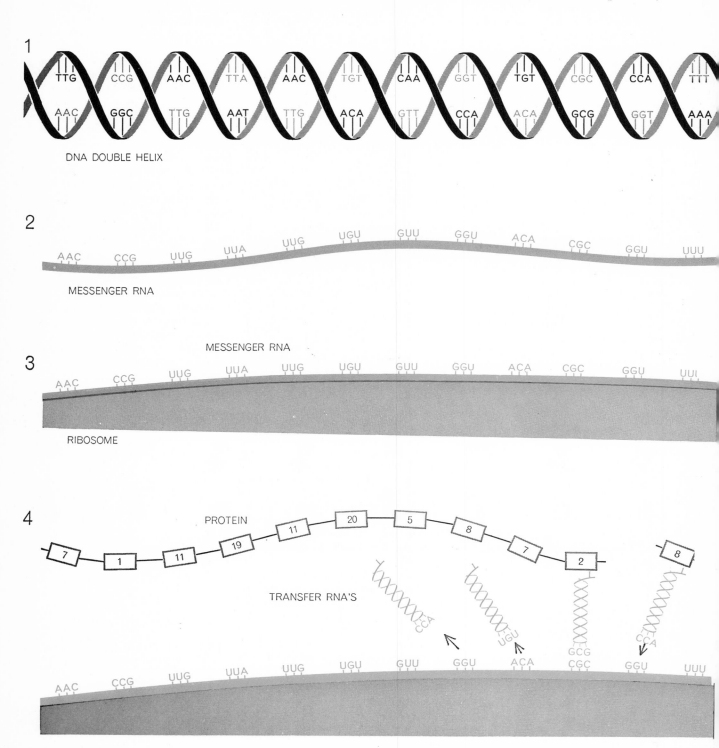

SYNTHESIS OF PROTEIN begins with the genetic code embodied in DNA (*1*). The code is transcribed into messenger RNA (*2*). In the diagram it is assumed that the message has been derived from the DNA strand bearing dark letters. The messenger RNA finds its way to a ribosome (*3*), the site of protein synthesis. Amino acids, indicated by numbered rectangles, are carried to proper sites on the messenger RNA by molecules of transfer RNA (*see illustration on opposite page*). Bases are actually equidistant, not

thesis provided an indirect approach to the coding problem. Tissières, Novelli and Bention Nisman, then at the Pasteur Institute, had reported that protein synthesis could be halted in cell-free extracts by adding deoxyribonuclease, or DNAase, an enzyme that specifically de-

stroys DNA. Matthaei and I also observed this effect and studied its characteristics. It seemed probable that protein synthesis stopped after the messenger RNA had been depleted. When we added crude fractions of messenger RNA to such extracts, we found that they stimulated protein synthesis. The development of this cell-free assay for messenger RNA provided the rationale for all our subsequent work.

We obtained RNA fractions from various natural sources, including viruses, and found that many of them were highly active in directing protein synthesis in the cell-free system of the colon bacillus. The ribosomes of the colon bacillus were found to accept RNA "blueprints" obtained from foreign organisms, including viruses. It should be emphasized that only minute amounts of protein were synthesized in these experiments.

It occurred to us that synthetic RNA containing only one or two bases might direct the synthesis of simple proteins containing only a few amino acids. Synthetic RNA molecules can be prepared with the aid of an enzyme, polynucleotide phosphorylase, found in 1955 by Marianne Grunberg-Manago and Severo Ochoa of the New York University School of Medicine. Unlike RNA polymerase, this enzyme does not follow the pattern of DNA. Instead it forms RNA polymers by linking bases together in random order.

A synthetic RNA polymer containing only uracil (called polyuridylic acid, or poly-U) was prepared and added to the active cell-free system together with mixtures of the 20 amino acids. In each mixture one of the amino acids contained radioactive carbon 14; the other 19 amino acids were nonradioactive. In this way one could determine the particular amino acid directed into protein by poly-U.

It proved to be the amino acid phenylalanine. This provided evidence that the RNA code word for phenylalanine was a sequence of U's contained in poly-U. The code word for another amino acid, proline, was found to be a sequence of C's in polycytidylic acid, or poly-C. Thus a cell-free system capable of synthesizing protein under the direction of chemically defined preparations of RNA provided a simple means for translating the genetic code.

The Code-Word Dictionary

Ochoa and his collaborators and our group at the National Institutes of

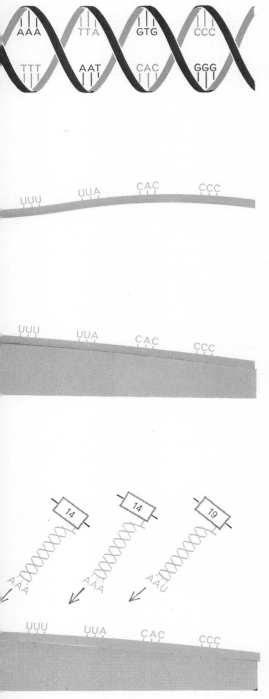

grouped in triplets, and mechanism of recognition between transfer RNA and messenger RNA is hypothetical. Linkage of amino acid subunits creates a protein molecule.

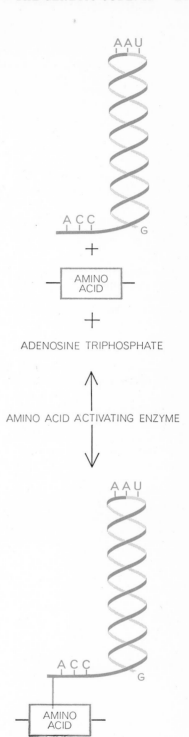

TRANSFER RNA is a special helical form of RNA that transports amino acids to their proper site in the protein chain. There is at least one transfer RNA for each of the 20 common amino acids. All, however, seem to carry the bases ACC where the amino acids attach and G at the opposite end. The attachment requires a specific enzyme and energy supplied by adenosine triphosphate. Unpaired bases in transfer RNA (AAU in the example) may provide the means by which the transfer RNA "recognizes" the place to deposit its amino acid package.

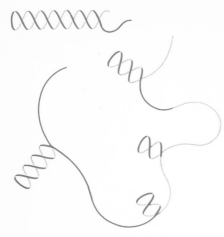

RNA STRUCTURE can take various forms. Transfer RNA (*top*) seems to be a fairly short double helix (probably less perfect than shown) that is closed at one end. Some RNA molecules contain a mixture of coiled and uncoiled regions (*bottom*).

Health, working independently, have now synthesized and tested polymers containing all possible combinations of the four RNA bases A, G, C and U. In the initial experiments only RNA polymers containing U were assayed, but recently many non-U polymers with high template activity have been found by M. Bretscher and Grunberg-Manago of the University of Cambridge, and also by Oliver W. Jones and me. All the results so far are summarized in the table at the bottom of pages 214 and 215. It lists the

RNA polymers containing the minimum number of bases capable of stimulating protein formation. The inclusion of another base in a polymer usually enables it to code for additional amino acids.

With only two kinds of base it is possible to make six varieties of RNA polymer: poly-AC, poly-AG, poly-AU, poly-CG, poly-CU and poly-GU. If the ratio of the bases is adjusted with care, each variety can be shown to code with great specificity for different sets of amino acids. The relative amount of one amino acid directed into protein compared with another depends on the ratio of bases in the RNA. Assuming a random sequence of bases in the RNA, the theoretical probabilities of finding particular sequences of two, three or more bases can be calculated easily if the base ratio is known. For example, if poly-UC contains 70 per cent U and 30 per cent C, the probability of the occurrence of the triplet sequence UUU is .7 × .7 × .7, or .34. That is, 34 per cent of the triplets in the polymer are expected to be UUU. The probability of obtaining the sequence UUC is .7 × .7 × .3, or .147. Thus 14.7 per cent of the triplets in such a polymer are probably UUC. This type of calculation, however, assumes randomness, and it is not certain that all the actual polymers are truly random.

It had been predicted by Gamow, Crick and others that for each amino acid there might be more than one code word, since there are 64 possible triplets and

only 20 amino acids. A code with multiple words for each object coded is termed degenerate. Our experiments show that the genetic code is indeed degenerate. Leucine, for example, is coded by RNA polymers containing U alone, or U and A, or U and C, or U and G.

It must be emphasized that degeneracy of this sort does not imply lack of specificity in the construction of proteins. It means, rather, that a specific amino acid can be directed to the proper site in a protein chain by more than one code word. Presumably this flexibility of coding is advantageous to the cell in ways not yet fully understood.

A molecular explanation of degeneracy has been provided recently in a striking manner. It has been known that some organisms contain more than one species of transfer RNA capable of recognizing a given amino acid. The colon bacillus, for example, contains two readily distinguishable species that transfer leucine. Bernard Weisblum and Seymour Benzer of Purdue University and Robert W. Holley of Cornell University separated the two leucine-transfer species and tested them in cell-free systems. They found that one of the species recognizes poly-UC but not poly-UG. The other species recognizes poly-UG but not poly-UC [see top illustration on page 213]. Although the number of transfer RNA species per cell is unknown, it is possible that each species corresponds to a different code word.

There is, however, the possibility of

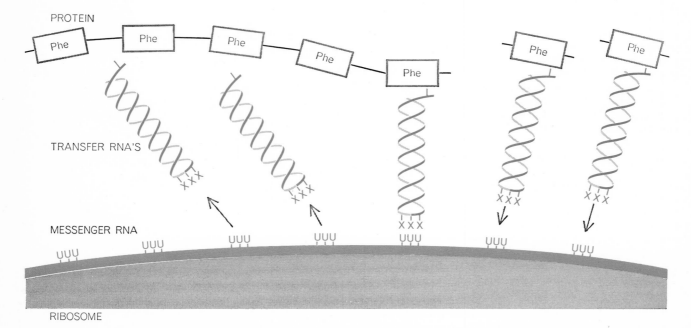

FIRST BREAK IN GENETIC CODE was the discovery that a synthetic messenger RNA containing only uracil (poly-U) directed the manufacture of a synthetic protein containing only one amino acid, phenylalanine (*Phe*). The finding was made by the author and J. Heinrich Matthaei. The X's in transfer RNA signify that the bases that respond to code words in messenger RNA are not known.

real ambiguity in protein synthesis. This would occur if one code word were to direct two or more kinds of amino acid into protein. So far only one such ambiguity has been found. Poly-U directs small amounts of leucine as well as phenylalanine into protein. The ratio of the two amino acids incorporated is about 20 or 30 molecules of phenylalanine to one of leucine. In the absence of phenylalanine, poly-U codes for leucine about half as well as it does for phenylalanine. The molecular basis of this ambiguity is not known. Nor is it known if the dual coding occurs in living systems as well as in cell-free systems.

Base sequences that do not encode for any amino acid are termed "nonsense words." This term may be misleading, for such sequences, if they exist, might have meaning to the cell. For example, they might indicate the beginning or end of a portion of the genetic message. An indirect estimate of the frequency of nonsense words can be obtained by comparing the efficiency of random RNA preparations with that of natural messenger RNA. We have found that many of the synthetic polymers containing four, three or two kinds of base are as efficient in stimulating protein synthesis as natural polymers are. This high efficiency, together with high coding specificity, suggests that relatively few base sequences are nonsense words.

In the preceding article, "The Genetic Code," F. H. C. Crick presented arguments for believing that the coding ratio is either three or a multiple of three. Recently we have determined the relative amounts of different amino acids directed into protein by synthetic RNA preparations of known base ratios, and the evidence suggests that some code words almost surely contain three bases. Yet, as the table at the bottom of the next two pages shows, 18 of the 20 amino acids can be coded by words containing only two different bases. The exceptions are aspartic acid and methionine, which seem to require some combination of U, G and A. (Some uncertainty still exists about the code words for these amino acids, because even poly-UGA directs very little aspartic acid or methionine into protein.) If the entire code indeed consists of triplets, it is possible that correct coding is achieved, in some instances, when only two out of the three bases read are recognized. Such imperfect recognition might occur more often with synthetic RNA polymers containing only one or two bases than it does with natural messenger RNA, which always contains a mixture of all four. The results obtained with synthetic RNA may dem-

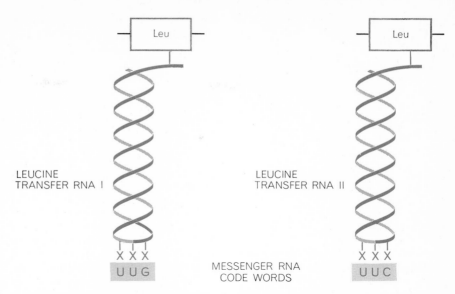

TWO KINDS OF TRANSFER RNA have been found, each capable of transporting leucine (*Leu*). One kind (*left*) recognizes the code word UUG; the other (*right*) recognizes UUC.

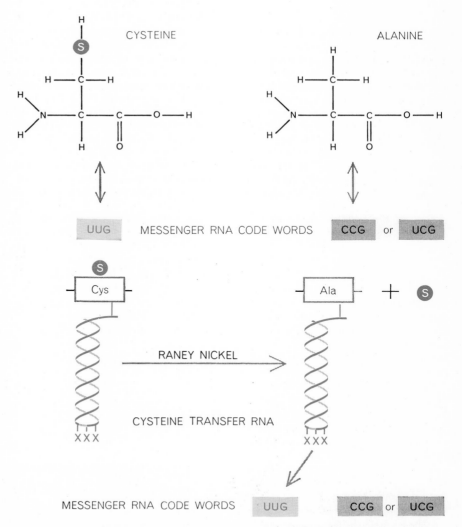

INGENIOUS EXPERIMENT showed that code-word recognition depends on the specificity of transfer RNA, not on the structure of the amino acid being transported. Cysteine is coded by UUG, alanine by CCG or UCG. Cysteine was hooked to its specific transfer RNA and sulfur was removed by a catalyst (Raney nickel). With sulfur removed from the molecule, cysteine became alanine. It was still directed into protein, however, as if it were cysteine.

SINGLET CODE (4 WORDS)
A
G
C
U

DOUBLET CODE (16 WORDS)			
AA	AG	AC	AU
GA	GG	GC	GU
CA	CG	CC	CU
UA	UG	UC	UU

TRIPLET CODE (64 WORDS)			
AAA	AAG	AAC	AAU
AGA	AGG	AGC	AGU
ACA	ACG	ACC	ACU
AUA	AUG	AUC	AUU
GAA	GAG	GAC	GAU
GGA	GGG	GGC	GGU
GCA	GCG	GCC	GCU
GUA	GUG	GUC	GUU
CAA	CAG	CAC	CAU
CGA	CGG	CGC	CGU
CCA	CCG	CCC	CCU
CUA	CUG	CUC	CUU
UAA	UAG	UAC	UAU
UGA	UGG	UGC	UGU
UCA	UCG	UCC	UCU
UUA	UUG	UUC	UUU

CODE-LETTER COMBINATIONS increase sharply with the length of the code word. Since at least 20 code words are needed to identify the 20 common amino acids, the minimum code length is a sequence of three letters, assuming that all words are the same length.

onstrate the coding potential of the cell; that is, it may reveal code words that function routinely in the living cell and potential words that would be recognized if appropriate mutations were to occur in the cellular DNA. The table on page 216 summarizes the code-word dictionary on the assumption that all code words are triplets.

The Universality of the Code

Does each plant or animal species have its own genetic code, or is the same genetic language used by all species on this planet? Preliminary evidence suggests that the code is essentially universal and that even species at opposite ends of the evolutionary scale use much the same code. For instance, a number of laboratories in the U.S. and England have recently reported that synthetic RNA polymers code the same way in mammalian cell-free systems as they do in the bacterial system. The base compositions of mammalian code words corresponding to about six amino acids have been determined so far. It nevertheless seems probable that some differences may be found in the future. Since certain amino acids are coded by multiple words, it is not unlikely that one species may use one word and another species a different one.

An indirect check on the validity of code words obtained in cell-free systems can be made by studying natural proteins that differ in amino acid composition at only one point in the protein chain. For example, the hemoglobin of an individual suffering from "sickle cell" anemia differs from normal hemoglobin in that it has valine at one point in the chain instead of glutamic acid. Another abnormal hemoglobin has lysine at the same point. One might be able to show, by examining the code-word dictionary, that these three amino acids—glutamic acid, valine and lysine—have similar code words. One could then infer that the two

abnormal hemoglobins came into being as a result of a mutation that substituted a single base for another in the gene that controls the production of hemoglobin. As a matter of fact, the code-word dictionary shows that the code words are similar enough for this to have happened. One of the code groups for glutamic acid is AGU. Substitution of a U for A produces UGU, the code group for valine. Substitution of an A for a U yields AGA, one of the code groups for lysine. Similar analyses have been made for other proteins in which amino acid substitutions are known, and in most cases the substitutions can be explained by alteration of a single base in code-word triplets. Presumably more code words will be found in the future and the correlation between genetic base sequences and amino acid sequences can be made with greater assurance.

The Nature of Messenger RNA

Does each molecule of messenger RNA function only once or many times in directing the synthesis of protein? The question has proved difficult because most of the poly-U in the experimental system is degraded before it is able to function as a messenger. We have found, nevertheless, that only about 1.5 U's in poly-U are required to direct the incorporation of one molecule of phenylalanine into protein. And George Spyrides and Fritz A. Lipmann of the Rockefeller Institute have reported that only about .75 U's are required per molecule of amino acid in their studies. If the coding is done by triplets, three U's would be required if the messenger functioned only once. Evidently each poly-U molecule directs the synthesis of more than one long-chain molecule of polyphenylalanine. Similar results have been obtained in intact cells. Cyrus Levinthal and his associates at the Massachusetts Institute

	U	A	C	G
AMINO ACIDS CODED	PHENYLALANINE	LYSINE	PROLINE●	
	LEUCINE■			

■ POLY U CODES PREFERENTIALLY FOR PHENYLALANINE
● REPORTED BY ONLY ONE LABORATORY; STILL TO BE CONFIRMED
▲ REQUIRES ONLY FIRST OF TWO BASES LISTED
△ REQUIRES ONLY SECOND OF TWO BASES LISTED

SPECIFICITY OF CODING is shown in this table, which lists 18 amino acids that can be coded by synthetic RNA polymers containing no more than one or two kinds of base. The only amino acids that seem to require more than two bases for coding are aspartic acid and methionine, which need U, A and G. The relative amounts of amino acids directed into proof Technology inhibited messenger RNA synthesis in living bacteria with the antibiotic actinomycin and found that each messenger RNA molecule present at the time messenger synthesis was turned off directed the synthesis of 10 to 20 molecules of protein.

We have observed that two factors in addition to base sequence have a profound effect on the activity of messenger RNA: the length of the RNA chain and its over-all structure. Poly-U molecules that contain more than 100 U's are much more active than molecules with fewer than 50. Robert G. Martin and Bruce Ames of the National Institutes of Health have found that chains of poly-U containing 450 to 700 U's are optimal for directing protein synthesis.

There is still much to be learned about the effect of structure on RNA function. Unlike DNA, RNA molecules are usually single-stranded. Frequently, however, one part of the RNA molecule loops back and forms hydrogen bonds with another portion of the same molecule. The extent of such internal pairing is influenced by the base sequence in the molecule. When poly-U is in solution, it usually has little secondary structure; that is, it consists of a simple chain with few, if any, loops or knots. Other types of RNA molecules display a considerable amount of secondary structure [see top illustration on page 212].

We have found that such a secondary structure interferes with the activity of messenger RNA. When solutions of poly-U and poly-A are mixed, they form double-strand (U-A) and triple-strand (U-A-U) helices, which are completely inactive in directing the synthesis of polyphenylalanine. In collaboration with Maxine F. Singer of the National Institutes of Health we have shown that poly-UG containing a high degree of ordered secondary structure (possibly due to G-G hydrogen-bonding) is unable to code for amino acids.

It is conceivable that natural messenger RNA contains at intervals short regions of secondary structure resembling knots in a rope. These regions might signify the beginning or the end of a protein. Alternative hypotheses suggest that the beginning and end are indicated by particular base sequences in the genetic message. In any case it seems probable that the secondary structure assumed by different types of RNA will be found to have great influence on their biological function.

The Reading Mechanism

Still not completely understood is the manner in which a given amino acid finds its way to the proper site in a protein chain. Although transfer RNA was found to be required for the synthesis of polyphenylalanine, the possibility remained that the amino acid rather than the transfer RNA recognized the code word embodied in the poly-U messenger RNA.

To distinguish between these alternative possibilities, a brilliant experiment was performed jointly by François Chapeville and Lipmann of the Rockefeller Institute, Günter von Ehrenstein of Johns Hopkins University and three Purdue workers: Benzer, Weisblum and William J. Ray, Jr. One amino acid, cysteine, is directed into protein by poly-UG. Alanine, which is identical with cysteine except that it lacks a sulfur atom, is directed into protein by poly-CG or poly-UCG. Cysteine is transported by one species of transfer RNA and alanine by another. Chapeville and his associates enzymatically attached cysteine, labeled with carbon 14, to its particular type of transfer RNA. They then exposed the molecular complex to a nickel catalyst, called Raney nickel, that removed the sulfur from cysteine and converted it

to alanine—without detaching it from cysteine-transfer RNA. Now they could ask: Will the labeled alanine be coded as if it were alanine or cysteine? They found it was coded by poly-UG, just as if it were cysteine [see bottom illustration on page 213]. This experiment shows that an amino acid loses its identity after combining with transfer RNA and is carried willy-nilly to the code word recognized by the transfer RNA.

The secondary structure of transfer RNA itself has been clarified further this past year by workers at King's College of the University of London. From X-ray evidence they have deduced that transfer RNA consists of a double helix very much like the secondary structure found in DNA. One difference is that the transfer RNA molecule is folded back on itself, like a hairpin that has been twisted around its long axis. The molecule seems to contain a number of unpaired bases; it is possible that these provide the means for recognizing specific code words in messenger RNA [see illustration at right on page 211].

There is still considerable mystery about the way messenger RNA attaches to ribosomes and the part that ribosomes play in protein synthesis. It has been known for some time that colon bacillus ribosomes are composed of at least two types of subunit and that under certain conditions they form aggregates consisting of two subunits (dimers) and four subunits (tetramers). In collaboration with Samuel Barondes, we found that the addition of poly-U to reaction mixtures initiated further ribosome aggregation. In early experiments only tetramers or still larger aggregates supported the synthesis of polyphenylalanine. Spyrides and Lipmann have shown that poly-U makes only certain "active" ribosomes aggregate and that the remaining monomers and dimers do not support polyphenylalanine syn-

BASES PRESENT IN SYNTHETIC RNA

UA	UC	UG	AC	AG	CG
PHENYLALANINE ▲	PHENYLALANINE ▲	PHENYLALANINE ▲	LYSINE ▲	LYSINE ▲	PROLINE ▲
LYSINE △	PROLINE △	LEUCINE	PROLINE △	GLUTAMIC ACID	ARGININE ●
TYROSINE	LEUCINE	VALINE	HISTIDINE	ARGININE ●	ALANINE ●
LEUCINE	SERINE	CYSTEINE	ASPARAGINE	GLUTAMINE ●	
ISOLEUCINE		TRYPTOPHAN	GLUTAMINE	GLYCINE ●	
ASPARAGINE ●		GLYCINE	THREONINE		

tein by RNA polymers containing two bases depend on the base ratios. When the polymers contain a third and fourth base, additional kinds of amino acids are incorporated into protein. Thus the activity of poly-UCG (an RNA polymer containing U, C and G) resembles that of poly-UC plus poly-UG. Poly-G has not been found to code for any amino acid. Future work will undoubtedly yield data that will necessitate revisions in this table. An RNA-code-word dictionary derived from the table appears on page 216.

AMINO ACID	RNA CODE WORDS			
ALANINE	CCG	UCG ■		
ARGININE	CGC	AGA	UCG ■	
ASPARAGINE	ACA	AUA		
ASPARTIC ACID	GUA			
CYSTEINE	UUG △			
GLUTAMIC ACID	GAA	AGU ■		
GLUTAMINE	ACA	AGA	AGU ■	
GLYCINE	UGG	AGG		
HISTIDINE	ACC			
ISOLEUCINE	UAU	UAA		
LEUCINE	UUG	UUC	UUA	UUU ▫
LYSINE	AAA	AAG ●	AAU ●	
METHIONINE	UGA ■			
PHENYLALANINE	UUU			
PROLINE	CCC	CCU ▲	CCA ▲	CCG ▲
SERINE	UCU	UCC	UCG	
THREONINE	CAC	CAA		
TRYPTOPHAN	GGU			
TYROSINE	AUU			
VALINE	UGU			

△ UNCERTAIN WHETHER CODE IS UUG OR GGU

■ NEED FOR U UNCERTAIN

▫ CODES PREFERENTIALLY FOR PHENYLALANINE

● NEED FOR G AND U UNCERTAIN

▲ NEED FOR U,A,G UNCERTAIN

GENETIC-CODE DICTIONARY lists the code words that correspond to each of the 20 common amino acids, assuming that all the words are triplets. The sequences of the letters in the code words have not been established, hence the order shown is arbitrary. Although half of the amino acids have more than one code word, it is believed that each triplet codes uniquely for a particular amino acid. Thus various combinations of AAC presumably code for asparagine, glutamine and threonine. Only one exception has been found to this presumed rule. The triplet UUU codes for phenylalanine and, less effectively, for leucine.

thesis.

A possibly related phenomenon has been observed in living cells by Alexander Rich and his associates at the Massachusetts Institute of Technology. They find that in reticulocytes obtained from rabbit blood, protein synthesis seems to be carried out predominantly by aggregates of five ribosomes, which may be held together by a single thread of messenger RNA. They have named the aggregate a polysome.

Many compelling problems still lie ahead. One is to establish the actual sequence of bases in code words. At present the code resembles an anagram. We know the letters but not the order of most words.

Another intriguing question is whether in living cells the double strand of DNA serves as a template for the production of a single strand of messenger RNA, or whether each strand of DNA serves as a template for the production of two different, complementary strands of RNA. If the latter occurs—and available evidence suggests that it does—the function of each strand must be elucidated.

Ultimately one hopes that cell-free systems will shed light on genetic control mechanisms. Such mechanisms, still undiscovered, permit the selective retrieval of genetic information. Two cells may contain identical sets of genes, but certain genes may be turned on in one cell and off in another in highly specific fashion. With cell-free systems the powerful tools of enzymology can be brought to bear on these and other problems, with the promise that the molecular understanding of genetics will continue to advance rapidly in the near future.

22 | *The Genetic Code: III*

F. H. C. CRICK · October 1966

The hypothesis that the genes of the living cell contain all the information needed for the cell to reproduce itself is now more than 50 years old. Implicit in the hypothesis is the idea that the genes bear in coded form the detailed specifications for the thousands of kinds of protein molecules the cell requires for its moment-to-moment existence: for extracting energy from molecules assimilated as food and for repairing itself as well as for replication. It is only within the past 15 years, however, that insight has been gained into the chemical nature of the genetic material and how its molecular structure can embody coded instructions that can be "read" by the machinery in the cell responsible for synthesizing protein molecules. As the result of intensive work by many investigators the story

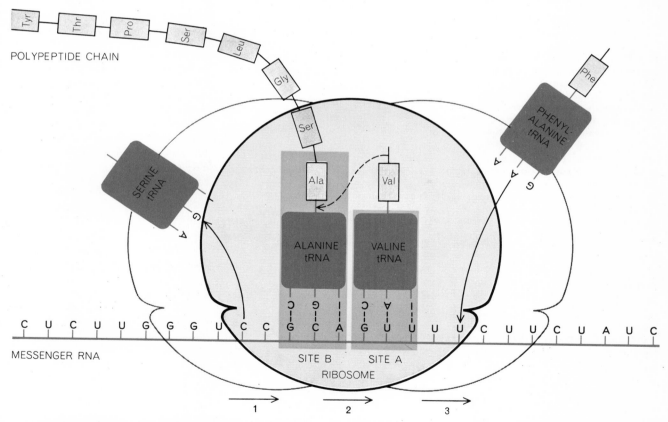

POLYPEPTIDE CHAIN

MESSENGER RNA

SITE B SITE A
RIBOSOME

1   2   3

SYNTHESIS OF PROTEIN MOLECULES is accomplished by the intracellular particles called ribosomes. The coded instructions for making the protein molecule are carried to the ribosome by a form of ribonucleic acid (RNA) known as "messenger" RNA. The RNA code "letters" are four bases: uracil (U), cytosine (C), adenine (A) and guanine (G). A sequence of three bases, called a codon, is required to specify each of the 20 kinds of amino acid, identified here by their abbreviations. (A list of the 20 amino acids and their abbreviations appears on the next page.) When linked end to end, these amino acids form the polypeptide chains of which proteins are composed. Each type of amino acid is transported to the ribosome by a particular form of "transfer" RNA (tRNA), which carries an anticodon that can form a temporary bond with one of the codons in messenger RNA. Here the ribosome is shown moving along the chain of messenger RNA, "reading off" the codons in sequence. It appears that the ribosome has two binding sites for molecules of tRNA: one site (*A*) for positioning a newly arrived tRNA molecule and another (*B*) for holding the growing polypeptide chain.

AMINO ACID	ABBREVIATION
ALANINE	Ala
ARGININE	Arg
ASPARAGINE	AspN
ASPARTIC ACID	Asp
CYSTEINE	Cys
GLUTAMIC ACID	Glu
GLUTAMINE	GluN
GLYCINE	Gly
HISTIDINE	His
ISOLEUCINE	Ileu
LEUCINE	Leu
LYSINE	Lys
METHIONINE	Met
PHENYLALANINE	Phe
PROLINE	Pro
SERINE	Ser
THREONINE	Thr
TRYPTOPHAN	Tryp
TYROSINE	Tyr
VALINE	Val

TWENTY AMINO ACIDS constitute the standard set found in all proteins. A few other amino acids occur infrequently in proteins but it is suspected in each case that they originate as one of the standard set and become chemically modified after they have been incorporated into a polypeptide chain.

of the genetic code is now essentially complete. One can trace the transmission of the coded message from its original site in the genetic material to the finished protein molecule.

The genetic material of the living cell is the chainlike molecule of deoxyribonucleic acid (DNA). The cells of many bacteria have only a single chain; the cells of mammals have dozens clustered together in chromosomes. The DNA molecules have a very long backbone made up of repeating groups of phosphate and a five-carbon sugar. To this backbone the side groups called bases are attached at regular intervals. There are four standard bases: adenine (A), guanine (G), thymine (T) and cytosine (C). They are the four "letters" used to spell out the genetic message. The exact sequence of bases along a length of the DNA molecule determines the structure of a particular protein molecule.

Proteins are synthesized from a standard set of 20 amino acids, uniform throughout nature, that are joined end to end to form the long polypeptide

chains of protein molecules [see illustration at left]. Each protein has its own characteristic sequence of amino acids. The number of amino acids in a polypeptide chain ranges typically from 100 to 300 or more.

The genetic code is not the message itself but the "dictionary" used by the cell to translate from the four-letter language of nucleic acid to the 20-letter language of protein. The machinery of the cell can translate in one direction only: from nucleic acid to protein but not from protein to nucleic acid. In making this translation the cell employs a variety of accessory molecules and mechanisms. The message contained in DNA is first transcribed into the similar molecule called "messenger" ribonucleic acid—messenger RNA. (In many viruses—the tobacco mosaic virus, for example—the genetic material is simply RNA.) RNA too has four kinds of bases as side groups; three are identical with those found in DNA (adenine, guanine and cytosine) but the fourth is uracil (U) instead of thymine. In this first transcription of the genetic message the code letters A, G, T and C in DNA give rise respectively to U, C, A and G. In other words, wherever A appears in DNA, U appears in the RNA transcription; wherever G appears in DNA, C appears in the transcription, and so on. As it is usually presented the dictionary of the genetic code employs the letters found in RNA (U, C, A, G) rather than those found in DNA (A, G, T, C).

The genetic code could be broken easily if one could determine both the amino acid sequence of a protein and the base sequence of the piece of nucleic acid that codes it. A simple comparison of the two sequences would yield the code. Unfortunately the determination of the base sequence of a long nucleic acid molecule is, for a variety of reasons, still extremely difficult. More indirect approaches must be used.

Most of the genetic code first became known early in 1965. Since then additional evidence has proved that almost all of it is correct, although a few features remain uncertain. This article describes how the code was discovered and some of the work that supports it.

Scientific American has already presented a number of articles on the genetic code. In one ["The Genetic Code," page 198 in this book] I explained that the experimental evidence (mainly indirect) suggested that the code was a triplet code: that the bases on the messenger RNA were read three at a time and that each group corresponded to a

particular amino acid. Such a group is called a codon. Using four symbols in groups of three, one can form 64 distinct triplets. The evidence indicated that most of these stood for one amino acid or another, implying that an amino acid was usually represented by several codons. Adjacent amino acids were coded by adjacent codons, which did not overlap.

In a sequel to that article ["The Genetic Code: II," page 206] Marshall W. Nirenberg of the National Institutes of Health explained how the composition of many of the 64 triplets had been determined by actual experiment. The technique was to synthesize polypeptide chains in a cell-free system, which was made by breaking open cells of the colon bacillus (*Escherichia coli*) and extracting from them the machinery for protein synthesis. Then the system was provided with an energy supply, 20 amino acids and one or another of several types of synthetic RNA. Although the exact sequence of bases in each type was random, the proportion of bases was known. It was found that each type of synthetic messenger RNA directed the incorporation of certain amino acids only.

By means of this method, used in a quantitative way, the *composition* of many of the codons was obtained, but the *order* of bases in any triplet could not be determined. Codons rich in G were difficult to study, and in addition a few mistakes crept in. Of the 40 codon compositions listed by Nirenberg in his article we now know that 35 were correct.

The Triplet Code

The main outlines of the genetic code were elucidated by another technique invented by Nirenberg and Philip Leder. In this method no protein synthesis occurs. Instead one triplet at a time is used to bind together parts of the machinery of protein synthesis.

Protein synthesis takes place on the comparatively large intracellular structures known as ribosomes. These bodies travel along the chain of messenger RNA, reading off its triplets one after another and synthesizing the polypeptide chain of the protein, starting at the amino end (NH$_2$). The amino acids do not diffuse to the ribosomes by themselves. Each amino acid is joined chemically by a special enzyme to one of the codon-recognizing molecules known both as soluble RNA (sRNA) and transfer RNA (tRNA). (I prefer the latter designation.) Each tRNA molecule has its own triplet of bases, called an anticodon, that recognizes the relevant codon on the messenger RNA by pairing bases with it [see illustration on page 217].

Leder and Nirenberg studied which amino acid, joined to its tRNA molecules, was bound to the ribosomes in the presence of a particular triplet, that is, by a "message" with just three letters. They did so by the neat trick of passing the mixture over a nitrocellulose filter that retained the ribosomes. All the tRNA molecules passed through the filter except the ones specifically bound to the ribosomes by the triplet. Which they were could easily be decided by using mixtures of amino acids

in which one kind of amino acid had been made artificially radioactive, and determining the amount of radioactivity absorbed by the filter.

For example, the triplet GUU retained the tRNA for the amino acid valine, whereas the triplets UGU and UUG did not. (Here GUU actually stands for the trinucleoside diphosphate GpUpU.) Further experiments showed that UGU coded for cysteine and UUG for leucine.

Nirenberg and his colleagues synthesized all 64 triplets and tested them for their coding properties. Similar results have been obtained by H. Gobind Khorana and his co-workers at the University of Wisconsin. Various other

groups have checked a smaller number of codon assignments.

Close to 50 of the 64 triplets give a clearly unambiguous answer in the binding test. Of the remainder some evince only weak binding and some bind more than one kind of amino acid. Other results I shall describe later suggest that the multiple binding is often an artifact of the binding method. In short, the binding test gives the meaning of the majority of the triplets but it does not firmly establish all of them.

The genetic code obtained in this way, with a few additions secured by other methods, is shown in the table below. The 64 possible triplets are set out in a regular array, following a plan

SECOND LETTER

FIRST LETTER		U	C	A	G		THIRD LETTER
U	UUU UUC	Phe	UCU UCC UCA UCG	Ser	UAU UAC	Tyr	UGU UGC	Cys	U C
	UUA UUG	Leu			UAA UAG	OCHRE AMBER	UGA UGG	? Tryp	A G
C	CUU CUC CUA CUG	Leu	CCU CCC CCA CCG	Pro	CAU CAC	His	CGU CGC CGA CGG	Arg	U C
					CAA CAG	GluN			A G
A	AUU AUC AUA	Ileu	ACU ACC ACA ACG	Thr	AAU AAC	AspN	AGU AGC	Ser	U C
	AUG	Met			AAA AAG	Lys	AGA AGG	Arg	A G
G	GUU GUC GUA GUG	Val	GCU GCC GCA GCG	Ala	GAU GAC	Asp	GGU GGC GGA GGG	Gly	U C
					GAA GAG	Glu			A G

GENETIC CODE, consisting of 64 triplet combinations and their corresponding amino acids, is shown in its most likely version. The importance of the first two letters in each triplet is readily apparent. Some of the allocations are still not completely certain, particularly for organisms other than the colon bacillus (*Escherichia coli*). "Amber" and "ochre" are terms that referred originally to certain mutant strains of bacteria. They designate two triplets, UAA and UAG, that may act as signals for terminating polypeptide chains.

that clarifies the relations between them.

Inspection of the table will show that the triplets coding for the same amino acid are often rather similar. For example, all four of the triplets starting with the doublet AC code for threonine. This pattern also holds for seven of the other amino acids. In every case the triplets XYU and XYC code for the same amino acid, and in many cases XYA and XYG are the same (methionine and tryptophan may be exceptions). Thus an amino acid is largely selected by the first two bases of the triplet. Given that a triplet codes for, say, valine, we know that the first two bases are GU, whatever the third may be. This pattern is true for all but three of the amino acids. Leucine can start with UU or CU, serine with UC or AG and arginine with CG or AG. In all other cases the amino acid is uniquely related to the first two bases of the triplet. Of course, the converse is often not true. Given that a triplet starts with, say, CA, it may code for either histidine or glutamine.

Synthetic Messenger RNA's

Probably the most direct way to confirm the genetic code is to synthesize a messenger RNA molecule with a strictly defined base sequence and then find the amino acid sequence of the polypeptide produced under its influence. The most extensive work of this nature has been done by Khorana and his colleagues. By a brilliant combination of ordinary chemical synthesis and synthesis catalyzed by enzymes, they have made long RNA molecules with various repeating sequences of bases. As an example, one RNA molecule they have synthesized has the sequence UGUG-UGUGUGUG.... When the biochemical machinery reads this as triplets the message is UGU–GUG–UGU–GUG.... Thus we expect that a polypeptide will be produced with an alternating sequence of two amino acids. In fact, it was found that the product is Cys–Val–Cys–Val.... This evidence alone would not tell us which triplet goes with which amino acid, but given the results of the binding test one has no hesitation in concluding that UGU codes for cysteine and GUG for valine.

In the same way Khorana has made chains with repeating sequences of the type XYZ... and also XXYZ.... The type XYZ...would be expected to give a "homopolypeptide" containing one amino acid corresponding to the triplet XYZ. Because the starting point is not clearly defined, however, the homopolypeptides corresponding to YZX... and ZXY... will also be produced. Thus poly-AUC makes polyisoleucine, polyserine and polyhistidine. This confirms that AUC codes for isoleucine, UCA for serine and CAU for histidine. A repeating sequence of four bases will yield a single type of polypeptide with a repeating sequence of four amino acids. The general patterns to be expected in each case are set forth in the table on this page. The results to date have amply demonstrated by a direct biochemical method that the code is indeed a triplet code.

Khorana and his colleagues have so far confirmed about 25 triplets by this method, including several that were quite doubtful on the basis of the binding test. They plan to synthesize other sequences, so that eventually most of the triplets will be checked in this way.

The Use of Mutations

The two methods described so far are open to the objection that since they do not involve intact cells there may be some danger of false results. This objection can be met by two other methods of checking the code in which the act of protein synthesis takes place inside the cell. Both involve the effects of genetic mutations on the amino acid sequence of a protein.

It is now known that small mutations are normally of two types: "base substitution" mutants and "phase shift" mutants. In the first type one base is changed into another base but the total number of bases remains the same. In the second, one or a small number of bases are added to the message or subtracted from it.

There are now extensive data on base-substitution mutants, mainly from studies of three rather convenient proteins: human hemoglobin, the protein of tobacco mosaic virus and the A protein of the enzyme tryptophan synthetase obtained from the colon bacillus. At least 36 abnormal types of human hemoglobin have now been investigated by many different workers. More than 40 mutant forms of the protein of the tobacco mosaic virus have been examined by Hans Wittmann of the Max Planck Institute for Molecular Genetics in Tübingen and by Akita Tsugita and Heinz Fraenkel-Conrat of the University of California at Berkeley [see "The Genetic Code of a Virus," by Heinz Fraenkel-Conrat; SCIENTIFIC AMERICAN Offprint 193]. Charles Yanofsky and his group at Stanford University have characterized about 25 different mutations of the A protein of tryptophan synthetase.

RNA BASE SEQUENCE	READ AS	AMINO ACID SEQUENCE EXPECTED
(XY)ₙ ...	X Y X | Y X Y | X Y X | Y X Y ...	αβαβ
(XYZ)ₙ ...	X Y Z | X Y Z | X Y Z ...	ααα
...	Y Z X | Y Z X | Y Z X ...	βββ
...	Z X Y | Z X Y | Z X Y ...	γγγ
(XXYZ)ₙ ...	X X Y | Z X X | Y Z X | X Y Z ...	αβγδαβγδ
(XYXZ)ₙ ...	X Y X | Z X Y | X Z X | Y X Z ...	αβγδαβγδ

VARIETY OF SYNTHETIC RNA's with repeating sequences of bases have been produced by H. Gobind Khorana and his colleagues at the University of Wisconsin. They contain two or three different bases (X, Y, Z) in groups of two, three or four. When introduced into cell-free systems containing the machinery for protein synthesis, the base sequences are read off as triplets (*middle*) and yield the amino acid sequences indicated at the right.

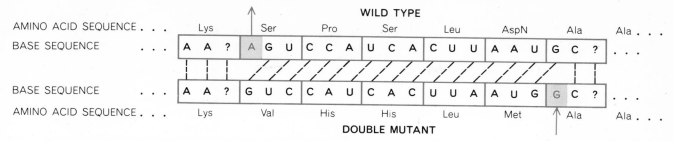

WILD TYPE

| AMINO ACID SEQUENCE . . . | Lys | Ser | Pro | Ser | Leu | AspN | Ala | Ala . . . |

BASE SEQUENCE . . . A A ? A G U C C A U C A C U U A A U G C ? . . .

BASE SEQUENCE . . . A A ? G U C C A U C A C U U A A U G C ? . . .

| AMINO ACID SEQUENCE . . . | Lys | Val | His | His | Leu | Met | Ala | Ala . . . |

DOUBLE MUTANT

"PHASE SHIFT" MUTATIONS help to establish the actual codons used by organisms in the synthesis of protein. The two partial amino acid sequences shown here were determined by George Streisinger and his colleagues at the University of Oregon. The sequences are from a protein, a type of lysozyme, produced by the bacterial virus T4. A pair of phase-shift mutations evidently removed one base, A, and inserted another, G, about 15 bases farther on. The base sequence was deduced theoretically from the genetic code.

The remarkable fact has emerged that in every case but one the genetic code shows that the change of an amino acid in a polypeptide chain could have been caused by the alteration of a single base in the relevant nucleic acid. For example, the first observed change of an amino acid by mutation (in the hemoglobin of a person suffering from sickle-cell anemia) was from glutamic acid to valine. From the genetic code dictionary on page 219 we see that this could have resulted from a mutation that changed either GAA to GUA or GAG to GUG. In either case the change involved a single base in the several hundred needed to code for one of the two kinds of chain in hemoglobin.

The one exception so far to the rule that all amino acid changes could be caused by single base changes has been found by Yanofsky. In this one case glutamic acid was replaced by methionine. It can be seen from the genetic code dictionary that this can be accomplished only by a change of *two* bases, since glutamic acid is encoded by either GAA or GAG and methionine is encoded only by AUG. This mutation has occurred only once, however, and of all the mutations studied by Yanofsky it is the only one not to back-mutate, or revert to "wild type." It is thus almost certainly the rare case of a double change. All the other cases fit the hypothesis that base-substitution mutations are normally caused by a single base change. Examination of the code shows that only about 40 percent of all the possible amino acid interchanges can be brought about by single base substitutions, and it is only these changes that are found in experiments. Therefore the study of actual mutations has provided strong confirmation of many features of the genetic code.

Because in general several codons stand for one amino acid it is not possible, knowing the amino acid sequence, to write down the exact RNA base sequence that encoded it. This is unfortu-nate. If we know which amino acid is changed into another by mutation, however, we can often, given the code, work out what that base change must have been. As an example, glutamic acid can be encoded by GAA or GAG and valine by GUU, GUC, GUA or GUG. If a mutation substitutes valine for glutamic acid, one can assume that only a single base change was involved. The only such change that could lead to the desired result would be a change from A to U in the middle position, and this would be true whether GAA became GUA or GAG became GUG.

It is thus possible in many cases (not in all) to compare the nature of the base change with the chemical mutagen used to produce the change. If RNA is treated with nitrous acid, C is changed to U and A is effectively changed to G. On the other hand, if double-strand DNA is treated under the right conditions with hydroxylamine, the mutagen acts only on C. As a result some C's are changed to T's (the DNA equivalent of U's), and thus G's, which are normally paired with C's in double-strand DNA, are replaced by A's.

If 2-aminopurine, a "base analogue" mutagen, is added when double-strand DNA is undergoing replication, it produces only "transitions." These are the same changes as those produced by hydroxylamine—plus the reverse changes. In almost all these different cases (the exceptions are unimportant) the changes observed are those expected from our knowledge of the genetic code.

Note the remarkable fact that, although the code was deduced mainly from studies of the colon bacillus, it appears to apply equally to human beings and tobacco plants. This, together with more fragmentary evidence, suggests that the genetic code is either the same or very similar in most organisms.

The second method of checking the code using intact cells depends on phase-shift mutations such as the addi-tion of a single base to the message. Phase-shift mutations probably result from errors produced during genetic recombination or when the DNA molecule is being duplicated. Such errors have the effect of putting out of phase the reading of the message from that point on. This hypothesis leads to the prediction that the phase can be corrected if at some subsequent point a nucleotide is deleted. The pair of alterations would be expected not only to change two amino acids but also to alter all those encoded by bases lying between the two affected sites. The reason is that the intervening bases would be read out of phase and therefore grouped into triplets different from those contained in the normal message.

This expectation has recently been confirmed by George Streisinger and his colleagues at the University of Oregon. They have studied mutations in the protein lysozyme that were produced by the T4 virus, which infects the colon bacillus. One phase-shift mutation involved the amino acid sequence ...Lys—Ser—Pro—Ser—Leu—AspN—Ala—Ala—Lys,... They were then able to construct by genetic methods a double phase-shift mutant in which the corresponding sequence was ...Lys–Val–His–His–Leu–Met–Ala–Ala–Lys....

Given these two sequences, the reader should be able, using the genetic code dictionary on page 219, to decipher uniquely a short length of the nucleic acid message for both the original protein and the double mutant and thus deduce the changes produced by each of the phase-shift mutations. The correct result is presented in the illustration above. The result not only confirms several rather doubtful codons, such as UUA for leucine and AGU for serine, but also shows which codons are actually involved in a genetic message. Since the technique is difficult, however, it may not find wide application.

Streisinger's work also demonstrates what has so far been only tacitly as-

ANTICODON	CODON
U	A G
C	G
A	U
G	U C
I	U C A

"WOBBLE" HYPOTHESIS has been proposed by the author to provide rules for the pairing of codon and anticodon at the *third* position of the codon. There is evidence, for example, that the anticodon base I, which stands for inosine, may pair with as many as three different bases: U, C and A. Inosine closely resembles the base guanine (G) and so would ordinarily be expected to pair with cytosine (C). Structural diagrams for standard base pairings and wobble base pairings are illustrated at the bottom of this page.

sumed: that the two languages, both of which are written down in a certain direction according to convention, are in fact translated by the cell in the same direction and not in opposite directions. This fact had previously been established, with more direct chemical methods, by Severo Ochoa and his colleagues at the New York University School of Medicine. In the convention, which was adopted by chance, proteins are written with the amino (NH_2) end on the left. Nucleic acids are written with the end of the molecule containing

a "5 prime" carbon atom at the left. (The "5 prime" refers to a particular carbon atom in the 5-carbon ring of ribose sugar or deoxyribose sugar.)

Finding the Anticodons

Still another method of checking the genetic code is to discover the three bases making up the anticodon in some particular variety of transfer RNA. The first tRNA to have its entire sequence worked out was alanine tRNA, a job done by Robert W. Holley and his collaborators at Cornell University [see "The Nucleotide Sequence of a Nucleic Acid," by Robert W. Holley, beginning on page 72 in this book]. Alanine tRNA, obtained from yeast, contains 77 bases. A possible anticodon found near the middle of the molecule has the sequence IGC, where I stands for inosine, a base closely resembling guanine. Since then Hans Zachau and his colleagues at the University of Cologne have established the sequences of two closely related serine tRNA's from yeast, and James Madison and his group at the U.S. Plant, Soil and Nutrition Laboratory at Ithaca, N.Y., have worked out the sequence of a tyrosine tRNA, also from yeast.

A detailed comparison of these three sequences makes it almost certain that the anticodons are alanine–IGC, serine–IGA and tyrosine–GΨA. (Ψ stands for pseudo-uridylic acid, which can form the same base pairs as the base uracil.) In addition there is preliminary evidence from other workers that an anticodon for valine is IAC and an anticodon for phenylalanine is GAA.

All these results would fit the rule that the codon and anticodon pair in an antiparallel manner, and that the pairing in the first two positions of the codon is of the standard type, that is, A pairs with U and G pairs with C. The pairing in the third position of the codon is more complicated. There is now good experimental evidence from both Nirenberg and Khorana and their co-workers that one tRNA can recognize several codons, provided that they differ only in the last place in the codon. Thus Holley's alanine tRNA appears to recognize GCU, GCC and GCA. If it recognizes GCG, it does so only very weakly.

The "Wobble" Hypothesis

I have suggested that this is because of a "wobble" in the pairing in the third place and have shown that a reasonable theoretical model will explain many of the observed results. The suggested rules for the pairing in the third position of the anticodon are presented in the table at the top of this page, but this theory is still speculative. The rules for the first two places of the codon seem reasonably secure, however, and can be used as partial confirmation of the genetic code. The likely codon-anticodon pairings for valine, serine, tyrosine, alanine and phenylalanine satisfy the standard base pairings in the first two places and the wobble hypothesis in the third place [see illustration on page 223].

Several points about the genetic code remain to be cleared up. For example, the triplet UGA has still to be allocated.

GUANINE   CYTOSINE   GUANINE   URACIL

STANDARD AND WOBBLE BASE PAIRINGS both involve the formation of hydrogen bonds when certain bases are brought into close proximity. In the standard guanine-cytosine pairing (*left*) it is believed three hydrogen bonds are formed. The bases are shown as they exist in the RNA molecule, where they are attached to 5-car-

bon rings of ribose sugar. In the proposed wobble pairing (*right*) guanine is linked to uracil by only two hydrogen bonds. The base inosine (I) has a single hydrogen atom where guanine has an amino (NH_2) group (*broken circle*). In the author's wobble hypothesis inosine can pair with U as well as with C and A (*not shown*).

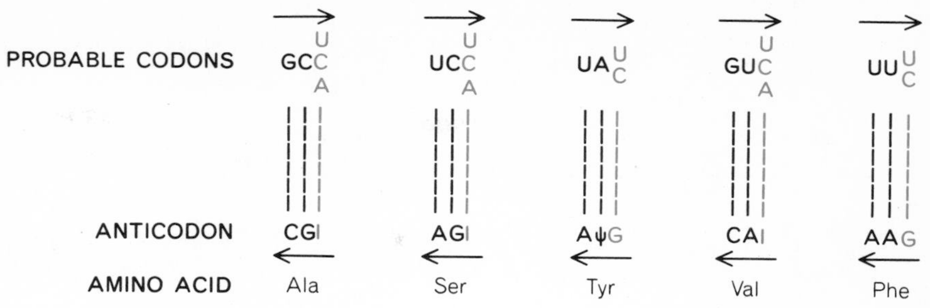

The punctuation marks—the signals for "begin chain" and "end chain"—are only partly understood. It seems likely that both the triplet UAA (called "ochre") and UAG (called "amber") can terminate the polypeptide chain, but which triplet is normally found at the end of a gene is still uncertain.

The picturesque terms for these two triplets originated when it was discovered in studies of the colon bacillus some years ago that mutations in other genes (mutations that in fact cause errors in chain termination) could "suppress" the action of certain mutant codons, now identified as either UAA or UAG. The terms "ochre" and "amber" are simply invented designations and have no reference to color.

A mechanism for chain initiation was discovered fairly recently. In the colon bacillus it seems certain that formylmethionine, carried by a special tRNA, can initiate chains, although it is not clear if all chains have to start in this way, or what the mechanism is in mammals and other species. The formyl group (CHO) is not normally found on finished proteins, suggesting that it is probably removed by a special enzyme. It seems likely that sometimes the methionine is removed as well.

It is unfortunately possible that a few codons may be ambiguous, that is, may code for more than one amino acid. This is certainly not true of most codons. The present evidence for a small amount of ambiguity is suggestive but not conclusive. It will make the code more difficult to establish correctly if ambiguity can occur.

Problems for the Future

From what has been said it is clear that, although the entire genetic code

PROBABLE CODONS	GCC^U_A	UCC^U_A	UA^U_C	GUC^U_A	UU^U_C
ANTICODON	CGI	AGI	AψG	CAI	AAG
AMINO ACID	Ala	Ser	Tyr	Val	Phe

CODON-ANTICODON PAIRINGS take place in an antiparallel direction. Thus the anticodons are shown here written backward, as opposed to the way they appear in the text. The five anticodons are those tentatively identified in the transfer RNA's for alanine, serine, tyrosine, valine and phenylalanine. Color indicates where wobble pairings may occur.

is not known with complete certainty, it is highly likely that most of it is correct. Further work will surely clear up the doubtful codons, clarify the punctuation marks, delimit ambiguity and extend the code to many other species. Although the code lists the codons that *may* be used, we still have to determine if alternative codons are used equally. Some preliminary work suggests they may not be. There is also still much to be discovered about the machinery of protein synthesis. How many types of tRNA are there? What is the structure of the ribosome? How does it work, and why is it in two parts? In addition there are many questions concerning the control of the rate of protein synthesis that we are still a long way from answering.

When such questions have been answered, the major unsolved problem will be the structure of the genetic code. Is the present code merely the result of a series of evolutionary accidents, so that the allocations of triplets to amino acids is to some extent arbitrary? Or are there profound structural reasons why phenylalanine has to be coded by UUU and UUC and by no other triplets? Such questions will be difficult to decide, since the genetic code originated at least three billion years ago, and it may be impossible to reconstruct the sequence of events that took place at such a remote period. The origin of the code is very close to the origin of life. Unless we are lucky it is likely that much of the evidence we should like to have has long since disappeared.

Nevertheless, the genetic code is a major milestone on the long road of molecular biology. In showing in detail how the four-letter language of nucleic acid controls the 20-letter language of protein it confirms the central theme of molecular biology that genetic information can be stored as a one-dimensional message on nucleic acid and be expressed as the one-dimensional amino acid sequence of a protein. Many problems remain, but this knowledge is now secure.

23 | Gene Structure and Protein Structure

CHARLES YANOFSKY · *May 1967*

The present molecular theory of genetics, known irreverently as "the central dogma," is now 14 years old. Implicit in the theory from the outset was the notion that genetic information is coded in linear sequence in molecules of deoxyribonucleic acid (DNA)

and that the sequence directly determines the linear sequence of amino acid units in molecules of protein. In other words, one expected the two molecules to be colinear. The problem was to prove that they were.

Over the same 14 years, as a conse-

quence of an international effort, most of the predictions of the central dogma have been verified one by one. The results were recently summarized in these pages by F. H. C. Crick, who together with James D. Watson proposed the helical, two-strand structure for DNA on

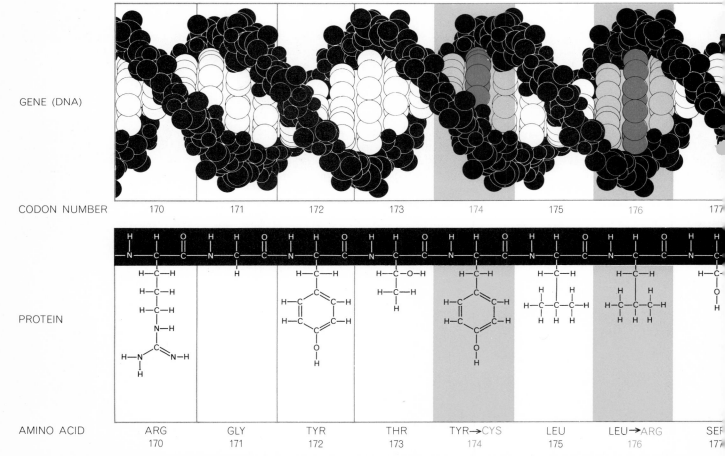

GENE (DNA)

CODON NUMBER   170   171   172   173   174   175   176   177

PROTEIN

AMINO ACID   ARG 170   GLY 171   TYR 172   THR 173   TYR→CYS 174   LEU 175   LEU→ARG 176   SER 177

STRUCTURES OF GENE AND PROTEIN have been shown to bear a direct linear correspondence by the author and his colleagues at Stanford University. They demonstrated that a particular sequence of coding units (codons) in the genetic molecule deoxyribonucleic acid, or DNA (*top*), specifies a corresponding sequence of amino acid units in the structure of a protein molecule (*bottom*).

In the DNA molecule depicted here the black spheres represent repeating units of deoxyribose sugar and phosphate, which form the helical backbones of the two-strand molecule. The white spheres connecting the two strands represent complementary pairs of the four kinds of base that provide the "letters" in which the genetic message is written. A sequence of three bases attached to

which the central dogma is based [see "The Genetic Code: III," by F. H. C. Crick, beginning on page 217 in this book]. Here I shall describe in somewhat more detail how our studies at Stanford University demonstrated the colinearity of genetic structure (as embodied in DNA) and protein structure.

Let me begin with a brief review. The molecular subunits that provide the "letters" of the code alphabet in DNA are the four nitrogenous bases adenine (A), guanine (G), cytosine (C) and thymine (T). If the four letters were taken in pairs, they would provide only 16 different code words—too few to specify the 20 different amino acids commonly found in protein molecules. If they are taken in triplets, however, the four letters can provide 64 different code words, which would seem too many for the efficient specification of the 20 amino acids. Accordingly it was conceivable that the cell might employ fewer than the 64 possible triplets. We now know that na-

ture not only has selected the triplet code but also makes use of most (if not all) of the 64 triplets, which are called codons. Each amino acid but two (tryptophan and methionine) are specified by at least two different codons, and a few amino acids are specified by as many as six codons. It is becoming clear that the living cell exploits this redundancy in subtle ways. Of the 64 codons, 61 have been shown to specify one or another of the 20 amino acids. The remaining three can act as "chain terminators," which signal the end of a genetic message.

A genetic message is defined as the amount of information in one gene; it is the information needed to specify the complete amino acid sequence in one polypeptide chain. This relation, which underlies the central dogma, is sometimes expressed as the one-gene-one-enzyme hypothesis. It was first clearly enunciated by George W. Beadle and Edward L. Tatum, as a result of their studies with the red bread mold *Neurospora crassa* around 1940. In some cases

a single polypeptide chain constitutes a complete protein molecule, which often acts as an enzyme, or biological catalyst. Frequently, however, two or more polypeptide chains must join together in order to form an active protein. For example, tryptophan synthetase, the enzyme we used in our colinearity studies, consists of four polypeptide chains: two alpha chains and two beta chains.

How might one establish the colinearity of codons in DNA and amino acid units in a polypeptide chain? The most direct approach would be to separate the two strands of DNA obtained from some organism and determine the base sequence of that portion of a strand which is presumed to be colinear with the amino acid sequence of a particular protein. If the amino acid sequence of the protein were not already known, it too would have to be established. One could then write the two sequences in adjacent columns and see if the same codon (or its synonym) always appeared adjacent to a particular amino acid. If it

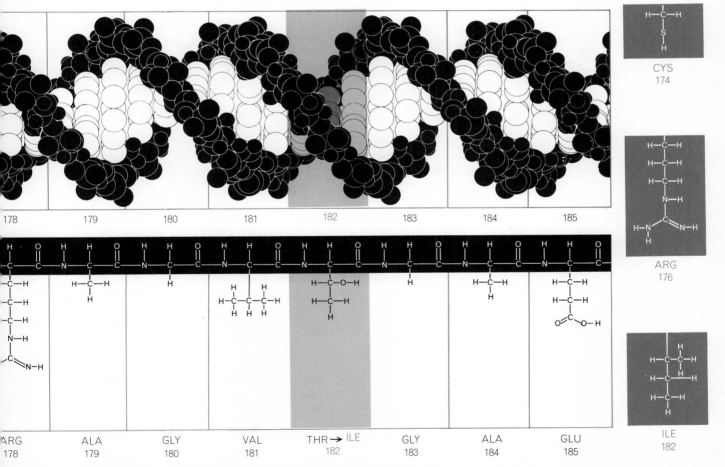

one strand of DNA is a codon and specifies one amino acid. The amino acid sequence illustrated here is the region from position 170 through 185 in the *A* protein of the enzyme tryptophan synthetase produced by the bacterium *Escherichia coli*. It was found that mutations in the *A* gene of *E. coli* altered the amino acids at three places (174, 176 and 182) in this region of the *A* protein. (A key to the amino acid abbreviations can be found on page 227.) The three amino acids that replace the three normal ones as a result of mutation are shown at the extreme right. Each replacement is produced by a mutation at one site (*dark color*) in the DNA of the *A* gene. In all, the author and his associates correlated mutations at eight sites in the *A* gene with alterations in the *A* protein.

did, a colinear relation would be established. Unfortunately this direct approach cannot be taken because so far it has not been possible to isolate and identify individual genes. Even if one could isolate a single gene that specified a polypeptide made up of 150 amino acids (and not many polypeptides are that small), one would have to determine the sequence of units in a DNA strand consisting of some 450 bases.

It was necessary, therefore, to consider a more feasible way of attacking the problem. An approach that immediately suggests itself to a geneticist is to construct a genetic map, which is a representation of the information contained in the gene, and see if the map can be related to protein structure. A genetic map is constructed solely on the basis of information obtained by crossing individual organisms that differ in two or more hereditary respects (a refinement of the technique originally

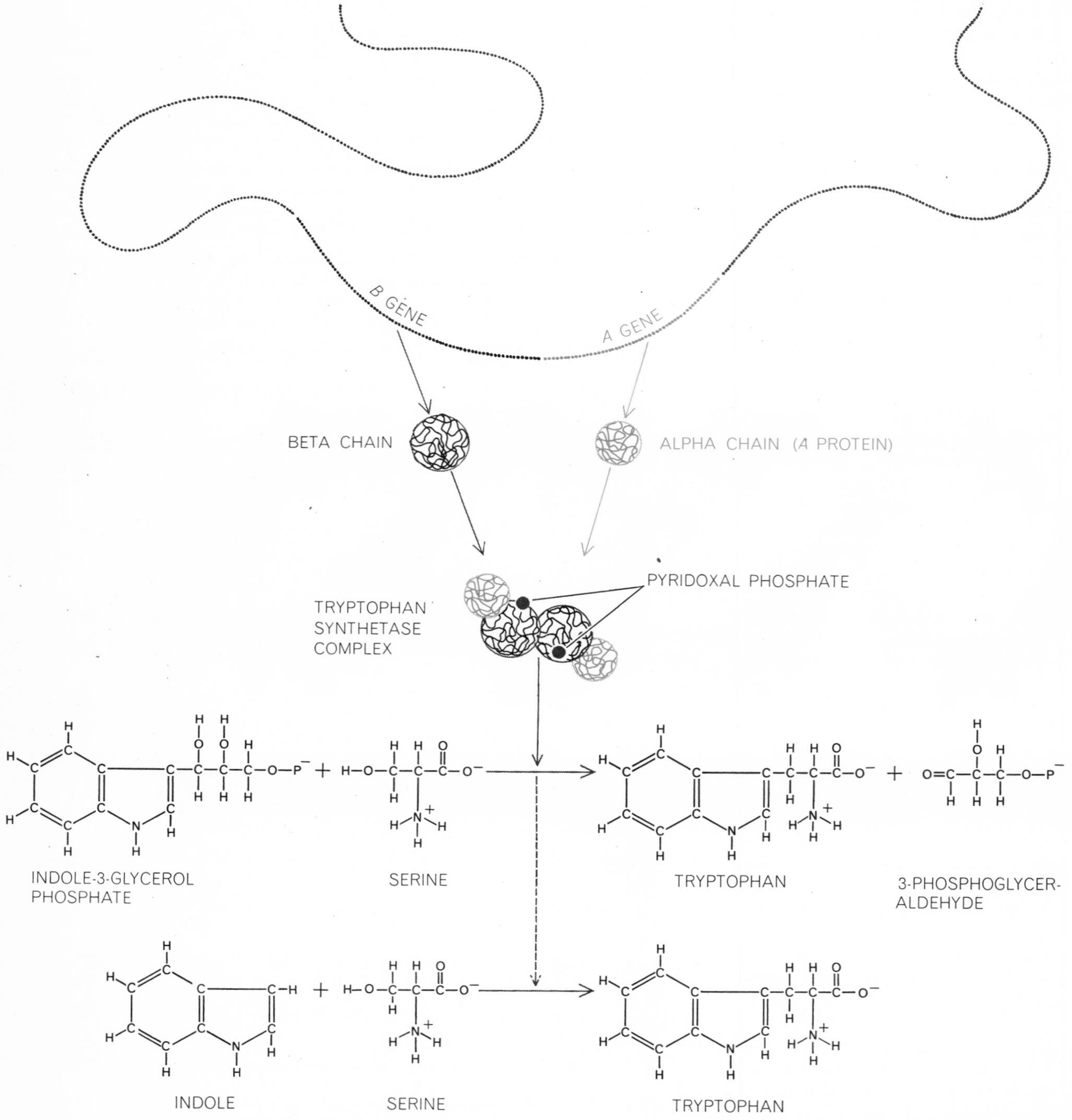

GENETIC CONTROL OF CELL'S CHEMISTRY is exemplified by the two genes in *E. coli* that carry the instructions for making the enzyme tryptophan synthetase. The enzyme is actually a complex of four polypeptide chains: two alpha chains and two beta chains. The alpha chain is the *A* protein in which changes produced by mutations in the *A* gene have provided the evidence for gene-pro- **tein colinearity. One class of *A*-protein mutants retains the ability to associate with beta chains but the complex is no longer able to catalyze the normal biochemical reaction: the conversion of indole-3-glycerol phosphate and serine to tryptophan and 3-phosphoglyceraldehyde. But the complex can still catalyze a simpler nonphysiological reaction: the conversion of indole and serine to tryptophan.**

used by Gregor Mendel to demonstrate how characteristics are inherited).

By using bacteria and bacterial viruses in such studies one can catalogue the results of crosses involving millions of individual organisms and thereby deduce the actual distances separating the sites of mutational changes in a single gene. The distances are inferred from the frequency with which parent organisms, each with at least one mutation in the same gene, give rise to offspring in which neither mutation is present. As a result of the recombination of genetic material the offspring can inherit a gene that is assembled from the mutation-free portions of each parental gene. If the mutational markers lie far apart on the parental genes, recombination will frequently produce mutation-free progeny. If the markers are close together, mutation-free progeny will be rare [see bottom illustration on next page].

In his elegant studies with the "rII" region of the chromosome of the bacterial virus designated T4, Seymour Benzer, then at Purdue University, showed that the number of genetically distinguishable mutation sites on the map of the gene approaches the estimated number of base pairs in the DNA molecule corresponding to that gene. (Mutations involve pairs of bases because the bases in each of the two entwined strands of the DNA molecule are paired with and are complementary to the bases in the other strand. If a mutation alters one base in the DNA molecule, its partner is eventually changed too during DNA replication.) Benzer also showed that the only type of genetic map consistent with his data is a map on which the sites altered by mutation are arranged linearly. Subsequently A. D. Kaiser and David Hogness of Stanford University demonstrated with another bacterial virus that there is a linear correspondence between the sites on a genetic map and the altered regions of a DNA molecule isolated from the virus. Thus there is direct experimental evidence indicating that the genetic map is a valid representation of DNA structure and that the map can be employed as a substitute for information about base sequence.

This, then, provided the basis of our approach. We would pick a suitable organism and isolate a large number of mutant individuals with mutations in the same gene. From recombination studies we would make a fine-structure genetic map relating the sites of the mutations. In addition we would have to be able to isolate the protein specified by that gene and determine its amino acid

sequence. Finally we would have to analyze the protein produced by each mutant (assuming a protein were still produced) in order to find the position of the amino acid change brought about in its amino acid sequence by the mutation. If gene structure and protein structure were colinear, the positions at which amino acid changes occur in the protein should be in the same order as the po-

sitions of the corresponding mutationally altered sites on the genetic map. Although this approach to the question of colinearity would require a great deal of work and much luck, it was logical and experimentally feasible. Several research groups besides our own set out to find a suitable system for a study of this kind.

The essential requirement of a suitable system was that a genetically

ALA	ALANINE	GLY	GLYCINE	PRO	PROLINE
ARG	ARGININE	HIS	HISTIDINE	SER	SERINE
ASN	ASPARAGINE	ILE	ISOLEUCINE	THR	THREONINE
ASP	ASPARTIC ACID	LEU	LEUCINE	TRP	TRYPTOPHAN
CYS	CYSTEINE	LYS	LYSINE	TYR	TYROSINE
GLN	GLUTAMINE	MET	METHIONINE	VAL	VALINE
GLU	GLUTAMIC ACID	PHE	PHENYLALANINE		

AMINO ACID ABBREVIATIONS identify the 20 amino acids commonly found in all proteins. Each amino acid is specified by a triplet codon in the DNA molecule (see below).

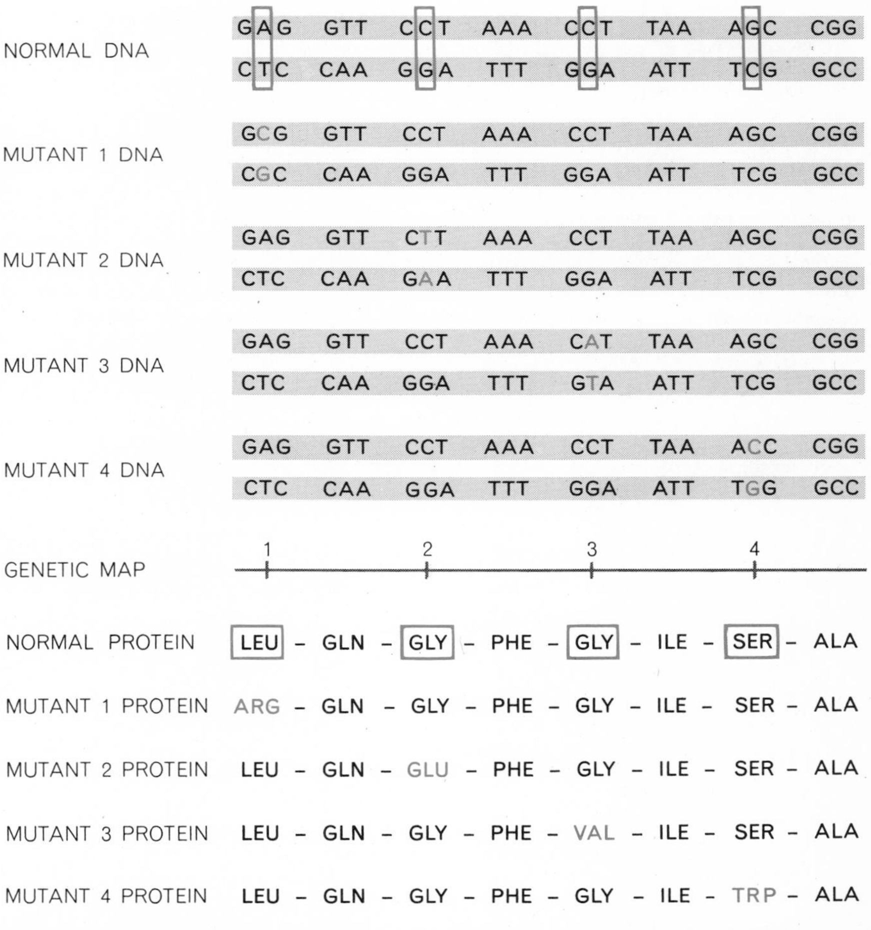

GENETIC MUTATIONS can result from the alteration of a single base in a DNA codon. The letters stand for the four bases: adenine (A), thymine (T), guanine (G) and cytosine (C). Since the DNA molecule consists of two complementary strands, a base change in one strand involves a complementary change in the second strand. In the four mutant DNA sequences shown here (top) a pair of bases (color) is different from that in the normal sequence. By genetic studies one can map the sequence and approximate spacing of the four mutations (middle). By chemical studies of the proteins produced by the normal and mutant DNA sequences (bottom) one can establish the corresponding amino acid changes.

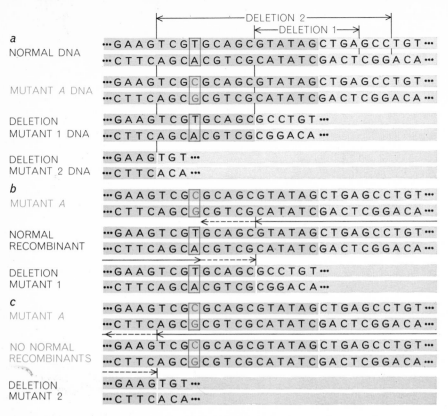

a
NORMAL DNA

···G A A G T C G T G C A G C G T A T A G C T G A G C C T G T···
···C T T C A G C A C G T C G C A T A T C G A C T C G G A C A···

MUTANT *A* DNA

···G A A G T C G C G C A G C G T A T A G C T G A G C C T G T···
···C T T C A G C G C G T C G C A T A T C G A C T C G G A C A···

DELETION
MUTANT 1 DNA

···G A A G T C G T G C A G C G C C T G T···
···C T T C A G C A C G T C G C G G A C A···

DELETION
MUTANT 2 DNA

···G A A G T G T···
···C T T C A C A···

b
MUTANT *A*

···G A A G T C G C G C A G C G T A T A G C T G A G C C T G T···
···C T T C A G C G C G T C G C A T A T C G A C T C G G A C A···

NORMAL
RECOMBINANT

···G A A G T C G T G C A G C G T A T A G C T G A G C C T G T···
···C T T C A G C A C G T C G C A T A T C G A C T C G G A C A···

DELETION
MUTANT 1

···G A A G T C G T G C A G C G C C T G T···
···C T T C A G C A C G T C G C G G A C A···

c
MUTANT *A*

···G A A G T C G C G C A G C G T A T A G C T G A G C C T G T···
···C T T C A G C G C G T C G C A T A T C G A C T C G G A C A···

NO NORMAL
RECOMBINANTS

···G A A G T C G C G C A G C G T A T A G C T G A G C C T G T···
···C T T C A G C G C G T C G C A T A T C G A C T C G G A C A···

DELETION
MUTANT 2

···G A A G T G T···
···C T T C A C A···

"DELETION" MUTANTS provide one approach to making a genetic map. Here (a) normal DNA and mutant *A* differ by only one base pair (*C–G* has replaced *T–A*) in a certain portion of the *A* gene (*colored area*). In deletion mutant 1 a sequence of 10 base pairs, including six pairs from the *A* gene, has been spontaneously deleted. In deletion mutant 2, 22 base pairs, including 15 pairs from the *A* gene, have been deleted. By crossing mutant *A* with the two different deletion mutants in separate experiments (*b, c*), one can tell whether the mutated site (*C–G*) in the *A* gene falls inside or outside the deleted regions. A normal-type recombinant will appear (*b*) only if the altered base pair falls outside the deleted region.

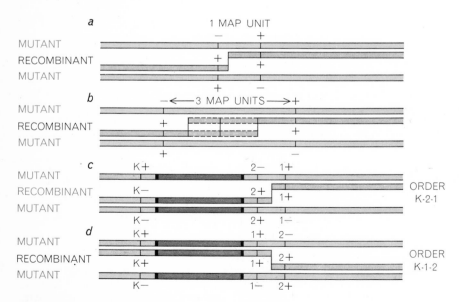

OTHER MAPPING METHODS involve determination of recombination frequency (*a, b*) and the distribution of outside markers (*c, d*). The site of a mutational alteration is indicated by "−," the corresponding unaltered site by "+." If the altered sites are widely spaced (*b*), normal recombinants will appear more often than if the altered sites are close together (*a*). In the second method the mutants are linked to another gene that is either normal (K^+) or mutated ($K^−$). Recombinant strains that contain 1^+ and 2^+ will carry the $K^−$ gene if the correct order is K–2–1. They will carry the K^+ gene if the order is K–1–2.

mappable gene should specify a protein whose amino acid sequence could be determined. Since no such system was known we had to gamble on a choice of our own. Fortunately we were studying at the time how the bacterium *Escherichia coli* synthesizes the amino acid tryptophan. Irving Crawford and I observed that the enzyme that catalyzed the last step in tryptophan synthesis could be readily separated into two different protein species, or subunits, one of which could be clearly isolated from the thousands of other proteins synthesized by *E. coli*. This protein, called the tryptophan synthetase *A* protein, had a molecular weight indicating that it had slightly fewer than 300 amino acid units. Furthermore, we already knew how to force *E. coli* to produce comparatively large amounts of the protein—up to 2 percent of the total cell protein—and we also had a collection of mutants in which the activity of the tryptophan synthetase *A* protein was lacking. Finally, the bacterial strain we were using was one for which genetic procedures for preparing fine-structure maps had already been developed. Thus we could hope to map the *A* gene that presumably controlled the structure of the *A* protein.

To accomplish the mapping we needed a set of bacterial mutants with mutational alterations at many different sites on the *A* gene. If we could determine the amino acid change in the *A* protein of each of these mutants, and discover its position in the linear sequence of amino acids in the protein, we could test the concept of colinearity. Here again we were fortunate in the nature of the complex of subunits represented by tryptophan synthetase.

The normal complex consists of two *A*-protein subunits (the alpha chains) and one subunit consisting of two beta chains. Within the bacterial cell the complex acts as an enzyme to catalyze the reaction of indole-3-glycerol phosphate and serine to produce tryptophan and 3-phosphoglyceraldehyde [*see illustration on page 226*]. If the *A* protein undergoes certain kinds of mutations, it is still able to form a complex with the beta chains, but the complex loses the ability to catalyze the reaction. It retains the ability, however, to catalyze a simpler reaction when it is tested outside the cell: it will convert indole and serine to tryptophan. There are still other kinds of *A*-gene mutants that evidently lack the ability to form an *A* protein that can combine with beta chains; thus these strains are not able to catalyze even the simpler reaction. The first class of mutants—those that produce an *A* protein that is still able to combine with beta chains and exhibit catalytic activity when they are tested outside the cell—proved to be the most important for our study.

A fine-structure map of the *A* gene was constructed on the basis of genetic crosses performed by the process called transduction. This employs a particular bacterial virus known as transducing phage *P1kc*. When this virus multiplies in a bacterium, it occasionally incorporates a segment of the bacterial DNA within its own coat of protein. When the virus progeny infect other bacteria, genetic material of the donor bacteria is introduced into some of the recipient cells. A fraction of the recip-

ients survive the infection. In these survivors segments of the bacterium's own genetic material pair with like segments of the "foreign" genetic material and recombination between the two takes place. As a result the offspring of an infected bacterium can contain characteristics inherited from its remote parent as well as from its immediate one.

In order to establish the order of mutationally altered sites in the *A* gene we have relied partly on a set of mutant bacteria in which one end of a deleted segment of DNA lies within the *A* gene. In each of these "deletion" mutants a segment of the genetic material of the bacterium was deleted spontaneously.

Thus each deletion mutant in the set retains a different segment of the *A* gene. This set of mutants can now be crossed with any other mutant in which the *A* gene is altered at only a single site. Recombination can give rise to a normal gene only if the altered site does not fall within the region of the *A* gene that is missing in the deletion mutant [*see top illustration on opposite page*]. By crossing many *A*-protein mutants with the set of deletion mutants one can establish the linear order of many of the mutated sites in the *A* gene. The ordering is limited only by the number of deletion mutants at one's disposal.

A second method, which more closely

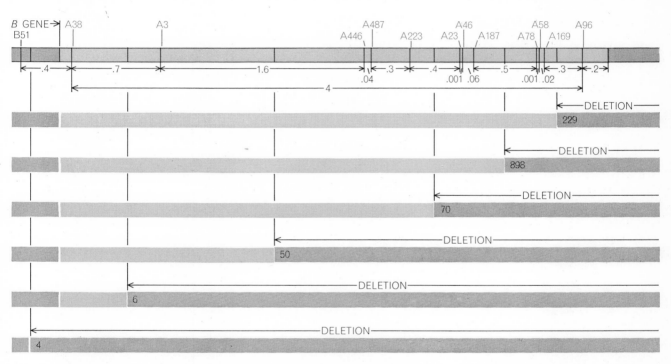

MAP OF *A* GENE shows the location of mutationally altered sites, drawn to scale, as determined by the three genetic-mapping methods illustrated on the opposite page. The total length of the *A* gene is slightly over four map units (probably 4.2). Below map are six deletion mutants that made it possible to assign each of the 12 *A*-gene mutants to one of six regions within the gene. The more sensitive mapping methods were employed to establish the order of mutations and the distance between mutation sites within each region.

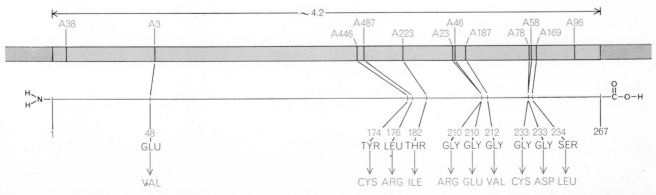

COLINEARITY OF GENE AND PROTEIN can be inferred by comparing the *A*-gene map (*top*) with the various amino acid changes in the *A* protein (*bottom*), both drawn to scale. The amino acid changes associated with 10 of the 12 mutations are also shown.

MET – GLN – ARG – TYR – GLU – SER – LEU – PHE – ALA – GLN – LEU – LYS – GLU – ARG – LYS – GLU – GLY – ALA – PHE – VAL –
1   20

PRO – PHE – VAL – THR – LEU – GLY – ASP – PRO – GLY – ILE – GLU – GLN – SER – LEU – LYS – ILE – ASP – THR – LEU – ILE –
21   40

A3

GLU – ALA – GLY – ALA – ASP – ALA – LEU – [GLU] – LEU – GLY – ILE – PRO – PHE – SER – ASP – PRO – LEU – ALA – ASP – GLY –
41   ↓   60
                               VAL

PRO – THR – ILE – GLN – ASN – ALA – THR – LEU – ARG – ALA – PHE – ALA – ALA – GLY – VAL – THR – PRO – ALA – GLN – CYS –
61   80

PHE – GLU – MET – LEU – ALA – LEU – ILE – ARG – GLN – LYS – HIS – PRO – THR – ILE – PRO – ILE – GLY – LEU – LEU – MET –
71   100

TYR – ALA – ASN – LEU – VAL – PHE – ASN – LYS – GLY – ILE – ASP – GLU – PHE – TYR – ALA – GLN – CYS – GLU – LYS – VAL –
101   120

GLY – VAL – ASP – SER – VAL – LEU – VAL – ALA – ASP – VAL – PRO – VAL – GLN – GLU – SER – ALA – PRO – PHE – ARG – GLN –
121   140

ALA – ALA – LEU – ARG – HIS – ASN – VAL – ALA – PRO – ILE – PHE – ILE – CYS – PRO – PRO – ASP – ALA – ASP – ASP – ASP –
141   160

A446   A487

LEU – LEU – ARG – GLN – ILE – ALA – SER – TYR – GLY – ARG – GLY – TYR – THR – [TYR] – LEU – [LEU] – SER – ARG – ALA – GLY –
161   ↓   ↓   180
                                                               CYS   ARG

A223

VAL – [THR] – GLY – ALA – GLU – ASN – ARG – ALA – ALA – LEU – PRO – LEU – ASN – HIS – LEU – VAL – ALA – LYS – LEU – LYS –
181   ↓   200
       ILE

A23   A46   A187

GLU – TYR – ASN – ALA – ALA – PRO – PRO – LEU – GLN – [GLY] – PHE – [GLY] – ILE – SER – ALA – PRO – ASP – GLN – VAL – LYS –
201   ↓   ↓   ↓   220
                                      ARG   GLU   VAL

A78   A58   A169

ALA – ALA – ILE – ASP – ALA – GLY – ALA – ALA – GLY – ALA – ILE – SER – [GLY] – [SER] – ALA – ILE – VAL – LYS – ILE – ILE –
221   ↓   ↓   240
                                                        CYS ASP   LEU

GLU – GLN – HIS – ASN – ILE – GLU – PRO – GLU – LYS – MET – LEU – ALA – ALA – LEU – LYS – VAL – PHE – VAL – GLN – PRO –
241   260

MET – LYS – ALA – ALA – THR – ARG – SER
261   267

AMINO ACID SEQUENCE OF *A* PROTEIN is shown side by side with a ribbon representing the DNA of the *A* gene. It can be seen that 10 different mutations in the gene produced alterations in the amino acids at only eight different places in the *A* protein. The explanation is that at two of them, 210 and 233, there were a total of four alterations. Thus at No. 210 the mutation designated A23 changed glycine to arginine, whereas mutation A46 changed glycine to glutamic acid. At No. 233 glycine was changed to cysteine by one mutation (A78) and to aspartic acid by another mutation (A58). On the genetic map A23 and A46, like A78 and A58, are very close.

resembles traditional genetic procedures, relies on recombination frequencies to establish the order of the mutationally altered sites in the *A* gene with respect to one another. By this method one can assign relative distances—map distances—to the regions between altered sites. The method is often of little use, however, when the distances are very close.

In such cases we have used a third method that involves a mutationally altered gene, or genetic marker, close to the *A* gene. This marker produces a recognizable genetic trait unrelated to the *A* protein. What this does, in effect, is provide a reading direction so that one can tell whether two closely spaced mutants, say No. 58 and No. 78, lie in the order 58–78, reading from the left on the map, or vice versa [see bottom illustration on page 228].

With these procedures we were able to construct a genetic map relating the altered sites in a group of mutants responsible for altered *A* proteins that could themselves be isolated for study. Some of the sites were very close together, whereas others were far apart [see upper illustration on page 229]. The next step was to determine the nature of the amino acid changes in each of the mutationally altered proteins.

It was expected that each mutant of the *A* protein would have a localized change, probably involving only one amino acid. Before we could hope to identify such a specific change we would have to know the sequence of amino acids in the unmutated *A* protein. This was determined by John R. Guest, Gabriel R. Drapeau, Bruce C. Carlton and me, by means of a well-established procedure. The procedure involves breaking the protein molecule into many short fragments by digesting it with a suitable enzyme. Since any particular protein rarely has repeating sequences of amino acids, each digested fragment is likely to be unique. Moreover, the fragments are short enough—typically between two and two dozen amino acids in length—so that careful further treatments can release one amino acid at a time for analysis. In this way one can identify all the amino acids in all the fragments, but the sequential order of the fragments is still unknown. This can be established by digesting the complete protein molecule with a different enzyme that cleaves it into a uniquely different set of fragments. These are again analyzed in detail. With two fully analyzed sets of fragments in hand, it is not difficult to

SEGMENT OF PROTEIN	MUTANT										NORMAL
	H11	C140	B17	B272	H32	B278	C137	H36	A489	C208	
I	+	+	+	+	+	+	+	+	+	+	+
II	−	+	+	+	+	+	+	+	+	+	+
III	−	−	+	+	+	+	+	+	+	+	+
IV	−	−	−	+	+	+	+	+	+	+	+
V	−	−	−	−	+	+	+	+	+	+	+
VI	−	−	−	−	−	+	+	+	+	+	+
VII	−	−	−	−	−	−	+	+	+	+	+
VIII	−	−	−	−	−	−	−	+	+	+	+
IX	−	−	−	−	−	−	−	−	+	+	+
X	−	−	−	−	−	−	−	−	−	+	+
XI	−	−	−	−	−	−	−	−	−	−	+

GENETIC MAP   H11 C140 B17 B272 H32   B278 C137   H36   A489 C208

INDEPENDENT EVIDENCE FOR COLINEARITY of gene and protein structure has been obtained from studies of the protein that forms the head of the bacterial virus T4D. Sydney Brenner and his co-workers at the University of Cambridge have found that mutations in the gene for the head protein alter the length of head-protein fragments. In the table "+" indicates that a given segment of the head protein is produced by a particular mutant; "−" indicates that the segment is not produced. When the genetic map was plotted, it was found that the farther to the right a mutation appears, the longer the fragment of head protein.

find short sequences of amino acids that are grouped together in the fragment of one set but that are divided between two fragments in the other. This provides the clue for putting the two sets of fragments in order. In this way we ultimately determined the identity and location of each of the 267 amino acids in the unmutated *A* protein of tryptophan synthetase.

Simultaneously my colleagues and I were examining the mutants of the *A* protein to identify the specific sites of mutational changes. For this work we used a procedure first developed by Vernon M. Ingram, now at the Massachusetts Institute of Technology, in his studies of naturally occurring abnormal forms of human hemoglobin. This procedure also uses an enzyme (trypsin) to break the protein chain into peptides, or polypeptide fragments. If the peptides are placed on filter paper wetted with certain solvents, they will migrate across

the paper at different rates; if an electric potential is applied across the paper, the peptides will be dispersed even more, depending on whether they are negatively charged, positively charged or uncharged under controlled conditions of acidity. The former separation process is chromatography; the latter, electrophoresis. When they are employed in combination, they produce a unique "fingerprint" for each set of peptides obtained by digesting the *A* protein from a particular mutant bacterium. The positions of the peptides are located by spraying the filter paper with a solution of ninhydrin and heating it for a few minutes at about 70 degrees centigrade. Each peptide reacts to yield a characteristic shade of yellow, gray or blue.

When the fingerprints of mutationally altered *A* proteins were compared with the fingerprint of the unmutated protein, they were found to be remarkably similar. In each case, however, there was a difference. The mutant fingerprint usually lacked one peptide spot that appears in the nonmutant fingerprint and exhibited a spot that the nonmutant fingerprint lacks. The two peptides would presumably be related to each other with the exception of the change resulting from the mutational event. One can isolate each of the peptides and compare their amino acid composition. Guest, Drapeau, Carlton and I, together with D. R. Helinski and U. Henning, identified the amino acid substitutions in

each of a variety of altered A proteins.

The final step was to compare the locations of these changes in the A protein with the genetic map of the mutationally altered sites. There could be no doubt that the amino acid sequence of the A protein and the map of the A gene are in fact colinear [see lower illustration on page 229].

One can also see that the distances between mutational sites on the map of the A gene correspond quite closely to the distances separating the corresponding

amino acid changes in the A protein. In two instances two separate mutational changes, so close as to be almost at the same point on the genetic map, led to changes of the same amino acid in the unmutated protein. This is to be expected if a codon of three bases in DNA is required to specify a single amino acid in a protein. Evidently the most closely spaced mutational sites in our genetic map represent alterations in two bases within a single codon.

Thus our studies have shown that each

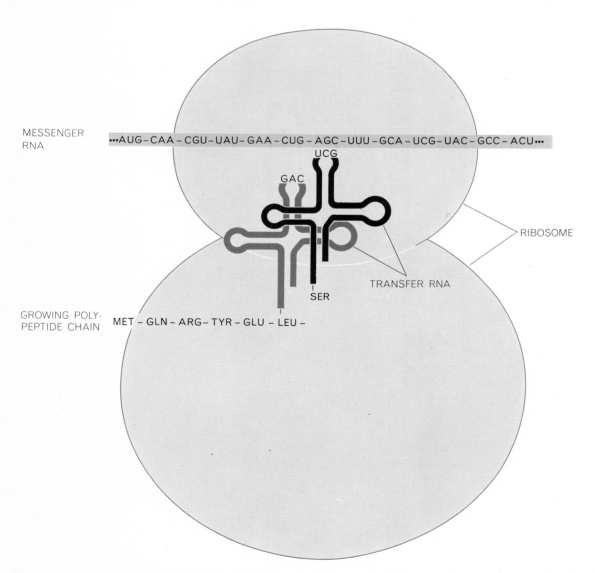

DNA

...ATG – CAA – CGT – TAT – GAA – CTG – AGC – TTT – GCA – TCG – TAC – GCC – ACT – GTT – TCT – ATT – GCA...

...TAC – GTT – GCA – ATA – CTT – GAC – TCG – AAA – CGT – AGC – ATG – CGG – TGA – CAA – AGA – TAA – CGT...

MESSENGER RNA

...AUG – CAA – CGU – UAU – GAA – CUG – AGC – UUU – GCA – UCG – UAC – GCC – ACU...

UCG

GAC

SER

RIBOSOME

TRANSFER RNA

GROWING POLY-PEPTIDE CHAIN   MET – GLN – ARG – TYR – GLU – LEU –

SCHEME OF PROTEIN SYNTHESIS, according to the current view, involves the following steps. Genetic information is transcribed from double-strand DNA into single-strand messenger ribonucleic acid (RNA), which becomes associated with a ribosome. Amino acids are delivered to the ribosome by molecules of transfer RNA, which embody codons complementary to the codons in messenger RNA. The next to the last molecule of transfer RNA to arrive (color) holds the growing polypeptide chain while the arriving molecule of transfer RNA (black) delivers the amino acid that is to be added to the chain next (serine in this example). The completed polypeptide chain, either alone or in association with other chains, is the protein whose specification was originally embodied in DNA.

	AGY							AGX	AGY									AGY		
CGZ	GGZ	UAX	ACZ	UAX	XUZ	CUZ	UCZ	CGZ	GCZ	GGZ	GUZ	ACW	GGZ	GCZ	GAY	AAX	CGZ	GCZ	GCZ	XUZ
– ARG –	GLY –	TYR –	THR –	TYR –	LEU –	LEU –	SER –	ARG –	ALA –	GLY –	VAL –	THR –	GLY –	ALA –	GLU –	ASN –	ARG –	ALA –	ALA –	LEU –

170 ... 190

CCZ	XUZ	AAX	CAX	XUZ	GUZ	GCZ	AAY	XUZ	AAY	GAY	UAX	AAX	GCZ	GCZ	CCZ	CCZ	XUZ	CAY	GGA
PRO –	LEU –	ASN –	HIS –	LEU –	VAL –	ALA –	LYS –	LEU –	LYS –	GLU –	TYR –	ASN –	ALA –	ALA –	PRO –	PRO –	LEU –	GLN –	GLY –

191 ... 210

	AGX																		
UUX	GGZ	AUW	UCZ	GCZ	CCZ	GAX	CAY	GUZ	AAY	GCZ	GCZ	AUW	GAX	GCZ	GGZ	GCZ	GCZ	GGZ	GCZ
PHE –	GLY –	ILE –	SER –	ALA –	PRO –	ASP –	GLN –	VAL –	LYS –	ALA –	ALA –	ILE –	ASP –	ALA –	GLY –	ALA –	ALA –	GLY –	ALA –

211 ... 230

	AGX																		
AUW	UCZ	GGX	UCZ	GCZ	AUW	GUZ	AAY	AUW	AUW	GAY	CAY	CAX	AAX	AUW	GAY	CCZ	GAY	AAY	AUG
ILE –	SER –	GLY –	SER –	ALA –	ILE –	VAL –	LYS –	ILE –	ILE –	GLU –	GLN –	HIS –	ASN –	ILE –	GLU –	PRO –	GLU –	LYS –	MET –

231 ... 250

W = U, C or A   X = U or C   Y = A or G   Z = U, C, A or G

PROBABLE CODONS IN MESSENGER RNA that determines the sequence of amino acids in the *A* protein are shown for 81 of the protein's 267 amino acid units. The region includes seven of the eight mutationally altered positions (*colored boxes*) in the *A* protein. The codons were selected from those assigned to the amino acids by Marshall Nirenberg and his associates at the National Institutes of Health and by H. Gobind Khorana and his associates at the University of Wisconsin. Codons for the remaining 186 amino acids in the *A* protein can be supplied similarly. In most cases the last base in the codon cannot be specified because there are usually several synonymous codons for each amino acid. With a few exceptions the synonyms differ from each other only in the third position.

unique sequence of bases in DNA—a sequence constituting a gene—is ultimately translated into a corresponding unique linear sequence of amino acids—a sequence constituting a polypeptide chain. Such chains, either by themselves or in conjunction with other chains, fold into the three-dimensional structures we recognize as protein molecules. In the great majority of cases these proteins act as biological catalysts and are therefore classed as enzymes.

The colinear relation between a genetic map and the corresponding protein has also been convincingly demonstrated by Sydney Brenner and his co-workers at the University of Cambridge. The protein they studied was not an enzyme but a protein that forms the head of the bacterial virus T4. One class of mutants of this virus produces fragments of the head protein that are related to one another in a curious way: much of their amino acid sequence appears to be identical, but the fragments are of various lengths. Brenner and his group found that when the chemically similar regions in fragments produced by many mutants were matched, the fragments could be arranged in order of increasing length. When they made a genetic map of the mutants that produced these fragments, they found that the mutationally altered sites on the genetic map were in the same order as the termination points in the protein fragments. Thus the length of the fragment of the head protein produced by a mutant increased as the site of mutation was displaced farther from one end of the genetic map [*see illustration on page 231*].

The details of how the living cell translates information coded in gene structure into protein structure are now reasonably well known. The base sequence of one strand of DNA is transcribed into a single-strand molecule of messenger ribonucleic acid (RNA), in which each base is complementary to one in DNA. Each strand of messenger RNA corresponds to relatively few genes; hence there are a great many different messenger molecules in each cell. These messengers become associated with the small cellular bodies called ribosomes, which are the actual site of protein synthesis [*see illustration on page 232*]. In the ribosome the bases on the messenger RNA are read in groups of three and translated into the appropriate amino acid, which is attached to the growing polypeptide chain. The messenger also contains in code a precise starting point and stopping point for each polypeptide.

From the studies of Marshall Nirenberg and his colleagues at the National Institutes of Health and of H. Gobind Khorana and his group at the University of Wisconsin the RNA codons corresponding to each of the amino acids are known. By using their genetic code dictionary we can indicate approximately two-thirds of the bases in the messenger RNA that specifies the structure of the *A*-protein molecule. The remaining third cannot be filled in because synonyms in the code make it impossible, in most cases, to know which of two or more bases is the actual base in the third position of a given codon [*see illustration*

above]. This ambiguity is removed, however, in two cases where the amino acid change directed by a mutation narrows down the assignment of probable codons. Thus at amino acid position 48 in the *A*-protein molecule, where a mutation changes the amino acid glutamic acid to valine, one can deduce from the many known changes at this position that of the two possible codons for glutamic acid, GAA and GAG, GAG is the correct one. In other words, GAG (specifying glutamic acid) is changed to GUG (specifying valine). The other position for which the codon assignment can be made definite in this way is No. 210. This position is affected by two different mutations: the amino acid glycine is replaced by arginine in one case and by glutamic acid in the other. Here one can infer from the observed amino acid changes that of the four possible codons for glycine, only one—GGA—can yield by a single base change either arginine (AGA) or glutamic acid (GAA).

Knowledge of the bases in the messenger RNA for the *A* protein can be translated, of course, into knowledge of the base pairs in the *A* gene, since each base pair in DNA corresponds to one of the bases in the RNA messenger. When the ambiguity in the third position of most of the codons is resolved, and when we can distinguish between two quite different sets of codons for arginine, leucine and serine, we shall be able to write down the complete base sequence of the *A* gene—the base sequence that specifies the sequence of the 267 amino acids in the *A* protein of the enzyme tryptophan synthetase.

24 | *How Proteins Start*

BRIAN F. C. CLARK AND *KJELD A. MARCKER* · *January 1968*

Over the past 15 years a tremendous amount of information has been amassed on how the living cell makes protein molecules. Step by step investigators in laboratories all over the world are clarifying the architecture of specific proteins, the nature of the genetic material that incorporates the instructions for building them, the code in which the instructions are written and the processes that translate the instructions into the work of construction. With the information now available experimenters have already synthesized a number of protein-like molecules from cell-free materials, and the day seems not far off when we shall be able to describe, and perhaps control, every step in the making of a protein.

How is the building of a protein initiated? Until recently this question seemed to create no special problems. Given a supply of the amino acids from which a protein is made, the cell assembles them into a polypeptide chain that grows into a protein molecule, and it did not appear that the cell used any special machinery to start the construction of the chain. We have now learned, however, that the cell does indeed possess a starting mechanism. With the discovery of this mechanism it has become possible to study in detail the first step in the production of a protein molecule.

In order to discuss this new development we must first review the general features of protein synthesis by the cell. Proteins are made up of some 20 varieties of amino acid. A protein molecule consists of a long chain of amino acid units, typically from 100 to 500 or more of them, linked together in a specific sequence. The instructions for the particular order in each protein (the cell manufactures hundreds of different proteins) reside in the chainlike molecule of deoxyribonucleic acid (DNA). The DNA molecule consists of units called nucleotides; each nucleotide contains a side group of atoms called a base, and the sequence of bases along the DNA chain specifies the sequence for amino acids in the protein. There are four different bases in DNA: adenine (A), guanine (G), thymine (T) and cytosine (C). A "triplet" (a sequence of three bases) constitutes the "codon" that specifies a particular amino acid. The four bases taken three at a time in various sequences provide 64 possible codons; thus the four-letter language of DNA provides a vocabulary that is more than sufficient to designate the 20 amino acids. (In fact, some amino acids can be indicated by more than one codon.)

DNA does not guide the construction of the protein directly. Its message is first transcribed into the daughter molecule called messenger ribonucleic acid (mRNA). Messenger RNA also has four bases; three of them (A, G and C) are the same as in DNA, but the fourth, taking the place of thymine, is uracil (U). The RNA molecule is generated from DNA by a coupling process based on the fact that U couples to A and G couples to C. Thus during the transcription of DNA into RNA the four bases A, G, T and C in DNA give rise respectively to U, C, A and G in RNA [see *illustration on opposite page*].

The coded message is then read off the messenger RNA and translated into the construction of a protein molecule. This process takes place on the cell particles known as ribosomes, and it requires the assistance of smaller RNA molecules called transfer RNA (tRNA) that bring amino acids to the indicated sites. Each transfer RNA is specific for a particular amino acid, to which it attaches itself with the aid of an enzyme. It possesses an "anticodon" corresponding to a particular codon on the messenger RNA molecule. The ribosome moves along the messenger RNA molecule, reading off each codon in succession, and in this way it mediates the placement of the appropriate amino acids as they are delivered. As the amino acids join the chain they are linked together through peptide bonds formed by means of enzymes.

The decipherment of the genetic code for protein synthesis began in 1961 when Marshall W. Nirenberg and J. Heinrich Matthaei of the National Institutes of Health synthesized a simplified form of messenger RNA, composed of just one type of nucleotide, and found that it could generate the formation of a protein-like chain molecule made up of one variety of amino acid. Their artificial messenger RNA was the polynucleotide called "poly-U," containing uracil as the base. When it was added to a mixture of amino acids, extracts from cells of the bacterium *Escherichia coli* and energy-supplying compounds, it caused the synthesis of a polypeptide chain composed of the amino acid phenylalanine. Thus the poly-U codon (UUU) was found to specify phenylalanine.

This breakthrough quickly led to the identification of the codons for a number of other amino acids by means of the same device: using synthetic forms of messenger RNA. The experiments suggested that the initiation of synthesis of a protein was a perfectly straightforward matter. It appeared that the first codon in the messenger RNA chain simply called forth the delivery and placement of the specified amino acid and that no special starting signal was required. In 1964, however, Frederick Sanger and one of the authors of this article (Marcker) discovered a peculiar form of an amino acid, in combination with its transfer RNA, that threw entirely new light on the situation.

Using extracts from the *E. coli* bacterium, we were studying the chemical characteristics of the combination of the amino acid methionine with its specific tRNA. In the course of this study we decided to investigate the breakdown of the compound by pancreatic ribonu- clease, an enzyme known to split RNA chains at certain specific bonds [*see top illustration on page 237*]. In order to facilitate identification of the products we labeled the methionine in advance with radioactive sulfur, and after treatment of the methionine-tRNA compound with

CARBON   A ADENINE
OXYGEN   T THYMINE
HYDROGEN   G GUANINE
NITROGEN   C CYTOSINE
SULFUR   U URACIL
PHOSPHORUS

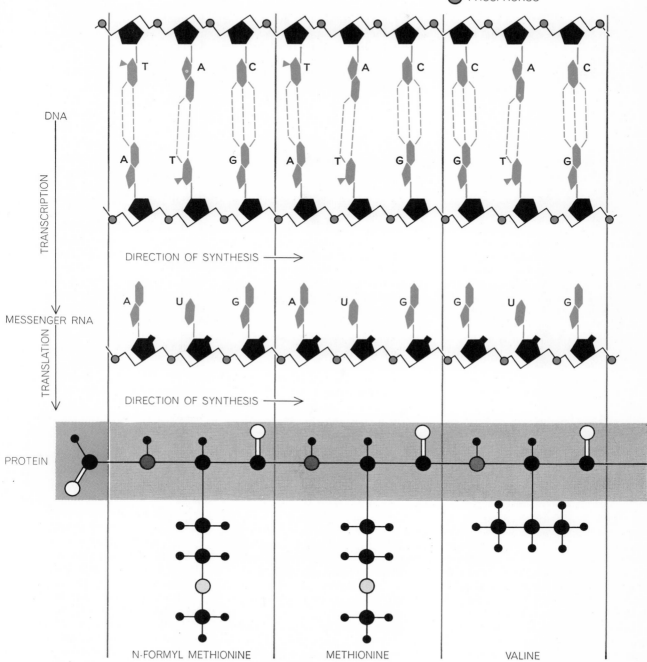

DNA

TRANSCRIPTION

DIRECTION OF SYNTHESIS →

MESSENGER RNA

TRANSLATION

DIRECTION OF SYNTHESIS →

PROTEIN

N-FORMYL METHIONINE   METHIONINE   VALINE

TRANSMISSION OF GENETIC INFORMATION takes place in two main steps. First the linear code specifying a particular protein is transcribed from deoxyribonucleic acid (DNA) into messenger ribonucleic acid (RNA). The code letters in DNA are the four bases adenine (A), thymine (T), guanine (G) and cytosine (C). Hydrogen bonds (*broken lines*) between the complementary bases A–T and G–C hold the two strands of the DNA molecule together. The strands, which run antiparallel, consist of alternating units of deoxyribose sugar (*pentagons*) and phosphate (PO₃H). The code letters in messenger RNA duplicate those attached to one strand of the DNA except that uracil (U) replaces thymine. In RNA the sugar is ribose. In the second step of the process messenger RNA is translated into protein. The code letters in RNA are read in triplets, or codons, each of which specifies one (or sometimes more) of the 20 amino acids that form protein molecules. It has now been found that the codon AUG can specify a modification of methionine known as formyl methionine, which signals the start of a protein chain. Inside the chain AUG specifies ordinary methionine. The codon GUG, which codes for valine inside the chain, can also specify formyl methionine and initiate chain synthesis.

the enzyme we separated the products by means of electrophoresis, the technique that segregates electrically charged molecules according to their charge, size and shape. As was to be expected, one of the products was the compound known as methionyl-adenosine, a combination of methionine with the terminal adenosine portion of the tRNA molecule. But we also found, to our surprise, that the products included a considerable amount of a formylated variety of this compound, that is, a variation in which a formyl group (CHO) replaced a hydrogen atom in the amino group

(NH₂) of the molecule. It turned out that this was by no means an artifact of the treatment to which the original compound had been subjected; growing cells proved to contain a high proportion of formylated methionine tRNA.

It was immediately evident that formylated methionine must occupy a special position in the protein molecule. The attachment of the formyl group to the amino group would prevent the amino group from forming a peptide bond [*see illustration below*]. Consequently the formylated amino acid must be an end unit in the protein molecule. Since an

amino group forms the "front" end of protein molecules when they are being assembled, formylated methionine must constitute the initial unit of the molecule.

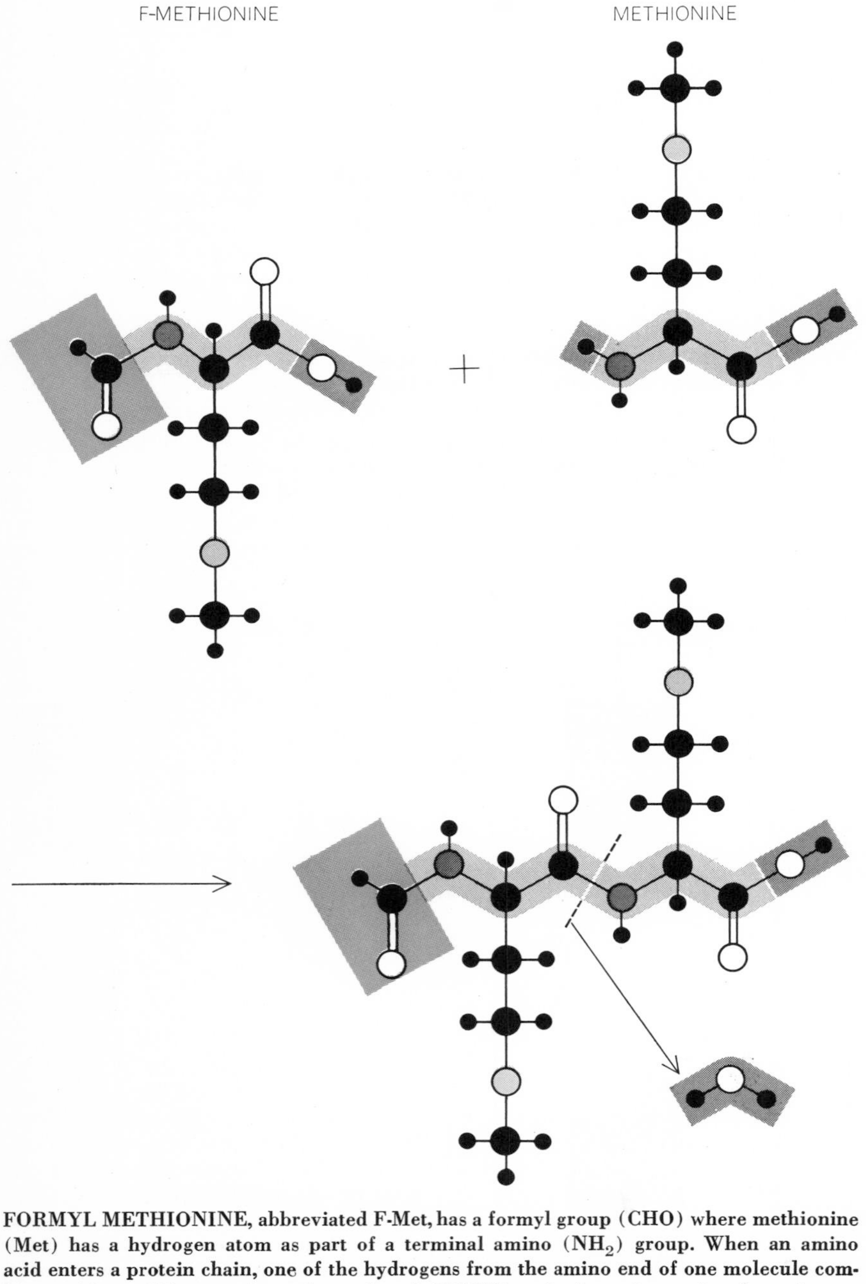

We were able to separate the methionine tRNA of *E. coli* into two distinct species, and found that only one can be formylated. The formylatable species constitutes about 70 percent of the bacterium's methionine tRNA [*see bottom illustration on opposite page*]. Recent work in our laboratory at the Medical Research Council in Cambridge has established that the compound is formylated (at methionine's amino group) only after the amino acid has become attached to the tRNA molecule. The donor of the formyl group is 10-formyl tetrahydrofolic acid, and the reaction is catalyzed by a specific enzyme that acts exclusively on the combination of methionine with the formylatable species of tRNA.

Our laboratory and others have proceeded to analyze the initiation of protein formation by several experimental techniques. We began by testing a number of different synthetic messenger RNA's for their ability to bring about synthesis of a polypeptide incorporating methionine. Only two of the synthetic polynucleotides we tried proved to be capable of doing this. One contained the bases uracil, adenine and guanine (poly-UAG); the other had only uracil and guanine (poly-UG). We found that in a mixture of amino acids and other cell-free materials where only the formylatable species of methionine tRNA was present, either poly-UAG or poly-UG would cause the synthesis of a polypeptide with methionine in the starting position—and only in that position. Surprisingly, this was true even when no formyl group was attached to the methionine-tRNA compound. We had to conclude that the formylatable version of the tRNA for methionine possessed a special adaptation that helped it to function as a polypeptide-chain initiator.

A thorough search was made for formylated varieties of other tRNA's: that is, of tRNA's for amino acids other than methionine. None were found. This raised an interesting question. In the proteins produced by *E. coli* cells the amino acid at the "front" end of the protein molecule is not always methionine; often it is alanine or serine. These amino acids are never found to be formylated. How, then, does either of them become the initial member of the protein chain?

Experiments with natural messenger RNA's (rather than synthetic polynucleotides) have suggested an explanation. Jerry Adams and Mario Capecchi, work-

F-METHIONINE   METHIONINE

FORMYL METHIONINE, abbreviated F-Met, has a formyl group (CHO) where methionine (Met) has a hydrogen atom as part of a terminal amino (NH₂) group. When an amino acid enters a protein chain, one of the hydrogens from the amino end of one molecule combines with an OH group from the carboxyl (COOH) end of another molecule to form a molecule of water. The two molecules are then linked by a peptide bond. The formyl group prevents this reaction, hence F-Met can appear only at the beginning of a protein chain.

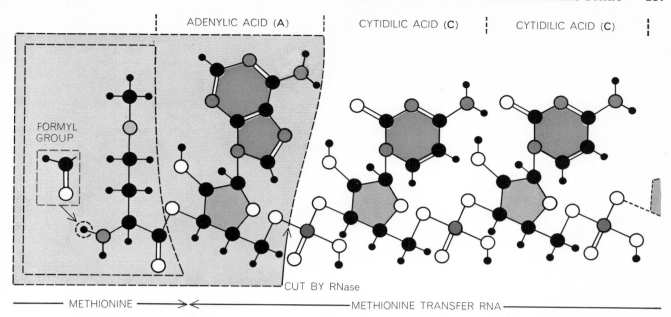

ADENYLIC ACID (A)   CYTIDILIC ACID (C)   CYTIDILIC ACID (C)

FORMYL GROUP

CUT BY RNase

METHIONINE → ← METHIONINE TRANSFER RNA

TRANSFER OF AMINO ACID to the site of protein synthesis is accomplished by molecules of transfer RNA (tRNA). There is at least one species of transfer RNA for each amino acid. All transfer RNA molecules contain the base sequence CCA at the terminal that holds the amino acid. Such a terminal is diagrammed here and shown coupled to methionine. Methionine that subsequently can be converted to formyl methionine is transferred by a different tRNA. When treated with the enzyme ribonuclease (RNase), the final base (adenine) and its coupled amino acid are split off from the rest of the transfer RNA. The fragment is called an aminoacyl adenosine.

ing in the laboratory of James D. Watson at Harvard University, and Norton D. Zinder and his collaborators at Rockefeller University have used messenger RNA's extracted from bacterial viruses. These RNA's direct the synthesis of the proteins that form the coat of the virus. The experimenters in Watson's and Zinder's laboratories found that when such an RNA was added to cell-free materials in the test tube, formylated methionine turned up at the starting end of the coat proteins that were synthesized. This was most surprising, because normally in living systems the initial amino acid of the viruses' coat protein is alanine. A significant clue was found, however, in the fact that the coat proteins synthesized in the cell-free systems invariably had an alanine in the second position, following the formyl methionine. From this it seems reasonable to deduce that in living systems, as in the cell-free system, the formation of the protein starts with formyl

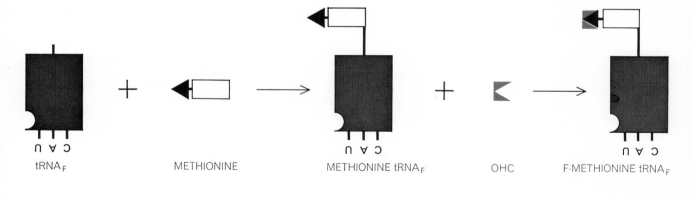

tRNA_F   METHIONINE   METHIONINE tRNA_F   OHC   F-METHIONINE tRNA_F

C A U

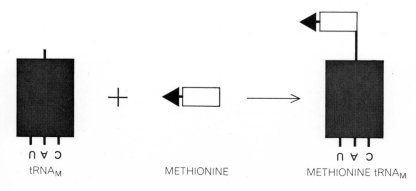

tRNA_M   METHIONINE   METHIONINE tRNA_M

C A U

TWO METHIONINE tRNA's, designated tRNA_F and tRNA_M, exhibit different characteristics. In the presence of an energy source (adenosine triphosphate) and a special coupling enzyme, both tRNA's combine with methionine. Only tRNA_F, however, forms a complex that is recognized by another enzyme that can convert methionine to formyl methionine. The formyl group is provided by 10-formyl tetrahydrofolic acid. The complex that results is F-Met·tRNA_F.

tRNA	CODONS
MET-tRNA$_M$	AUG
MET-tRNA$_F$	AUG
F-MET-tRNA$_F$	GUG

CODON ASSIGNMENTS show the bases in messenger RNA that cause the two Met-tRNA's to deliver methionine or formyl methionine for insertion in a protein chain.

methionine, and that the bacterial cells supply an enzyme that chops off the formyl methionine later, leaving alanine in the first position.

Experiments with *E. coli* RNA in our laboratory and others have produced similar results. Messenger RNA extracted from these bacteria, like that extracted from bacterial viruses, causes cell-free systems to synthesize proteins with formyl methionine in the first position. On the other hand, the proteins extracted from living *E. coli* cells usually have unformylated methionine or alanine or serine in the lead position. It therefore seems likely that the living cells remove the formyl group from methionine or split off the entire formyl methionine unit after synthesis of the protein chain has got under way. The significance of the frequent appearance of alanine and serine at the front end of *E. coli* proteins is not clear; no satisfactory explanation has yet been found for the cell's selection of alanine and serine to follow formyl methionine. At all events, what does seem plausible now is that in *E. coli* the synthesis of all proteins starts with formyl methionine as the first unit.

How does the messenger RNA convey the message calling for formyl methionine as the starting unit? Does it use a special codon addressed specifically to the formylatable variety of methionine tRNA? We tested various codons for their ability to bring about the delivery of formyl methionine to the protein-synthesizing ribosomes. A codon for methionine was already known: it is AUG. We found that AUG was "read" by both varieties of methionine tRNA—the formylatable and the unformylatable. Either variety of tRNA delivered and bound methionine to the ribosome in response to AUG. We found that the formylatable tRNA (but not the other variety) also recognized and responded to another codon: GUG.

These findings were consistent with our earlier observation that either poly-UAG or poly-UG could effect the incorporation of methionine into a polypeptide in a cell-free system. Poly-UAG, of course, can contain the codons AUG and GUG, depending on the sequence in which the bases happen to be arranged in this polynucleotide; poly-UG provides the codon GUG. That both AUG and GUG can initiate the synthesis of a methionine polypeptide was confirmed and clearly spelled out in detail by experiments in the laboratory of H. Gobind Khorana at the University of Wisconsin. Using synthetic messenger RNA's in which the bases were arranged only in these triplet sequences (AUG and GUG), Khorana's group showed that both codons led to the formation of a chain with formyl methionine in the starting position. AUG also placed methionine in internal positions in the chain, but GUG, which can code only for the formylatable version of the tRNA, incorporated methionine only at the starting end [*see illustration below*].

Investigators in the laboratories of Severo Ochoa at New York University and Paul M. Doty at Harvard obtained the same results. They also noted that both codons possess a certain versatility as signals, depending on their location in the messenger RNA. Located at or near the beginning of the messenger RNA chain, the AUG triplet is recognized by the formylatable variety of tRNA and leads to the placement of formylated methionine at the starting end of the polypeptide; farther on in the messenger RNA chain the same triplet is recognized by unformylatable tRNA and causes the placement of unformylated methionine in the internal part of the polypeptide. In short, at the "front" end of the RNA message the AUG codon says to the cell's synthesizing machinery, "Start the formation of a protein"; when it is located internally in the message, AUG simply says, "Place a methionine here." Similarly, the codon GUG was found to have two possible meanings: located at the beginning of the message, it orders the initiation of a protein with formylated methionine; in an internal position in the message it is the code word for placement not of methionine but of the amino acid valine.

How is it that each of these codons signifies a starting signal in one position and has a different meaning in another? Obviously this question will have to be answered in order to clarify the language of the protein-starting mechanism. Indeed, we cannot be sure that a codon in itself constitutes the entire message for the initiation of a protein. The signaling mechanism may be more complex than one might assume from the findings developed so far. Those findings are based almost entirely on work done with artificial messenger RNA's, and it is possible that the messages they provide are only approximations—meaningful enough to stimulate the cell machinery but not the full story.

When we consider how important the

SYNTHETIC MESSENGER	SOURCE OF METHIONINE			POSITION OF METHIONINE IN POLYPEPTIDE		CODONS USED
	MET-tRNA$_M$	MET-tRNA$_F$	F-MET-tRNA$_F$	INTERNAL	N-TERMINAL	
RANDOM POLY-UG	−	+		−	+	GUG
RANDOM POLY-AUG	+	+		+	+	AUG, GUG
POLY-(UG)$_n$	−	+		−	+	GUG
POLY-(AUG)$_n$	+	+		+	+	AUG

INCORPORATION OF METHIONINE in protein-like chains has been studied with synthetic messenger RNA's and the two species of methionine transfer RNA: tRNA$_M$ and tRNA$_F$. The plus sign indicates combinations that lead to incorporation. In random poly-UG and random poly-AUG the bases can occur in any sequence, but presumably the only effective sequences are GUG and AUG. Poly-(UG)$_n$ and poly-(AUG)$_n$ are synthetic chains of RNA consisting of 30 or more repetitions of the base sequences indicated.

codons AUG and GUG are in initiating the synthesis of polypeptides, it is certainly odd that a synthetic messenger RNA such as poly-U, which of course cannot supply those codons, nevertheless manages to cause the ribosomes to produce a polypeptide. We can only conclude that they do so by mistake, so to speak, that is, by acting in a way not entirely specified by the available information. (It is ironic that the genetic code was broken because artificial systems were able to make the right kind of mistake!) Are there circumstances that tend to assist these systems in accomplishing proper mistakes? One influential factor has been found. It is the concentration of magnesium in the cell-free system of building materials. A high magnesium concentration makes it possible for many kinds of synthetic messenger RNA to generate polypeptides; when the magnesium concentration is lowered, only the RNA's that contain AUG or GUG succeed in doing so. What magnesium may have to do with polypeptide initiation is still unclear.

Let us come back to the placement of the initial methionine as the normal first step in the construction of a protein. We have noted that the methionine-tRNA complex that places the amino acid in the initial position does not necessarily contain a formyl group. Evidently under conditions of a relatively high concentration of magnesium the formyl group of itself plays no essential role in the installation of the amino acid. What seems to be important is the character of the tRNA: only the formylatable variety of methionine tRNA can initiate the synthesis, and it can do so even when it is not formylated. What, then, are the specific properties that account for its role as an initiator?

A reasonable supposition is that this variety of tRNA has a special shape or configuration that helps it to fit into a particular site on the ribosome. As a matter of fact there is evidence that ribosomes possess two kinds of site for the attachment of tRNA's. One kind, called an amino acid site, simply receives and positions the tRNA when it arrives with its amino acid; the other kind, called a peptide site, holds the tRNA while a peptide bond is formed between its amino acid and an adjacent neighbor [see illustration at right]. It is therefore plausible to suppose that the formylatable variety of the tRNA for methionine may have a shape that helps it to fit into a peptide site on the ribosome and thus be in a position to start the linking together of amino acids.

Evidence in support of this hypothesis has been obtained in our laboratory by Mark S. Bretscher and one of us (Marcker) and by Philip Leder and his associates at the National Institutes of Health in experiments using the antibiotic puromycin. The structure of puromycin is similar to that of the end of a tRNA molecule that attaches to an amino acid [see illustration on next page]. Because it has an NH_2 group, puromycin can form a peptide bond with an amino acid, but since it lacks the free carboxyl (COOH) group of a normal amino acid it cannot form a second peptide bond.

Thus it cannot participate in chain elongation. Various experiments indicate that puromycin will add on to—and terminate—a growing polypeptide chain only when the tRNA holding the chain is bound in the peptide site.

In other experiments it has been found that the formylatable variety of methionine tRNA, when bound to a ribosome, will combine with puromycin; the unformylatable variety of the tRNA, on the other hand, will not react with puromycin. The experimental results therefore indicate that there are indeed two kinds of ribosomal site or state: one where a

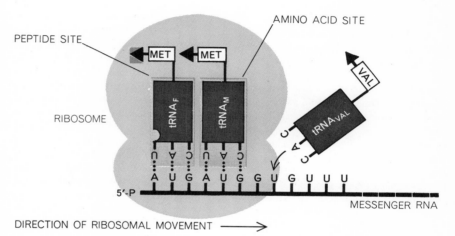

DIRECTION OF RIBOSOMAL MOVEMENT ⟶

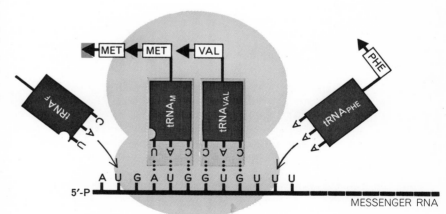

DIRECTION OF RIBOSOMAL MOVEMENT ⟶

PROTEIN SYNTHESIS takes place on cellular particles called ribosomes, which travel along the "instruction tape" of messenger RNA, reading off the genetic message. The ribosome evidently has two sites for accommodating molecules of transfer RNA: a peptide site and an amino acid site. It appears that the structure of tRNA$_F$ enables it to go directly to the peptide site, thereby initiating the protein chain. This special structure is symbolized by a notch in tRNA$_F$. Other tRNA's may acquire the configuration needed for the peptide site after first occupying the amino acid site. In step 1 (top) the codon AUG at the front end (5'-phosphate end) of messenger RNA pairs with the anticodon CAU that is believed to exist on tRNA$_F$, which delivers a molecule of formyl methionine to start the protein chain. The codon AUG in the second position is paired with the CAU anticodon of tRNA$_M$, which delivers a molecule of ordinary methionine. In step 2 (bottom) the tRNA$_F$ molecule has moved away and the peptide site has been occupied by tRNA$_M$, which is now coupled to the growing protein chain. Valine transfer RNA has moved into the amino acid site.

peptide bond cannot be formed between the peptide chain and puromycin and one where it can. Most likely the latter is the peptide site. Furthermore, the experiments have strengthened the suspicion that the formylatable tRNA possesses a unique structure that somehow helps it to move into the peptide site on a ribosome. Apparently the structure of the formylatable tRNA has been particularly tailor-made for its function as a chain initiator.

The question therefore arises: What is the precise role of the formyl group? If the formyl group per se has nothing to do with placing methionine in the starting position, what function does it have? Our earlier experiments, in which we used a relatively high magnesium concentration, suggested that the formyl group is involved somehow in the formation of the first peptide bond, which launches the building of the polypeptide chain. When the methionine tRNA complex is formylated, synthesis of the polypeptide proceeds much faster than when it is not. This effect can be ascribed to the fact that the presence of the formyl group somehow facilitates the entry into the peptide site. It still remains to be determined just how the formyl group helps to promote such an effect.

Further light has been shed on the problem of protein-chain initiation in the past year by the work of several laboratories, including our own. Special protein agents, still poorly defined, have been implicated together with a cofactor in the formation of the initiation complex on the ribosome. When these new components are present and the supply of magnesium is low, the formyl group is necessary if the formylatable methionine tRNA is to be attached to the ribosomal peptide site by a messenger. Quite recently the cofactor has been identified as being a nucleotide derivative: guanosine triphosphate. Hence we are coming to the view that the conditions prevailing within the living cell are approached by these low-magnesium conditions, where there is strict specificity for forming the initiation complex and for unambiguous polypeptide formation. In our present state of knowledge, however, it is still unclear how these new components help to ensure the placement of the formylated methionine tRNA in the peptide site on the ribosome.

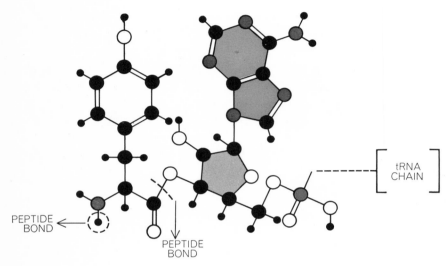

TYROSINE tRNA

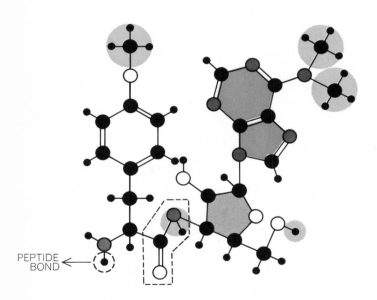

PUROMYCIN

PROTEIN-CHAIN TERMINATION can be induced by adding puromycin, an antibiotic, to a protein-synthesizing system. The structure of puromycin closely resembles the structure formed by the amino acid tyrosine and the terminal base of tRNA. Colored disks mark the atomic differences. Tyrosine can be inserted in a protein chain because it can form two peptide bonds. Puromycin can form only one peptide bond because the —CONH— linkage (*inside broken line*) is less reactive than the —COO— linkage in tyrosine tRNA.

The specific findings concerning the initiation of protein synthesis that we have discussed in this article apply only to bacterial cells. So far no such form of tRNA (containing the formyl group or any other blocking agent) has been found in the cells of mammals. Accordingly the mechanism of protein-chain initiation is possibly different in mammalian cells from the mechanism discussed here. The process of polypeptide initiation in the cells of higher organisms is currently under study in several laboratories.

Meanwhile the investigation of the *E. coli* system is being pursued with experiments that promise to yield further insights. The way in which the vaguely characterized protein agents and guanosine triphosphate are involved in the initiation of a polypeptide chain is being explored. Much work is under way on analyzing the sequence of nucleotides in natural messenger RNA's, with a view to determining whether or not AUG or GUG constitutes a complete coding signal for protein initiation. We are searching for differences between the formylatable and unformylatable varieties of methionine tRNA, in their nucleotide sequences and in their three-dimensional structures, that may throw light on their respective interactions with the ribosomes.

IV

MODIFICATION OF GENE ACTION

The Regulation of Cellular Activity

Many thousands of different biochemical reactions must occur simultaneously in coordinated fashion in the living cell. Virtually all of these reactions are catalyzed by specific enzymes. The synthesis of new cells might be likened to an automobile assembly line: the proper parts must be ready in the right amounts at the right place and at the right time, as the finished product is gradually assembled. But, more than that, the biological assembly line must be extremely flexible; it must be able to adjust quickly to momentary or developing shortages of particular raw materials. Thus, a bacterium growing in a synthetic medium with glucose as its sole source of both energy and carbon is able to adapt readily to new growth media in which, for example, the sugar, lactose, replaces glucose. To accomplish this feat of biochemical dexterity the cell proceeds to synthesize an enzyme not normally present in significant amounts in the glucose-grown culture. This enzyme, called betagalactosidase, is capable of breaking the lactose molecule into the simpler sugars, galactose and glucose, which are then metabolized as before. What general systems of regulation, or control, could operate in such an intricate biochemical factory?

There are evidently a number of mechanisms through which such control might operate. Obviously the control of the transcription rate of a particular gene will regulate the rate of synthesis of the corresponding enzyme and in turn the biochemical reaction it catalyzes. However, this type of regulation might not be sensitive enough to very sudden or very drastic changes in intracellular conditions. A more direct kind of control is that which operates upon the enzyme itself, and which has the effect of increasing or decreasing its activity. It turns out that both of these mechanisms are essential to the coordinated activity of every biological system. They are described in the article by Jean-Pierre Changeux on "The Control of Biochemical Reactions." Just as the details of the structure of a protein are responsible for the protein's specificity as an enzyme, this structure also influences the regulation of the enzymes.

Although most studies of gene and enzyme regulation have been carried out on simple bacterial systems, it is likely that the mechanisms that have been discovered also operate in the cells of multicellular organisms. However, in these more complex organisms there exists an additional problem, that of coordinating the activity of many cells to operate in concert for the benefit of the organism as a whole. For this sort of regulation, a special class of proteins function as chemical messengers. These molecules, called hormones, are produced by certain glands in higher organisms, and they are carried by the circulation to various organs or target cells throughout the organism. In "Hormones and Genes," Eric H. Davidson shows that many hormones affect the transcription of the genetic message.

The next article in this section, "Antibiotics and the Genetic Code" by Luigi Gorini, might equally well have been included in the section on protein synthesis. The studies on the effect of streptomycin upon the translation of the messenger RNA in ribosomes have contributed much to our understanding of the role that the ribosome plays in this process. It now appears that this organelle is not merely a passive site for protein synthesis, since modification of ribosome structure has been shown to have a profound effect upon the translation of the encoded message. Streptomycin and other antibiotics alter ribosome structure in such a way that incorrect amino acids may be inserted in place of the correct amino acids in certain positions of the proteins being synthesized. Such biochemical tampering with the molecular process of translation has already had widespread practical application in the pharmacological treatment of disease. It is possible that there will be found new compounds that have very selective effects on the ribosomes of certain classes of cells, even, for example, malignant cells. Whereas the multiplication of most animal cells is very stringently regulated, the malignant cell does not respond to the normal growth controls of the organism. In addition, the cancer cell seems to undergo permanent genetic changes so great that it is no longer even recognizable as belonging to the individual in which it is found. The understanding of how this "malignant transformation" is brought about may provide an important clue to the eventual control of the disease. In "The Induction of Cancer by Viruses," Renato Dulbecco describes an exciting line of work being pursued in his laboratory: cells in tissue culture are being infected by certain viruses that cause them to become transformed into cancer-like cells. This article helps one to appreciate how the detailed study of the molecular processes of life in simple systems may be extended to the understanding of these same processes in more complex systems. You will note the immediate similarities between the cancer-producing polyoma virus described by Dulbecco and the T4 bacterial virus considered in Part II. The study of the molecular mechanism of gene regulation is probably the most promising avenue to the eventual control of the diseases of regulation, more commonly classified as cancer.

In multicellular organisms cells are sometimes able to recognize infectious agents such as viruses. Neutralization of these invaders is accomplished by another class of specialized proteins known as antibodies. Many types of antibodies are produced, each having a special configuration that allows it to counteract the specific foreign substance that has stimulated its production. In the last article in this section, "The Structure of Antibodies," R. R. Porter discusses those structural features that enable the antibodies to carry out their all-important functions in defending the body against disease.

25 | The Control of Biochemical Reactions

JEAN-PIERRE CHANGEUX · *April 1965*

The analogy between a living organism and a machine holds true to a remarkable extent at all levels at which it is investigated. To be sure, living things are machines with exceptional powers, set apart from other machines by their ability to adapt to the environment and to reproduce themselves. Yet in all their functions they seem to obey mechanistic laws. An organism can be compared to an automatic factory. Its various structures work in unison, not independently; they respond quantitatively to given commands or stimuli; the system regulates itself by means of automatic controls consisting of specific feedback circuits.

These principles have long been recognized in the behavior of living organisms at the physiological level. In response to the tissues' need for more oxygen during exercise the heart speeds up its pumping of blood; in response to a rise in the blood-sugar level the pancreas increases its secretion of insulin. Now analogous systems have been discovered at work within the living cell. The new findings of molecular biology show that the cell is a mechanical microcosm: a chemical machine in which the various structures are interdependent and controlled by feedback systems quite similar to the systems devised by engineers who specialize in control theory. In this article we shall survey the experimental findings and hypotheses that have developed from the viewpoint that the cell is a self-regulating machine.

We can think of the cell as a completely automatic chemical factory designed to make the most economical use of the energy available to it. It manufactures certain products—for example proteins—by means of series of reactions that constitute its production lines, and most of the energy goes to power these processes. Regulating the production lines are control circuits that themselves require very little energy. Typically they consist of small, mobile molecules that act as "signals" and large molecules that act as "receptors" and translate the signals into biological activity.

The elementary machines of the cellular factory are the biological catalysts known as enzymes. The synthesis of any product (for example a specific protein) entails a series of steps, each of which calls for a specific enzyme. Obviously there are two possible ways in which the cell can control its output of a given product: (1) it may change the number of machines (enzyme molecules) available for some step in the chain or (2) it may change their rate of operation. Therefore in order to reduce the output of the product in question the cell may cut down the number of enzyme molecules or inhibit some of them or do both.

An excellent demonstration of such control has been obtained in experiments with the common bacterium *Escherichia coli*. The experiments involved the bacterial cell's production of the amino acid L-isoleucine, which it uses, along with other amino acids, to make proteins. Would the cell go on synthesizing this amino acid if it already had more than it needed for building proteins? L-isoleucine labeled with radioactive atoms was added to the medium in which the bacteria were growing; the experiments showed that when the substance was present in excess, the bacteria ceased to produce it. The amount of the amino acid in the cell in this case serves as the signal controlling its synthesis: if the amount is below a certain level, the cell produces more L-isoleucine; if it rises above that level, the cell stops producing L-isoleucine. Like the temperature level in a house with a thermostatically regulated heating system, the level of L-isoleucine in the cell exerts negative-feedback control on its own production.

How is the control carried out? H. Edwin Umbarger and his colleagues, working in the laboratory of the Long Island Biological Association, found that the presence of an excess of L-isoleucine has two effects on the cell: it inhibits the activity of the enzyme (L-threonine deaminase) needed for the first step in the chain of synthesizing reactions, and it stops production by the cell of all the enzymes (including L-threonine deaminase) required for L-isoleucine synthesis. Curiously it turned out that the two control mechanisms are independent of each other. By experiments with mutant strains of *E. coli* it was found that one mutation deprived the cell of the ability represented by the inhibition of L-threonine deaminase by L-isoleucine; another mutation deprived it of the ability to halt production of the entire set of enzymes. The two mutations were located at different places on the bacterial chromosome. Therefore it is clear that the two control mechanisms are completely separate.

Let us first examine the type of mechanism that controls the manufacture of enzymes. It was Jacques Monod and Germaine Cohen-Bazire of the Pasteur Institute in Paris who discovered the phenomenon of repression: the inhibition of enzyme synthesis by the presence of the product, the product serving as a signal that the enzymes are not needed. The signal substance

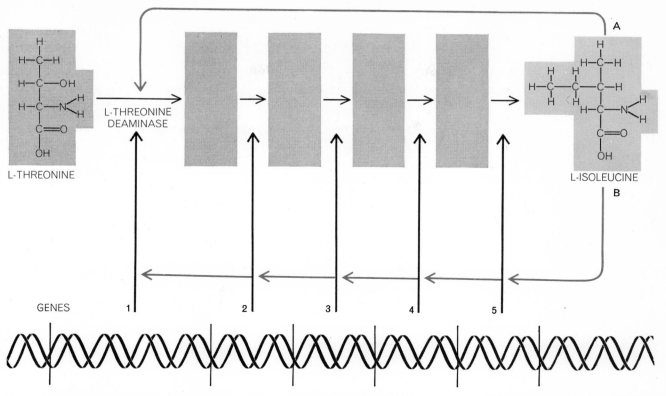

TWO FEEDBACK SYSTEMS control the biosynthesis of cell products, as shown here for the synthesis of the amino acid L-isoleucine in the bacterium *Escherichia coli*. The end product of the synthesizing chain acts as a regulatory signal that inhibits the activity of the first enzyme in the chain, L-threonine deaminase (*A*), and also represses the synthesis of all the enzymes (*B*).

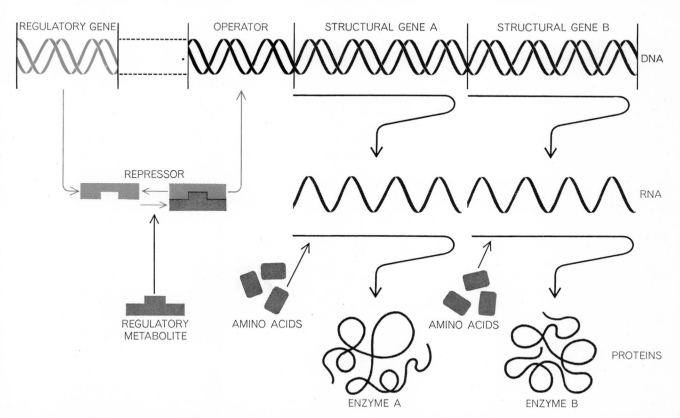

CONTROL OF PROTEIN SYNTHESIS by a genetic "repressor" was proposed by François Jacob and Jacques Monod. A regulatory gene directs the synthesis of a molecule, the repressor, that binds a metabolite acting as a regulatory signal. This binding either activates or inactivates the repressor, depending on whether the system is "repressible" or "inducible." In its active state the repressor binds the genetic "operator," thereby causing it to switch off the structural genes that direct the synthesis of the enzymes.

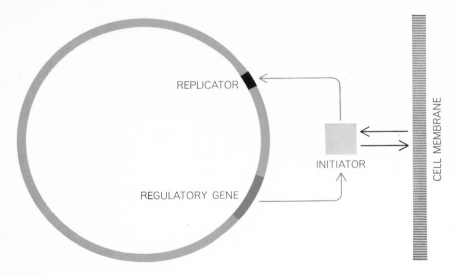

REPLICATION OF DNA of a bacterial chromosome may be under a control like that of protein synthesis. A regulatory gene directs the synthesis of an "initiator," which receives a signal (perhaps from the cell membrane) that makes it act on the "replicator."

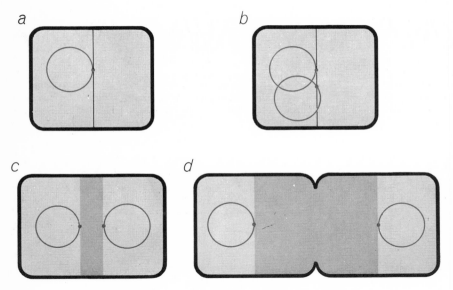

ROLE OF CELL MEMBRANE in replication is suggested by the fact that a bacterial chromosome is attached to a point on the membrane (*a*). It could be a signal from the membrane that initiates the formation of daughter chromosomes (*b*). Then the membrane begins to grow, separating the points of attachment (*c*) until the cell is ready to divide (*d*).

in their experiments was the amino acid tryptophan. They found that when the medium in which *E. coli* cells were growing contained an abundance of tryptophan, the cells stopped producing tryptophan synthetase, the enzyme required for the synthesis of the amino acid. This efficient behavior has since been demonstrated in many cells, not only bacteria but also the cells of higher organisms. The addition of an essential product to the cells' growth medium results in a negative-feedback signal that causes them to stop synthesizing enzymes they do not need.

In other systems the response of the cell is not negative but positive. We have been considering signals that repress the synthesis of enzymes; the cell can also respond to signals calling on it to produce enzymes. An example of such a situation is that the cell is confronted with a compound it must break down into substances it requires for growth.

The "induction" of enzyme synthesis in cells was discovered at the turn of the century by Frédéric Dienert of the Agronomical Institute in France. He was studying the effect of a yeast (*Sac-*

charomyces ludwigii) in fermenting the milk sugar lactose. He found that strains of the yeast that had been grown for several generations in a medium containing lactose would begin to work on the sugar immediately, causing it to start fermenting within an hour. These cells had a high level of lactase, an enzyme that specifically breaks down lactose. Yeast cells that had not been grown in lactose lacked this enzyme, and not surprisingly they failed to ferment lactose on being introduced to the sugar. After 14 hours, however, fermentation of the sugar did get under way; it developed that the presence of the lactose had induced the yeast to produce the enzyme lactase. The adaptation was quite specific: only lactose caused the yeast to synthesize this enzyme; other sugars failed to do so.

In recent years Monod and François Jacob of the Pasteur Institute have worked out some of the basic mechanisms of enzymatic adaptation by the cell, in both the repression and induction aspects. First they discovered that a single mutation in *E. coli* could eliminate the control of lactase synthesis by lactose: the mutant cells produced lactase just as well in the absence of lactose as in its presence. In these cells only the triggering effect was changed; the enzyme they produced was exactly the same as that synthesized by nonmutant strains. In other words, it appeared that the rate of production of the enzyme was controlled by one gene and that the structure of the enzyme was determined by quite another gene. This was confirmed by genetic experiments that showed that the "regulatory gene" and the "structural gene" were indeed in separate positions on the bacterial chromosome.

How does the regulatory gene work? Arthur B. Pardee, Jacob and Monod found that it causes the cell to produce a "repressor" molecule that controls the functioning of the structural gene. In the absence of lactose the repressor molecule prevents the structural gene from directing the synthesis of lactase molecules. The repressor does not act on the structural gene directly; it binds itself to a special structure that is closely linked on the chromosome with the structural gene for the enzyme and with several other genes involved in lactose metabolism. This special genetic structure is called an "operator." The binding of the repressor to the operator causes the latter to switch off the activity of the adjacent structural genes, and in this way it blocks the complex series of events that would lead to synthesis of the enzyme.

Jacob and Monod have shown that this scheme of control applies to any category of "adaptive" enzymes [*see bottom illustration on page 245*]. The repression and induction of enzymes can be regarded as opposite sides of the same coin. In a repressible system the binding of the regulatory signal on the repressor activates the repressor so that it blocks the synthesis of the enzyme. In an inducible system, on the other hand, the binding of the inducing signal on the repressor *inactivates* the repressor, thus releasing the cell machinery to synthesize the enzyme. Mutant cells that lose the repressive machinery need no inducer: they synthesize the enzyme almost limitlessly without requiring any induction signal.

In brief, the various repressors in the cell are specialized receptors, each capable of recognizing a specific signal. And within its chromosomes a cell possesses instructions for synthesizing a wide variety of enzymes, each of which can be evoked simply by the presenta-

tion of the appropriate signal to the appropriate repressor.

The cell's selection of chromosomal records for transcription is so efficient as to seem almost "conscious." Actually, however, the responses of the cell are automatic, and like any other automatic mechanism they can be "tricked." It is as though a vending machine were made to work by a false coin: certain artificial compounds closely resembling lactose are excellent inducers of lactase but cannot be broken down by the enzyme. This means that the cell is tricked into spending energy to make an enzyme it cannot use. The signal works, but it is a false alarm. Trickery in the opposite direction is also possible. There is an analogue of tryptophan, called 5-methyl tryptophan, that acts as a repressive signal, causing the cell to stop its production of tryptophan. But 5-methyl tryptophan cannot be incorporated into protein in place of the genuine amino acid. Without that essential amino acid the cell stops growing and dies of starvation. Thus the false signal in effect acts as an antibiotic.

If chemical signals control the pro-

duction of enzymes, may they not also control the more generalized activities of the cell, notably its self-replication? Jacob, Sydney Brenner and François Cuzin, working cooperatively at the Pasteur Institute and at the Laboratory of Molecular Biology at the University of Cambridge, recently discovered evidence of such a chemical control. They investigated the replication of the unique circular chromosome of *E. coli*. The synthesis of the deoxyribonucleic acid (DNA) of the chromosome, they found, is initiated by a signaling molecule that corresponds to the repressor of enzyme synthesis. The "initiator" has a positive effect rather than a repressive one. Like the repressor of enzyme synthesis, it is synthesized under the direction of a regulatory gene for replication. As the cell prepares for division, the initiator receives orders from the cell membrane and triggers the replication of its DNA by activating a genetic structure called the replicator (analogous to the "operator" of enzyme synthesis). Not much information has been gathered so far about the signal that prompts the initiator or about the

TWO NUCLEOTIDES, adenosine triphosphate (ATP) and cytidine triphosphate (CTP), are required by the cell in fixed proportions, so their production is regulated by interconnected feedback mechanisms operating on the first enzymes in the synthetic chains. In the case of CTP the enzyme is aspartate transcarbamylase (ATCase). It is inhibited by an excess of CTP (*1*), activated by an excess of ATP (*2*) and must also recognize and respond to the "cooperative" effects of aspartate, its substrate (*3*), which also plays a role in protein synthesis. Notice that ATP, CTP and aspartate have different shapes. How, then, can they all "fit" ATCase chemically?

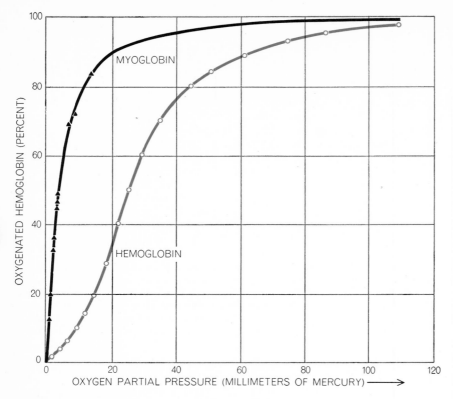

HEMOGLOBIN, like an enzyme, is a large molecule that binds a small one (oxygen) at specific sites. The curves show the rate of oxygen-binding by hemoglobin (*color*) and myoglobin (*black*), a related oxygen-carrier in muscle. The myoglobin curve is a hyperbola but the hemoglobin curve is S-shaped. Hemoglobin binds best at higher oxygen concentrations (in the lungs); the binding of a few oxygen molecules favors the binding of more.

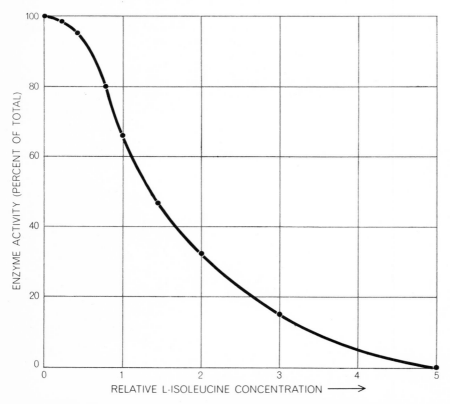

"COOPERATIVE EFFECT" occurs in regulatory enzymes as in hemoglobin. This curve shows the inhibition of L-threonine deaminase by L-isoleucine. The curve's S shape indicates that the effect of the regulatory signal is significant only above a threshold value.

details of the machinery it sets in motion, but it seems clear that cell division has its own system of chemical control and that it can adjust itself to the composition of the growth medium.

We have been considering the control of the synthesis of enzymes; now let us turn to the control of their activity. As I have mentioned, Umbarger and his colleagues found that the presence of L-isoleucine would not only cause *E. coli* to stop synthesizing the enzymes needed for its production but also inhibit the activity of the first enzyme in the chain leading to the formation of the amino acid. The phenomenon of control of enzyme activity had already been noted earlier in the 1950's by Aaron Novick and Leo Szilard of the University of Chicago. They had shown that an excess of tryptophan in the *E. coli* cell halted the cell's production of tryptophan immediately, which means that the signal inhibited the activity of enzymes already present in the cell. Umbarger went on to investigate the direct effect of L-isoleucine on the enzymes that synthesize it; these had been extracted from the cell. He demonstrated that L-isoleucine inhibited the first enzyme in the chain (L-threonine deaminase), and only the first. This action was extremely specific; no other amino acid—not even D-isoleucine, the mirror image of L-isoleucine—had any effect on the enzyme's activity.

One must pause to remark on the extraordinary economy and efficiency of this control system. As soon as the supply of L-isoleucine reaches an adequate level, the cell stops making it at once. The signal acts simply by turning off the activity of the first enzyme; that is enough to stop the whole production line. Most remarkable of all, once this first enzyme has been synthesized the control costs the cell no expenditure of energy whatever; this is shown by the fact that the amino acid will act to inhibit the enzyme outside the cell without any energy being supplied. A factory with control relays that require no energy for their operation would be the ultimate in industrial efficiency!

The L-isoleucine control system of *E. coli* is only one example of this type of regulation in the living cell. It has now been demonstrated that similar circuits control the cell's production of the other amino acids, vitamins and other major substances, including the purine and pyrimidine bases that are the precursors of DNA.

In all these cases the control is nega-

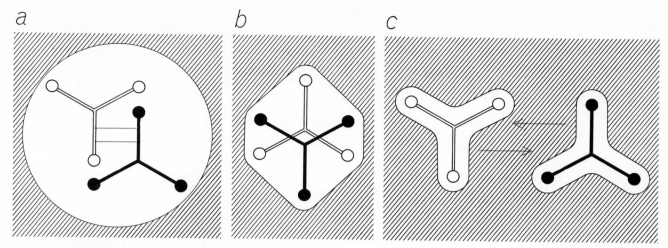

a   b   c

REGULATORY PROPERTY of an enzyme might be explained in three different ways. A regulatory signal (*open shape*) might combine with the substrate (*black shape*), participating directly in the chemical reaction it is controlling (*a*). But no such compounds have been found. A signal could simply get in the way of the substrate, excluding it from the enzyme's active site by "steric hindrance" (*b*).

The different shapes of substrates and signals preclude this, and in any case steric hindrance could only account for enzyme inhibition, not activation. The only plausible hypothesis, confirmed by experiments with several enzymes, is that the signals and the substrate fit different sites on the enzyme and that the regulatory interactions of these sites are "allosteric," or indirect (*c*).

tive; that is, it involves the inhibition of enzymes. There are opposite situations, of course, in which the control system *activates* an enzyme when the circumstances call for it. An excellent example of such a positive control has to do with the cell's storage and use of energy.

Animal cells store reserve energy in the form of glycogen, or animal starch. Glycogen is synthesized from a precursor—glucose-6-phosphate—in three enzymatic steps. First glucose-6-phosphate is made into glucose-1-phosphate; then glucose-1-phosphate is made into uridine diphosphate D-glucose. Finally uridine diphosphate D-glucose is made into glycogen. When

the cell has a good supply of energy, it produces considerable amounts of glucose-6-phosphate. This serves as a signal for stimulating the synthesis of glycogen. The signal works at the third step: the presence of a high level of glucose-6-phosphate strongly activates the enzyme that brings about the conversion of uridine diphosphate D-glucose into glycogen. On the other hand, when the supply of working energy in the cell falls to a low level, so that it must draw on the reserve stored in glycogen, it becomes necessary to activate an enzyme that splits the glycogen (the enzyme known as glycogen phosphorylase). One chemical signal known

to be capable of activating this enzyme is adenosine monophosphate (AMP). AMP is a product of the splitting of adenosine triphosphate (ATP), the principal source of the cell's working energy, and an accumulation of AMP therefore indicates that the cell has used up its energy. The AMP signal activates the glycogen-splitting enzyme; the enzyme splits the glycogen molecule; the splitting releases energy, and the energy then is used to regenerate ATP.

The cell thus possesses mechanisms for two types of control of enzyme activity: negative (inhibited enzymes) and positive (activated enzymes). There are

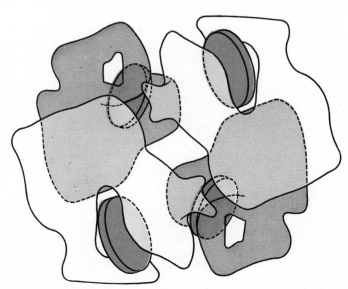

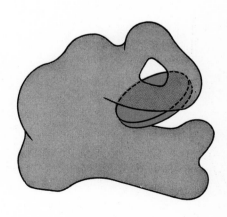

MOLECULE OF HEMOGLOBIN, shown (*left*) in very simplified form, has four heme groups (*color*), each of which is borne on a subunit, or chain, that is very similar to a myoglobin molecule

(*right*). The heme groups of hemoglobin, each of which is a binding site for an oxygen molecule, are relatively far apart. Cooperative interactions among them must therefore be "allosteric."

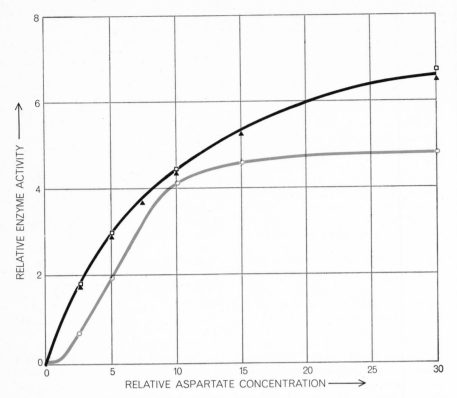

DESENSITIZATION of an enzyme affects all its regulatory properties. The substrate saturation curve of natural ATCase (*color*) is S-shaped as a result of the cooperative effect. If the enzyme is denatured by heating, the cooperative effect is lost (*black curve*). So is the effect of feedback inhibition by CTP, as shown by the fact that the curve is the same whether the enzyme is assayed without CTP (*triangles*) or with CTP added (*squares*).

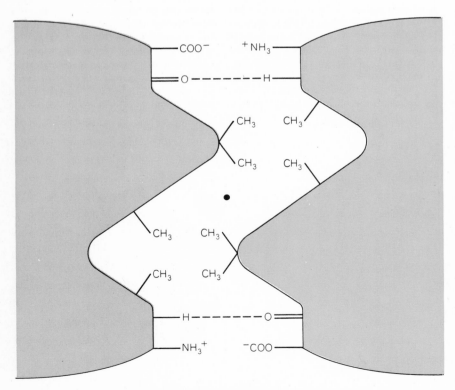

ALLOSTERIC PROTEINS are assumed by Monod, Jeffries Wyman and the author to be polymers, molecules composed of identical subunits, that have a definite axis of symmetry (*black dot*). A cross section through such a molecule (made up in this case of two subunits) shows how the symmetry results from the chemical bonds by which the units are associated.

situations in which both methods operate simultaneously. Consider, for example, the synthesis of a nucleic acid. It is assembled from purine and pyrimidine bases, combined in certain definite proportions. The purines and pyrimidines are synthesized on parallel production lines. For the sake of economy they should be produced roughly in the proportions in which they will be used.

This implies that the rate of production by each production line should feed back to control the output by the other. Such a system of mutual regulation must employ both negative and positive controls. Exactly this kind of system has been demonstrated in experiments with *E. coli* conducted by John C. Gerhart and Pardee at the University of California at Berkeley and at Princeton University. They showed that the output of the pyrimidine production line is controlled not only by its own end product (which inhibits the first enzyme in the synthetic sequence) but also by the end product of the purine production line, which counteracts the inhibition by the pyrimidine end product in vitro. Indeed, the purine end product can activate the pyrimidine production directly when no pyrimidine product is present! In short, the enzyme involved here is inhibited by one signal and activated by another.

Several enzymes involved in regulation have also been found to respond in this way to different signals. Moreover, this is not the only exceptional property of these enzymes. Let us now consider another property that will clarify the mechanism by which they are controlled.

A clue to this property seems to lie in the shape of the curve describing the rate at which the enzymes react with their substrates: the substances whose changes they catalyze. Ordinarily the rate of reaction of an enzyme increases as the concentration of substrate is increased. The increase is described by an experimental curve that fits a hyperbola. This kind of curve expresses the fact that the first step in the transformation of the substrate by the enzyme is the binding of the substrate to a specific attachment site on the enzyme.

When the concentration of substrate is increased, molecules of substrate tend to occupy more and more binding sites. Since the number of enzyme molecules is limited, at high concentrations of substrate nearly all the binding sites are occupied. At this point the rate of reaction levels off, hence the hyperbolic shape of the curve. The regulatory enzymes, surprisingly, do not exactly follow this pattern: their reaction rate increases with the concentration of substrate but often the curve is sigmoid (S-shaped) rather than hyperbolic.

When one reflects on the saturation curve of the regulatory enzymes, one notes that it is strikingly like the curve describing the saturation of the hemoglobin of the blood with oxygen. There too the reaction rate traces a sigmoid curve; this remarkable property is related to hemoglobin's physiological function of carrying oxygen from the lungs to other tissues. In the lungs, where the oxygen pressure is high, the hemoglobin is readily charged with the gas; in the tissues, where the oxygen pressure is low, the hemoglobin readily discharges its oxygen. Consider now, however, the myoglobin of muscle tissue. It takes on oxygen, but its oxygenation follows a hyperbolic curve like the classical one for enzymes. A comparative chart shows that when the pressure of oxygen is increased, the amount of oxygen bound by hemoglobin increases faster than the amount bound by myoglobin [*see top illustration on page 248*]. It looks as if the first oxygen molecules picked up by the hemoglobin favor the binding of others—as if there is cooperation among the oxygen molecules in binding themselves to the carrier. Oxygen thus plays the role of a regulatory signal for its own binding.

Similarly, cooperation may be the key to the sigmoid pattern of binding activity in many of the regulatory enzymes. An example of such an enzyme is threonine deaminase. Here again physiological function is evident. The substrate of threonine deaminase is the amino acid threonine. If the amount of this amino acid falls to a very low level in the cell, the cell cannot synthesize proteins. In the absence of threonine, it would be a waste of energy to make isoleucine, the end product of the chain of which threonine deaminase is the first step; hence the economy-geared control system of the cell calls off the production of the second amino acid. In other words, threonine deaminase will not be active and isoleucine will not be produced unless at least threshold concentrations of threonine are present in the cell. In this situation threonine plays the role of regulatory signal for the reaction of which it is the specific substrate; it is an activator of its own transformation.

The most remarkable part of the story is that such cooperative effects are not restricted to the binding of substrate but also operate in the binding of more familiar regulatory signals: specific inhibitors or activators. Regulatory enzymes appear to be built in such a way that they not only recognize the configuration of specific substrates as signals but also gauge their response to whether or not the substrates and regulatory signals are present in certain threshold concentrations. (This is strongly reminiscent, of course, of electric relays—and, one may add, of nerve cells—which react only if the signal has a certain threshold strength.) The regulatory enzymes are thus capable of integrating several signals—both positive and negative—that modulate their activity.

We come now to the question: How do the regulatory relays work? The signals (either activators or inhibitors) are usually small molecules, and the receptor is a regulatory enzyme. In chemical terms, how does the enzyme translate and integrate the signals it receives? The answer to this question applies not only to regulatory enzymes but also to any other molecule that mediates a regulatory interaction. Since little is known about many of these molecules, the model I shall now describe is based on the experimental results obtained from regulatory enzymes. It seems legitimate, however, to extend the model to any category of regulatory molecule.

The question presents a biochemist with a difficult paradox. A molecule can "recognize" a message only in terms of geometry, that is, the shape or configuration of the molecule bearing the message. In this case the message is supposed to cause the enzyme to carry out (or refrain from carrying out) a certain reaction: conversion of a specific substrate into a specific product. Yet the molecule bearing the message often has no structural likeness to either the substrate or the product! How, then, can it promote or interfere with the enzyme's performance of its specific catalytic action on this substrate?

Considering several possible explana-

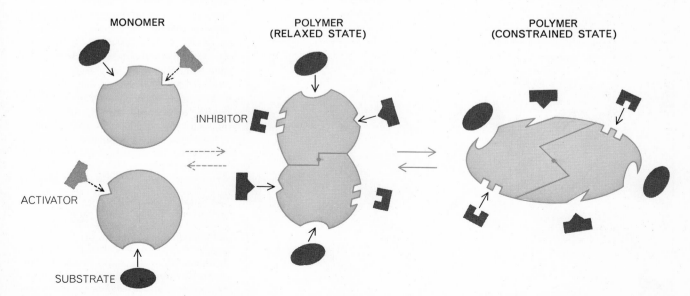

MONOMER

POLYMER (RELAXED STATE)

POLYMER (CONSTRAINED STATE)

INHIBITOR

ACTIVATOR

SUBSTRATE

REGULATORY CHANGES in an allosteric molecule are conceived of as arising from its shifting back and forth between two states. The polymeric molecule is made up of several monomers (two in this case), as shown at left. The polymer can exist in a "relaxed" state (*middle*) or a "constrained" state (*right*). In one condition it binds substrate and activators; in the other state it binds inhibitors. The binding of a signal tilts the balance toward one or the other state but the molecule's symmetry is preserved.

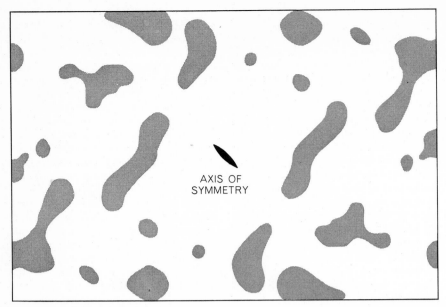

AXIS OF
SYMMETRY

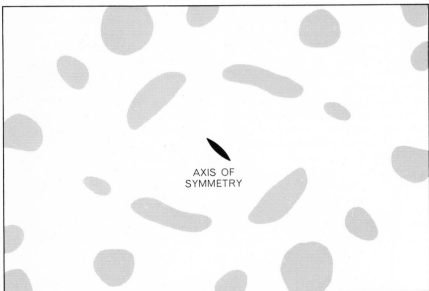

AXIS OF
SYMMETRY

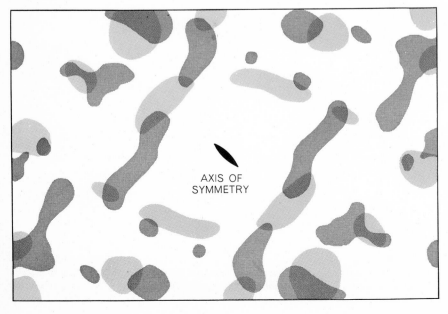

AXIS OF
SYMMETRY

tions, Monod, Jacob and I have concluded that the only plausible one is that the signal and the substrate fit into separate binding sites on the enzyme and that the signal takes effect by an interaction between these sites [*see top illustration on page 249*]. There is strong experimental evidence in favor of this model. One of the most convincing lines of evidence is the recent discovery by Gerhart that the regulatory enzyme aspartate transcarbamylase has a binding site for its substrate on one subunit of the molecule and a site for an inhibitor of its activity on another subunit. When the subunits are split apart, one retains the ability to recognize the substrate, the other the ability to recognize the inhibitor.

We must now inquire into the nature of the interaction of these two categories of sites on the enzyme. How does the binding of a molecule at one site affect the binding of another molecule at the other site? The best clue to an understanding of the mechanism of the interaction seems to lie in a property of regulatory enzymes that I have already mentioned: the sigmoid curve describing their binding of substrate or of signal molecules, which indicates a cooperative effect among those molecules. Again it is instructive to consider the analogy of the binding of oxygen molecules by hemoglobin.

The hemoglobin molecule has four hemes that are well separated from one another; each is a binding site for an oxygen molecule. In view of the separation between the sites, their cooperation in binding oxygen must be "allosteric," or indirect. Myoglobin, which has only one binding site, binds oxygen hyperbolically (that is, without any control); hemoglobin, with its four sites, binds oxygen in a sigmoid pattern. It seems, therefore, that the key to hemoglobin's cooperative, controlled binding of oxygen lies in the molecule's four-part structure.

Now consider a regulatory enzyme. The binding of any particular molecule

EXPERIMENTAL DATA supporting the allosteric model come from X-ray diffraction maps of hemoglobin made by M. F. Perutz and his colleagues at the University of Cambridge. The contour lines based on electron densities suggest the shapes of the subunit chains of oxygenated hemoglobin (*top*), reduced hemoglobin (*middle*) and the two superposed (*bottom*). A conformational change of the kind proposed in the model on the preceding page is evident, as is preservation of the molecule's axis of symmetry.

(substrate, inhibitor or activator) is sigmoid and therefore a cooperative affair; this implies that there is a set of reception sites for each specific molecule. There also appears to be interaction among the binding sites for different molecules, such as substrate and activator or substrate and inhibitor. Surprisingly the experimental evidence suggests that both types of allosteric interaction—that among the sites binding a particular molecule and that among the sites binding different molecules—may depend on one and the same mechanism, embodied in the structure of the enzyme molecule.

The most striking evidence comes from experiments in the alteration of the structure of regulatory enzyme molecules. Gerhart and Pardee at Berkeley and Princeton and I at the Pasteur Institute, working independently, have found that by changing the molecular structure of aspartate transcarbamylase or L-threonine deaminase (by means of heat, bacterial mutation or certain other procedures) it is possible to "desensitize" these regulatory enzymes so that they are no longer affected by a feedback inhibitor. They are still capable, however, of reacting with their respective substrates. The interesting point is that a change in the enzyme's structure eliminates, along with the negative interaction of the feedback inhibitor and the substrate, all the cooperative interactions in the enzyme molecule. This applies particularly to the binding of the substrate, which changes from a sigmoid to a hyperbolic pattern.

What, then, is the crucial structural feature that accounts for the allosteric interactions within the enzyme molecule? Again hemoglobin offers a clue.

We have noted that the hemoglobin molecule is a four-part structure. It comprises four heme units, each of which is attached to a distinct chain of amino acid units. This molecule is thus made up of four subunits, each of which is so similar to a myoglobin molecule that hemoglobin can be considered essentially a combination of four myoglobin molecules. Hemoglobin displays cooperative interaction, whereas myoglobin does not; hence this property evidently is associated with its four-part structure. Now, experiments show that the binding of oxygen by hemoglobin is connected in some way with an adjustment in the bonding between the subunits making up the mole-

cule [see "The Hemoglobin Molecule," by M. F. Perutz, which begins on page 39 in this book]. The same turns out to be true of many of the regulatory enzymes; their binding of smaller molecules also depends on the adjustment of the bonds holding together their subunits.

On the strength of the experimental findings, Monod, Jeffries Wyman and I have proposed a model picturing the working of the regulatory enzyme system [see illustration on page 251]. It suggests that the enzyme molecule consists of a set of identical subunits, each subunit containing just one specific site for each of the molecules it may bind to itself, either substrate molecules or regulatory signals. Now, if a molecule is made up of a definite and limited number of subunits, the implication is that it has an axis of symmetry. Let us say that the enzyme molecule can switch back and forth between two states, and that in each state its symmetry is preserved. The two symmetrical states differ in the energy of bonding between the subunits: in the more relaxed state the enzyme molecule will preferentially bind activator and substrate; in the more constrained state it will bind inhibitor. Whichever compound it binds (substrate, inhibitor or

activator) will tip the balance so that it then favors the binding of that category of small molecule. A change in the relative concentrations of substrate and signals may, depending on their molecular structure, tip the balance one way or the other. Thus the model indicates how the enzyme molecule's binding sites may interact, either cooperatively or antagonistically. It suggests that the enzyme may integrate different messages simply by adopting a characteristic state of spontaneous equilibrium between two states.

The major conclusion from the study of the regulatory enzymes is that their powers of control and regulation depend entirely on the form of their molecular structure. Built into that structure, as into a computer, is the capacity to recognize and integrate various signals. The enzyme molecule responds to the signals automatically with structural modifications that will determine the rate of production of the product in question. How did these biological "computers" come into being? Obviously they must owe their remarkable properties to nature's game of genetic mutation and selection, which in eons of time has refined their construction to a peak of exquisite efficiency.

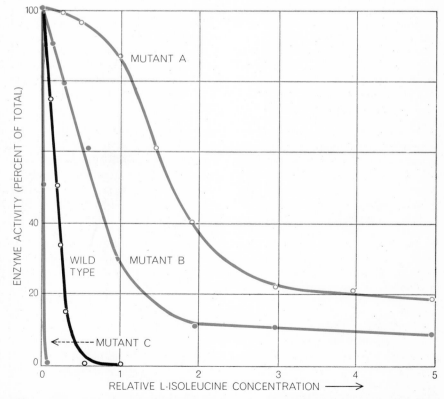

MUTATIONS in the structural gene for L-threonine deaminase in *E. coli* affect the regulatory properties of the enzyme. Mutant enzymes respond differently to feedback inhibition.

26 | Hormones and Genes

ERIC H. DAVIDSON · June 1965

In the living cell the activities of life proceed under the direction of the genes. In a many-celled organism the cells are marshaled in tissues, and in order for each tissue to perform its role its cells must function in a cooperative manner. For more than a century biologists have studied the ways in which tissue functions are controlled, providing the organism with the flexibility it needs to adapt to a changing environment. Gradually it has become clear that among the primary controllers are the hormones. Thus whereas the genes control the activities of individual cells, these same cells constitute the tissues that respond to the influence of hormones.

New experimental evidence is now making it possible to complete this syllogism: it is being found that hormones can affect the activity of genes. Hormones of the most diverse sources, molecular structure and physiological influence appear able to rapidly alter the pattern of genetic activity in the cells responsive to them. The establishment of a link between hormones and gene action completes a conceptual bridge stretching from the molecular level to ecology and animal behavior.

In order to understand the nature of the link between hormones and genes it will be useful to review briefly what is known of how genes function in differentiated, or specialized, cells. One of the most striking examples of cell specialization in animals is the red blood cell, the protein content of which can be more than 90 percent hemoglobin. It has been shown that in man the ability to manufacture a given type of hemoglobin is inherited; this provides a clear case of a differentiated-cell function under genetic control. Hemoglobin also furnishes an example of another principle that is fundamental to the study of differentiation: the specialized character of a cell depends on the type and quantity of proteins in it, and therefore the process of differentiation is basically the process of developing a specific pattern of protein synthesis. Some cells, such as red blood cells and the cells of the pancreas that produce digestive enzymes, specialize in synthesizing one kind of protein; other cells specialize in synthesizing an entire set of protein enzymes to manufacture nonprotein end products, for example glycogen, or animal starch (which is made by liver cells), and steroid hormones (which are made by cells of the adrenal cortex).

If one understood the means by which the type and quantity of protein made by cells was controlled, one would have taken a long step toward understanding the nature of the differentiated cell. Part of this objective has been attained: we now know something of how genes act and how proteins are synthesized. A protein owes its properties to the sequence of amino acid subunits in its chainlike molecule. The genes of most organisms consist of deoxyribonucleic acid (DNA), the chainlike molecules of which are made up of nucleotide subunits. The sequence of nucleotides in a single gene determines the sequence of amino acids in a single protein.

The protein is not assembled directly on the gene; instead the cell copies the sequence of nucleotides in the gene by synthesizing a molecule of ribonucleic acid (RNA). This "messenger" RNA moves away from the gene to the small bodies called ribosomes. On the ribosomes, which contain their own unique kind of RNA, the amino acids are assembled into protein. In the assembly process each molecule of amino acid is identified and moved into position through its attachment to a specific molecule of a third kind of RNA: "transfer" RNA. It can therefore be said that the characteristics of the cell are determined at the level of "gene transcription"—the synthesis of messenger and ribosomal RNA.

Each differentiated cell in a many-celled organism contains a complete set of the organism's genes. It is obvious, however, that in such a cell only a small fraction of the genes are actually functioning; the gene for hemoglobin is not active in a skin cell and the assortment of genes active in a liver cell is not the same as the assortment active in an adrenal cell. The active genes release their information in the form of messenger RNA and the inactive genes do not. Exactly how the inactive genes are repressed is not clearly understood, but the repression seems to involve a chemical combination between DNA and the proteins called histones; it has been shown that histones inhibit the synthesis of messenger RNA in the isolated nuclei of calf-thymus cells, and similar results have been obtained with the nuclei of other kinds of cell. In any case it is clear that the characteristics of the cell are the result of variable gene activity. The prime question becomes: How are the genes selectively turned on or selectively repressed during the life of the cell?

Gene action is often closely linked to cell function in terms of time. It has been demonstrated that genes can exercise immediate control over the activities of differentiated cells—particularly very active or growing cells—and over cells that are going through some change of state. In many specialized cells at least part of the messenger RNA

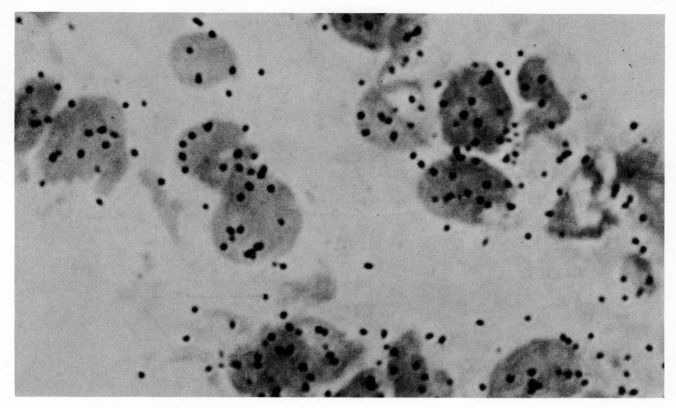

HORMONE IS LOCALIZED IN NUCLEI of cells in this radio-autograph made by George A. Porter, Rita Bogoroch and Isidore S. Edelman of the University of California School of Medicine (San Francisco). The hormone aldosterone was radioactively labeled and administered to a preparation of toad bladder tissue. When the tissue was radioautographed, the hormone revealed its presence by black dots. The dots appear predominantly in the nuclei (*dark gray areas*) of the cells rather than in the cytoplasm (*light gray areas*).

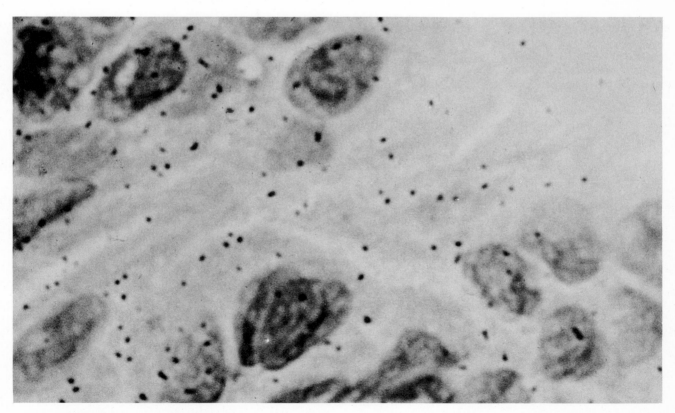

ANOTHER HORMONE IS NOT LOCALIZED in the nuclei in this radioautograph made by the same investigators. Here the hormone was progesterone, and it too was labeled and administered to toad bladder tissue. The dots are distributed more or less at random.

HORMONE	SOURCE		CHEMICAL NATURE	FUNCTION
ECDYSONE	INSECT PROTHORACIC GLAND 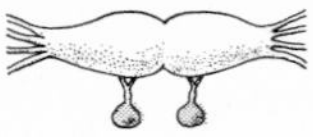		STEROID	Causes molting, initiation of adult development and puparium formation.
GLUCOCORTICOIDS (CORTISONE)	ADRENAL CORTEX 		STEROID	Causes glycogen synthesis in liver. Causes redistribution of fat throughout organism. Alters nitrogen balance. Causes complete revision of white blood cell type frequencies. Is required for muscle function. Alters central nervous system excitation threshold. Affects connective tissue differentiation. Promotes healing. Induces appearance of new enzymes in liver. Affects almost all tissues.
INSULIN	PANCREAS (ISLETS OF LANGERHANS) 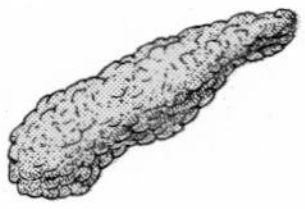		POLYPEPTIDE	Affects entry rate of carbohydrates, amino acids, cations and fatty acids into cells. Promotes protein synthesis. Affects glycogen synthetic activity. Stimulates fat synthesis. Stimulates acid mucopolysaccharide synthesis. Affects almost all tissues.
ESTROGEN	OVARY 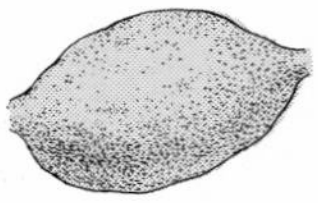		STEROID	Promotes appearance of secondary sexual characteristics. Increases synthesis of contractile and other proteins in uterus. Increases synthesis of yolk proteins in fowl liver. Increases synthesis of polysaccharides. Affects rates of glycolysis, respiration and substrate uptake into cells. Probably affects almost all tissues.
ALDOSTERONE	ADRENAL CORTEX 		STEROID	Controls sodium and potassium excretion and cation flux across many internal body membranes.
PITUITARY ACTH	ANTERIOR PITUITARY 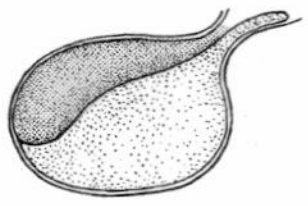		POLYPEPTIDE	Stimulates glucocorticoid synthesis by adrenal cortex. Stimulates adrenal protein synthesis and glucose uptake. Inhibits protein synthesis in adipose tissue. Stimulates fat breakdown.
PITUITARY GH	ANTERIOR PITUITARY 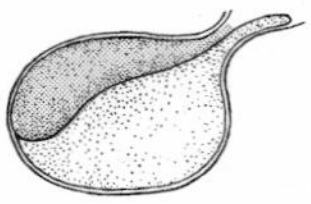		PROTEIN	Stimulates all anabolic processes. Affects nitrogen balance, water balance, growth rate and all aspects of protein metabolism. Stimulates amino acid uptake and acid mucopolysaccharide synthesis. Affects fat metabolism. Probably affects all tissues.
THYROXIN	THYROID 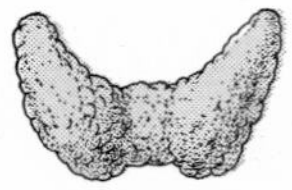		THYRONINE DERIVATIVE	Affects metabolic rate, growth, water and ion excretion. Promotes protein synthesis. Is required for normal muscle function. Affects carbohydrate levels, transport and synthesis. Probably affects all tissues.

HORMONES DISCUSSED IN THIS ARTICLE are listed according to their source, their chemical nature and their effects, which are usually quite diverse. Pituitary GH is the pituitary growth hormone. The steroid hormones share a basic molecular skeleton consisting of adjoining four-ring structures. The polypeptide hormones and the protein hormones consist of chains of amino acid subunits.

produced by the active genes decays in a matter of hours, and therefore the genes must be continuously active for protein synthesis to continue normally. Other differentiated cells display the opposite characteristic, in that gene activity occurs at a time relatively remote from the time at which the messenger RNA acts. The very existence of this time element in gene control of cell function indicates how extensive that control is. Furthermore, certain genes can be alternately active and inactive over a short period; for example, if a leaf is bleached by being kept in the dark and is then exposed to light, it immediately begins to manufacture messenger RNA for the synthesis of chlorophyll.

The sum of such observations is that the patterns of gene activity in the living cell are in a state of continuous flux. For a cell in a many-celled organism, however, it is essential that the genetic apparatus be responsive to external conditions. The cell must be able to meet changing situations with altered metabolism, and if all the cells in a tissue are to alter their metabolism in a coordinated way, some kind of organized external control is needed. Evidence obtained from experiments with a number of biological systems suggests that such control is obtained by externally modulating the highly variable activity of the cellular genetic apparatus. The studies that will be reviewed here are cases of this general proposition; in these cases the external agents that alter the pattern of gene activity are hormones.

Many efforts have been made to explain the basis of hormone action. It has been suggested that hormones are coenzymes (that is, cofactors in enzymatic reactions), that they activate key enzymes, that they modify the outer membrane of cells and that they directly affect the physical state of structures within the cell. For each hypothesis there is evidence from studies of one or several hormones. As an example, experiments with the pituitary hormone vasopressin, which causes blood vessels to constrict and decreases the excretion of urine by the kidney, strongly support the conclusion that the hormone attaches itself to the outer membrane of the cells on which it acts.

To these hypotheses has been added the new one that hormones act by regulating the genetic apparatus, and many investigators have undertaken to study the effects of hormones on gene activity. It turns out that the gene-regulation hypothesis is more successful than the others in explaining some of the most puzzling features of hormone activity, such as the time lag between the administration of some hormones and the initial appearance of their effects, and also the astonishing variety of these effects [see illustration on opposite page]. There can be no doubt that some hormone action is independent of gene activity, but it has now been shown that a wide variety of hormones can affect such activity. This conclusion is strongly supported by the fact that each of these same hormones is powerless to exert some or all of its characteristic effects when the genes of the cells on which it acts are prevented from functioning.

The genes can be blocked by the remarkably specific action of the antibiotic actinomycin D. The antibiotic penetrates the cell and forms a complex with the cell's DNA; once this has happened the DNA cannot participate in the synthesis of messenger RNA. The specificity of actinomycin is indicated by the fact that it does not affect other activities of the cell: protein synthesis, respiration and so on. These activities continue until the cellular machinery stops because it is starved for messenger RNA. In high concentrations actinomycin totally suppresses the synthesis of messenger RNA; in lower concentrations it depresses this synthesis and appears to prevent it from developing at new sites.

So far the greatest number of studies of the effects of hormones on genes have been concerned with the steroid hormones, particularly the estrogens produced by the ovaries. This work has been carried forward by many investigators in many laboratories. It has been found that when the ovaries are removed from an experimental animal and then estrogen is administered to the animal at a later date, the synthesis of protein by cells in the uterus of the animal increases by as much as 300 percent. The increase is detected by measuring the incorporation of radioactively labeled amino acids into uterine protein, or by testing the capacity for protein synthesis of homogenized uterine tissue removed from the animal at various times after the administration of estrogen. Added proof that these observations have to do with the synthesis of protein is provided by the fact that the stimulating effects of estrogen are blocked by the antibiotic puromycin, which specifically inhibits protein synthesis.

In these experiments the principal rise in protein synthesis is first observed between two and four hours after estrogen treatment. Less than 30 minutes after the treatment, however, there is a dramatic increase in the rate of RNA synthesis. When actinomycin is used to block the rise in RNA synthesis, the administration of estrogen has no effect on protein synthesis! What this means is that since the diverse metabolic changes brought about in uterine cells by estrogen are all mediated by protein enzymes, none of the changes can occur unless the estrogen has induced gene action. Among the changes are the increased synthesis of amino acids from glucose, the increased evolution of carbon dioxide and the increased synthesis of the fatty lipids and phospholipids. It is not surprising to find that none of these metabolic changes in uterine cells can be detected when estrogen is administered to an animal that has first been treated with actinomycin.

The effect of estrogen on the synthesis of RNA is not limited to messenger RNA. There is also an increase in the manufacture of the other two kinds of RNA: transfer RNA and ribosomal RNA. The administration of estrogen first stimulates the production of messenger RNA and transfer RNA. The genes responsible for the synthesis of ribosomal RNA become active somewhat later, and the number of ribosomes per cell increases. One of the earliest changes brought about by estrogen, however, is an increase in the activity of the enzyme RNA-DNA polymerase. This enzyme appears to be responsible for all RNA synthesis in such cells.

Two main conclusions can be drawn from these various observations. First, there can be no reasonable doubt that treatment with estrogenic hormones results in activation at the gene level, and that many of the well-known effects of estrogen on uterine cells result from this gene activation. Second, it is clear that a considerable number of genes must be activated in order to account for the many different responses of the cells to estrogen. Consider only the fact that estrogen stimulates the production of three different kinds of RNA. At least two different genes are known to be associated with the synthesis of ribosomal RNA, and each cell needs to manufacture perhaps as many as 60 species of transfer RNA. As for messenger RNA, the variety of the changes induced by estrogen implies that under such influences it too must be produced

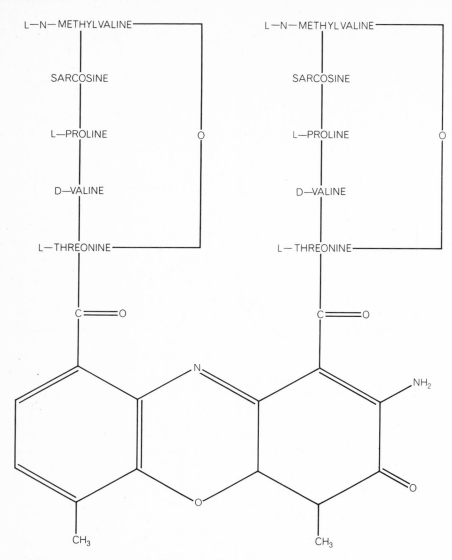

ANTIBIOTIC ACTINOMYCIN D has a complex chemical structure. The antibiotic blocks the participation of the genetic material in the synthesis of ribonucleic acid (RNA); thus it can be used in studies to determine whether or not a given hormone stimulates gene activity.

in a number of molecular species. We are therefore confronted with a major mystery of gene regulation: How can a single hormone activate an entire set of functionally related but otherwise quite separate genes, and activate them in a specific sequence and to a specific degree?

The question can be sharpened somewhat by considering the effect of estrogen not on uterine cells but on the cells of the liver. When an egg is being formed in a hen, the estrogen produced by the hen's ovaries stimulates its liver to produce the yolk proteins lipovitellin and phosvitin. Obviously a rooster does not need to synthesize these proteins, but if it is treated with estrogen, its liver will make them in large amounts! A more unequivocal example of the

selective activation of repressed genes by a hormone could scarcely be imagined. What is more, experiments by E. N. Carlsen and his co-workers at the University of California School of Medicine (Los Angeles) have demonstrated that this gene-activating effect of estrogen is remarkably specific. Phosvitin is an unusual protein in that nearly half of its subunits are of one kind: they are residues of the amino acid serine. Carlsen and his colleagues found that estrogen most strongly stimulates liver cells to produce the particular species of transfer RNA that is associated with the incorporation of this amino acid into protein.

The effect of estrogen on liver cells is thus quite different from its effect on uterine cells. Indeed, it has long been

recognized that hormonal specificity resides less in the hormone than in the "target" cell. We are now, however, able to ask new questions: How are the sets of genes that are activated by a given hormone selected? Are these genes somehow preset for hormonal activation? How does the hormone interact not only with the gene itself but also with the cell's entire system of genetic regulation?

The male hormone testosterone has also been shown to operate by gene activation. Like the estrogens, the male sex hormones can give rise to dramatic increases of RNA synthesis in various cells. In experiments on male and female rats it has been found that the effect of testosterone on the liver cells of a female is somewhat different from that on the liver cells of a castrated male. In both cases the hormone causes an increase in the *amount* of messenger RNA produced, but in the female it also brings about the synthesis of a new *variety* of messenger RNA. This effect, like the ability of estrogen to stimulate a rooster's liver cells to produce egg-yolk proteins, provides a new approach for examining the whole question of sexual differentiation.

Apart from the sex hormones, the principal steroids in mammals are those secreted by the adrenal cortex. One group of adrenocortical hormones is typified by cortisone; this hormone and its relatives are known for their quite different effects in different tissues. Only a fraction of these effects have been studied from the standpoint of gene activation, and there is much evidence to indicate that some of them are not mediated by the genes. Some responses to cortisone, however, do appear to be the consequence of gene activation.

If the adrenal glands are removed from an experimental animal and cortisone is administered later, the hormone induces in the liver cells of the animal the production of a number of new proteins. Among these proteins are enzymes required for the synthesis of glucose (but not the breakdown of glucose) and enzymes involved in the metabolism of amino acids. Moreover, cortisone steps up the total production of protein by the liver cells. The effect of cortisone on the synthesis of messenger RNA is apparent as soon as five minutes after the hormone has been administered; within 30 minutes the amount of RNA produced has increased two to three times and probably includes not

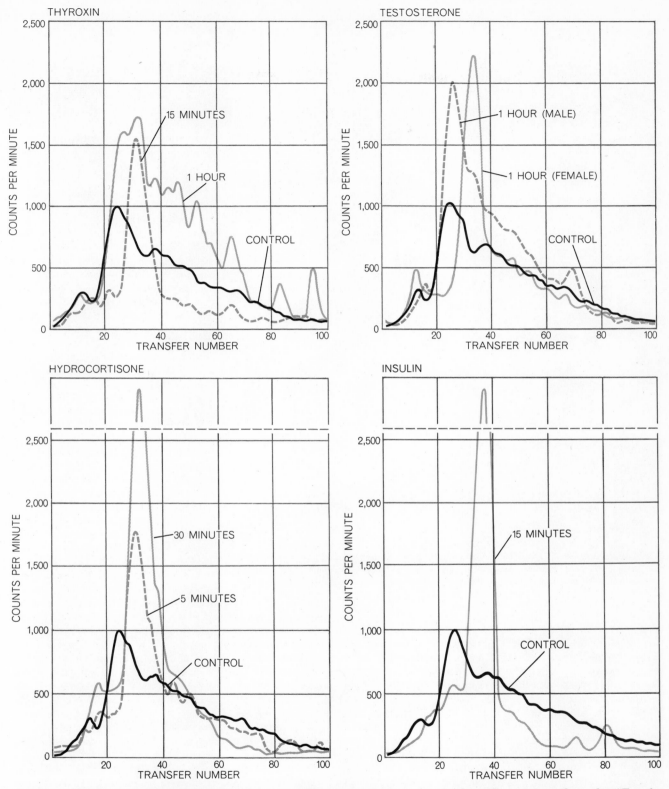

GENETIC ACTIVITY OF SEVERAL HORMONES is indicated by measurements made by Chev Kidson and K. S. Kirby of the Chester Beatty Research Institute in London. Their basic technique was first to administer to rats radioactively labeled orotic acid, which is a precursor of RNA. The tissues of the rat then incorporated the radioactive label into new RNA. Next liver tissue was removed from the rat and the species of RNA called "messenger" RNA was extracted from its cells. When the messenger RNA was analyzed by the method of countercurrent distribution, it gave rise to a charac-

teristic curve (*black "Control" curve in each graph*); "Transfer number" refers to a stage of transfer in the countercurrent-distribution process and "Counts per minute" to the radioactivity of the solution at that point. Then, in separate measurements, rats were first given one of a number of hormones (*top left of each graph*) and shortly thereafter radioactively labeled orotic acid. The curves (*color*) of the messenger RNA obtained from such rats were entirely different, depending on the time that had elapsed before the administration of the orotic acid or on the sex of the animal (*top right*).

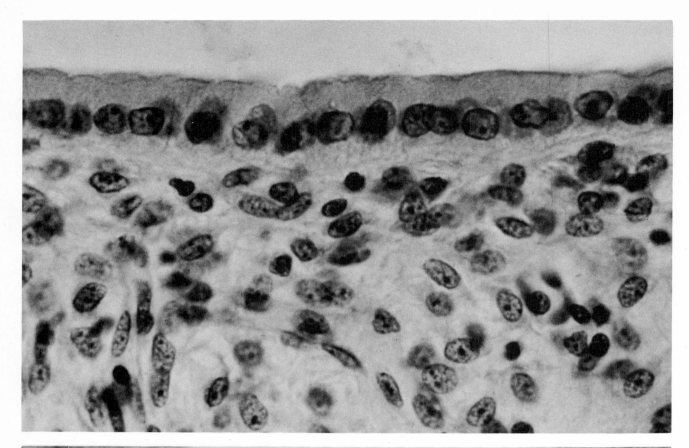

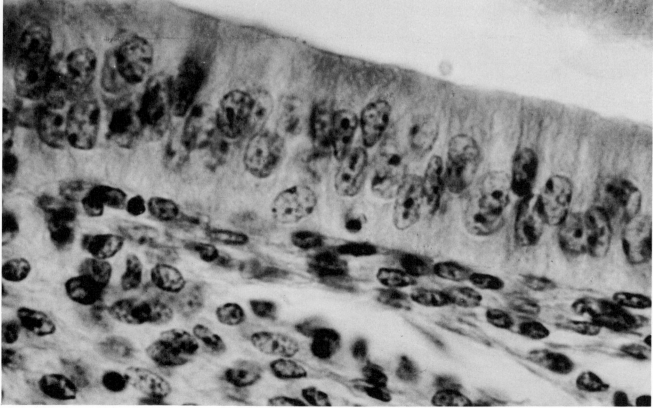

EFFECT OF ESTROGEN ON CELLS in the uterus of rats is demonstrated in these photomicrographs made by Sheldon J. Segal and G. P. Talwar of the Rockefeller Institute. The photomicrograph at top shows uterine cells from a rat that had not been treated with estrogen; the layer of cells at the surface of the tissue is relatively thin. The photomicrograph at bottom shows uterine cells from a rat that had been treated with the hormone; the layer of cells is much thicker. The effect involves enhanced synthesis of protein.

only messenger RNA but also ribosomal RNA. These events are followed by the increase in enzyme activity. Olga Greengard and George Acs of the Institute for Muscle Disease in New York have shown that if the animal is treated with actinomycin before cortisone is administered, the new enzymes fail to appear in its liver cells.

Another clear case of the activation of genes by an adrenocortical hormone has been demonstrated by Isidore S. Edelman, Rita Bogoroch and George A. Porter of the University of California School of Medicine (San Francisco). They employed the hormone aldosterone, which regulates the passage through the cell membrane of sodium and potassium ions. Tracer studies with radioactively labeled aldosterone showed that when the bladder cells of a toad were exposed to the hormone, the molecules of hormone penetrated all the way into the nuclei of the cells [see illustrations on page 255]. About an hour and a half after the aldosterone has reached its peak concentration within the cells the movement of sodium ions across the cell membrane increases. It appears that this facilitation of sodium transport is brought about by proteins the cell is induced to make, because it will not occur if the cells have been treated beforehand with puromycin, the drug that blocks the synthesis of protein. Moreover, treatment of the cells with actinomycin will block the aldosterone-induced increase in sodium transport through the membrane. Thus the experiments indicate that aldosterone activates genes in the nucleus and gives rise to proteins—that is, enzymes—that speed up the passage of sodium ions across the membrane.

Ecdysone, a steroid hormone of insects, is also believed to be a gene activator. The evidence for this conclusion has been provided by Wolfgang Beermann and his colleagues at the Max Planck Institute for Biology in Tübingen [see "Chromosome Puffs," by Wolfgang Beermann and Ulrich Clever; SCIENTIFIC AMERICAN Offprint 180]. If the larva of an insect lacks ecdysone, the development of the larva is indefinitely arrested at a stage preceding its metamorphosis into a pupa. Only when, in the course of normal development, the concentration of ecdysone in the tissues of the larva begins to rise does further differentiation take place; the larva then advances to metamorphosis. Ecdysone has been of especial interest to cell biologists because it has been observed

ROOSTER TREATED WITH ESTROGEN (*bottom*) is compared with a normal rooster (*top*). The signs of femaleness induced by estrogen include changes in comb and plumage.

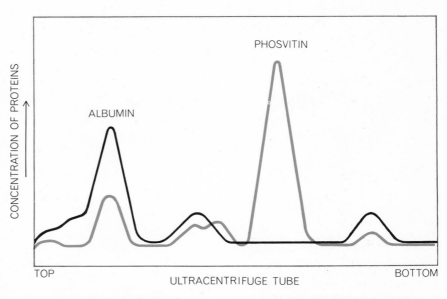

ULTRACENTRIFUGE PATTERNS show that phosvitin, a yolk protein found only in hens, is present in serum extracted from a bird that had been injected with estrogen (*colored curve*) but not in serum from a bird used as a control (*black curve*). Each curve gives the concentration of proteins as they are separated out of a mixture by an ultracentrifuge.

to cause startling changes in the chromosomes within the nuclei of the cells affected by it. Studies of this kind are possible in insects because the cells of certain insect tissues have giant chromosomes that can easily be examined in the microscope. These "polytene" chromosomes develop in many kinds of differentiated cell by means of a process in which the chromosomes repeatedly replicate but do not separate.

In some polytene chromosomes genetic loci, or specific regions, have a distended, diffuse appearance [see illustration below]. Biologists regard these regions, which have been named "puffs," as sites of intense gene activity. Evidence for this conclusion is provided by radioautograph studies, which show that the puffs are localized sites of intense RNA synthesis. In such studies a molecular precursor of RNA is radioactively labeled and after it has been incorporated into RNA reveals its presence as a black dot in the emulsion of the radioautograph. According to the view of differentiation presented in this article, different genes should be active in different types of cell, and this appears to be the case in insect cells with polytene chromosomes. In many different kinds of cell—salivary-gland cells, rectal-gland cells and excretory-tubule cells—the giant chromosomes have a different constellation of puffs; this suggests that different sets of genes are active, a given gene being active in one cell and quiescent in another.

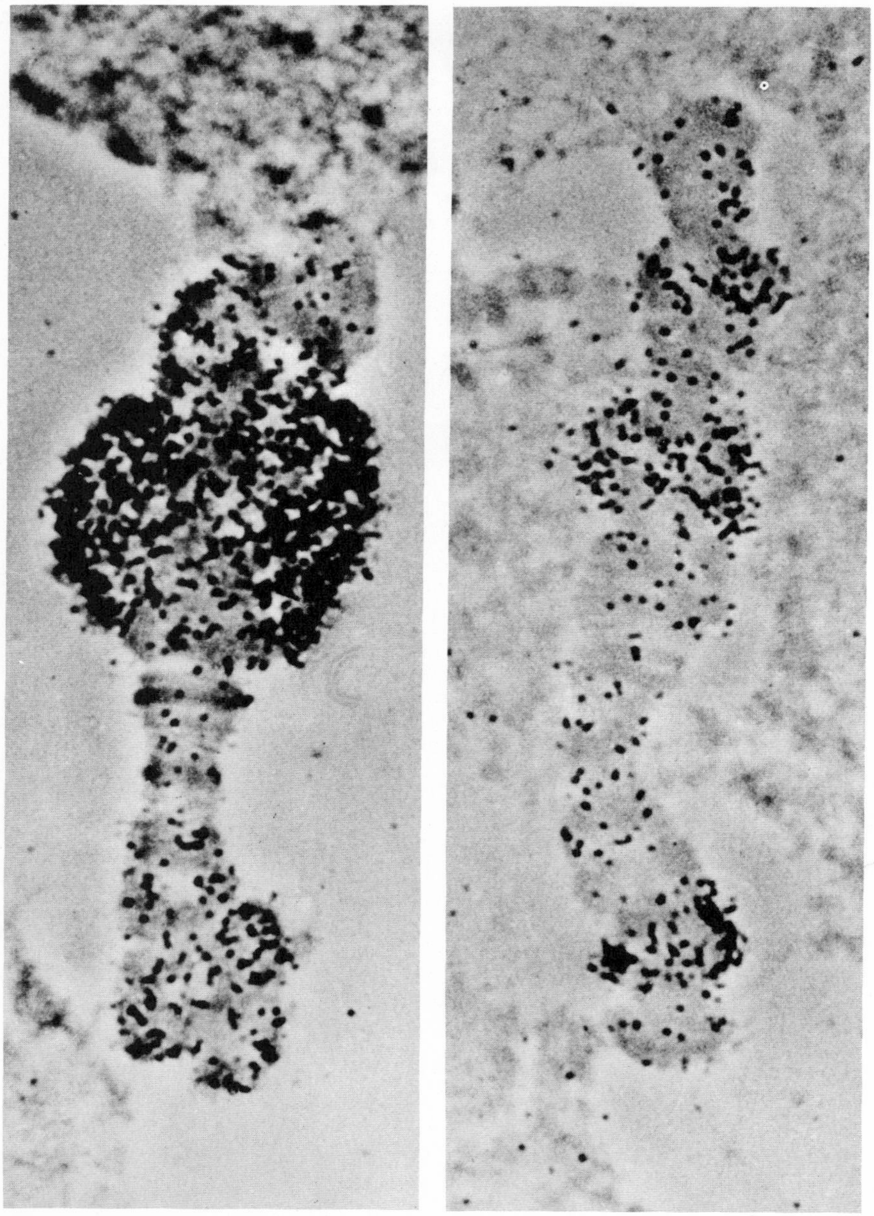

On the polytene chromosomes of insect salivary-gland cells new puffs develop as metamorphosis begins. This is where ecdysone comes into the picture: the hormone seems to be capable of inducing the appearance of specific new puffs. When a minute amount of ecdysone is injected into an insect larva, a specific puff appears on one of its salivary-gland chromosomes; when a slightly larger amount of ecdysone is injected, a second puff materializes at a different chromosomal location. In the normal course of events the concentration of ecdysone increases as the larva nears metamorphosis; therefore there exists a mechanism whereby the more sensitive genetic locus can be aroused first. This example of hormone action at the gene level, which is directly visible to the investigator, seems to have provided some of the strongest evidence for the regulation of gene action by hormones. The effect of ecdysone, which is clearly needed for differentiation, appears to be to arouse quiescent genes to visible states of activity. In this way the specific patterns of gene activity required for differentiation are provided.

What about nonsteroid hormones? Here the overall picture is not as clearcut. The effects of some hormones are quite evidently due to gene activation, and yet other effects of the same hormones are not blocked by the administration of actinomycin; a small sample of these effects is listed in the illustration on the opposite page. As for the hormonal effects that are quite definitely not genetic, they fall into one of the following categories.

(1) Some hormones act on specific enzymes; for example, the thyroid hormone thyroxin promotes the dissociation of the enzyme glutamic dehydrogenase. (2) Other hormones, for instance insulin and vasopressin, act on systems that transport things through cell mem-

"PUFF" ON A GIANT CHROMOSOME from the salivary gland of the midge *Chironomus tentans* appears after administration of the insect hormone ecdysone. In the radioautograph at left the round area at top center is a puff. The black dots result from the fact that the midge was given radioactively labeled uridine, which is a precursor of RNA. The concentration of dots in the puff indicates that it is actively synthesizing RNA. In the radioautograph at right is a chromosome from a fly that had been treated with actinomycin before receiving ecdysone. No puff has occurred and RNA synthesis appears to be muted. The radioautographs were made by Claus Pelling of the Max Planck Institute for Biology in Tübingen.

HORMONE	EVIDENCE FOR HORMONAL ACTION BY GENE ACTIVATION.	EVIDENCE THAT HORMONAL ACTION IS CLEARLY INDEPENDENT OF IMMEDIATE GENE ACTIVATION.
PITUITARY GROWTH HORMONE	General stimulation of protein synthesis. Stimulation of rates of synthesis of ribosomal RNA, transfer RNA and messenger RNA within 90 minutes in liver. Effect blocked with actinomycin.	
PITUITARY ACTH	Stimulates adrenal protein synthesis. Messenger RNA and total RNA synthesis stimulated.	Steroid synthesis in isolated adrenal sections is independent of RNA synthesis and is insensitive to actinomycin D.
THYROXIN	Promotes new messenger RNA synthesis within 10 to 15 minutes of administration, promotes stimulation of all classes of RNA by 60 minutes. Promotes increase in RNA–DNA polymerase at 10 hours, later promotes general increase in protein synthesis.	Causes isolated, purified glutamic dehydrogenase to dissociate to the inactive form. Affects isolated mitochondria in vitro.
INSULIN	Promotes 100 percent increase in rate of RNA synthesis. Causes striking change in messenger RNA profile within 15 minutes of administration to rat diaphragm; effect blocked with actinomycin. Actinomycin-sensitive induction of glucokinase activity.	Actinomycin-insensitive increase in ATP synthesis and in glucose transport into cells; mechanism appears to involve insulin binding to cell membrane, occurs at 0 degrees C.
VASOPRESSIN		Actinomycin-insensitive promotion of water transport in isolated bladder preparation under same conditions in which aldosterone action is blocked by actinomycin.

SUMMARY OF EXPERIMENTAL EVIDENCE is given in table. Facts indicating that hormones activate the genes (*middle column*) are compared with facts suggesting that hormonal action does not entail the immediate activation of the genes (*column at right*).

branes; indeed, it is believed that both of these hormones attach themselves directly to the membranes whose function they affect. (3) Still other hormones rapidly activate a particular enzyme; phosphorylase, a key enzyme in determining the overall rate at which glycogen is broken down, is converted from an inactive form by several hormones, including epinephrine, glucagon and ACTH.

This does not alter the fact that many nonsteroid hormones operate at the gene level. Some of the best evidence for this statement is provided by studies of several hormones made by Chev Kidson and K. S. Kirby of the Chester Beatty Research Institute of the Royal Cancer Hospital in London. They separately injected rats with thyroxin, testosterone, cortisone and insulin and then mea-

sured the synthesis of messenger RNA by the rats' liver cells [*see illustration on page 259*]. The most striking aspect of their measurements is the extremely short time lag between the administration of the hormone and the change in the pattern of gene activity. The activation of genes in the nuclei of the affected cells occurs so quickly that one is tempted to assume that it is an initial effect of the hormone.

Here, however, we come face to face with a basic problem that must be solved in any attempt to explain the exact molecular mechanism of hormone action. The problem is simply that of identifying the initial site of reaction in a cell exposed to a hormone. Does a hormone move directly to the chromosome and exert its effect, so to speak, "in person"? As we have seen, aldoste-

rone does appear to enter the nucleus, but there is little real evidence that other hormones do so.

For many years biologists have been looking for the "receptor" substance of various hormones. The discovery that hormones ultimately act on genes makes this search all the more interesting. The evidence presented here only goes as far as to prove that an early stage in the operation of many hormones is the selective stimulation of genetic activity in the target cell. The molecules of the hormones range in size and structure from the tiny molecule of thyroxin to the unique multi-ring molecule of a steroid and the giant molecule of a protein; how these various molecules similarly affect the genetic apparatus of their target cells remains an intriguing mystery.

27 | Antibiotics and the Genetic Code

LUIGI GORINI · April 1966

A cell is characterized by the metabolic activities that occur within its boundaries. These activities proceed along chemical pathways involving numerous steps, each catalyzed by a different enzyme. The cell's characteristics are therefore maintained by its enzymes, and the conservation of these characteristics in a hereditary line of cells depends on their ability to synthesize the same set of enzymes in successive generations. Enzymes are proteins; their catalytic specificity is determined by their structure and that structure is encoded in the genetic material of the cell. It has become common knowledge that the transmission of genetic information from one generation to another is subject to mutations, or occasional errors, and that these mutations are the basis of biological evolution. Until recently, however, the possibility that errors might occur in the transfer of information within the cell, from the genetic material to the protein, was overlooked.

As molecular biologists and geneticists have learned more about the mechanism of this transfer they have wondered if it too might not be subject to error. It is. Not only can mutations affect the transfer mechanism, as one might have expected; in our laboratory at the Harvard Medical School we have discovered that the genetic information encoded within a cell is sometimes ambiguous and can be misunderstood. The ambiguity results from unexpected complex variations in the structure of the cell components known as ribosomes. And the misunderstanding can be prompted by antibiotics such as streptomycin in a manner that explains at least in part how such antibiotics kill cells.

Our work can best be understood in the context of much that has gone before, and so I must briefly review some of that history. In science a line of investigation may often be based on a postulate that in time proves not to have been correct but that nevertheless has great suggestive value. That is, the postulate serves as a starting point for valuable discoveries, with the result that a solid structure of knowledge may be erected in spite of an original oversimplification. So it has been with the celebrated "one gene, one enzyme" postulate put forward in 1941 by George W. Beadle and Edward L. Tatum at Stanford University. Their assumption that each gene defines the structure of one and only one protein ignored the possibility that a gene might make slightly different proteins at different times, but it nevertheless opened the door to biochemical genetics. It did so by providing experimenters with a set of principles: A mutant deficient in a specific enzyme must have a defect in the gene controlling the synthesis of that enzyme; if several metabolic products are lacking as the result of a single mutation, a single enzyme must be responsible and so the products must have a single precursor; a substance that allows the growth of a mutant with a defective enzyme must be the product of a step subsequent to that enzyme's action or of a reaction bypassing the missing enzyme.

By isolating and studying defective mutants and applying these few principles, investigators learned a great deal about the enzyme-catalyzed reactions that build up and break down small molecules in the cell. The principles were close enough to being correct to work well at that level. Their limited validity became apparent, however, as new information made it possible to look behind conventional enzymatic reactions and study the synthesis of the enzymes themselves. The synthesis of enzymes utilizes novel reactions that are directed by the template molecules deoxyribonucleic acid (DNA) and ribonucleic acid (RNA) and that involve the translation of a code.

Proteins are made up of one or more peptide chains, which are in turn linear arrays of linked subunits: the 20 amino acids. It is the sequence in which these amino acids are linked into structures several hundred units long that determines the coiling and folding, and hence the specific characteristics, of each protein. The synthesis of a protein involves the selection, from the pool of amino acids in the cell, of the proper amino acids and their linkage in the proper sequence. This is accomplished in several steps [see *illustrations on opposite page*].

The first step involves the transcription of the inherited instructions in a structural gene—a segment of DNA—into a template molecule of RNA. This "messenger RNA" is the basic link between a gene and its enzyme. Like other kinds of RNA, it is a polynucleotide chain: a strand made up of the nucleotide bases adenine, cytosine, guanine and uracil. The sequence of these bases follows that of the corresponding DNA bases and constitutes the code that establishes the order in which amino acids are assembled to form the protein. The codon, or code word, for each amino acid is a group of three "letters": a nucleotide triplet [see "The Genetic Code: II," by Marshall W. Nirenberg, which begins on page 206 in this book].

The second, or translation, step is to "plug in" the right amino acid at each codon of the messenger RNA

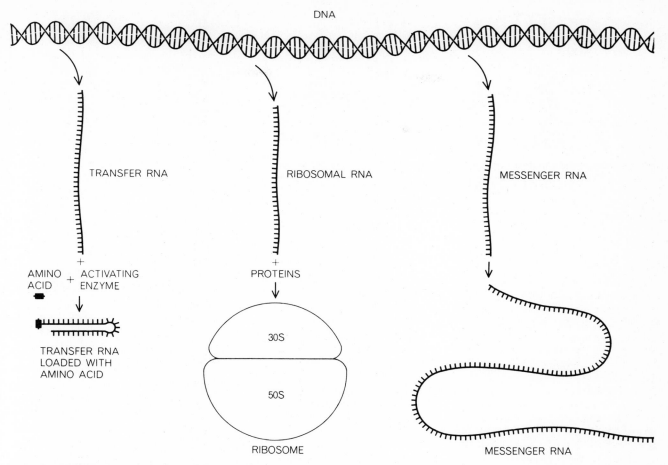

PROTEIN SYNTHESIS involves transcription of deoxyribonucleic acid (*DNA*) into several kinds of ribonucleic acid (*RNA*). Messenger RNA is a sequence of three-base codons, or code words, indicating the amino acid sequence of a protein. Each molecule of transfer RNA is loaded with a specific amino acid through the action of an activating enzyme. Ribosomal RNA and ribosomal proteins combine to constitute ribosomes, the components that are the sites of protein synthesis. The ribosomes have two subunits.

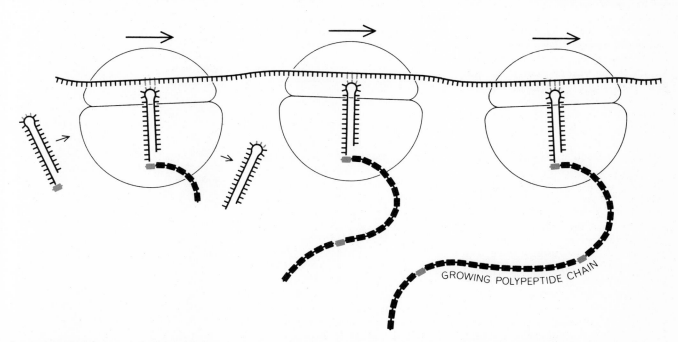

TRANSLATION of genetic instructions from RNA into protein involves the assembly of amino acids into a peptide chain in the sequence coded for by the codons of the messenger RNA. Transfer RNA loaded with an amino acid is thought to "recognize" the codon for that amino acid, perhaps through the binding to the codon of an anticodon of three complementary bases on transfer RNA.

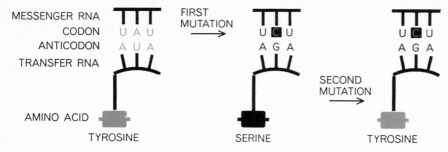

SUPPRESSION of a mutation can occur through the agency of a second mutation affecting transfer RNA or an activating enzyme. The triplet UAU normally codes for tyrosine, for example, perhaps by binding the anticodon AUA on tyrosine transfer RNA according to base-pairing rules (*left*). Mutated to UCU, it would encode serine (*middle*). Another mutation might insert correct amino acid again, perhaps by loading it on serine transfer RNA (*right*).

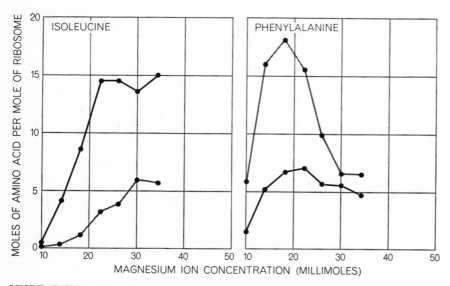

MISREADING is induced in a preparation containing ribosomes from streptomycin-sensitive cells and polyuridylic acid (UUU). The amino acid incorporated in the absence of streptomycin (*gray curves*) is primarily phenylalanine. When streptomycin is added (*black*), incorporation of phenylalanine is inhibited and incorporation of isoleucine is stimulated.

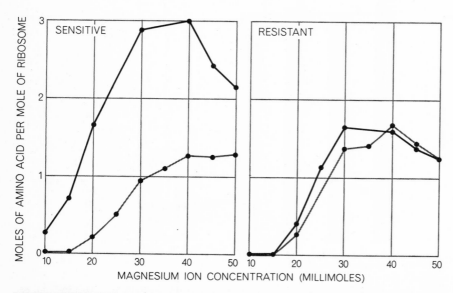

MORE ISOLEUCINE is incorporated in the presence of streptomycin (*black curves*) than in its absence (*gray*) in this system only if the ribosomes in the system are from streptomycin-sensitive cells (*left*). The incorporation varies with magnesium-ion concentration.

template. This is accomplished by a set of enzymes and specialized molecules of "transfer RNA." Each enzyme is able to "recognize," or interact with, one of the amino acids. Each transfer RNA molecule has two specificities: it can interact with one of the enzymes and so become "loaded" with the corresponding amino acid, and it can interact with the codon in the messenger RNA that designates that amino acid. In doing so it inserts the amino acid in the proper position in the developing peptide chain. The site on the transfer RNA that accomplishes this recognition is thought to be an "anticodon" of three bases that fit the three bases of the codon according to the rules of base-pairing: adenine pairs with uracil and guanine with cytosine. That is to say, an adenine-guanine-cytosine (AGC) codon would pair with a uracil-cytosine-guanine (UCG) anticodon. Now, in a code utilizing four letters, 64 triplets are possible, but there are only 20 amino acids to be coded for. The fact is that the code is "degenerate": most amino acids are indicated by several synonymous codons. In each case one of these synonyms seems to appear more frequently than the others—to be the "preferred" codon, in effect.

The translation step takes place in the ribosomes: ultramicroscopic particles made up of nucleic acid and protein. Each ribosome has a large and a small subunit designated (on the basis of their rates of sedimentation in a centrifuge) 50S and 30S. During protein synthesis the messenger RNA is apparently attached to the 30S subunit, the growing protein to the 50S subunit and the transfer RNA to both. The protein-synthesizing system seems to consist of groups of several ribosomes, or polyribosomes, traveling along a messenger RNA strand, each carrying an elongating peptide chain [see "Polyribosomes," by Alexander Rich, beginning on page 188 in this book]. The assumption has been that the ribosomes serve as inert jigs to hold the various reactants of the translation process in position with respect to one another.

Among the mutational events that might account for a defective mutant the most obvious (and the only one predicted by the one-gene, one-enzyme postulate) is one that occurs in the gene controlling the structure of a messenger RNA. Clearly a mutation that changes even one codon could either alter the message or deprive it of any sense at all and thus result in an altered or missing protein. As for the converse event, the "reversion" of a defective mutant to its parental characteristics, that would presumably be due to an analogous situation: the occurrence of a second mutation, with a "backward" effect, in the defective gene for the same messenger RNA.

Quite frequently, however, one finds a revertant in which the second mutation can be shown to occur in a gene different from that of the defective messenger RNA. Somehow this second mutation suppresses the effect of the original one; it enables the mutant cell to produce an active enzyme even though the gene for that enzyme is producing a defective messenger RNA. Such "suppressor" mutations have been known for more than 40 years. Barring a few cases for which conventional explanations could be found, however, they remained puzzling anomalies, quite in conflict with the one-gene, one-enzyme postulate.

In 1960, on the basis of the new knowledge of the steps in protein synthesis, Charles A. Yanofsky of Stanford University suggested that suppressor genes might be genes that control the structure of activating enzymes or of transfer RNA. A mutation altering the specificity of one of these tools of translation could result in the plugging in of an amino acid other than the one designated by the messenger RNA, and this substitution could reinstate the original structure of the affected enzyme. Such suppressor mutations have since been found. In them an incorrect messenger RNA is "read" by a transfer RNA carrying an amino acid other than the one coded for, and the net result of the double error is the synthesis of a correct protein. Since any given mutation in the tools of translation will suppress any messenger RNA mutations that stand to benefit by the given amino acid substitution, the one-gene, one-enzyme rule is violated: a single mutation can simultaneously produce changes in several proteins quite unrelated in their metabolic function.

In 1961, before much was known about translation errors, we isolated a peculiar mutant in our laboratory. We were working with a strain of the intestinal bacterium *Escherichia coli* that was unable to manufacture a necessary growth factor, the amino acid arginine. In the course of an experiment we "plated" some streptomycin-resistant mutants of these defective cells (which ordinarily could not grow unless arginine was supplied in their medium) on a medium containing streptomycin but no argi-

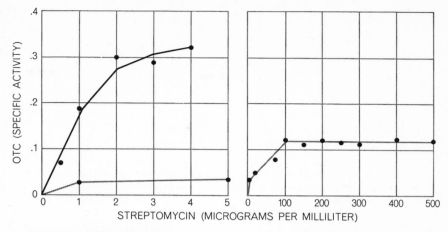

STREPTOMYCIN SUPPRESSION of a mutation affecting the synthesis of an enzyme (*OTC*) occurs at much lower concentrations in streptomycin-sensitive cells (*black curve*) than in resistant cells (*gray curves*). The concentration must be kept sublethal with sensitive cells. The curve for resistant cells has been shown on an expanded scale at the right.

nine. We expected no growth, but to our surprise we found that some of the resistant mutants no longer required arginine; streptomycin fulfilled their requirement. The requirement was due to a defective enzyme, ornithine transcarbamylase (OTC), and the peculiar thing was that OTC activity, which was lacking in cells grown in arginine, was present in cells grown in streptomycin. This meant that the antibiotic was not simply providing a chemical bypass that made arginine synthesis possible without OTC. Various experiments elimi-

nated several other conventional explanations involving the control of enzyme synthesis. We were left with the possibility that streptomycin was acting at the level of protein synthesis, somehow counteracting the effect of a mutation in a structural gene. The idea seemed too radical to pursue. We reported the finding, consigned the mutant to the category of the "funny mutants" one occasionally encounters and cannot explain, and paid no more attention to it.

It was only two years later, after the annual symposium on genetics held in

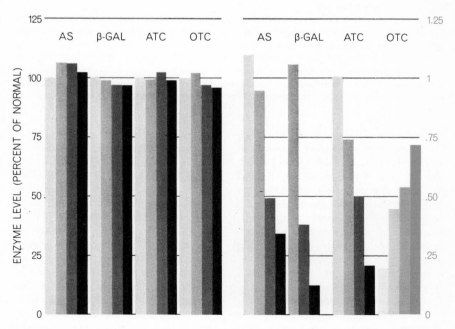

ERRORS are imposed in good enzymes as the error in OTC is suppressed. When the misreading level is too high, "oversuppression" may occur. In a streptomycin-resistant parent strain (*left*) synthesis of four enzymes is unaffected as the streptomycin concentration increases (*successively darker bars*) from zero to five, eight and 12 micrograms per milliliter. In an "oversuppressible" derivative of the conditionally streptomycin-dependent mutant (*right*) the drug increases the OTC level but decreases the level of the other three enzymes.

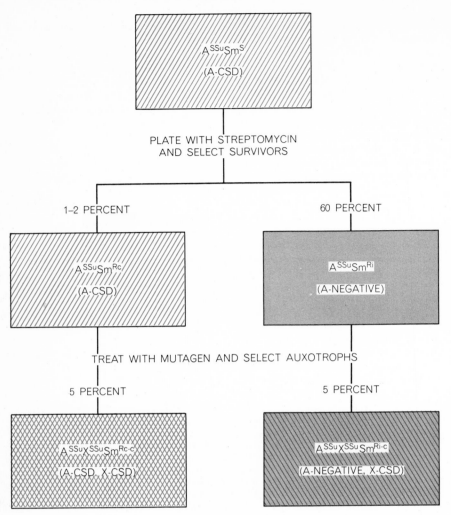

GENETIC EXPERIMENT begins with a strain that has an arginine defect suppressible by streptomycin (A^{SSu}) and is sensitive to streptomycin (Sm^S). Its behavior is conditionally streptomycin-dependent as to arginine (*A-CSD*). Plated on streptomycin medium, it yields three mutants (*middle row*): 1 or 2 percent drug-resistant and "competent" for suppression of the defect (Sm^{Rc}), about 60 percent resistant and "incompetent" (Sm^{Ri}) and about 40 percent dependent on the drug (*not shown*). A second crop of mutants (*bottom row*) includes some with a new drug-suppressible defect (X^{SSu}). A few of the cells that were incompetent for the suppression of the first defect are competent for the suppression of the new one.

Cold Spring Harbor, N.Y., at which there was much discussion of mutations in the genetic-code-reading mechanism, that I became aware of the parallel between streptomycin's effect in our funny mutant and the mechanism being proposed for suppressor mutations. I wondered if streptomycin could interfere with the accuracy of the reading machinery in such a way that the incorrect reading of an incorrect messenger RNA could result in the production of a correct protein.

To support such a hypothesis it was absolutely necessary to show that streptomycin was not merely counteracting the effect of an enzyme specifically involved in arginine synthesis—that the correction induced by streptomycin was associated not with particular metabolic pathways but with particular kinds of mutation, regardless of the structural gene in which they might occur. The crucial experiment was performed by Eva Kataja, a graduate student. She treated a streptomycin-resistant strain of *E. coli* with a mutagen, isolated all the auxotrophs, or cells ordinarily requiring a growth factor, and screened them for the ability to multiply without the growth factor in the presence of streptomycin. She found that from 2 to 5 percent of the auxotrophs requiring different amino acids that were unrelated as to their synthesis were actually "conditional" auxotrophs: their need for the growth factor was conditional on the absence of streptomycin. We designated this new class of mutants "conditionally streptomycin-dependent."

The name has proved not broad enough, because this kind of suppression has now been reported by a number of laboratories to be prompted by other antibiotics and to involve various kinds of mutation other than auxotrophy, including the inability of certain mutant bacterial viruses to grow in a given strain of bacteria. We also find mutants that are in effect "conditionally streptomycin-resistant" in that streptomycin makes them dependent on, rather than independent of, some growth requirement; in this case streptomycin is apparently "impressing" an error rather than suppressing one. All these examples illustrate the same basic finding: Whatever its genetic inheritance (genotype), a cell's characteristics (phenotype) may vary under the influence of certain comparatively small molecules that change the meaning of the genetic code. The idea that the information encoded in DNA may not be inviolate had already been accepted, but it was assumed that the code could be interfered with only by a mutation in the tools of translation. Here we have examples of phenotypic interference with translation, brought about by small molecules present in the cell or in its surroundings.

At the time of our original experiment the relative infrequency of the conditionally streptomycin-dependent mutants among auxotrophs obtained from a single parent indicated that the reading inaccuracy induced by the antibiotic was profitable only to a restricted class of defects in the structural genes. It appeared, moreover, that the mutation to streptomycin resistance did not always result in cells that were "competent" for streptomycin-induced suppression of auxotrophy. That indicated a linkage between the suppressibility phenomenon and the particular mutation to streptomycin resistance. We suggested, therefore, that suppressibility might be dependent on the structure of the ribosome, because it was already known that the mutation from "wild type" streptomycin-sensitive cells to streptomycin-resistant cells involves a change in the structure of the ribosome. Charles R. Spotts and Roger Y. Stanier of the University of California at Berkeley had predicted as much in 1961, and Julian E. Davies of the Harvard Medical School and Joel G. Flaks of the University of Pennsylvania School of Medicine had each proved it in 1963.

They had done so by experimenting with the cell-free amino-acid-incorporating system perfected by Marshall W.

Nirenberg and J. Heinrich Matthaei of the National Institutes of Health in 1961 and since utilized for most of the research on the genetic code. In a system containing purified ribosomes, transfer RNA and enzymes from *E. coli* together with amino acids and a synthetic polynucleotide as an artificial messenger RNA, only the amino acids encoded by the polynucleotide are incorporated in peptide chains. A "homopolymer" such as polyuridylic acid (UUU) codes for phenylalanine, for example. Confirming and broadening previous reports, Davies and Flaks found that if streptomycin was added to a cell-free system containing polyuridylic acid and phenylalanine, it prevented the incorporation of the amino acid unless the ribosomes—and specifically the 30S subunit—had been extracted from streptomycin-resistant cells. Apparently streptomycin acted by somehow "poisoning" the 30S ribosomal subunit.

The behavior of the conditionally streptomycin-dependent mutants suggested, however, that streptomycin was altering code translation rather than simply inhibiting it. Davies, Walter Gilbert and I confirmed this prediction with an experiment in which we put all the amino acids, rather than just the one that should properly be incorporated, into a synthetic-nucleotide preparation with ribosomes, transfer RNA and enzymes from streptomycin-sensitive cells. We found that streptomycin not only inhibited incorporation of the correct polypeptide but also caused incorporation of incorrect ones. With polyuridylic acid as the messenger, for example, streptomycin decreased the incorporation of phenylalanine and also caused the misincorporation of substantial amounts of isoleucine, serine, tyrosine and leucine—amino acids for which UUU is not the correct codon. This misreading did not occur when the cell components came from streptomycin-resistant cells. By interchanging the components we established that the streptomycin misreading depended on the source of the 30S subunit of the ribosome only; the origin of the 50S subunit, the transfer RNA and the activating enzymes did not matter, so apparently these components were unaffected by the antibiotic.

It became evident that streptomycin, by altering the configuration of the 30S subunit (the subunit that attaches to the messenger RNA), disturbs the reading of the RNA code, and therefore that the ribosome controls the accuracy of codon-anticodon binding and that misreading is the result of misrecog-

nition between codon and anticodon. Nirenberg and his colleagues S. Pestka and R. Marshall tested the effect of streptomycin on the binding of amino-acid-loaded transfer RNA to ribosomes and got essentially the same results as we did studying incorporation. By examining this intermediate step in the translation process they confirmed that it is at the recognition stage and through ribosomal intervention that streptomycin-induced misreadings occur. Finally David Old and I analyzed the amino acid composition of the growing polypeptide attached to the ribosome. With polyuridylic acid as the messenger RNA and with no streptomycin, the peptide is a chain of phenylalanine. With streptomycin added, the polypeptide contains about 40 percent isoleucine.

To be sure, various ways of producing misreading in cell-free preparations are known. Misreading can be induced

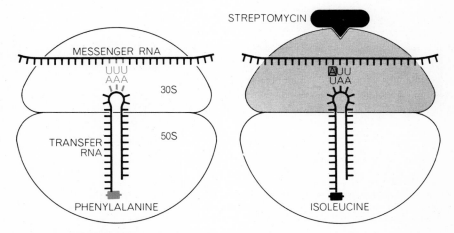

ACTION OF STREPTOMYCIN can be conceived of as an alteration, perhaps some kind of distortion, of the 30S subunit of the ribosome such that the codon is "read" incorrectly, binds the wrong transfer RNA and thus incorporates into the peptide chain an amino acid other than the one it coded for. This highly schematic diagram shows how a UUU codon should incorporate phenylalanine (*left*). Altered by a streptomycin molecule (*right*), the ribosome causes the UUU to be read as if it were AUU, and thus to incorporate isoleucine.

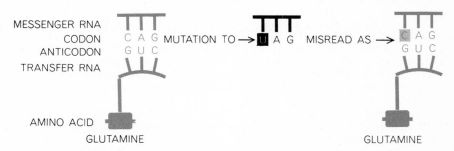

"NONSENSE" mutant is one in which the correct codon (*left*) is mutated to one that encodes no amino acid (*middle*), so no protein can be formed. Streptomycin might suppress the error by causing the nonsense codon to be misread as if it were the correct one (*right*).

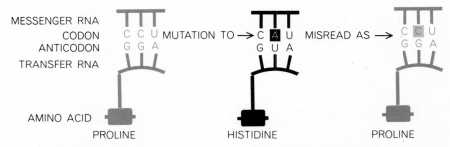

"MISSENSE" MUTANT is one in which the codon (*left*) is mutated to one incorporating a different amino acid (*middle*), making an inactive or perhaps unstable enzyme. Streptomycin-induced misreading might cause incorporation of the correct amino acid (*right*).

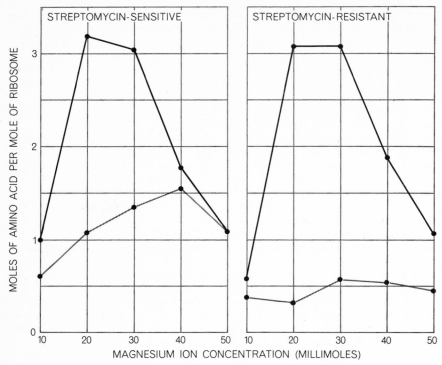

NEOMYCIN, a related antibiotic, stimulates the misincorporation of serine in a poly-uridylic acid preparation whether the ribosomes are from streptomycin-sensitive or resistant cells (*black curves*). In contrast, streptomycin (*gray curves*) has no effect on ribosomes from resistant cells (*right*); incorporation is the same as it is in the absence of the drug.

by changing the concentration of positive ions, the acidity or the temperature, or by adding certain organic solvents. The effects of these changes may be laboratory artifacts, however, quite without biological significance. In the case of the streptomycin effect it has been possible to throw a bridge between misreading in cell-free preparations on one hand and suppression in living mutant cells on the other.

At first there was some conflict between the two. Whereas the conditionally streptomycin-dependent cells had been streptomycin-resistant, ribosomes from resistant cells were not subject to misreading in our cell-free preparations. In those preparations it was ribosomes from drug-sensitive cells that seemed subject to misreading, but we had not tested the sensitive cells in vivo because we assumed that the streptomycin would kill them. We subsequently found that it is indeed possible to isolate conditionally streptomycin-dependent mutants among auxotrophs obtained from wild-type, sensitive strains, provided that streptomycin is added to the medium at a very low concentration. Sensitive cells respond readily to these small amounts of streptomycin. Resistant cells, however, respond sluggishly and require much more of the streptomycin in order to synthesize the

enzyme in which they are defective [*see top illustration on page 267*]. This weak response in resistant conditionally streptomycin-dependent cells suggested that our failure to find even a little misreading with resistant ribosomes in the cell-free preparations was due to the low efficiency of our biochemical system. Sure enough, when we developed a highly purified system, we found that even some streptomycin-resistant ribosomes were subject to misreading.

All these experiments pointed to a picture of the ribosome as a cell component with a very complex function. The structure and function of ribosomes can be investigated by isolating and examining ribosomal mutants in much the same way that other mutants have been followed in genetic experiments to unravel the structure of enzymes. In this task one can select for altered ribosomes by taking advantage of the fact that streptomycin and other "aminoglycoside" antibiotics related to it cause changes in ribosome structure. So far it is clear that two classes of streptomycin-resistant cell can be isolated from a strain bearing a defect that can be suppressed by streptomycin. One is "competent" for the suppression and the other "incompetent." A graduate student in our laboratory, Lee Brecken-

ridge, succeeded in isolating a second crop of conditionally streptomycin-dependent mutants from competent and incompetent parents and found that a mutant that is incompetent for one defect may be competent for another. This confirms our impression that there is a relation between a specific change in ribosome structure and the defect that can be corrected. This is equivalent to saying that as a result of mutation or of the presence of streptomycin or related drugs a ribosome can assume different conformations that are specific for different types of misreading.

Other findings support this conclusion. For one thing, the pattern of misreading induced in a cell-free system by streptomycin and related drugs such as kanamycin and neomycin varies with the drug. Moreover, in experiments with living cells certain auxotrophs are suppressed by one drug and not by another. Even in the absence of inducing drugs, variations in ribosome structure play a role in the accuracy of translation. There seems to be a steady low level of misreading, and that level varies with specific ribosomal mutations. It has also been noted that a single mutation from drug-sensitive to resistant—which means a change in ribosome structure—is often accompanied by the appearance of other defects, such as auxotrophy, that suggest errors in translation.

All of this means that ambiguity of translation is inherent in the process of protein synthesis; the genetic script transcribed into messenger RNA is not read in only one way. A cell is capable of a certain frequency of misreading, and drugs or other agents in the environment can increase this frequency by acting on the ribosomes.

The misreading caused by streptomycin is not random; it makes poly-uridylic acid, for example, code for only a few incorrect amino acids. The results of experiments conducted in Nirenberg's laboratory and by Davies in our laboratory make it possible tentatively to define a simple pattern for these misreadings and to obtain some insight into the way in which antibiotics cause them and thus into the mechanism of translation. According to the available data and the code "dictionary" compiled to date, it is possible to suggest that streptomycin distorts the configuration of the ribosome in a way that affects the reading of only one base of a triplet at a time. It follows that the codon is read as if it were one of the triplets "connected" to it, that is, differing from it by only one base substitution. The ambiguity, as is evident in cell-free preparations, is still more selective in that the misreadings we find do not include all the possible connected codons but only some of them. This selectivity largely accounts for the relative infrequency of conditionally streptomycin-dependent mutants among all the auxotrophs derived from a given parent.

Another reason for this infrequency could be that a streptomycin-induced misreading can often lead to the incorporation of the same amino acid encoded by the messenger RNA, because connected codons are often synonymous. This might explain why a large fraction of the conditionally streptomycin-dependent auxotrophs we find are really "leaky," or incomplete, auxotrophs stimulated by streptomycin rather than strictly dependent on it: they produce too small a quantity of some growth factor rather than none at all, and streptomycin makes them produce more. A reasonable hypothesis is that their mutation was to a rarely used codon and that streptomycin suppresses that codon, reading instead a more frequently utilized synonym—that they too are corrected by streptomycin through misreading, but the correction is "silent" in the sense that one cannot demonstrate actual amino acid substitution.

This is only a hypothesis, however; the leaky auxotrophs might suggest, on the contrary, that streptomycin always acts in living cells by somehow stimulating enzyme production—a process for which several explanations other than codon misreading can be imagined. To convince ourselves that the misreading obtained in cell-free preparations does indeed account for the suppression observed in living cells, we need unequivocal demonstrations of the occurrence of misreading in such cells. The most direct approach would be to isolate, purify and analyze an enzyme and demonstrate that in the presence of streptomycin one actually gets a mixture of molecules with slightly different amino acid compositions. Unfortunately, this seems to be a very laborious and difficult task. Streptomycin correction is of the order of less than 1 percent, and the few corrected molecules may be impossible to distinguish from impurities.

Fortunately there is another way in which misreading can be demonstrated unequivocally. That is to inquire directly whether the two well-known types of mutation are susceptible to streptomycin correction. One is the "nonsense" mutation, in which the affected triplet codes for no amino acid at all, and the

protein corresponding to the mutated messenger is therefore missing. The mechanism of suppression of these mutations is well established and consists in making sense of the nonsense triplet, causing the protein to be formed [see "The Genetics of a Bacterial Virus," by R. S. Edgar and R. H. Epstein, which begins on page 145 in this book]. Since it has been demonstrated, particularly in bacterial viruses, that streptomycin corrects mutants harboring a well-known and easily detected nonsense mutation, it is clear that streptomycin corrects by misreading a nonsense triplet into a "sense" amino acid codon. In a "missense" mutation, on the other hand, the wrong amino acid is encoded, resulting in an altered or inactive enzyme. Here streptomycin suppression through misreading could insert either the correct amino acid or another one that permits some enzyme activity. A mutant both conditionally streptomycin-dependent and temperature-sensitive—one that ordinarily produces an altered enzyme that is stable at one temperature but not stable at a higher temperature, but that in the presence of streptomycin produces at least some stable enzyme—offers unequivocal evidence of amino acid substitution. We have isolated such mutants and we are studying them.

Streptomycin-induced translation errors can of course hurt the cell as well as help it, since they affect certain codons in certain ways whether or not those codons are mutated. We studied the effect of misreading on the synthesis of four enzymes in a conditionally streptomycin-dependent mutant in which the effect of the drug was enhanced by a

second mutation. Increasing concentrations of streptomycin raised the level of the defective enzyme (OTC), but it also markedly reduced the level of the other three enzymes. We call this effect "oversuppression." It tends to flood a cell with faulty proteins.

Intuitively, misreading would seem to be the reason why streptomycin acts as an antibiotic, and there is very suggestive evidence that it is indeed the basis for an explanation of the aminoglycoside drugs' bactericidal effect. Bacteria resistant to the antibiotic effect of streptomycin are also resistant to its close relatives dihydrostreptomycin and bluensomycin, but they are killed by neomycin and kanamycin. The parallel to this is that in cell-free preparations in which streptomycin-resistant ribosomes are resistant to misreading induced by streptomycin and its close relatives they are nevertheless susceptible to misreading induced by neomycin and kanamycin, and neomycin-resistant mutants are susceptible to misreading induced by streptomycin. Although a flood of bad protein might well stop cell growth, however, its effect should be reversible. Special types of misreading or other effects would seem necessary to account fully for the killing of cells.

Apart from its pharmacological implications, our work with streptomycin adds a new dimension—the ribosomal dimension—to investigations into the mechanism of protein synthesis and provides the genetic tools with which to investigate it. Our findings also raise the broad question of the meaning of ambiguity in the genetic code. That ambiguity and the flexibility to which it gives rise may play an important role in the life of cells and in their evolution.

POLYRIBOSOMES from rabbit reticulocytes, the cells that make hemoglobin, are enlarged 370,000 diameters in this electron micrograph made by Henry S. Slayter of the Children's Cancer Research Foundation. They appear to be groups of ribosomes connected by strands of RNA, presumably the messenger RNA encoding the amino acid sequence of a protein.

28 | The Induction of Cancer by Viruses

RENATO DULBECCO · April 1967

Cancer, one of the major problems of modern medicine, is also a fascinating biological problem. In biological terms it is the manifestation of changes in one of the more general properties of the cells of higher organisms: their ability to adjust their growth rate to the architectural requirements of the organism. To learn more about cancer is therefore to learn more about this basic control mechanism. Over the past decade dramatic advances in our knowledge of cancer have resulted from the use of viruses to elicit the disease in simple model systems. A certain understanding of the molecular aspects of cancer has been attained, and the foundation has been laid for rapid progress in the foreseeable future.

A cancer arises from a single cell that undergoes permanent hereditary changes and consequently multiplies, giving rise to billions of similarly altered cells. The development of the cancer may require other conditions, such as failure of the immunological defenses of the organism. The fundamental event, however, is the alteration of that one initial cell.

There are two main changes in a cancer cell. One change can be defined as being of a regulatory nature. The multiplication of the cells of an animal is carefully regulated; multiplication takes place only when it is required, for example by the healing of a wound. The cancer cell, on the other hand, escapes the regulatory mechanisms of the body and is continuously in a multiplication cycle.

The other change of the cancer cell concerns its relations with neighboring cells in the body. Normal cells are confined to certain tissues, according to rules on which the body's overall architecture depends. The cancer cell is not confined to its original tissue but invades other tissues, where it proliferates.

The basic biological problem of cancer is to identify the molecular changes that occur in the initial cancer cell and determine what causes the changes. The particular site in the cell affected by the changes can be approximately inferred from the nature of the changes themselves. For example, a change in the regulation of cell growth and multiplication must arise from a change in the regulation of a basic process in the cell, such as the synthesis of the genetic material deoxyribonucleic acid (DNA). The alterations in relations with neighboring cells are likely to flow from changes in the outside surface of the cell, which normally recognizes and responds to its immediate environment.

Experimental work directed toward the solution of this central problem makes use of cancers induced artificially rather than cancers that occur spontaneously. Spontaneous cancers are not suitable for experiments because by definition their occurrence cannot be controlled; moreover, when a spontaneous cancer becomes observable, its cells have often undergone numerous changes in addition to the initial one. In recent years model systems for studying cancers have been developed by taking advantage of the fact that animal cells can easily be grown in vitro—in test tubes or boxes of glass or plastic filled with a suitable liquid medium. This is the technique of tissue culture.

Since the use of tissue culture has many obvious experimental advantages, methods for the induction of cancer in vitro have been developed. The most successful and most widely employed systems use viruses as the cancer-inducing agent. In these systems the initial cellular changes take place under controlled conditions and can be followed closely by using an array of technical tools: genetic, biochemical, physical and immunological.

It may seem strange that viruses, which are chemically complex structures, would be preferable for experimental work to simple cancer-inducing chemicals, of which many are available. The fact is that the action of cancer-inducing chemicals is difficult to elucidate; they have complex chemical effects on a large number of cell constituents. Furthermore, even if one were to make the simple and reasonable assumption that chemicals cause cancer by inducing mutations in the genetic material of the cells, the problem would remain enormously difficult. It would still be almost impossible to know which genes are affected, owing to the large number of genes in which the cancer-causing mu-

NORMAL AND TRANSFORMED cells are shown on the opposite page in three stages of density, or growth, increasing to the right in each row. Normal cells (*A*, *C*) tend to adhere to one another and form either a pattern of bundles (*A*) or a mosaic-like arrangement referred to as pavement (*C*). Cells that have been transformed by viruses (*B*, *D*, *E*) generally overlap one another and form irregular patterns. The cellular bodies are dark gray and contain a lighter round or oval nucleus in which two or more dark nuclei are embedded. Two of the cultures (*A*, *B*) are a strain of hamster cells identified as "BHK." The other three cultures are "3T3" cells derived from a mouse. Two of the cultures (*B*, *E*) have been transformed by polyoma virus; one (*D*) has been transformed by simian virus 40, also known as SV 40. The cells were photographed in the living state by the author, using a phase-contrast microscope, at the Salk Institute for Biological Studies.

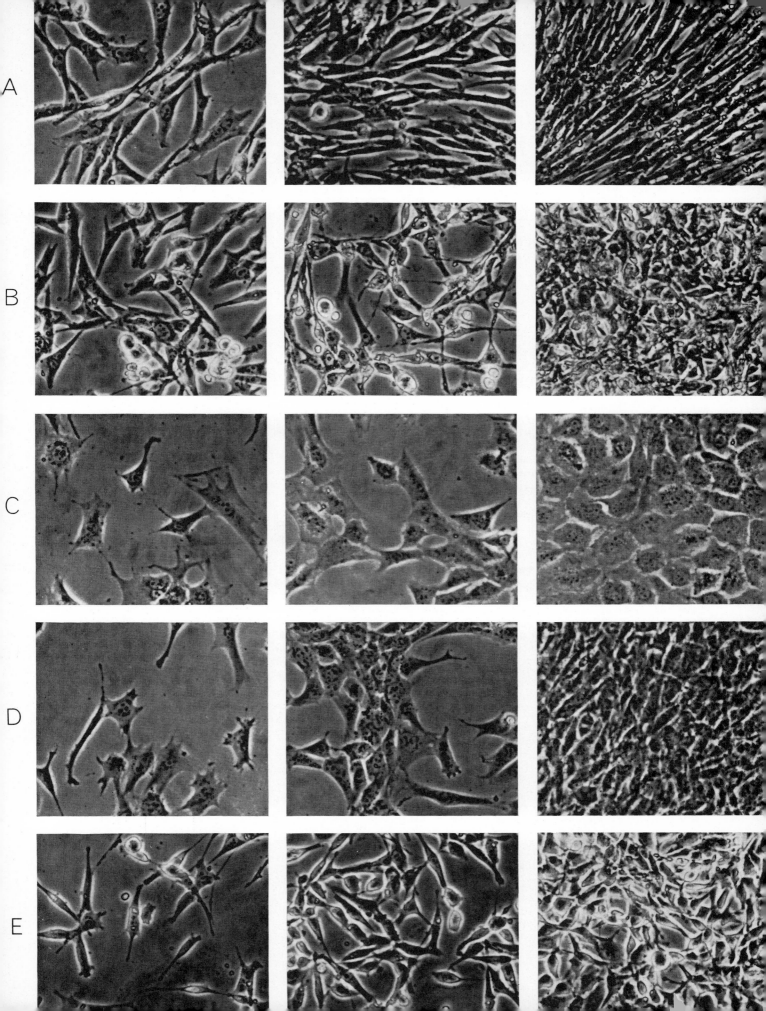

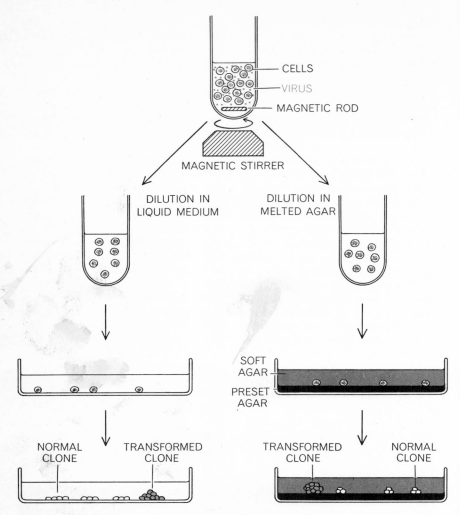

TRANSFORMATION EXPERIMENT produces cell colonies that differ in appearance, depending on the nature of the culture medium. BHK (hamster) cells are first incubated with polyoma virus for about an hour at 37 degrees centigrade, being stirred constantly. During this time viral particles enter the cells. The infected cells are then diluted either in a liquid medium or in melted agar and transferred to culture dishes. In the agar system the melted agar is poured on a layer of preset agar. The dishes are incubated at 37 degrees C. Cell colonies in the liquid medium develop in contact with the bottom of the container, whereas those in agar form spherical colonies above the preset agar layer. The results of using the two kinds of media are shown in the photographs on the opposite page.

tation could occur. It is estimated that there are millions of genes in an animal cell, and the function of most of them is unknown. With viruses the situation can be much simpler. As I shall show, cancer is induced by the genes of the virus, which, like the genes of animal cells, are embodied in the structure of DNA. Since the number of viral genes is small (probably fewer than 10 in the system discussed in this article), it should be possible to identify those responsible for cancer induction and to discover how they function in the infected cells. The problem can thus be reduced from one of cellular genetics to one of viral genetics. The reduction is of several orders of magnitude.

A number of different viruses have the ability to change normal cells into cancer cells in vitro. In our work at the Salk Institute for Biological Studies we employ two small, DNA-containing viruses called the polyoma virus and simian virus 40 (SV 40), both of which induce cancer when they are inoculated into newborn rodents, particularly hamsters, rats and, in the case of the polyoma virus, mice. Together these viruses are referred to as the small papovaviruses.

In tissue-culture studies two types of host cell are employed with each virus. In one cell type—the "productive" host cell—the virus causes what is known as a productive infection: the virus multiplies unchecked within the cell and finally kills it. In another type of cell—the "transformable" host cell—the virus

causes little or no productive infection but induces changes similar to those in cancer cells. This effect of infection is called transformation rather than cancer induction because operationally it is recognized from the altered morphology of the cells in vitro rather than from the production of cancer in an animal.

In the experimental work it is convenient to employ as host cells, particularly for transformation studies, permanent lines of cellular descent, known as clonal lines, that are derived from a single cell and are therefore uniform in composition. By using these clonal lines the changes caused by the virus can be studied without interference from other forms of cellular variation; one simply compares the transformed cells with their normal counterparts. Two lines that are widely employed are the "BHK" line, which was obtained from a hamster by Ian A. Macpherson and Michael G. P. Stoker of the Institute of Virology of the University of Glasgow, and the "3T3" line, which was obtained from a mouse by George J. Todaro and Howard Green of the New York University School of Medicine. BHK cells are particularly suitable for transformation by the polyoma virus; 3T3 cells are readily transformed by SV 40 and less easily by the polyoma virus.

In a typical transformation experiment a suspension of cells in a suitable liquid medium is mixed with the virus [*see illustration at left*]. The cells are incubated at 37 degrees centigrade for an hour; they are stirred constantly to prevent them from settling and clumping together. A sample of the cells is then distributed in a number of sterile dishes of glass or plastic that contain a suitable nutrient medium. The dishes are incubated at 37 degrees C. for a period ranging from one to three weeks. The cells placed in the dishes settle and adhere to the bottom. There they divide, each cell giving rise to a colony [*see illustration at left on opposite page*]. If the number of cells is sufficiently small, the colonies remain distinct from one another and are recognizable to the unaided eye after about 10 days' incubation; they can be studied sooner with a low-power microscope. When the colonies are fully developed, they are usually fixed and stained. Colonies of normal and transformed cells can be recognized on the basis of morphological characters I shall describe. By picking a colony of transformed cells and reseeding its cells in a fresh culture, clonal lines of transformed cells can be easily prepared. The transformation of BHK cells can also be studied by a selective method that involves suspending the cells in melted agar, which then sets. Transformed cells give rise to spherical colonies, visible to the unaided eye, whereas normal cells grow little or not at all [see illustration at right below].

Colonies of transformed cells, and cultures derived from such colonies, differ morphologically from their normal counterparts in two obvious ways; these differences show that changes have occurred in the regulatory properties of the cells and also in the way they relate to their neighbors. The transformed cultures are thicker because they continue to grow rapidly, whereas normal cultures slow down or stop; in addition the transformed cells are not regularly oriented with respect to each other because they fail to respond to cell-to-cell contact. The altered response to contacts can be best appreciated in time-lapse motion pictures of living cultures.

In sparse BHK cultures the cells move around actively; if a cell meets another cell in its path, it usually stops moving and slowly arranges itself in contact with and parallel to the other cell. In this way a characteristic pattern of parallel lines and whorls is generated, since the cells do not climb over each other. In a culture of a derivative of the BHK line transformed by polyoma virus the same active movement of the cells is observed. When a cell meets another in its path, however, it continues to move, climbing over the other. In this way the arrangement of the cells becomes chaotic, without any discernible pattern [see illustration on page 273].

These alterations of the transformed cells indicate their intimate relatedness to cancer cells. The relatedness is shown in a more dramatic way by the ability of the transformed cells to grow into a cancer when injected, in sufficient number, into a live host that does not present an insurmountable immunological barrier to their survival. For example, BHK cells, which were originally obtained from a hamster, can be transplanted into hamsters; similarly, cells of inbred strains of mice can easily be transplanted into mice of the same strain. The injection of roughly a million transformed cells into a hamster or mouse will be followed by the development of a walnut-sized tumor at the site of inoculation in about three weeks. Untransformed cells, on the other hand, fail to produce tumors.

A crucial finding is that the transformation of healthy cells is attributable to the genes present in the viral DNA that penetrates the cells at infection. The viral genes are the units of information that determine the consequences of infection. Each viral particle contains a long, threadlike molecule of DNA wrapped in a protein coat. Each of these molecules is made up of two strands twisted around each other. Attached to the molecular backbone of each strand is the sequence of nitrogenous bases that contains the genetic information of the virus in coded form. There are four kinds of base, and the DNA molecule of a papovavirus has some 5,000 bases on each strand. Each species of virus has a unique sequence of bases in its DNA; all members of a species have the same base sequence, except for isolated differences caused by mutations.

The double-strand molecule of DNA is so constructed that a given base in one strand always pairs with a particular base in the other strand; these two associated bases are called complementary. Thus the two DNA strands are also complementary in base sequence. Complementary bases form bonds with each other; the bonds hold the two strands firmly together. The two strands fall apart if a solution of DNA is heated to a fairly high temperature, a process

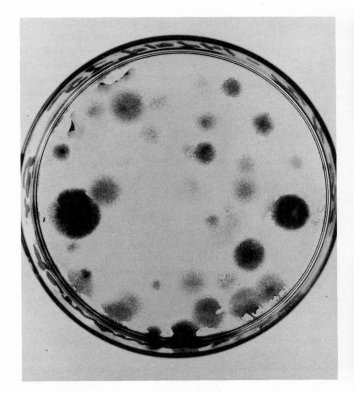

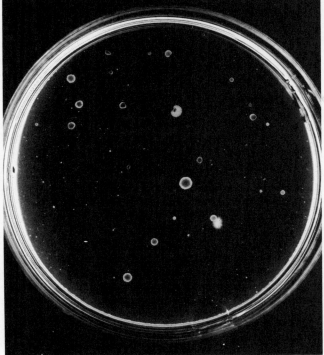

TWO KINDS OF CELL COLONY are depicted in these photographs made in the author's laboratory. Colonies formed by 3T3 (mouse) cells exposed to SV 40 particles grow on the bottom of a plastic dish under a liquid nutrient medium (left). The two large, dark colonies on opposite sides of the culture dish consist of transformed cells. The other colonies are made up of normal cells. Colonies formed by BHK (hamster) cells exposed to polyoma virus are suspended in agar (right). Transformed cells create large spherical colonies, which appear as white disks with gray centers. Colonies of normal cells are small or invisible.

called denaturation. If the heated solution is then slowly cooled, a process called annealing, the complementary strands unite again and form double-strand molecules identical with the original ones.

When suitable cells are exposed to a virus, a large number of viral particles are taken up into the cells in many small vesicles, or sacs, which then accumulate around the nucleus of the cell. Most of the viral particles remain inert, but the protein coat of some is removed and their naked DNA enters the inner compartments of the cell, ultimately reaching the nucleus. Evidence that cell transformation is caused by the viral DNA, and by the genes it carries, is supplied by two experimental results.

The first result is that cell transformation can be produced by purified viral DNA, obtained by removing the protein coat from viral particles; this was first shown by G. P. Di Mayorca and his colleagues at the Sloan-Kettering Institute. The extraction of the DNA is usually accomplished by shaking the virus in concentrated phenol. In contrast, the empty viral coats do not cause transformation. These DNA-less particles are available for experimentation because they are synthesized in productively infected cells together with the regular DNA-containing particles. The empty coats have a lower density than the complete viral particles; hence the two can be separated if they are spun at high speed in a heavy salt solution, the technique known as density-gradient centrifugation.

A more sophisticated experiment performed at the University of Glasgow also rules out the possibility that the transforming activity resides in contaminant molecules present in the extracted DNA. The basis for this experiment is the shape of the DNA molecules of papovaviruses. The ends of each molecule are joined together to form a ring. When the double-strand filaments that consti-

tute these ring molecules are in solution, they form densely packed supercoils. If one of the strands should suffer a single break, the supercoil disappears and the molecule becomes a stretched ring. Supercoiled molecules, because of their compactness, settle faster than stretched-ring molecules when they are centrifuged. Thus the two molecular types can be separated in two distinct bands.

By this technique polyoma virus DNA containing both molecular types can be separated into fractions, each of which contains just one type. Examination of the biological properties of these fractions shows that the transforming efficiency is strictly limited to the two bands of the viral DNA. Similarly, only the material in the two bands will give rise to productive infection. This result, among others, rules out the possibility that transformation is due to fragments of cellular DNA, which are known to be present in some particles of polyoma virus and therefore contaminate the preparations of viral DNA. The contaminant molecules have a very different distribution in the gradient.

The second result demonstrates directly that the function of a viral gene is required for transformation, by showing that a mutation in the viral genetic material can abolish the ability of the virus to transform. This important finding was made by Mike Fried of the California Institute of Technology, who studied a temperature-sensitive mutant line of polyoma virus called Ts-a. The virus of this line behaves like normal virus in cells at 31 degrees C., causing either transformation or productive infection, depending on the cells it infects. At 39 degrees C., however, the effect of the mutation is manifest, and the virus is unable to cause either transformation or infection; it is simply inactive [see top illustration on opposite page].

We can now inquire whether the viral gene functions needed to effect transformation are transient or continuous. In other words, do the genes act only once and produce a permanent transformation of the cell line or must they act continuously to keep the cell and its descendants transformed?

A result pertinent to this question is that the transformed cells contain functional viral genes many cell generations after transformation has occurred, although they never contain, or spontaneously produce, infectious virus. The presence of viral genes has been demonstrated particularly well by T. L. Benjamin at Cal Tech, who has shown that the transformed cells contain virus-specific

PRODUCTIVE
INFECTION

TRANSFORMATION

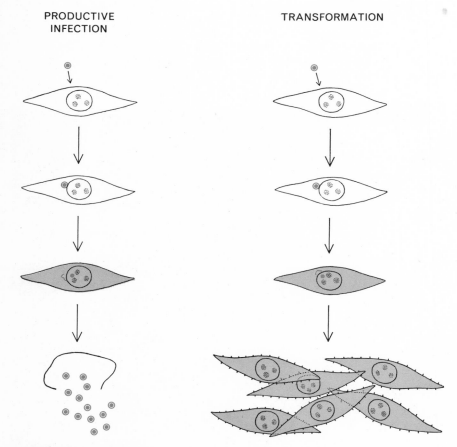

VIRAL INVASION OF CELLS can have two different results. One result is "productive infection" (*left*), **in which viral particles** (*color*) **mobilize the machinery of the cell for making new viral particles, complete with protein coats. The cell eventually dies, releasing the particles. The other result is transformation** (*right*), **in which the virus alters the cell so that it reproduces without restraint and does not respond to the presence of neighboring cells. Viral particles cannot be found in the transformed cells. The tint of color in these cells indicates the presence of new functions induced by the genes of the virus. The change in the cell membrane** (*lower right*) **denotes the presence of a virus-specific antigen.**

ribonucleic acid (RNA). To make the significance of this finding clear it should be mentioned that the instructions contained in the base sequence of the DNA in cells or viruses are executed by first making a strand of RNA with a base sequence complementary to that of one of the DNA strands. This RNA, called messenger RNA, carries the information of the gene to the cellular sites where the proteins specified by the genetic information are synthesized. Each gene gives rise to its own specific messenger RNA. If one could show that viral messenger RNA were present in transformed cells, one would have evidence not only that the cells contain viral genes but also that these genes are active. The viral RNA molecules can be recognized among those extracted from transformed cells, which are mostly cellular RNA, by adding to the mixture of RNA molecules heat-denatured, single-strand viral DNA. When the mixture of RNA and DNA is annealed, only the viral molecules of RNA enter into double-strand molecules with the viral DNA. The reaction is extremely sensitive and specific.

It is likely, therefore, that the viral genes persisting in the transformed cells are instrumental in maintaining the transformed state of the cells. This idea is supported by the observation that the form of the transformed cells is controlled by the transforming virus. This is seen clearly in cells of the line 3T3, which can be transformed by either SV 40 or polyoma virus. The transformed cells, although descended from the same clonal cell line, are strikingly different [*see illustration on page 273*]. Similar differences are also observed in other cell types transformed by the two viruses. Since the cells were identical before infection, the differences that accompany transformation by two different viruses can be most simply explained as the result of the continuing function of the different viral genes in the same type of cell. In fact, it is difficult to think of a satisfactory alternative hypothesis.

It must be clear, however, that there is no conclusive evidence for this continuing role of the viral genes. It is therefore impossible to exclude an entirely different interpretation of the observation. One can argue, for example, that the persistence of the viral genes is irrelevant for transformation, and that the genes remain in the cells as an accidental result of the previous exposure of the cells, or of their ancestors, to the virus. Indeed, under many other circumstances viruses are often found in association with cells without noticeably affecting them. A conclusive clarification of the

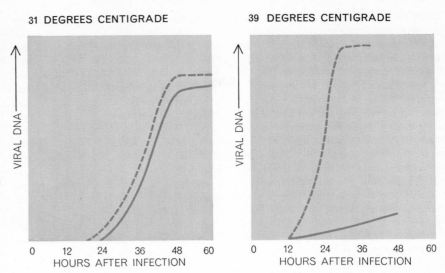

TEMPERATURE-DEPENDENT STRAINS OF POLYOMA VIRUS act normally at a temperature of 31 degrees C. (*left*) but exhibit mutated behavior at 39 degrees C. (*right*). The solid curves show the amount of viral deoxyribonucleic acid (DNA) synthesized in productive host cells containing the mutant virus. Broken curves show the viral DNA output in cells containing "wild type" (ordinary) polyoma virus. The mutant virus is called Ts-a.

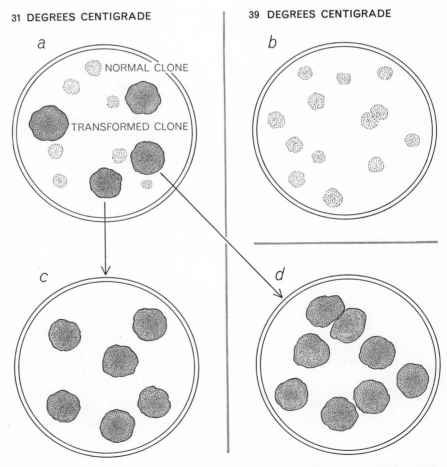

TRANSIENT ROLE OF TS-A GENE, which gives rise to temperature-dependent mutants of polyoma virus, can be demonstrated by raising the temperature of experimental cultures after the cells have been transformed by the virus. The mutant virus is able to transform cells at low temperature (*a*) but not at high temperature (*b*). Transformed cell colonies, or clones, remain transformed, as expected, at low temperature (*c*), but they also remain transformed when the temperature is raised (*d*). This experiment provides evidence that the Ts-a gene is needed for the initial transformation of the cell but is not needed thereafter.

role of the persisting viral genes is being sought by using temperature-dependent viral mutants analogous to the Ts-a mutant I have mentioned. A virus bearing a temperature-dependent mutation in a gene whose function is required for maintaining the cells in the transformed state would cause transformation at low temperature. The cells, however, would revert to normality if the ambient temperature were raised. A small-scale search for mutants with these properties has already been carried out in our laboratory but without success; a large-scale search is being planned in several laboratories.

It should be remarked that no protein of the outer coat of the viral particles is ever found in the transformed cells. Thus the gene responsible for the coat protein is always nonfunctional. This could be either because the transformed cells have an incomplete set of viral genes and the coat gene is absent or because some genes remain "silent." The silence of these genes in turn could be attributed to failure either of transcription of the DNA of the gene into messenger RNA or of translation of the messenger RNA into protein. If failure of transcription were the mechanism, transformed cells would be similar to lysogenic bacteria. Such bacteria have a complete set of genes of a bacteriophage (a virus that infects bacteria), but most of the viral genes are not transcribed into RNA. No other significant similarities exist, however, between ordinary lysogenic bacteria and transformed cells; therefore it is more likely that the coat gene is either absent or, if it is present, produces messenger RNA that is not translated into coat protein. Whatever the mechanism, the lack of expression of the coat-protein gene, and probably of other genes as well, is essential for the survival of the transformed cells, since it prevents productive infection that would otherwise kill the cells.

So far we have considered the genes of the virus in abstract terms. Let us now consider them in concrete ones by asking how many genes each viral DNA molecule possesses and what their functions are. The function of a viral gene is the specification, through its particular messenger RNA, of a polypeptide chain, which by folding generates a protein subunit; the subunits associate to form

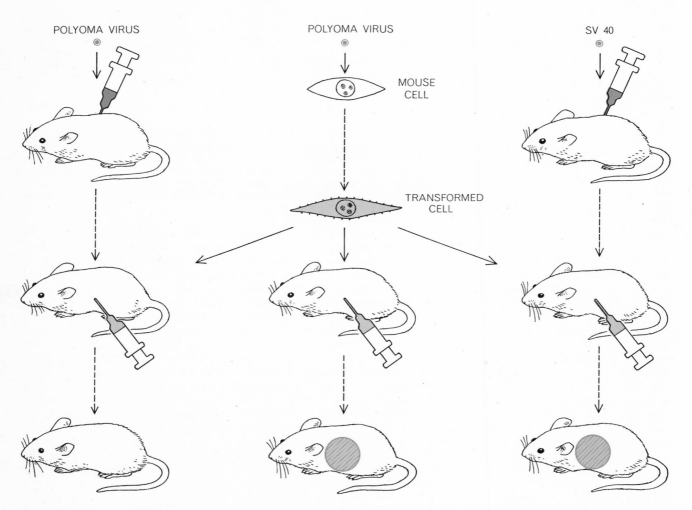

IMMUNIZATION EXPERIMENT shows that an animal will not develop a tumor after receiving a massive injection of transformed cells if it has previously received a mild inoculation of the virus used to transform the cells. Thus the animal at left, which has been immunized by an injection of polyoma virus, does not develop a tumor when injected with cells transformed by polyoma virus. The animal in the middle, not so immunized, develops a tumor following the injection of polyoma-transformed cells. The animal at right, which has received an injection of a different virus, SV 40, is not immunized against cells transformed by polyoma virus, hence it too develops a tumor. It would not develop a tumor, however, if injected with cells transformed by SV 40. Cells transformed by either polyoma virus or SV 40 contain a new antigen in their surface that makes them foreign to the animal strain from which they derive and therefore subject to its immunological defenses. These defenses can be mobilized by direct injection of the virus.

a functional viral protein. The final product can be an enzyme or a regulator molecule that can control the function of other genes (viral or cellular), or it can be a structural protein such as the coat protein of the viral particles.

As I have said, each strand of the DNA of the small papovaviruses contains about 5,000 bases. Three bases are required to specify one amino acid, or one building block, in a polypeptide chain; therefore 5,000 bases can specify some 1,700 amino acids. It can be calculated from the total molecular weight of the coat protein of the viral particles and from the number of subunits it has that between a third and a fourth of the genetic information of the virus is tied up in specifying the coat protein. This genetic information is irrelevant for transformation, because no coat protein is made in the transformed cells. What remains, therefore, is enough genetic information to specify about 1,200 amino acids, which can constitute from four to eight small protein molecules, depending on their size. This is the maximum number of viral genetic functions that can be involved in the transformation of a host cell.

In order to discover these viral genetic functions the properties of normal cells have been carefully compared with the properties of cells that have been either transformed or productively infected. Characteristics present in the infected cultures can be considered to result, directly or indirectly, from the action of viral genes. We shall call these new characteristics "new functions." In this way six new functions have been discovered in the infected cells, in addition to the specification of the viral coat protein [see illustration on page 281]. Some of the new functions can be recognized biochemically; others can be shown by immunological tests to act as new cellular antigens.

The genetic studies with the papovaviruses have not gone far enough to reveal whether each of the new functions indeed represents the function of a separate viral gene, or whether all the gene functions have been identified. On the basis of the possible number of genes and the number of new functions it is likely that most, if not all, of the gene functions have been detected. At present the new functions are being attributed to the genes, and a large-scale effort is being made to produce temperature-sensitive mutants that will affect each of the genes separately. By studying the effect of such mutations on transformation it will

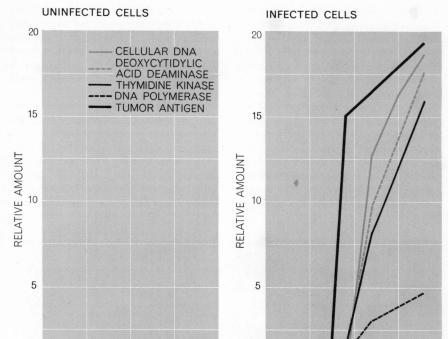

ACTIVATION OF DNA SYNTHESIS, along with activation of enzymes needed for its production, is a major consequence of viral infection of animal cells. Resting, uninfected cells make little DNA or enzymes associated with its synthesis (left). The values plotted are for kidney cells of an African monkey. When the cells are infected with SV 40, the output of DNA and associated enzymes rises steeply (right). Before these cellular syntheses are activated a new virus-specific protein, the "T antigen," whose role is unknown, appears.

be possible to establish the role of each gene in an unambiguous way.

For the moment we must limit ourselves to examining the various new functions and making educated guesses about their possible role in transformation. If transformation is continuously maintained by the function of viral genes, two new functions are particularly suspect as agents of transformation. One function involves a virus-specific antigen present on the surface of transformed cells; the other is the activation of the synthesis of cellular DNA and of cellular enzymes required for the manufacture of DNA by productively infected cells.

The induction of a virus-specific antigen on the cell surface was detected independently by Hans Olof Sjögren of the Royal Caroline Institute in Stockholm and by Karl Habel of the National Institutes of Health. They have shown that if an animal is inoculated with a mild dose of SV 40 or polyoma virus, it will develop an immune response that will enable it to reject cells transformed by the virus. Whereas the cells grow to form a tumor in the untreated animals, they

are immunologically rejected by and form no tumor in the immunized animals [see illustration on opposite page]. Rejection occurs only if the animals were immunized by the same virus used for transforming the cells. For instance, immunity against cells transformed by polyoma virus is induced by polyoma virus but not by SV 40, and vice versa. This shows that the antigen is virus-specific. The antigenic change is an indication of structural changes in the cellular surface, which may be responsible for the altered relations of transformed cells and their neighbors.

The activation of cellular syntheses, discovered independently in several laboratories, can be demonstrated in crowded cultures. If the cells in the culture are uninfected, they tend to remain in a resting stage. In these cells the synthesis of DNA, and of enzymes whose operation is required for DNA synthesis (such as deoxycytidylic acid deaminase, DNA polymerase and thymidine kinase), proceeds at a much lower rate than it does in growing cells. After infection by a small papovavirus a burst of new synthesis of both DNA and enzymes occurs; a viral function thus activates a group of cellular genes that were previously inactive [see illustration on preceding page]. If the infection of the cells is productive, the activation of cellular syntheses occurs before the cells are killed. The activating viral function must act centrally, presumably at the level of transcription or translation of cellular genes that receive regulatory signals from the periphery of the cell; the signals themselves should be unchanged, since the cell's environment, in which the signals originate, is not changed. If the viral gene

responsible for the activating function persists and operates in the transformed cells, it will make the cells insensitive to regulation of growth. Direct evidence for the operation of this mechanism in the transformed cells, however, has not yet been obtained.

A third viral function may be connected with such activation. This is the synthesis of a protein detected as a virus-specific antigen and called the T antigen (for tumor antigen). This antigen, discovered by Robert J. Huebner and his colleagues at the National Institute of Allergy and Infectious Diseases, differs

in immunological specificity from either the protein of the viral coat or the transplantation antigen [see lower illustration on this page]. The T antigen is present in the nucleus of both productively infected and transformed cells. In productive infection the T antigen appears before the induction of the cellular syntheses begins, and before the viral DNA replicates. Therefore the T antigen may represent a protein with a control function; for instance, it may be the agent that activates the cellular syntheses. For this assumption also direct evidence is lacking.

A fourth viral function relevant to transformation is the function of the gene bearing the Ts-a mutation, which we can call the Ts-a gene. The reader will recall that a virus line carrying this mutation transforms cells at low temperature but not at high temperature. Cells transformed at low temperature, however, remain transformed when they are subjected to the higher temperature, in spite of the inactivation of the gene [see bottom illustration on page 277]. Thus the function of the Ts-a gene is only transiently required for transformation. In order to evaluate the significance of this result we must also recall that in productive infection the function of the Ts-a gene is required for the synthesis of the viral DNA. Therefore the transient requirement of this function in transformation may simply mean that the viral DNA must replicate before transformation takes place. If so, the Ts-a gene is not directly involved in transformation.

Another interpretation is possible. The function of the Ts-a gene is likely to be the specification of an enzyme involved in the replication of the viral DNA, for example a DNA polymerase, or a nuclease able to break the viral DNA at specific points, or even an enzyme with both properties. The action of a specific nuclease seems to be required for the replication of the viral DNA because the viral DNA molecules are in the form of closed rings. A nuclease, in breaking one of the strands, could provide a swivel around which the remainder of the molecule could rotate freely, allowing the two strands to unwind. The enzyme, although required for the replication of the viral DNA, may also affect the cellular DNA, for instance by causing breaks and consequently mutations. Such breaks have been observed in the DNA of cells that have been either productively infected or transformed by papovaviruses. If the Ts-a gene indeed acts on the DNA of the host cell, it could play a direct role in the transformation of the cell. Its actions would appear to

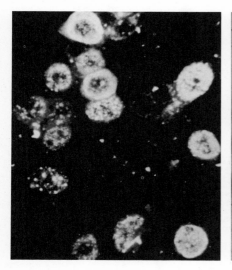
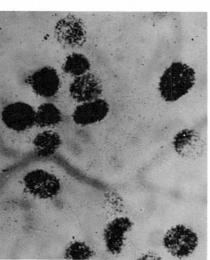

SITE OF VIRAL-COAT PROTEIN SYNTHESIS in infected cells is found to coincide with the site of DNA synthesis. A culture of mouse kidney cells was exposed to radioactive thymidine (needed in DNA synthesis) some 20 hours after infection with polyoma virus. Six hours later the culture was fixed and stained with antibodies coupled to a fluorescent dye that are specific for the coat protein of the virus. When the culture was photographed in ultraviolet light (left), the brilliant fluorescence of the bound antibodies showed that some of the cell nuclei were rich in coat protein. Then the culture was coated with a photographic film to disclose where beta rays emitted by the radioactive thymidine would expose grains of silver. The result (right) shows that the nuclei rich in coat protein were the same ones that had accumulated thymidine and were thus the site of DNA synthesis.

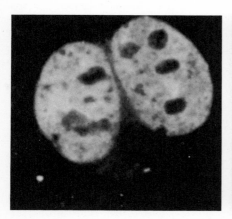
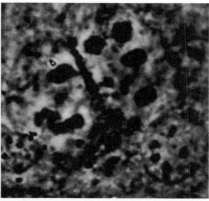

LOCATION OF T ANTIGEN in mouse cells transformed by SV 40 can be established by staining the cells with fluorescent antibodies that are specific for the T antigen (left). The same cells were also photographed in the phase-contrast microscope to show details of cell structure (right). It can be seen that the fluorescent antibodies nearly fill two large nuclei.

be transient, however, since mutations in the cellular DNA would not be undone if the Ts-a gene were subsequently inactivated by raising the temperature of the system. A more definite interpretation of the Ts-a results must await the completion of the biochemical and genetic studies now in progress in several laboratories.

The last two of the six new viral functions observed in infected cells are not sufficiently well known to permit evaluation of their possible roles in cell transformation. One of these two functions is the induction of a thymidine kinase enzyme that is different from the enzyme of the same type normally made by the host cell. Thymidine kinase participates at an early stage in a synthetic pathway leading to the production of a building block required in DNA synthesis. There are reasons to believe, however, that the thymidine kinase induced by the virus may have a general regulatory effect in activating the DNA-synthesizing machinery of the cell after infection. One reason is that the viral thymidine kinase has not been found in transformed cells. Since this enzyme is induced by many viruses containing DNA, whether or not they cause transformation, its induction by the papovaviruses may be connected exclusively with productive infection.

The last new function is one observed so far only with SV 40. After cells have been productively infected with this virus they are changed in some way so that they become productive hosts for a completely different kind of virus, an adenovirus, even though they are normally not a suitable host for such viruses. Little is known about the biochemical steps involved.

The central mechanism of cell transformation and cancer induction would appear to be contained within the half-dozen viral functions I have discussed, perhaps together with a few others as yet unknown. Thus the problem is narrowly restricted. It is likely that the dubious points still remaining will be resolved in the near future, since the dramatic advances of the past several years have set the stage for rapid further progress.

This article should not be concluded without an attempt's being made to answer a question that will undoubtedly have arisen in the minds of many readers: Why are viruses able to induce cancer at all? For the two viruses discussed in this article, at least, it seems likely that the viral functions that are probably responsible for cell transformation have been selected by evolutionary processes

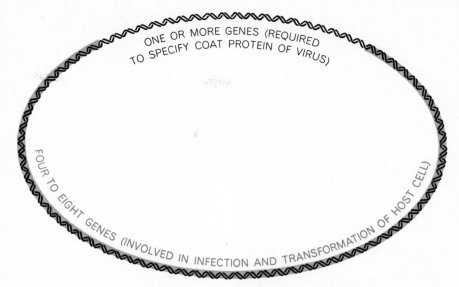

ONE OR MORE GENES (REQUIRED TO SPECIFY COAT PROTEIN OF VIRUS)

FOUR TO EIGHT GENES (INVOLVED IN INFECTION AND TRANSFORMATION OF HOST CELL)

SEVEN FUNCTIONS IDENTIFIED WITH VIRUS ACTIVITY

1. Specification of antigen found on surface of transformed cells.

2. Specification of factor that activates synthesis of cellular DNA.

3. Specification of antigen (T antigen) found in nuclei of infected and transformed cells.

4. Specification of enzyme involved in initial replication of viral DNA. (Attributed to the Ts-a gene.)

5. (Facilitation of cell infection by other viruses.)

6. (Induction of thymidine kinase enzyme.)

7. (Specification of coat protein of virus.)

SEVEN VIRAL FUNCTIONS have been identified in the infection and transformation of cells. The DNA present in the polyoma virus and SV 40 takes the form of a single ring-shaped molecule consisting of two helically intertwined strands (*top*). Each strand contains some 5,000 molecular subunits called bases that embody the genetic information of the virus in coded form. These bases, in groups of three, specify the amino acids that link together to form protein molecules. Thus 5,000 bases can specify some 1,700 amino acids, or enough to construct some six to 12 proteins. By definition it takes one gene to specify one protein. It is estimated that a third to a fourth of the bases in the viral DNA are needed to specify the protein in the coat of the virus. The remaining bases, enough for four to eight genes, specify the proteins involved in infection and transformation. Little is yet known about the fifth function in this list of seven. Functions 6 and 7 are not involved in cell transformation.

to further the multiplication of the virus. Because the virus is small and cannot contain much genetic information it must exploit the synthetic mechanisms of the cell, including a large number of cellular enzymes, to achieve its own replication. Furthermore, in the animal hosts in which these viruses normally multiply, most cells that can undergo productive infection are in a resting stage and have their DNA-synthesizing machinery turned off. Thus the evolution of a viral function capable of switching on this machinery is obviously quite advantageous to the virus. This function must be very similar to the function of the cellular gene that regulates cellular DNA synthesis (and overall growth) in the absence of viral infection. The functions of the viral gene and of the cellular

gene, however, must differ in one point, again for selective reasons: the cellular function must be subject to control by external signals, whereas the viral function must not be. The virus-induced alteration of the cellular surface seems also to be connected, in a way not yet understood, with viral multiplication, since in many viral infections viral proteins appear on the surface of cells.

The cancer-producing action of the papovaviruses can therefore be considered a by-product of viral functions developed for the requirements of viral multiplication. These viral functions lead to cancer development because they are similar to cellular functions that control cell multiplication, but they somehow escape the regulatory mechanisms that normally operate within the cell.

The Structure of Antibodies

29

R. R. PORTER · *October 1967*

It has been known for millenniums that a person who survives a disease such as plague or smallpox is usually able to resist a second infection. Indeed, such immune people were often the only ones available to nurse the sick during severe epidemics. A general understanding of immunity had to await the discovery that microorganisms are the causative agents of infectious disease. Then progress was rapid. A key step was taken in 1890 by Emil Von Behring and Shibasaburo Kitasato, working in the Institute of Robert Koch in Berlin. They showed that an animal could be made immune to tetanus by an injection of the blood serum obtained from an animal that had survived the disease and had

developed immunity to it. Serum is the clear fluid that is left behind when a blood clot forms; it contains most of the blood proteins. Thus immunity to tetanus is a function of a substance or substances in the blood. These substances were named antibodies.

Antibodies are produced by all vertebrates as a defense against invasion by certain foreign substances, known collectively as antigens. The most effective antigens are large molecules such as proteins or polysaccharides (and of course the microorganisms that contain these molecules). The demonstration of the appearance of antibodies in the blood is most dramatic if the antigen is a lethal toxin or a pathogenic microorganism:

the immune animals live and the non-immune die when injected with the antigen. Innocuous substances such as egg-white protein or the polysaccharide coat of bacteria, however, are equally effective as antigens. The antibodies formed against them can be detected by their ability to combine with antigen. This can be shown in many ways. Perhaps the simplest demonstration is provided by the precipitate that appears in a test tube when a soluble antigen combines with antibody contained in a sample of serum. The most remarkable aspect of this phenomenon is the specificity of the antibody for the antigen injected. That is, the antibody formed will combine only with the antigen injected

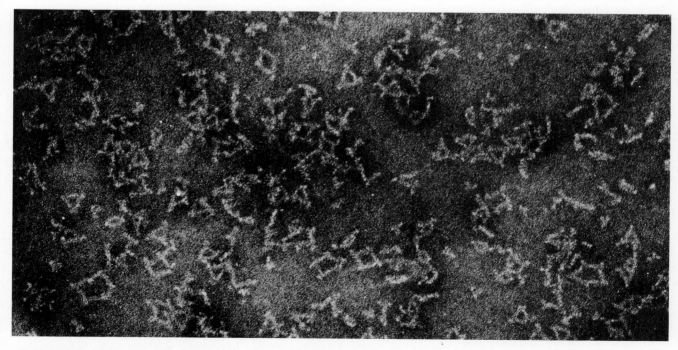

ANTIBODIES BOUND TO ANTIGENS are depicted in this electron micrograph made by Michael Green and Robin Valentine of the National Institute for Medical Research in London. The antigen itself is too small to be visible, but it evidently acts as the coupling agent that binds antibody molecules together to form the various multisided structures. The magnification is about 275,000 diameters.

F R A G M E N T   A N T I G E N   B I N D I N G   (Fab)

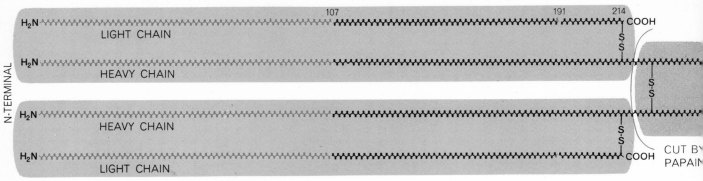
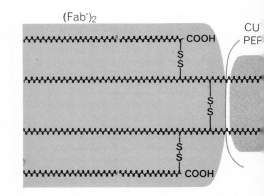

IMMUNOGLOBULIN GAMMA, the chief class of antibody, is a protein molecule consisting of four polypeptide chains held together by disulfide (S—S) bonds. The two light chains are identical, as are the two heavy chains. Depending on the source, the light chains contain from about 210 to 230 amino acid units; the heavy chains vary from about 420 to 440 units. Thus the lengths, the spacing between disulfide bonds and enzyme cleavage points shown here are approximate. The enzyme papain splits the molecule into three fragments (*above*): a fragment that forms crystals (F*c*) and two fragments (F*ab*) that do not crystallize but contain the antigen binding sites. Approximately half of each F*ab* fragment (*color*) is variable in amino acid composition. Site 191 is genetically variable. When immunoglobulin gamma is split by the enzyme pepsin (*right*), the F*ab* fragments remain bonded together (F*ab'*)₂ because the cleavage occurs on the other side of the central disulfide bond.

or with other substances whose structure is closely related.

Numerous different antibodies can be formed. Although an individual animal may respond poorly, or perhaps not at all, to a particular antigen, there is no known limit to the number of specific antibodies that one species, for example the rabbit, can synthesize. Conceptually there is a great difference between the capability of one species to synthesize a very large but limited number of antibodies and the capacity to synthesize an infinite number, but an experimental decision as to which is correct is not possible at present.

All antibodies are found in a group of related serum proteins known as immunoglobulins. The challenge to the protein chemist lies in the fact that antibody molecules are surprisingly similar even though they possess an enormous range of specific combining power. Although it is clear that there must be significant differences among antibodies, no chemical or physical property has yet been found that can distinguish between two antibody molecules: one able to combine specifically, say, with an aromatic compound such as a benzene derivative and the other with a sugar, although the benzene compound and the sugar have no common structural features. Antibodies of quite unrelated specificity appear to be identical,

within the limits of present experimental techniques, except, of course, in their specific combination with antigen.

An antibody can be isolated from the serum of an immunized animal only by using the special property of allowing it to combine with the antigen, freeing the complex from the other serum proteins and then dissociating and separating the antibody and antigen. This can be done by allowing a precipitate to form, washing the precipitate well with salt solution and then suspending the precipitate in weak acid. Under these

conditions the antibody-antigen precipitate will dissolve and dissociate, and the antibody and antigen can be separated from each other to yield the purified antibody. As we shall see, however, even this purified material usually contains a variety of antibody molecules that differ slightly in their molecular structure.

If an animal has not been immunized, it will still have a good concentration of immunoglobulin in its blood, usually about 1 percent by weight. This material is believed to be made up of many thousands of different antibodies

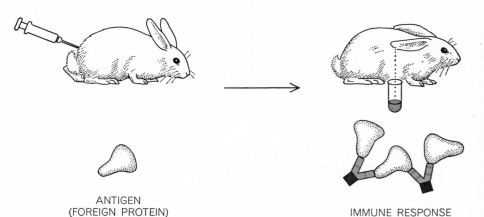

MIXTURE OF SIMILAR ANTIBODIES can be produced by injecting a rabbit or other animal with a purified antigen, typically a large protein of foreign origin. In response the animal produces antibodies, primarily immunoglobulin gamma, that are able to bind specifically to the antigen. Evidently a given antigen provides many different binding sites, thus giving rise to many different antibody molecules. If blood is removed from the animal

FRAGMENT CRYSTALLINE (Fc)

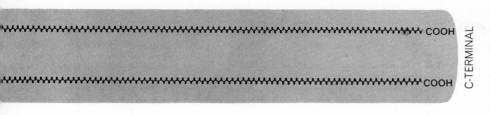

C-TERMINAL

COOH

COOH

Fc

carbohydrate content and amino acid analysis. Antibodies of any specificity can be found in any of the classes; hence there is no correlation between class and specificity. The class present in the largest amounts in the blood and the most easily isolated is called immunoglobulin gamma. Since most of the work has been done with this material I shall limit my discussion to it.

Immunoglobulin gamma has a molecular weight of about 150,000, corresponding to some 23,000 atoms, of which a carbohydrate fraction forms no more than 2 or 3 percent. Chemical studies have shown that the immunoglobulin gamma molecule is built up of four polypeptide chains, which, as in all proteins, are formed from strings of amino acids joined to one another through peptide bonds. The four chains are paired so that the molecule consists of two identical halves, each consisting of one long, or heavy, chain and one short, or light, chain. The four chains are held to one another by the disulfide bonds of the amino acid cystine [see illustration at top of these two pages]. If the disulfide bonds are split, the heavy and light chains are still bound to each other. If, however, they are put in an acid solution or one containing a substance such as urea, they dissociate and can be separated by their difference in size.

Immunoglobulin gamma molecules can also be split by proteolytic enzymes such as papain, which breaks the molecule into three pieces of about equal size. Two, known as Fab (for "fragment antigen binding"), appear to be identical, and the third, known as Fc (fragment crystalline), is quite different. Fab is so named because it will still combine with the antigen although it will not pre-

The immunoglobulins can be isolated from serum by the usual methods of protein separation. Hence the protein chemist has available for study two general kinds of immunoglobulin fraction: a complex mixture of many antibodies and purified antibodies that have been isolated by virtue of their specific affinity for the antigen. It would seem to be a relatively straightforward task, after the great progress made in the techniques of protein chemistry in recent years, to carry out detailed studies of such material and pinpoint the differences. Clearly structural differences responsible for the specific combining power of antibodies must exist among them and should become apparent.

Major difficulties have arisen, however, because the immunoglobulins have been found to be a very complex mixture of molecules and the complexity is not necessarily due to the presence of the many different kinds of antibody. One difficulty is that there are three main classes of immunoglobulins distinguished chemically from one another by size,

against microorganisms the animal has encountered during its lifetime or against other antigenic substances that accidentally entered its body. Evidence that this view is correct comes from experiments in which small animals have been born and raised in an entirely germ-free environment. Under these conditions the immunoglobulin content of the blood is much lower, perhaps only 10 percent of the immunoglobulin in the blood of a normal animal, suggesting that mild infections are the main source of antigens.

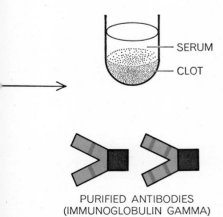

SERUM

CLOT

PURIFIED ANTIBODIES
(IMMUNOGLOBULIN GAMMA)

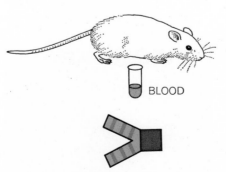

BLOOD

MYELOMA PROTEIN
(IMMUNOGLOBULIN GAMMA)

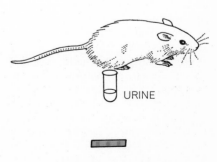

URINE

BENCE-JONES PROTEIN
(LIGHT CHAIN OF
IMMUNOGLOBULIN GAMMA)

and allowed to coagulate, antibodies can be isolated from the serum fraction. Even when purified by recombination with the original antigen, immunoglobulin gamma molecules produced in this way vary slightly.

IDENTICAL ANTIBODY-LIKE MOLECULES are produced in large numbers by mice and humans who suffer from myelomatosis, a cancer of the cells that synthesize immunoglobulin. These abnormal immunoglobulins, all alike, can be isolated from the animal's blood (left). Often an abnormal protein also appears in the urine (right). Called a Bence-Jones protein, it seems to be the light chain of the abnormal immunoglobulin.

cipitate with it. Each *Fab* fragment carries one combining site; thus the two fragments together account for the two combining sites that each antibody molecule had been deduced to possess. The F*c* fragment prepared from rabbit immunoglobulin gamma crystallizes readily, but neither the F*ab* fragments nor the whole molecule has ever been crystallized.

Since crystals form easily only from identical molecules, it was guessed that the halves of the heavy chain that comprise the F*c* fragment are probably the same in all molecules and that the complexity is mainly in the F*ab* fragments where the combining sites are found. The enzyme papain, which causes the split into three pieces, can hydrolyze a

great variety of peptide bonds, and yet only a few in the middle of the heavy chain are in fact split; it looks as if in the F*ab* and F*c* fragments the peptide chains are tightly coiled in such a way that the enzyme cannot gain access. This suggests a picture in which three compact parts of the molecule are joined by a short flexible section near the middle of the heavy chain.

The full structure of a protein molecule showing the arrangement in space of the peptide chains and the positioning of the amino acids along them can at present only be achieved by X-ray crystallography. Such work has been started at Johns Hopkins University with the F*c* fragment. Electron microscopy, however, can provide much information about the shape of protein molecules, and successful electron microscope studies have been made recently with rabbit antibodies. When the antibodies are free, no clear pictures are obtained, which suggests that the molecules have a loose structure that is without definite shape. If they are combined with antigen, however, good pictures can be made. Michael Green and Robin Valentine of the National Institute for Medical Research in London prepared antibodies in rabbits that would combine with a benzene derivative known as a dinitrophenyl group. This can be done, as Karl Landsteiner showed many years ago, by injecting into the rabbit a protein on which dinitrophenyl groups have been substituted. Antibodies are formed, some of which combine specifically with the substituent dinitrophenyl coupled onto other proteins or into smaller molecules.

Green and Valentine investigated the smallest compound carrying two dinitrophenyl groups that would cross-link two or more antibody molecules. This proved to be an eight-carbon chain with a dinitrophenyl group at each end. This material does not form a precipitate with antibody, but with the electron microscope one can see ringlike structures that appear to contain three to five antibody molecules [*see illustrations on page 283 and at left*]. The small antigen molecule is not visible. The three-component structure is believed to consist of three antibody molecules linked by three molecules of invisible antigen. The lumps protruding from the corners are thought to be F*c* fragments. This interpretation is supported by using the proteolytic enzyme pepsin to digest off the F*c* fragment, leaving two F*ab* molecules held together by a disulfide bond and referred to as (F*ab'*)₂. When these (F*ab'*)₂ molecules are combined

ANTIBODY-ANTIGEN COMPLEX seen in electron micrographs *(below and page 283)* is thought to have this triangular structure. Below it, drawn to a large scale, is the synthetic antigen: an eight-carbon chain with a dinitrophenyl group at each end. Three such antigen molecules appear able to bind together three immunoglobulin gamma molecules.

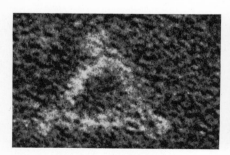 

EFFECT OF PEPSIN COMPLEX is demonstrated in electron micrographs taken by Green and Valentine. In the normal complex formed by immunoglobulin gamma and the dinitrophenyl compound *(left)* a typical triangular structure contains a small lobe, or lump, at each corner, which is thought to be the F*c* part of the immunoglobulin molecule. If the antibody is first treated with pepsin, which splits off the F*c* fragment, the remaining (F*ab'*)₂ molecule still reacts with the antigen but the corner lobes are missing *(right)*.

with antigen, rings are formed as before, but the lumps at the corners are now gone, confirming the idea that they were indeed the F*c* part of the molecule.

Since most interest centers on the antibody combining site, the next problem to solve is whether the site is to be found in the light chain, which is entirely in the F*ab* fragment, or in the half of the heavy chain that is also present, or whether the site is formed by both chains together. It has not been possible to get a clear answer to this problem because the chains cannot be separated except in acid or urea solutions; this causes a partial loss of the affinity for antigen, which is not recovered even after the acid or urea is removed. Present evidence suggests that the heavy chain is the most important but that the light chain plays a role. This may be because it actually forms a part of the site or because it helps to stabilize the shape that the heavy chain assumes and hence plays a secondary role that may be only partially specific.

In any case, the field is clear for a direct attempt at comparative studies of the chemical structure of the light chain as well as of the half of the heavy chain that lies in the F*ab* part of the molecule. The shape and hence the specificity of the combining site must depend on the configuration of the peptide chains of the F*ab* fragment; this is believed to be determined only by the sequence of the different amino acids in the chain. Therefore it is reasonable to expect that if the amino acid sequence is worked out for the F*ab* half of the heavy chain and perhaps also for the light chain, then in some sections sequences will be found that determine the configuration of the combining site and that will be characteristic for each antibody specificity. Attempts to carry out such sequence studies, however, seemed unattractive because of convincing evidence that all preparations of immunoglobulin gamma—even samples of purified antibodies obtained by precipitation with a specific antigen—were actually mixtures of many slightly different molecules with presumably different amino acid sequences.

Although the complexity of immunoglobulin gamma (and of the other classes of immunoglobulins) has presented investigators with a most difficult puzzle, considerable progress has now been made in solving much of it [*see illustration on this page*]. First, there are two kinds of light chain, named kappa and lambda, but in any one molecule both light chains are of the same type.

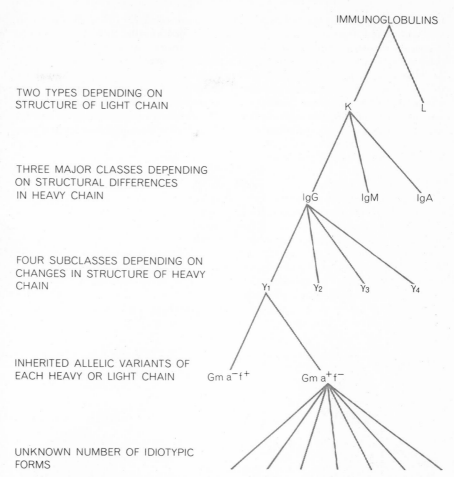

IMMUNOGLOBULINS

TWO TYPES DEPENDING ON STRUCTURE OF LIGHT CHAIN

K   L

THREE MAJOR CLASSES DEPENDING ON STRUCTURAL DIFFERENCES IN HEAVY CHAIN

IgG   IgM   IgA

FOUR SUBCLASSES DEPENDING ON CHANGES IN STRUCTURE OF HEAVY CHAIN

Y₁   Y₂   Y₃   Y₄

INHERITED ALLELIC VARIANTS OF EACH HEAVY OR LIGHT CHAIN

Gm a⁻f⁺   Gm a⁺f⁻

UNKNOWN NUMBER OF IDIOTYPIC FORMS

SUBDIVISIONS OF HUMAN IMMUNOGLOBULIN presented investigators with a difficult problem to unravel. For simplicity, subdivisions are shown for only one branch at each level. The abbreviation "*IgG*" stands for immunoglobulin gamma, the antibody found in largest amounts and the one most easily isolated. Idiotypic forms are apparently unique to individual animals and may involve alterations in both the light and the heavy chains.

The molecules containing kappa chains are known as *K* type and those with lambda chains as *L* type. Then in some species (probably in all) the immunoglobulin gamma class contains several subclasses; four have been identified in human gamma globulin. The subclasses differ in their heavy chains, which carry not only the characteristic features of the class but also small differences that distinguish the subclasses. In any one individual, molecules will be found of both *K* and *L* type, and they belong to all the subclasses. In addition each of the kinds of chain shows differences, known as allelic forms, that are inherited according to Mendelian principles. In an individual homozygous for this property only one allelic form of, say, the kappa chain will be present, but in a heterozygous individual there will be two forms of the kappa chain. It scarcely need be stressed that all these phenomena lead to a very complex mixture of molecules of immunoglobulin gamma in the serum of any

individual. Yet there is still another kind of complexity termed idiotypic. In certain circumstances it is possible for an animal to synthesize antibody molecules that are unique to itself, distinct from other antibody molecules of the same specificity in other individuals of the same species—and distinct from all other immunoglobulins in its own blood.

Perhaps the most remarkable aspect of all of this is that the complexity seems to bear no relation to the structure of the antibody combining site. As far as we know at present, any antibody specificity may be found on any of these many different kinds of molecule.

All such variations are likely to be based on differences in amino acid sequence, and already some differences relating to subclass and allelic changes have been identified. The structural differences are so small, however, that it is not possible to separate out single kinds of molecule by the methods available for the fractionation of proteins.

Thus it was a great step forward when it was recognized that in certain forms of cancer, immunoglobulin molecules of apparently a single variety appear in the blood. Such immunoglobulins have only one type of light chain and one subclass of heavy chain, and each chain belongs to one or the other allelic form. As far as we know each chain has only one amino acid sequence and therefore belongs to only one idiotypic form.

The disease responsible for this unique production of antibody is known as myelomatosis. Observed in both mice and men, it is a cancer of the cells that synthesize immunoglobulin, often those in the bone marrow. Apparently a single cell, one of the great number that synthesize immunoglobulins, starts to divide rapidly and leads to an excessive production of a single kind of immunoglobulin. This provides evidence, incidentally, that the complexity of immunoglobulin molecules arises from their synthesis by many different kinds of cells. These abnormal immunoglobulins are known as myeloma proteins. Because they are often present in the blood in a concentration several times higher than all the other immunoglobulins together, they can be isolated rather easily.

Moreover, in about half of all myeloma patients an abnormal protein appears in the urine in large amounts. This substance was first observed by Henry Bence-Jones at Guy's Hospital in London in 1847 and has been known ever since as Bence-Jones protein. Its nature, however, was not recognized until five years ago, when Gerald M. Edelman and J. A. Gally of Rockefeller University and independently Frank W. Putnam of the University of Florida showed that Bence-Jones protein is probably identical with the light chains of the myeloma protein in the serum of the same patient. Because Bence-Jones proteins can be obtained easily, without any inconvenience to the patient, they were the first materials used for amino-acid-sequence studies.

Although complete sequences have been worked out for only two Bence-Jones proteins in the mouse and only three human Bence-Jones proteins, perhaps 20 more have been partially analyzed. A remarkable fact has emerged. It seems that all Bence-Jones proteins of the same type have exactly the same sequence of amino acids in the half of the molecule that ends in the chemical group COOH (hence known as the C-terminal half) but show marked variation in the half that ends in the group

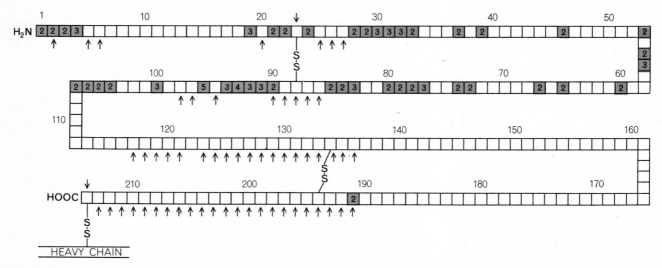

IMMUNOGLOBULIN LIGHT CHAIN, represented by analyses of human Bence-Jones proteins of the *K* type, has 214 amino acid units. Colored squares show where amino acids have been found to vary from one protein to another; blank squares show where no variation has yet been found. Numbers in the squares indicate how many different amino acids have been identified so far at a given site. Arrows mark positions where a particular amino acid has been found in at least five different proteins. Complete amino acid sequences are now known for three human Bence-Jones proteins and partial sequences for about 20 others. All variations occur in the first half of the chain with one exception, the variation at position 191. This is related to the allelic, or inherited, character of light *K* chains, hence differs from the alterations in the variable half of the chain. The diagram is based on one recently published by S. Cohen of Guy's Hospital Medical School in London and C. Milstein of the Laboratory of Molecular Biology in Cambridge.

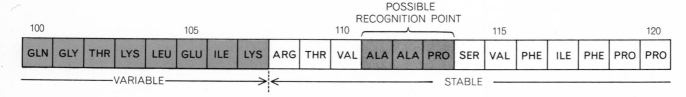

ALA	ALANINE	LYS	LYSINE
ARG	ARGININE	PHE	PHENYL-
GLN	GLUTAMINE		ALANINE
GLU	GLUTAMIC ACID	PRO	PROLINE
GLY	GLYCINE	SER	SERINE
ILE	ISOLEUCINE	THR	THREONINE
LEU	LEUCINE	VAL	VALINE

MIDDLE PART OF LIGHT CHAIN, as determined for one human Bence-Jones protein (*K* type), includes the amino acids at positions 111, 112 and 113 that are common to both *K*- and *L*-type Bence-Jones proteins of humans and to *K*-type Bence-Jones proteins of mice. It has been suggested that the section of the gene coding for this sequence may provide a special "recognition point" for the joining of two different genes responsible for the variable and stable sections of the light chain or, possibly, for bringing into play a mechanism to change the amino acid sequence in the variable section (*see illustration on page 290*).

NH$_2$ (the N-terminal half). Of 107 amino acid positions in this half, at least 40 have been found to vary. No two Bence-Jones proteins have yet been found to be identical in the N-terminal half, so that the possibility of molecular variation is clearly great. Given the possibility of variation at 40 sites and supposing that only two different amino acids can occupy these sites, it would be possible to construct 2^{40}, or more than 10 billion, different sequences. Actually as many as five different amino acids have been found to occupy one of the variable sites [*see upper illustration on opposite page*].

The amino acid sequence studies of the heavy chain are less advanced than those with the Bence-Jones proteins because the material is more difficult to obtain and is more than twice the length. Results with the heavy chain of two human myeloma proteins, however, have shown them to have many differences in sequence for more than 100 amino acids from the N-terminal end, whereas the remainder of the chain appears to be identical in both cases. Accordingly it seems certain that the heavy chains will show the same phenomena as the light chains; it is possible that the length of the variable section in both chains will be similar.

Inasmuch as both variable sections are in the F*ab* fragment of the molecule it seems obvious that these sections must participate in creating the many different antibody combining sites. All the work discussed here has been done with myeloma proteins, and since each has a single amino acid sequence in both heavy and light chains, it would follow that each will be a specific antibody against one of an untold number of different antigenic sites. The chances, therefore, of finding a myeloma protein in which antibody specificity is directed to a known, well-defined antigenic site seemed small. Nevertheless, several myeloma proteins have recently been found to possess antibody-like activity against known antigens. A comparison of the sequences of their heavy and light chains may give a lead as to where the combining site is located.

It has been believed with good reason that myeloma proteins are typical of normal molecules of immunoglobulin gamma, each being a homogeneous example of the many different forms present. It thus seemed likely that any attempt to determine the amino acid sequence of immunoglobulin gamma from a normal animal would be impossible, especially in the variable region that is

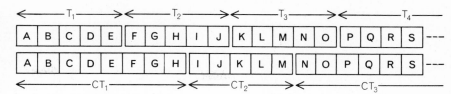

DETERMINATION OF AMINO ACID SEQUENCE in the polypeptide chains of proteins depends on the use of enzymes that cleave the chains into short fragments next to particular amino acids. The sequence in the resulting fragments can then be established. Thus trypsin might split a chain into fragments T_1, T_2, T_3 and T_4. Another enzyme, chymotrypsin, might split the same chain into fragments CT_1, CT_2 and CT_3. Since these fragments must overlap one can establish their order unequivocally and thereby the sequence of the entire chain.

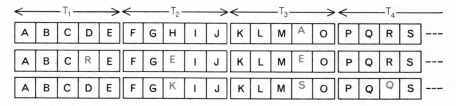

IMMUNOGLOBULIN SEQUENCE should be amenable to analysis even though a particular antibody sample might contain a variety of slightly different molecules. Slight variations at certain positions (*color*) should not prevent the ordering of similar fragments.

of particular interest. One would expect normal immunoglobulin gamma to be a mixture of many thousands of different molecules, each with a different sequence in the variable region.

Amino acid sequences of polypeptide chains are found by using enzymes to break the chains into pieces from 10 to 20 amino acids long. It is then possible to work out the sequence of each piece. By using different enzymes the original chain can be broken at different places, with the result that some pieces overlap. This provides enough clues for the whole sequence to be put together, rather like a one-dimensional jigsaw puzzle [*see upper illustration above*]. When the protein is pure, there is only one order of amino acids possible, and all the sequences of the individual fragments will fit into it.

One can see that if this method were attempted with a protein that was in fact a mixture of many slightly different proteins, each with a different sequence, a hopelessly confusing picture would probably result. The work with the myeloma protein suggested, however, that there would be a constant part as well as a variable part, and it seemed worthwhile to see what progress could be made in determining at least the constant part. Work at Duke University showed that the whole of the F*c* section of the heavy chain of normal rabbit immunoglobulin gamma gave a coherent sequence and was therefore part of the stable section, as had been expected. Recent work in our laboratory has now

shown that the coherence continues well into the other half of the heavy chain. Although the work is far from complete, it seems possible that a full sequence will be established right through the entire heavy chain. Variations have been picked up in a number of positions and no doubt many more will be found, but the results are not completely confusing, as might have been expected if normal immunoglobulin gamma were a mixture of many thousands of myeloma proteins, each with substantially different sequences in the variable parts of the chain. The conflict between the results with the myeloma proteins and the recent results with normal rabbit immunoglobulin may be more apparent than real.

What does all this mean in terms of the structure of antibodies and their power to combine specifically with antigens? The phenomenon of a variable section and a stable section in both heavy and light chains is extraordinary and is unique to immunoglobulins; the variable section is in the part of the molecule known to contain the combining site. It therefore seems certain that this must be the basis of the specific configuration of the combining site.

It should be emphasized that all this work is very incomplete. In another year or so it will undoubtedly be much easier to see just how different one myeloma protein is from another in both the heavy and the light chains. It may be that the differences between any two

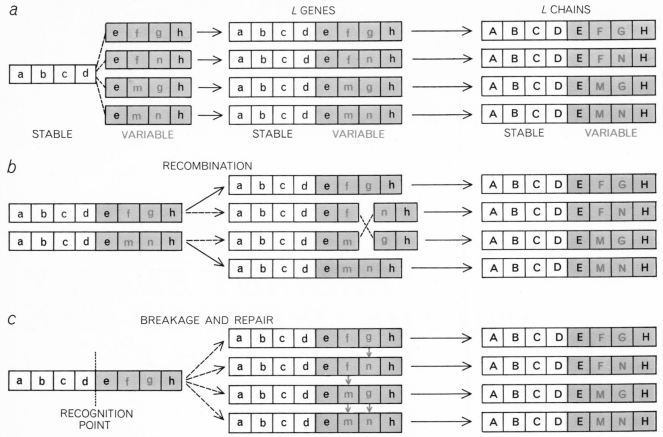

VARIABILITY OF IMMUNOGLOBULIN MOLECULES has been explained by three principal hypotheses. The simplest (a) suggests that one gene codes for the stable section of each chain and that a great number, perhaps hundreds of thousands, code for the variable section. A second idea (b) is that several genes are divided into stable and variable sections and that the latter inter-change parts during cell division. A third proposal (c) suggests that there may be a recognition point in the gene (see lower il-lustration on page 288) and that an enzyme partially splits, or breaks, the gene on the variable side of that point. When repaired by other enzymes (arrows), mistakes are made, thus giving rise to many different amino acid sequences in the antibody molecule.

will on the average be small, so that for a mixture of many molecules the amino acid in any one position will be common to 80 or 90 percent of the molecules [see lower illustration on page 289]. Presumably this explains how it is possible to find a comprehensible amino acid sequence in normal immunoglobulin gamma.

It may also be, however, that myeloma proteins are not quite typical of normal antibodies. Because they are the result of a disease they may exaggerate a normal phenomenon. Although they are invaluable in drawing attention to a fundamental mechanism, they may mislead us by exhibiting greater variability than is present in normal immunoglobulin gamma.

Whatever the answer, the existence of a stable section and a variable section, which has been shown so clearly in the Bence-Jones proteins and which also occurs in the heavy chains, is a remarkable phenomenon. The mechanism of its biological origin has aroused intense interest. Many hypotheses have been put forward, but there are perhaps three principal ones [see illustration above].

A straightforward mechanism would be to have a single gene coding for each stable section in the antibody molecule and as many genes as necessary (tens of thousands or hundreds of thousands) coding for the variable sections. The cell would also be provided with a means for fusing the product of the two kinds of gene to construct the complete immunoglobulin molecule. (In this as in the other suggestions, the presence of an antigen would somehow trigger production of the appropriate antibody.)

A second proposal invokes the concept of genetic recombination, which involves the exchange of parts of genes. One can imagine several genes that are divided into a stable portion and a variable portion. During cell division, when genes are pairing and duplicating, the variable portion would interchange sections, thereby giving rise to many different genes capable of coding the variable parts of the antibody molecule.

The third suggestion visualizes that the gene for, say, the light chain may contain a "recognition point" midway in its structure [see lower illustration on page 288]. This might provide a specific attachment site for an enzyme that can split the nucleic acid of the gene only on the side coding for the variable section. When the broken portion is repaired by other enzymes, mistakes are made, thereby giving rise to many different sequences of nucleotides—the nucleic acid building blocks that embody the genetic message. These differences are then translated into different amino acid sequences in the variable portion of the antibody molecule.

There is no clear answer as to which methods, if any or all, are the operative mechanisms, but a continuation of the structural studies may provide a clearer understanding. When this understanding is attained, it should lead to ideas about how to change, stimulate or suppress immune reactions as medical practice requires and therefore should be of great practical value as well as solving one of the most intriguing problems in biology.

V

RADIANT ENERGY
AND THE ORIGIN OF LIFE

Molecular Evolution

*I*n the previous sections of this book we have surveyed many aspects of the molecular architecture and mode of operation of the living cell. In this final section the most basic question of all will be treated: How did life begin?

Although the detailed processes involved in the formation of our planet are still subject to speculation, it is generally agreed that the earth was molten at an early stage in its history. Obviously no living thing could exist at such extreme temperatures, and so the planet was sterile. When it had cooled sufficiently, life became possible and it eventually appeared. It was once suggested that present-day organisms arose from an "infection" of the sterile earth by microorganisms carried here from some other celestial body. This is no solution to the problem of the origin of life, for this hypothesis merely removes the problem to another, unknown planet. Furthermore, it is now realized that it would have been virtually impossible even for a bacterial spore to survive the radiation received during a long trip through space.

Not only was the primitive earth sterile, but it was composed of only the simplest inorganic molecules and its early atmosphere contained no oxygen. Oxygen, hydrogen, nitrogen, and carbon are the most abundant and essential elements found in all forms of life. Cells are composed of relatively complex organic molecules—such as the amino acids, sugars, and the purine and pyrimidine bases of the nucleic acids—that contain these elements. A long period of "chemical evolution," during which these essential molecules were formed, must have preceded the origin of anything we might have designated as alive. It has been found that most of these molecules are formed in mixtures of water vapor, ammonia, methane, and other simple substances upon exposure to ultraviolet light and other forms of radiation. Such photochemical reactions would have occurred on the surface of the primitive earth because at that time ultraviolet light from the sun was not blocked by the layer of ozone that now exists in our upper atmosphere. (The ozone layer is derived photochemically from the oxygen given off by green plants.) Thus, radiant energy from the sun not only sustains the life now present on earth but was probably essential for the origin of life.

This final section begins with an article by George Wald, titled "Life and Light," in which he describes the intimate and essential connection between sunlight and life. This vital coupling between the earth and the sun resides primarily in the ultimate dependence of all living things on nutrient materials whose synthesis (photosynthesis) by green plants requires sunlight as an energy source. The wavelengths of light involved in most of the photochemical reactions required for chemical evolution and photosynthesis correspond closely to the most abundant wavelengths emitted by the sun. Thus, it is not really surprising that life has evolved in our solar system, because the photochemical reactions necessary for life are precisely those that depend upon the predominant wavelengths emitted by the sun. The radiation from an X-ray star might be deficient in the essential ultraviolet and visible regions of the spectrum that both initiate chemical evolution and sustain life once it is established.

No one knows how the first primitive organisms arose in the dilute solution of organic molecules that was produced by the action of sunlight on the earth's watery surface. Among the earliest organisms, plant-like forms developed that were able to use sunlight as an energy source for their biochemical activities. In "The Role of Chlorophyll in Photosynthesis," Eugene I. Rabinowitch and Govindjee describe the molecular basis of the process of photosynthesis as it now occurs in green plants and certain microorganisms. The process depends on the unique photochemical properties of a certain class of pigment molecule, chlorophyll being the most important example of this class.

Primitive photosynthetic microorganisms were still many steps away from the complex animal species that we see around us today. After a billion years of chemical evolution culminated in the appearance of the first organisms, there ensued the present epoch of Darwinian evolution that has persisted now for about three billion years. More complex organisms developed that were capable of exploiting the various sources of nutrient materials that had become available, partly because of the progress of life itself. (It is interesting to note that once genuine organisms have arisen, subsequent, or independent, "origins of life" may be impossible: for the first organisms would tend to consume the "organic soup" in which they themselves were formed.) The increase of more and more kinds of evolving forms required the appearance of an increasing variety of proteins. The study of evolutionary changes in protein structure is only now beginning, as a result of the advances in macromolecular chemistry described in earlier sections of this volume. Here we offer one example of this area of study: in "The Evolution of Hemoglobin," Emile Zuckerkandl describes the differences in the amino acid sequences of hemoglobin obtained from several different animals. On the basis of these differences, and our knowledge of the genetic code, it is possible to deduce evolutionary relations among the animals studied. The studies by Zuckerkandl and others provide a molecular basis for the phylogenetic relations deduced by classical biologists from the comparative studies of the morphology and embryology of these same species. The molecular approach to the study of evolution is still in its infancy, but it is clear that definitive answers to our questions about evolution will be found in the similarities among proteins and in homologies among nucleic acid base sequences in the many species that now inhabit the earth.

Geoffrey Eglinton and Melvin Calvin discuss in "Chemical Fossils" some of the chemical studies that should ultimately put current speculations as to the origin of life on a more certain observational basis.

We conclude our collection with another article by George Wald, "The Origin of Life," in which he reviews the philosophical controversy that has long surrounded studies on the origin of life. In it he also describes the classic experiment of Stanley Miller and Harold Urey in which amino acids were first synthesized from simple inorganic molecules in a simulated prebiotic environment. The present generally accepted view of the origin of life is none other than the old theory of "spontaneous generation" in a modern guise. But, as Wald notes, today's version attributes the beginning of life to perfectly natural phenomena. You may notice that the last micrograph in Wald's article is of the protein collagen; and since we began with collagen in the first article of this book, it is probably an appropriate place to end.

30 | Life and Light

GEORGE WALD · October 1959

All life on this planet runs on sunlight, that is, on photosynthesis performed by plants. In this process light supplies the energy to make the organic molecules of which all living things are principally composed. Those plants and animals which are incapable of photosynthesis live as parasites on photosynthetic plants. But light—that form of radiant energy which is visible to the human eye—comprises only a narrow band in the spectrum of the radiant energy that pervades the universe. From gamma rays, which may be only one ten-billionth of a centimeter long, the wavelengths of electromagnetic radiation stretch through the enormous range of 10^{16}—10,000 million million times—up to radio waves, which may be miles in length. The portion of this spectrum that is visible to man is mainly contained between the wavelengths 380 to 760 millimicrons (a millimicron is ten millionths of a centimeter). By using very intense artificial sources one can stretch the limits of human vision somewhat more widely: from about 310 to 1,050 millimicrons. The remarkable fact is that, lying altogether within this slightly wider range of wavelengths, and mainly enclosed between 380 and 760 millimicrons, we also find the vision of all other animals, the bending of plants toward light, the oriented movements of animals toward or away from light and, most important, all types of photosynthesis. This is the domain of photobiology.

Why these wavelengths rather than others? I believe that this choice is dictated by intrinsic factors which involve the general role of energy in chemical reactions, the special role that light energy plays in photochemical reactions, and the nature of the molecules that mediate the utilization of light by living organisms. It is not merely a tautology to say that photobiology requires the particular range of wavelengths we call light. This statement must be as applicable everywhere in the universe as here. Now that many of us are convinced that life exists in many places in the universe (it is hard to see how to avoid this conclusion), we have good reason to believe that everywhere we should find photobiology restricted to about the same range of wavelengths. What sets this range ultimately is not its availability, but its suitability to perform the tasks demanded of it. There cannot be a planet on which photosynthesis or vision occurs in the far infrared or far ultraviolet, because these radiations are not appropriate to perform these functions. It is not the range of available radiation that sets the photobiological domain, but rather the availability of the proper range of wavelengths that decides whether living organisms can develop and light can act upon them in useful ways.

We characterize light by its wave motion, identifying the regions of the spectrum by wavelength or frequency [see illustration at top of pages 296 and 297]. But in its interactions with matter—its absorption or emission by atoms and molecules—light also acts as though it were composed of small packets of energy called quanta or photons. These are in fact a class of ultimate particles, like protons and electrons, though they have no electric charge and very little mass. Each photon has the energy content: $E = hc/\lambda$, in which h is Planck's universal constant of action (1.58 $\times$ 10^{-34} calorie seconds), c is the velocity of light (3 $\times$ 10^{10} centimeters per second in empty space) and λ is the wavelength. Thus, while the intensity of light is the rate of delivery of photons, the work that a single photon can do (its energy content) is inversely proportional to its wavelength. With the change in the energy of photons, from one end of the electromagnetic spectrum to the other, their effects upon matter vary widely. For this reason photons of different wavelengths require different instruments to detect them, and the spectrum is divided arbitrarily on this basis into regions called by different names.

In the realm of chemistry the most useful unit for measuring the work that light can do is the "einstein," the energy content of one mole of quanta (6.02 $\times$ 10^{23} quanta). One molecule is excited to enter into a chemical reaction by absorbing one quantum of light; so one mole of molecules can be activated by absorbing one mole of quanta. The energy content of one einstein is equal to 2.854 $\times$ 10^7 gram calories, divided by the wavelength of the photon expressed in millimicrons. With this formula one can easily interconvert wavelength and energy content, and so assess the chemical effectiveness of electromagnetic radiations.

Energy enters chemical reactions in two separate ways: as energy of activation, exciting molecules to react; and as heat of reaction, the change in energy of the system resulting from the reaction. In a reacting system, at any moment, only the small fraction of "hot" molecules react that possess energies equal to or greater than a threshold value called the energy of activation. In ordinary chemical reactions this energy is acquired in collisions with other molecules. In a photochemical reaction the energy of activation is supplied by light. Whether light also does work on the reaction is an entirely separate issue. Sometimes, as in photosynthesis, it does so; at other times, as probably in vision, it seems to do little or no work.

Almost all ordinary ("dark") chemical

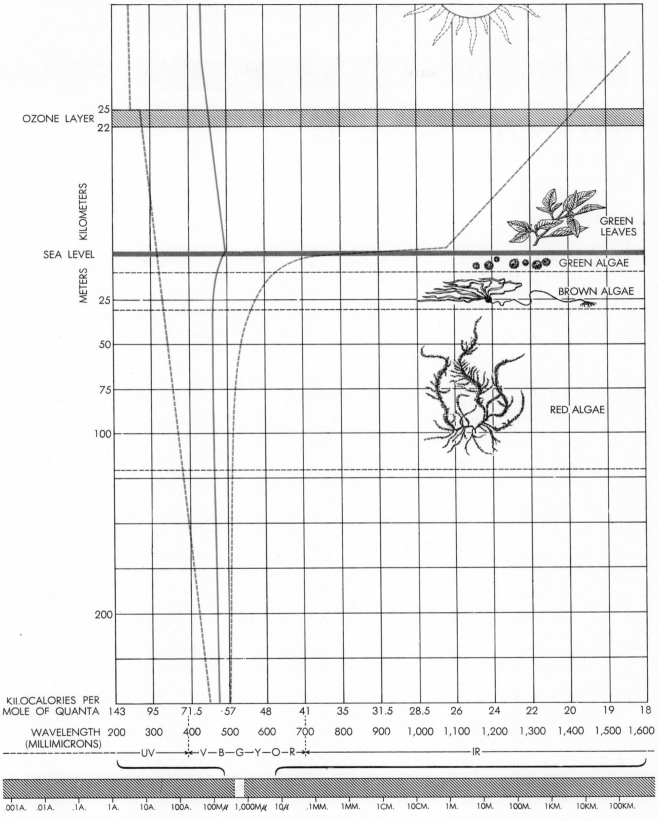

KILOCALORIES PER MOLE OF QUANTA	143	95	71.5	57	48	41	35	31.5	28.5	26	24	22	20	19	18
WAVELENGTH (MILLIMICRONS)	200	300	400	500	600	700	800	900	1,000	1,100	1,200	1,300	1,400	1,500	1,600

UV ——•←— V – B – G – Y – O – R —→•←———————————— IR ————————————

.001A. .01A. .1A. 1A. 10A. 100A. 100Mμ 1,000Mμ 10μ .1MM. 1MM. 1CM. 10CM. 1M. 10M. 100M. 1KM. 10KM. 100KM.

SPECTRUM OF SUNLIGHT at the earth's surface is narrowed by atmospheric absorption to the range of wavelengths (from 320 to 1,100 millimicrons) that are effective in photobiological processes. The sunlight reaching the domain of life in the sea is further narrowed by absorption in the sea water. The solid colored line locates the wavelengths of maximum intensity; the broken colored lines, the wavelength-boundaries within which 90 per cent of the solar energy is concentrated at each level in the atmosphere and ocean. The letters above the spectrum of wavelengths at bottom represent ultraviolet (UV), violet (V), blue (B), green (G), yellow (Y), orange (O), red (R) and infrared (IR). Other usages in the chart are explained in the illustration at top of next two pages.

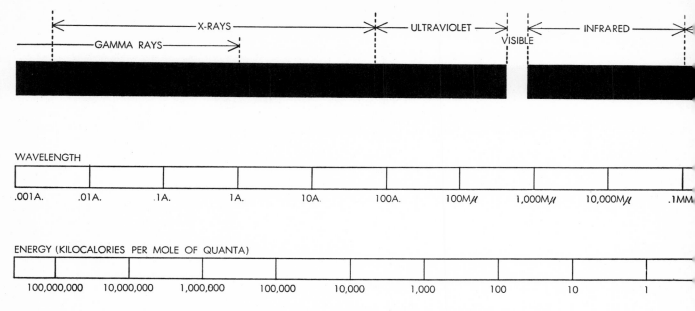

ELECTROMAGNETIC SPECTRUM is divided by man into qualitatively different regions (*top bar*), although the only difference between one kind of radiation and another is difference in wavelength (*middle bar*). From gamma rays, measured here in angstrom units, or hundred millionths of centimeter (A.), through light waves, measured here in millimicrons, or ten millionths of a centi-

reactions involve energies of activation between 15 and 65 kilogram calories (kilocalories) per mole. This is equivalent energetically to radiation of wavelengths between 1,900 and 440 millimicrons. The energies required to break single covalent bonds—a process that, through forming free radicals, can be a potent means of chemical activation—almost all fall between 40 and 90 kilocalories per mole, corresponding to radiation of wavelengths 710 to 320 millimicrons. Finally, there is the excitation of valence electrons to higher orbital levels that activates the reactions classified under the heading of photochemistry; this ordinarily involves energies of about 20 to 100 kilocalories per mole, corresponding to the absorption of light of wavelengths 1,430 to 280 millimicrons. Thus, however one approaches the activation of molecules for chemical reactions, one enters into a range of wavelengths that coincides approximately with the photobiological domain.

Actually photobiology is confined within slightly narrower limits than photochemistry. Radiations below 300 millimicrons (95 kilocalories per mole) are incompatible with the orderly existence of such large, highly organized molecules as proteins and nucleic acids. Both types of molecule consist of long chains of units bound to one another by primary valences. Both types of molecule, however, are held in the delicate and specific configurations upon which their functions in the cell depend by the relatively

weak forces of hydrogen-bonding and van der Waals attraction.

These forces, though individually weak, are cumulative. They hold a molecule together in a specific arrangement, like zippers. Radiation of wavelengths shorter than 300 millimicrons unzips them, opening up long sections of attachment, and permitting the orderly arrangement to become random and chaotic. Hence such radiations denature proteins and depolymerize nucleic acids, with disastrous consequences for the cell. For this reason about 300 millimicrons represents the lower limit of radiations capable of promoting photoreactions, yet compatible with life.

From this point of view we live upon a fortunate planet, because the radiation that is useful in promoting orderly chemical reactions comprises the great bulk of that of our sun. The commonly stated limit of human vision—400 to 700 millimicrons—already includes 41 per cent of the sun's radiant energy before it reaches our atmosphere, and 46 per cent of that arriving at the earth's surface. The entire photobiological range— 300 to 1,100 millimicrons—includes about 75 per cent of the sun's radiant energy, and about 83 per cent of that reaching the earth.

From about 320 to 1,100 millimicrons —virtually the photobiological range— the sun's radiation reaches us with little modification. The atmosphere directly above us causes an attenuation, mainly by scattering rather than absorption of

light, which is negligible at 700 millimicrons and increases exponentially toward shorter wavelengths, so that at 400 millimicrons the radiation is reduced by about half. In the upper atmosphere, however, a layer of ozone, at a height of 22 to 25 kilometers, begins to absorb the sun's radiation strongly at 320 millimicrons, and at 290 millimicrons forms a virtually opaque screen. It is only the presence of this layer of ozone, removing short-wave antibiotic radiation, that makes terrestrial life possible.

At long wavelengths the absorption bands of water vapor cut strongly into the region of solar radiation from 720 to 2,300 millimicrons. Beyond 2,300 millimicrons the infrared radiation is absorbed almost completely by the water vapor, carbon dioxide and ozone of the atmosphere. The sun's radiation, therefore, which starts toward the earth in a band reaching from about 225 to 3,200 millimicrons, with its maximum at about 475 millimicrons, is narrowed by passing through the atmosphere to a range of about 310 to 2,300 millimicrons at the earth's surface.

The differential absorption of light by water confines more sharply the range of illumination that reaches living organisms in the oceans and in fresh water. The infrared is removed almost immediately in the surface layers. Cutting into the visible spectrum, water attenuates very rapidly in succession the red, orange, yellow and green. The short-wavelength limit is also gradually drawn

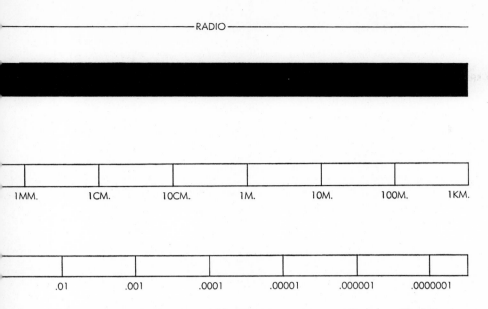

RADIO

1MM.	1CM.	10CM.	1M.	10M.	100M.	1KM.

.01	.001	.0001	.00001	.000001	.0000001

meter (Mμ), the waves range upward in length to the longest radio waves. The difference in wavelength is associated with a decisive difference in the energy conveyed by radiation at each wavelength. This energy content (*bottom bar*) is inversely proportional to wavelength.

---

matter once every 300 years. All the oxygen in our atmosphere, having been bound by various oxidation processes, is renewed by photosynthesis once in about 2,000 years.

In the original accumulation of this capital of carbon dioxide and oxygen, early in the history of the earth, it is thought that the process of photosynthesis itself profoundly modified the character of the earth's atmosphere and furnished the essential conditions for the efflorescence and evolution of life. Some of the oldest rock formations have lately been discovered to contain recognizable vestiges of living organisms, including what appear to have been photosynthetic forms. So for example iron gunflint cherts found in southern Ontario contain microscopic fossils, among which appear to be colonial forms of blue-green algae. These deposits are estimated to be at least 1.5 billion years old, so that if this identification can be accepted, photosynthesis has existed at least that long on this planet.

It now seems possible that the original development of the use of light by organisms, through the agency of chlorophyll pigments, may have involved not primarily the synthesis of new organic matter, but rather the provision of stores of chemical energy for the cell. A few years ago the process called photosynthetic phosphorylation was discovered, and has since been intensively explored,

in, so that the entire transmitted radiation is narrowed to a band centered at about 475 millimicrons, in the blue.

Photosynthesis

Each year the energy of sunlight, via the process of photosynthesis, fixes nearly 200 billion tons of carbon, taken up in the form of carbon dioxide, in more complex and useful organic molecules: about 20 billion tons on land and almost 10 times this quantity in the upper layers of the ocean. All the carbon dioxide in our atmosphere and all that is dissolved in the waters of the earth passes into this process, and is completely renewed by respiration and the decay of organic

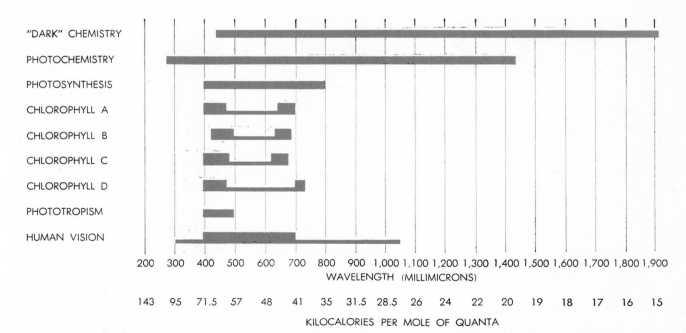

ENERGY CONTENT OF LIGHT is matched to the energy requirements of chemistry and photobiological processes and to the absorption spectra of photoreactive substances. The thicker segments of the bars opposite the chlorophylls indicate the regions of maximum absorption of light in each case, and the thicker segment in the bar opposite human vision indicates the normal boundaries.

mainly by Daniel I. Arnon of the University of California. By a still-unknown mechanism light forms the terminal high-energy phosphate bonds of adenosine triphosphate (ATP), which acts as a principal energy-carrier in the chemistry of the cell. One of the most interesting features of this process is that it is anaerobic; it neither requires nor produces oxygen. At a time when our atmosphere still lacked oxygen, this process could have become an efficient source of ATP. Among the many things ATP does in cells one of the most important is to supply the energy for organic syntheses. This direct trading of

the energy of sunlight for usable chemical energy in the form of ATP would therefore already have had as by-product the synthesis of organic structures. Mechanisms for performing such synthesis directly may have been a later development, leading to photosynthesis proper.

The essence of the photosynthetic process is the use of the energy of light to split water. The hydrogen from the water is used to reduce carbon dioxide or other organic molecules; and, in photosynthesis as performed by algae and higher plants, the oxygen is released into the atmosphere.

We owe our general view of photosynthesis in great part to the work of C. B. van Niel of the Hopkins Marine Station of Stanford University. Van Niel had examined the over-all reactions of photosynthesis in a variety of bacteria. Some of these organisms—green sulfur bacteria—require hydrogen sulfide to perform photosynthesis; van Niel discovered that in this case the net effect of photosynthesis is to split hydrogen sulfide, rendering the hydrogen available to reduce carbon dioxide to sugar, and liberating sulfur rather than oxygen. Still other bacteria—certain nonsulfur purple bacteria, for example—require organic

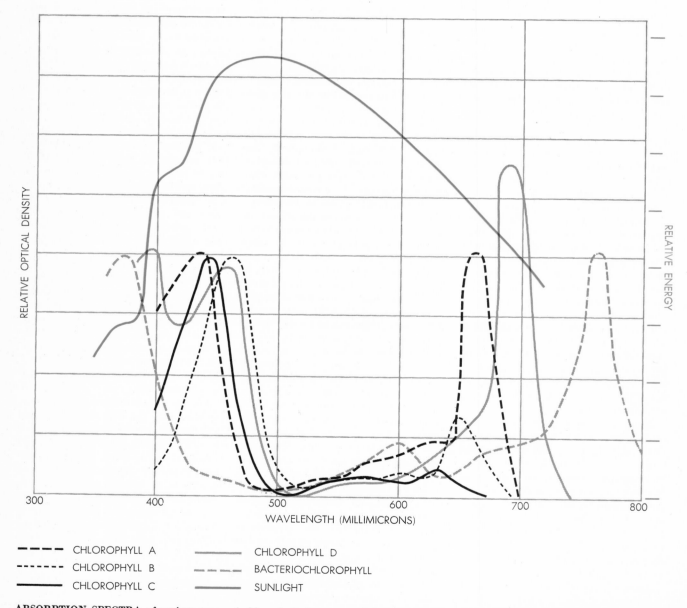

RELATIVE OPTICAL DENSITY

RELATIVE ENERGY

WAVELENGTH (MILLIMICRONS)

- - - - -   CHLOROPHYLL A
- - - - - -   CHLOROPHYLL B
————   CHLOROPHYLL C

————   CHLOROPHYLL D
- - - - -   BACTERIOCHLOROPHYLL
————   SUNLIGHT

ABSORPTION SPECTRA of various types of chlorophyll show the regions of the spectrum in which these substances absorb sunlight most effectively, measured on scale of relative optical density at left. Paradoxically the chlorophylls absorb best at the ends of the spectrum of sunlight, where energy, shown on scale at right, falls off steeply from the maximum around middle of the spectrum.

substances in photosynthesis. Here van Niel found that the effect of photosynthesis is to split hydrogen from these organic molecules to reduce carbon dioxide, liberating in this case neither oxygen nor sulfur but more highly oxidized states of the organic molecules themselves. Finally there are forms of purple bacteria that use molecular hydrogen directly in photosynthesis to reduce carbon dioxide, and liberate no by-product.

The efficiency of photosynthesis in algae and higher green plants is extraordinarily high—just how high is a matter of continuing controversy. The work of reducing one mole of carbon dioxide to the level of carbohydrate is in the neighborhood of 120 kilocalories. This energy requirement, though the exact figure is approximate, cannot be evaded through any choice of mechanism. Thanks to the selective absorption of the green chlorophyll pigment, light is made available for this process in quanta whose energy content is 41 or 42 kilocalories per mole, corresponding to quanta of red light of wavelength about 680 millimicrons. It is apparent, therefore, that several such quanta are required to reduce one molecule of carbon dioxide. If the energy of light were used with perfect efficiency, three quanta might perhaps suffice.

About 35 years ago the great German biochemist Otto Warburg performed experiments which appeared to show that in fact about four quanta of light of any wavelength in the visible spectrum are enough to reduce a molecule of carbon dioxide to carbohydrate. This might have meant an efficiency of about 75 per cent. Later a variety of workers in this country and elsewhere insisted that when such experiments are performed more critically, from eight to 12 quanta are required per molecule of carbon dioxide reduced. This discrepancy led to one of the bitterest controversies in modern science.

Many of us have grown tired of this controversy, which long ago bogged down in technical details and fruitless recriminations. I think it significant, however, that a number of recent, non-Warburgian, investigations have reported quantum demands of about six, and in at least one case the reported demand was as low as five. These numbers represent very high efficiencies (50 to 60 per cent), though not quite as high as Warburg prefers to set them.

Investigators have now turned from the question of efficiency to a more fruitful study of the specific uses to which quanta are put in photosynthesis. This is yielding estimates of quantum demand related to specific mechanisms rather than to controversial details of experimentation.

To reduce one molecule of carbon dioxide requires four hydrogen atoms and apparently three high-energy phosphate bonds of ATP. If we allow one quantum for each hydrogen atom (a point not universally conceded), that yields directly a quantum demand of four. If the ATP can be supplied in other ways, for example by respiration, four may be enough. If, however, light is needed also to supply ATP, by photosynthetic phosphorylation, then more quanta are needed; how many is not yet clear. Yet if one quantum were to generate one phosphate bond, the theoretical quantum-demand of photosynthesis, with all the energy supplied by light, would be four plus three, or seven. That would represent a high order of efficiency in the conversion of the energy of light to the energy of chemical bonds.

It is curious to put this almost obsessive concentration on the efficiency of photosynthesis together with what I think to be one of the most remarkable facts in all biology. Chlorophylls, the pigments universally used in photosynthesis, have absorption properties that seem just the opposite of what is wanted in a photosynthetic pigment. The energy of sunlight as it reaches the surface of the earth forms a broad maximum in the blue-green to green region of the spectrum, falling off at both shorter and longer wavelengths. Yet it is precisely in the blue-green and green, where the energy of sunlight is maximal, that the chlorophylls absorb light most poorly; this, indeed, is the reason for their green color. Where the absorption by chlorophyll is maximal—in widely separated bands in the violet and red—the energy of sunlight has fallen off considerably [see illustration on opposite page].

After perhaps two billion years of selection, involving a process whose efficiency is more important than that of any other process on earth, this seems an extraordinarily poor performance. It is a curious fact to put together with Warburg's comment (at one point in the quantum-demand controversy) that in a perfect nature, photosynthesis also is perfect. I think that the question it raises may be put more usefully as follows: What properties do the chlorophylls have that are so profoundly advantageous for photosynthesis as to override their disadvantageous absorption spectra?

We have the bare beginnings of an answer; it is emerging from a deeper understanding of the mechanism of photosynthesis, in particular as it is expressed in the structure and function of chlorophyll itself. Chlorophyll a, the type of chlorophyll principally involved in the photosynthesis of algae and higher plants, owes its color, that is, its capacity for absorbing light, to the possession of a long, regular alternation of single and double bonds, the type of arrangement called a conjugated system [see illustration on next two pages]. All pigments, natural and synthetic, possess such conjugated systems of alternate single and double bonds. The property of such systems that lends them color is the possession of particularly mobile electrons, called pi electrons, which are associated not with single atoms or bonds but with the conjugated system as a whole. It requires relatively little energy to raise a pi electron to a higher level. This small energy-requirement corresponds with the absorption of radiation of relatively long wavelengths, that is, radiation in the visible spectrum; and also with a high probability, and hence a strong intensity, of absorption.

In chlorophyll this conjugated system is turned around upon itself to form a ring of rings, a so-called porphyrin nucleus, and this I think is of extraordinary significance. On the one hand, as the illustration on these two pages shows, it makes possible a large number of rearrangements of the pattern of conjugated single and double bonds in the ring structure. Each such arrangement corresponds to a different way of arranging the external electrons, without moving any of the atoms. The molecule may thus be conceived to resonate among and be a hybrid of all these possible arrangements. In such a structure the pi electrons can not only oscillate, as in a straight-chain conjugated system; they can also circulate.

The many possibilities of resonance, together with the high degree of condensation of the molecule in rings, give the chlorophylls a peculiar rigidity and stability which I think are among the most important features of this type of structure. Indeed, porphyrins are among the most inert and stable molecules in the whole of organic chemistry. Porphyrins, apparently derived from chlorophyll, have been found in petroleum, oil shales and soft coals some 400 million years old.

This directs our attention to special features of chlorophyll, which are directly related to its functions in photosynthesis. One such property is not to utilize the energy it absorbs immediately in

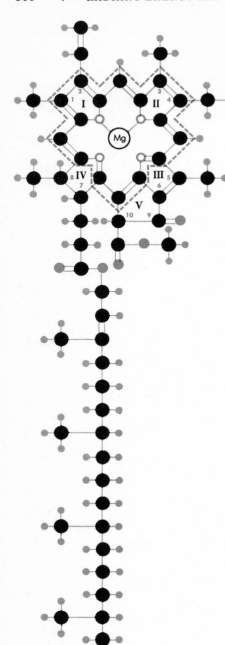

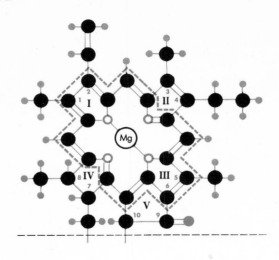

● CARBON   (Mg) MAGNESIUM

● OXYGEN   ○ NITROGEN

● HYDROGEN

CHLOROPHYLL MOLECULE, diagrammed in its entirety at left, owes its photobiological activity to the rigid and intricate porphyrin structure at top. The arrangement of the bonds in this structure may resonate among the configurations

reaction, but to trap it for a time, and pass it on intact to other, neighboring chlorophyll molecules. It has been shown that chlorophyll forms a long-lived metastable state, which, upon absorption of a quantum of light, retains a large part of the energy for a half-life of the order of five ten-thousandths of a second, perhaps 1,000 times longer than might otherwise be the case. In the structure of the chloroplasts, the functional assemblages of chlorophyll molecules in the cell, the chlorophyll molecules are in position to transfer energy from one to another, by a radiationless transfer akin to the way electrical energy is trans-

ferred in an induction motor. This capacity for transferring the energy about, so that it virtually belongs to a region of the chloroplast rather than to the specific molecule of chlorophyll that first absorbed it, makes possible the high efficiency of photosynthesis. While photosynthesis is proceeding rapidly, many chlorophyll molecules, having just reacted, are still in position to absorb light, but not to utilize it. In this way large amounts of absorbed energy that would otherwise be degraded into heat are retained and passed about intact until used photosynthetically.

One sign of the capacity to retain the energy absorbed as light and pass it on relatively intact is the strong fluorescence exhibited by chlorophyll. This green or blue-green pigment fluoresces red light; and however short the wavelengths that are absorbed—that is, however large the quanta—the same red light is fluoresced, corresponding to quanta of energy content about 40 kilocalories per mole. This is the quantity of energy that is passed from molecule to molecule in the chloroplast and eventually made available for photosynthesis.

The generally inert structure of chlorophyll must somewhere contain a chemically reactive site. Such a site seems to exist in the five-membered carbon ring, usually designated ring V in the structural diagrams. James Franck of the University of Chicago some years ago called attention to the possibility that it is here that the reactivity of chlorophyll is localized. Recent experiments by Wolf

Vishniac and I. A. Rose of Yale University, employing the radioactive isotope of hydrogen (tritium), have shown that chlorophyll, both in the cell and in solution, can take up hydrogen in the light though not in the dark, and can transfer it to the coenzyme triphosphopyridine nucleotide, which appears to be principally responsible for transferring hydrogen in photosynthesis. There is some evidence to support Franck's suggestion that the portion of chlorophyll involved in these processes is the five-membered ring.

Chlorophyll thus possesses a triple combination of capacities: a high receptivity to light, an inertness of structure permitting it to store the energy and relay it to other molecules, and a reactive site equipping it to transfer hydrogen in the critical reaction that ultimately binds hydrogen to carbon in the reduction of carbon dioxide. I would suppose that these properties singled out the chlorophylls for use by organisms in photosynthesis in spite of their disadvantageous absorption spectrum.

Photosynthetic organisms cope with the deficiencies of chlorophyll in a variety of ways. In 1883 the German physiologist T. W. Engelmann pointed out that in the various types of algae other pigments must also function in photosynthesis. Among these are the carotenoid pigments in the green and brown algae, and the phycobilins, phycocyanin and phycoerythrin (related to the animal bile-pigments) in the red and blue-green algae. Engelmann showed that each type

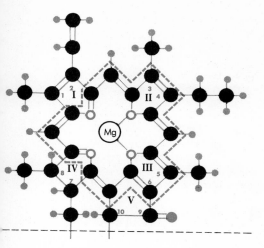

diagrammed in the middle and at the right. These and other possible configurations of the bonds help to make it possible for the chlorophyll molecule to trap and store energy which is conveyed to it by light quanta.

of alga photosynthesizes best in light of the complementary color: green algae in red light, brown algae in green light, red algae in blue light. He pointed out that this is probably the basis of the layering of these types of algae at various depths in the ocean.

All these pigments act, however, by transferring the energy they absorb to one another and eventually to chlorophyll *a;* whatever pigments have absorbed the light, the same red fluorescence of chlorophyll *a* results, with its maximum at about 670 to 690 millimicrons. The end result is therefore always the same: a quantum with an energy content of about 40 kilocalories per mole is made available to chlorophyll *a* for photosynthesis. The accessory pigments, including other varieties of chlorophyll, perform the important function of filling in the hole in the absorption spectrum of chlorophyll.

Still another device helps to compensate for the failure of chlorophyll to absorb green and blue-green light efficiently: On land and in the sea the concentration of chlorophyll and the depth of the absorbing layer are maximized by plant life. As a result chlorophyll absorbs considerable energy even in the wavelengths at which its absorption is weakest. Leaves absorb green light poorly, yet they do absorb a fraction of it. One need only look up from under a tree to see that the cover of superimposed leaves permits virtually no light to get through, green or otherwise. The lower leaves on a tree, though plentifully supplied with chloro-

plasts, may receive too little light to contribute significantly to photosynthesis. By being so profligate with the chlorophylls, plants compensate in large part for the intrinsic absorption deficiencies of this pigment.

Phototropism

The phototropism of plants—their tendency to bend toward the light—is excited by a different region of the spectrum from that involved in photosynthesis. The red wavelengths, which are most effective in photosynthesis, are wholly ineffective in phototropism, which depends upon the violet, blue and green regions of the spectrum. This relationship was first demonstrated early in the 19th century by a worker who reported that when he placed a flask of port wine between a growing plant and the light from a window, the plant grew about as well as before, but no longer bent toward the light. Recently, more precise measurements with monochromatic lights have shown that the phototropism of both molds and higher plants is stimulated only by light of wavelengths shorter than approximately 550 millimicrons, lying almost completely within the blue-green, blue and violet regions of the spectrum.

Phototropism must therefore depend on yellow pigments, because only such pigments absorb exclusively the short wavelengths of the visible spectrum. All types of plant that exhibit phototropism appear to contain such yellow pigments, in the carotenoids. In certain instances the carotenoids are localized specifically in the region of the plant that is phototropically sensitive. The most careful measurements of the effectiveness of various wavelengths of light in stimulating phototropism in molds and higher plants have yielded action spectra which resemble closely the absorption spectra of the carotenoids that are present.

A number of lower invertebrates—for example, hydroids, marine organisms that are attached to the bottom by stalks —bend toward the light by differential growth, just as do plants. The range of wavelengths which stimulate this response is also about the same as that in plants. It appears that here also carotenoids, which are usually present in considerable amount, may be the excitatory agents. Phototactic responses, involving motion of the whole animal toward or away from the light, also abound throughout all groups of invertebrates. Unfortunately no one has yet correlated accurately the action spectra for such re-

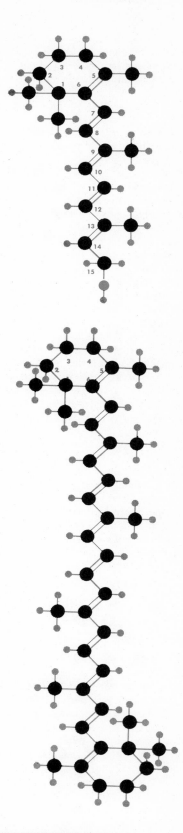

CAROTENE MOLECULE *(bottom)* is probable light-receptor in phototropism and is synthesized by plants. In structure it is a double vitamin A molecule *(top)*. Vitamin A, in turn, is precursor of retinine molecule *(illustration on page 302)*, which mediates vision.

sponses with the absorption spectra of the pigments that are present, so that no rigorous identification of the excitatory pigments can be made at present. This is a field awaiting investigation.

Vision

Only three of the 11 major phyla of animals have developed well-formed, image-resolving eyes: the arthropods (insects, crabs, spiders), mollusks (octopus, squid) and vertebrates. These three types of eye are entirely independent developments. There is no connection among them, anatomical, embryological or evolutionary. This is an important realization, for it means that three times, in complete independence of one another, animals on this planet have developed image-forming eyes.

It is all the more remarkable for this reason that in all three types of eye the chemistry of the visual process is very nearly the same. In all cases the pigments which absorb the light that stimulates vision are made of vitamin A, in the form of its aldehyde, retinene, joined with specific retinal proteins called opsins. Vitamin A ($C_{20}H_{29}OH$) has the structure of half a beta-carotene ($C_{40}H_{56}$), with a hydrogen and a hydroxyl radical (OH) added at the broken double bond.

Thus animal vision not only employs substances of the same nature as the carotenoids involved in phototropism of plants; there is also a genetic connection. Animals cannot make vitamin A *de novo*, but derive it from the plant carotenoids consumed in their diet. All photoreception, from phototropism in lower and higher plants to human vision, thus appears to depend for its light-sensitive pigments upon the carotenoids.

The role of light in vision is fundamentally different from its role in photosynthesis. The point of photosynthesis is to use light to perform chemical work, and the more efficiently this conversion is accomplished, the better the process serves its purpose. The point of vision is excitation; there is no evidence that the light also does work. The nervous structures upon which the light acts, so far as we know, are ready to discharge, having been charged through energy supplied by internal chemical reactions. Light is required only to trigger their responses.

Because this distinction is not always understood, attempts are frequently made to force parallels between vision and photosynthesis. In fact, these processes differ so greatly in their essential natures that no deep parallelism can be expected. The problem of quantum demand, for example, raises entirely different issues in vision as compared with photosynthesis. In photosynthesis one is interested in the minimum number of quanta needed to perform a given chemical task. In vision the problem hinges not on energetic efficiency but on differential sensitivity. The light intensities within which animals must see range from starlight to noonday sunlight; the latter is about a billion times brighter than the former. It is this enormous range of intensities that presents organisms with their fundamental visual problem: how to see at the lowest intensities without having vision obliterated by glare at the highest.

In the wholly dark-adapted state a vertebrate rod, the receptor principally involved in night vision, can respond to the absorption of a single quantum of visible light. To be sure, in the human eye, in which this relationship has been studied most completely, this minimal response of a single rod does not produce a visual sensation. In the dark-adapted state, seeing requires that at least five such events occur almost simultaneously within a small area of retina. This arrangement is probably designed to place the visual response above the "noise level" of the retina. From careful electrophysiological measurements it seems that a retina, even in total darkness, transmits a constant barrage of randomly scattered spontaneous responses to the brain. If the response of a single rod entered consciousness, we should be seeing random points of light flickering over the retina at all times.

The eye's extraordinary sensitivity to light is lost as the brightness of the illumination is increased. The threshold of human vision, which begins at the level of a few quanta in the dark-adapted state, rises as the brightness of the light increases until in bright daylight one million times more light may be needed just to stimulate the eye. But the very low quantum-efficiency in the light-adapted condition nonetheless represents a high visual efficiency.

The statement that the limits of human vision are 380 and 760 millimicrons is actually quite arbitrary. These limits are the wavelengths at which the visual sensitivity has fallen to about a thousandth of its maximum value. Specific investigations have pursued human vision to about 312 millimicrons in the near ultraviolet, and to about 1,050 in the near infrared.

In order to see at 1,050 millimicrons, however, 10,000 million times more light energy is required if cones are being stimulated, and over a million million times more energy if rods are being stimulated. This result came out of measurements made in our laboratory at Harvard University during World War II in association with Donald R. Griffin and Ruth Hubbard. As we exposed our eyes to flashes of light in the neighborhood of 1,000 millimicrons, we could not only see the flash but feel a momentary flush of heat on the cornea of the eye. At about 1,150 millimicrons, just a little farther into the infrared than our ex-

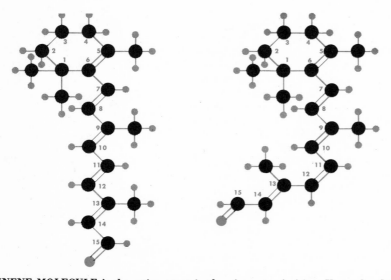

RETINENE MOLECULE is the active agent in the pigments of vision. Upon absorbing energy of light the geometry of the molecule changes from the so-called *cis* arrangement at left to the *trans* arrangement at right. This change in structure triggers process of vision.

periments had taken us, the radiation should have become a better stimulus as heat than as light.

The ultraviolet boundary of human vision, as that of many other vertebrates, raises a special problem. Ordinarily our vision is excluded from the ultraviolet, not primarily because the retina or its visual pigments are insensitive to that portion of the spectrum, but because ultraviolet light is absorbed by the lens of the eye. The human lens is yellow in color and grows more deeply yellow with age. One curious consequence of this arrangement is that persons who have had their lenses removed in the operation for cataract have excellent ultraviolet vision.

One may wonder how it comes about that man and many other vertebrates have been excluded from ultraviolet vision by the yellowness of their lenses. Actually this effect is probably of real advantage. All lens systems made of one material refract shorter wavelengths more strongly than longer wavelengths, and so bring blue light to a shorter focus than red. This phenomenon is known as chromatic aberration, or color error, and even the cheapest cameras are corrected for it. In default of color correction the lens seems to do the next best thing; it eliminates the short wavelengths of the spectrum for which the color error is greatest.

One group of animals, however, makes important use of the ultraviolet in vision. These are the insects. The insect eye is composed of a large number of independent units, the ommatidia, each of which records a point in the object, so that the image as a whole is composed as a mosaic of such points. Projection by a lens plays no part in this system, and chromatic aberration is of no account.

How does it happen that whenever vision has developed on our planet, it has come to the same group of molecules, the A vitamins, to make its light-sensitive pigments? I think that one can include plant phototropism in the same question, and ask how it comes about that all photoreception, animal and plant, employs carotenoids to mediate excitation by light. We have already asked a similar question concerning the chlorophylls and photosynthesis; and what chlorophylls are to photosynthesis, carotenoids are to photoreception.

Both the carotenoids and chlorophylls owe their color to the possession of conjugated systems. In the chlorophylls these are condensed in rings; in the carotenoids they are mainly in straight

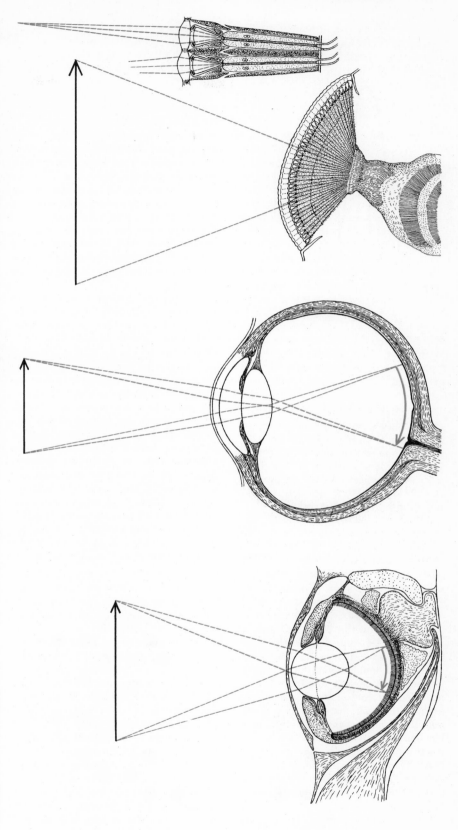

EYES of three kinds have evolved quite independently in three phyla: insects (*top*), vertebrates (*center*) and mollusks (*bottom*). In all three types of eye, however, the chemistry of vision is mediated by retinene derived from the carotenoids synthesized by plants.

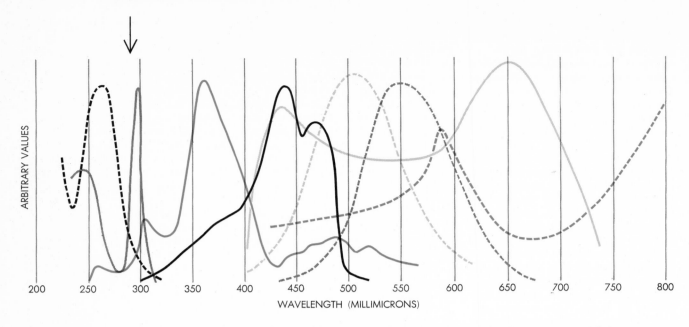

PHOTOBIOLOGICAL PROCESSES are activated by different regions 'of the spectrum: killing of a bacillus (A), sunburn in human skin (B), insect vision (C), phototropism in an oat plant (D), photosynthesis in wheat (E), human "night" vision (F), human "day" vision (G), photosynthesis in a bacterium (H). Arrow at left marks limit of solar short waves.

chains. The chlorophylls fluoresce strongly; the carotenoids, weakly or not at all. Much of the effectiveness of the chlorophylls in photosynthesis is associated with a high capacity for energy transfer; there is as yet no evidence that such energy transfer has a place in vision.

I think that the key to the special position of the carotenoids in photoreception lies in their capacity to change their shapes profoundly on exposure to light. They do this by the process known as *cis-trans* isomerization. Whenever two carbon atoms in a molecule are joined by a single bond, they can rotate more or less freely about this bond, and take all positions with respect to each other. When, however, two carbon atoms are joined by a double bond, this fixes their position with respect to each other. If now another carbon atom is joined to each of this pair, both the new atoms may attach on the same side of the double bond (the *cis* position) or on opposite sides, diagonally (the *trans* position). These are two different structures, each of them stable until activated to undergo transformation—isomerization—into the other.

Carotenoids, possessing as they do long straight chains of conjugated double bonds, can exist in a great variety of such *cis-trans* or geometrical isomers. No other natural pigments approach them in this regard. Porphyrins and other natural pigments may have as

many or more double bonds, but are held in a rigid geometry by being bound in rings.

Cis-trans isomerization involves changes in shape. The all-*trans* molecule is relatively straight, whereas a *cis* linkage at any point in the chain represents a bend. In the composition of living organisms, which depends in large part on the capacity of molecules to fit one another, shape is all-important.

We have learned recently that all the visual pigments known, in both vertebrate and invertebrate eyes, are made with a specifically bent and twisted isomer of retinene. Only this isomer will do because it alone fits the point of attachment on the protein opsin. The intimate union thus made possible between the normally yellow retinene and opsin greatly enhances the color of the retinene, yielding the deep-orange to violet colors of the visual pigments. The only action of light upon a visual pigment is to isomerize—to straighten out—retinene to the all-*trans* configuration. Now it no longer fits opsin, and hence comes away. The deep color of the visual pigment is replaced by the light yellow color of free retinene. This is what is meant by the bleaching of visual pigments by light.

In this succession of processes, however, it is some process associated with the *cis-trans* isomerization that excites vision. The subsequent cleavage of reti-

nene from opsin is much too slow to be responsible for the sensory response. Indeed, in many animals the visual pigments appear hardly to bleach at all. This seems to be the case in all the invertebrate eyes yet examined, in which the entire transformation in light and darkness appears to be restricted to the isomerization of retinene. It seems possible that similar *cis-trans* isomerizations of carotenoid pigments underlie phototropic excitation in plants. Experiments are now in progress in our laboratory to explore this possibility.

Bioluminescence

In addition to responding to light in their various ways, many bacteria, invertebrates and fishes also produce light. All bioluminescent reactions require molecular oxygen; combustions of one kind or another supply the energy that is emitted as light. In photosynthesis light performs organic reductions, releasing oxygen in the process. In bioluminescence the oxidation of organic molecules with molecular oxygen emits light. I used to think that bioluminescence is like vision in reverse; but in fact it is more nearly like photosynthesis in reverse.

What function bioluminescence fulfills in the lives of some of the animals that display it is not yet clear. The flashing of fireflies may act as a signal for integrating their activities, and perhaps as a sexual excitant. What role may be fulfilled by the extraordinary display of red, green and yellow illumination in a railroad worm is altogether conjectural. There is one major situation, however, in which bioluminescence must play an exceedingly important role. This is in the sea, at depths lower than those reached by surface light, and at night at all depths. It would be difficult otherwise to understand how fishes taken from great depths, far below those to which light from the surface can penetrate, frequently have very large eyes. For vision at night or at great depths, it is not necessary that the organisms and objects that are visible themselves be bioluminescent. Bioluminescent bacteria abound in the ocean, and many submerged objects are coated sufficiently with luminous bacteria to be visible to the sensitive eye.

It has lately been discovered that the rod vision of deep-sea fishes is adapted to the wavelengths of surface light that penetrate most deeply into the water: the blue light centered around 475 millimicrons. Furthermore, sensitive new devices for measuring underwater illumination have begun to reveal the remarkable fact that deep-sea bioluminescence may also be most intense at about 475 millimicrons. The same selection of visual pigments that best equips deep-sea fishes to see by light penetrating from the surface seems best adapted to the bioluminescent radiation.

Just as light quanta must be of a certain size to activate or provide the energy for useful chemical reactions, so chemical reactions emit light in the same range of wavelengths. It is for this reason, and no accident, that the range of bioluminescent radiations coincides well with the range of vision and other photobiological processes.

Light and Evolution

The relationship between light and life is in one important sense reciprocal. Over the ages in which sunlight has activated the processes of life, living organisms have modified the terrestrial environment to select those wavelengths of sunlight that are most compatible with those processes. Before life arose, much more of the radiation of the sun reached the surface of the earth than now. We believe this to have been because the atmosphere at that time contained very little oxygen (hence negligible amounts of ozone) and probably very little carbon dioxide. Very much more of the sun's infrared and hard ultraviolet radiation must have reached the surface of the earth then than now.

Some of the short-wave radiation, operating in lower reaches of the atmosphere and also probably in the surface layers of the seas, must have been important in activating the synthesis and interactions of organic molecules which formed the prelude to the eventual emergence of the first living organisms. These organisms, coming into an anaerobic world, surrounded by the organic matter that had accumulated over the previous ages, must have lived by fermentation, and in this process must have produced as a by-product very large quantities of carbon dioxide. Part of this remained dissolved in the oceans; part entered the atmosphere.

Eventually the availability of large amounts of carbon dioxide, much larger than are in the atmosphere today, made possible the development of the process of photosynthesis. This began to remove carbon dioxide from the atmosphere, fix-ing it in organic form. Simultaneously, through the most prevalent and familiar form of photosynthesis, it began to produce oxygen, and in this way oxygen first became established in our atmosphere. As oxygen accumulated, the layer of ozone that formed high in the atmosphere—itself a photochemical process—prevented the short-wavelength radiation from the sun from reaching the surface of the earth. This relief from antibiotic radiation permitted living organisms to emerge from the water onto the land.

The presence of oxygen also led to the development of the process of cellular respiration, which involves gas exchanges just the reverse of those of photosynthesis. Eventually respiration and photosynthesis came into approximate balance, as they must have been for some ages past.

One may wonder how much of this history could have occurred in darkness,

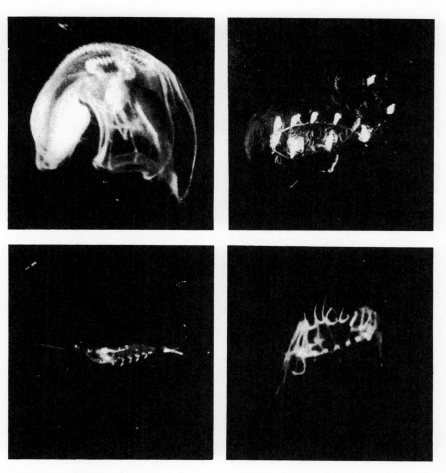

BIOLUMINESCENT CREATURES of the ocean were made to take these photographs of themselves by means of a camera designed by Harold E. Edgerton of Massachusetts Institute of Technology and L. R. Breslau of the Woods Hole Oceanographic Institution. The feeble luminescence of the animals was harnessed to trigger a high-speed electronic flash.

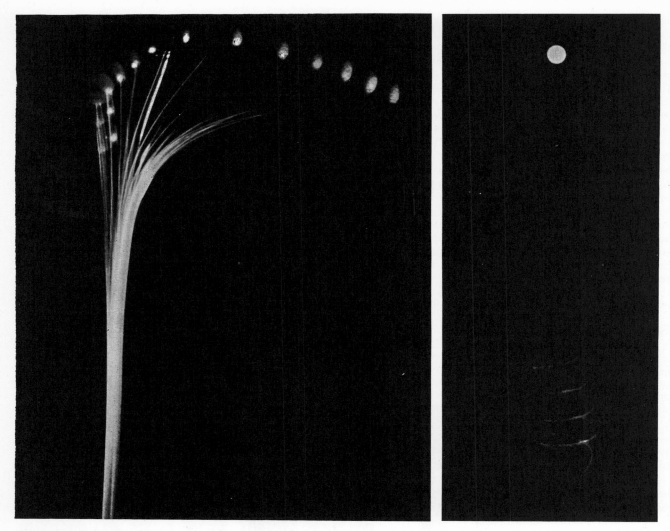

PHOTOTROPISM in the fruiting body of the mold *Phycomyces* is demonstrated in these photographs from the laboratory of Max Delbrück at the California Institute of Technology. The multiple photograph at left, with exposures made at intervals of five minutes, shows the fruiting body growing toward the light source. In the photograph at right, the stalk of the fruiting body has been made to grow in an ascending spiral by placing it on a turntable which revolved once every two hours in the presence of a fixed light-source.

by which I mean not merely the absence of external radiation but a much more specific thing: the absence of radiation in the range between 300 and 1,100 millimicrons. A planet without this range of radiation would virtually lack photochemistry. It would have a relatively inert surface, upon which organic molecules could accumulate only exceedingly slowly. Granted even enough time for such accumulation, and granted that eventually primitive living organisms might form, what then? They could live for a time on the accumulated organic matter. But without the possibility of photosynthesis how could they ever become independent of this geological heritage and fend for themselves? Inevitably they must eventually consume the organic molecules about them, and with that life must come to an end.

It may form an interesting intellectual exercise to imagine ways in which life might arise, and having arisen might maintain itself, on a dark planet; but I doubt very much that this has ever happened, or that it can happen.

The Role of Chlorophyll in Photosynthesis

EUGENE I. RABINOWITCH AND GOVINDJEE · July 1965

31

Any effort to understand the basis of life on this planet must always come back to photosynthesis: the process that enables plants to grow by utilizing carbon dioxide (CO_2), water (H_2O) and a tiny amount of minerals. Photosynthesis is the one large-scale process that converts simple, stable, inorganic compounds into the energy-rich combination of organic matter and oxygen and thereby makes abundant life on earth possible. Photosynthesis is the source of all living matter on earth, and of all biological energy.

The overall reaction of photosynthesis can be summarized in the following equation: $CO_2 + H_2O + light \rightarrow (CH_2O) + O_2 + 112,000$ calories of energy per mole. (CH_2O) stands for a carbohydrate; for example, glucose: $(CH_2O)_6$. "Mole" is short for "gram molecule": one gram multiplied by the molecular weight of the substances in question—in this case carbohydrate and oxygen.

When one of us first summarized the state of knowledge of photosynthesis 17 years ago, the whole process was still heavily shrouded in fog [see "Photosynthesis," by Eugene I. Rabinowitch; SCIENTIFIC AMERICAN Offprint 34]. Five years later investigation had penetrated the mists sufficiently to disclose some of the main features of the process [see "Progress in Photosynthesis," by Eugene I. Rabinowitch; SCIENTIFIC AMERICAN, November, 1953]. Since then much new knowledge has been accumulated; in particular the sequence of chemical steps that convert carbon dioxide into carbohydrate is now understood in considerable detail [see "The Path of Carbon in Photosynthesis," by J. A. Bassham; SCIENTIFIC AMERICAN Offprint 122]. The fog has also thinned out in other areas, and the day when the entire sequence of physical and chemical events in photosynthesis will be well understood seems much closer.

The photosynthetic process apparently consists of three main stages: (1) the removal of hydrogen atoms from water and the production of oxygen molecules; (2) the transfer of the hydrogen atoms from an intermediate compound in the first stage to one in the third stage, and (3) the use of the hydrogen atoms to convert carbon dioxide into a carbohydrate [see illustration on page 309].

The least understood of these three stages is the first: the removal of hydrogen atoms from water with the release of oxygen. All that is known is that it entails a series of steps probably requiring several enzymes, one of which contains manganese. The third stage—the production of carbohydrates from carbon dioxide—is the best understood, thanks largely to the work of Melvin Calvin and his co-workers at the University of California at Berkeley. The subject of our article is the second stage: the transfer of hydrogen atoms from the first stage to the third. This is the energy-storing part of photosynthesis; in it, to use the words of Robert Mayer, a discoverer of the law of the conservation of energy, "the fleeting sun rays are fixed and skillfully stored for future use."

The light energy to be converted into chemical energy by photosynthesis is first taken up by plant pigments, primarily the green pigment chlorophyll. In photosynthesis chlorophyll functions as a photocatalyst: when it is in its energized state, which results from the absorption of light, it catalyzes an energy-storing chemical reaction. This

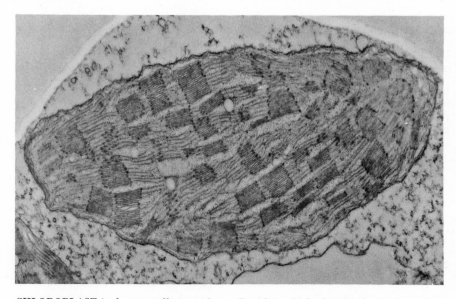

CHLOROPLAST is the organelle in a plant cell within which photosynthesis takes place. The chlorophyll is contained in the "grana," stacks of membranous sacs called lamellae, seen here in cross section. A maize-cell chloroplast is enlarged 19,000 diameters in this electron micrograph made by A. E. Vatter of the University of Colorado Medical Center.

PHOTOSYNTHETIC UNITS may be the small elements, looking somewhat like cobblestones, visible in this electron micrograph made by Roderic B. Park and John Biggins of the University of California at Berkeley. In the micrograph a single lamella and a part of another one are shadowed with chromium and enlarged 175,000 diameters. Where the membrane is torn away one can see an ordered array of the units, which Park and Biggins call quantasomes and calculate could contain 230 chlorophyll molecules each.

reaction is the primary photochemical process; it is followed by a sequence of secondary "dark"—that is, nonphotochemical—reactions in which no further energy is stored.

Once it was thought that in photosynthesis the primary photochemical process is the decomposition of carbon dioxide into carbon and oxygen, followed by the combination of carbon and water. More recently it has been suggested that the energy of light serves primarily to dissociate water, presumably into hydroxyl radicals (OH) and hydrogen atoms; the hydroxyl radicals would then react to form oxygen molecules. It is better than either of these two formulations to say that the primary

photochemical process in photosynthesis is the boosting of hydrogen atoms from a stable association with oxygen in water molecules to a much less stable one with carbon in organic matter. The oxygen atoms "left behind" combine into oxygen molecules, an association also much less stable than the one between oxygen and hydrogen in water. The replacement of stable bonds (between oxygen and hydrogen) by looser bonds (between oxygen and oxygen and between hydrogen and carbon) obviously requires a supply of energy, and it explains why energy is stored in photosynthesis.

The transfer of hydrogen atoms from one molecule to another is called oxida-

tion-reduction. The hydrogen atom is transferred from a donor molecule (a "reductant") to an acceptor molecule (an "oxidant"); after the reaction the donor is said to be oxidized and the acceptor to be reduced. The transfer of an electron can often substitute for the transfer of a hydrogen atom: in an aqueous system (such as the interior of the living cell) there are always hydrogen ions (H^+), and if such an ion combines with the electron acceptor, the acquisition of an electron becomes equivalent to the acquisition of a hydrogen atom (electron $+ H^+$ ion $\rightarrow$ H atom).

The chain of oxidation-reduction reactions in photosynthesis has some links that involve electron transfers and others that involve hydrogen-atom transfers. For the sake of simplicity we shall speak of electron transfers, with the understanding that in some cases what is actually transferred is a hydrogen atom. Indeed, the end result of the reactions undoubtedly *is* the transfer of hydrogen atoms.

In the oxidation-reduction reactions of photosynthesis the electrons must be pumped "uphill"; that is why energy must be supplied to make the reaction go. The tiny chlorophyll-containing chloroplasts of the photosynthesizing plant cell act as chemical pumps; they obtain the necessary power from the absorption of light by chlorophyll (and to some extent from absorption by other pigments in the chloroplast). It is important to realize that the energy is stored in the two products organic matter and free oxygen and not in either of them separately. To release the energy by the combustion of the organic matter (or by respiration, which is slow, enzyme-catalyzed combustion) the two products must be brought together again.

How much energy is stored in the transfer of electrons from water to carbon dioxide, converting the carbon dioxide to carbohydrate and forming a proportionate amount of oxygen?

Oxidation-reduction energy can conveniently be measured in terms of electrochemical potential. Between a given donor of electrons and a given acceptor there is a certain difference of oxidation-reduction potentials. This difference depends not only on the nature of the two reacting substances but also on the nature of the products of the reaction; it is characteristic of the two oxidation-reduction "couples." For example, when oxygen is reduced to water (H_2O) its potential is $+.81$ volt, but when it is reduced to hydrogen peroxide (H_2O_2) the potential is $+.27$ volt. The more positive the potential, the stronger is the oxidative power of the couple; the more negative the potential, the stronger is its reducing power.

When two oxidation-reduction couples are brought together, the one containing the stronger oxidant tends to oxidize the one containing the stronger reductant. In photosynthesis, however, a weak oxidant (CO_2) must oxidize a weak reductant (H_2O), producing a strong oxidant (O_2) and a strong reductant (a carbohydrate). This calls for a massive investment of energy. The specific amount needed is given by the difference between the oxidation-reduction potentials of the two couples involved in the reaction: oxygen-water and carbon-dioxide–carbohydrate. The oxygen-water potential is about $+.8$ volt; the carbon-dioxide–carbohydrate potential, about $-.4$ volt. The transfer of a single electron from water to carbon dioxide thus requires $+.8$ minus $-.4$, or 1.2, electron volts of energy. For a molecule of carbon dioxide to be reduced to CH_2O—the elementary molecular group of a carbohydrate—*four* electrons (or hydrogen atoms) must be transferred; hence the total energy needed is 4.8 electron volts. This works out to $112,000$ calories per mole of carbon dioxide reduced and of oxygen liberated. In short, the pumping of electrons in the second stage of photosynthesis entails the storage of $112,000$ calories of energy per mole for each set of four electrons transferred.

We know the identity of the primary electron donor in photosynthesis (water) and of the ultimate electron acceptor (carbon dioxide), but what are the intermediates involved in the transfer of electrons from the first stage to the third? This has become the focal problem in recent studies of the photosynthetic process. As a matter of fact, it is not yet definitely known what compound releases electrons from the first stage, and what compound receives them in the third; that is why these compounds are respectively labeled ZH and X in the illustration at the left. About the donor, ZH, we have almost no information; the following considerations suggest the possible nature of the primary acceptor, X.

From the study of the mechanism of respiration we are familiar with an important oxidation-reduction catalyst: nicotinamide adenine dinucleotide phosphate, or NADP (formerly known as triphosphopyridine nucleotide, or TPN). NADP has an oxidation-reduction potential of about $-.32$ volt, thus in itself it is not a strong enough reductant to provide the $-.4$-electron-volt potential needed to reduce carbon dioxide to carbohydrate. NADP can achieve this feat, however, if it is supplied with additional energy in the form of the high-energy compound adenosine triphosphate, or ATP. A molecule of ATP supplies about $10,000$ calories per mole when its terminal phosphate group is split off, and this is enough to provide the needed boost to the reducing power of NADP. Furthermore, we know that NADP is reduced when cell-free preparations of chloroplasts are illuminated. Put together, these two facts led to the now widely accepted hypothesis that the sec-

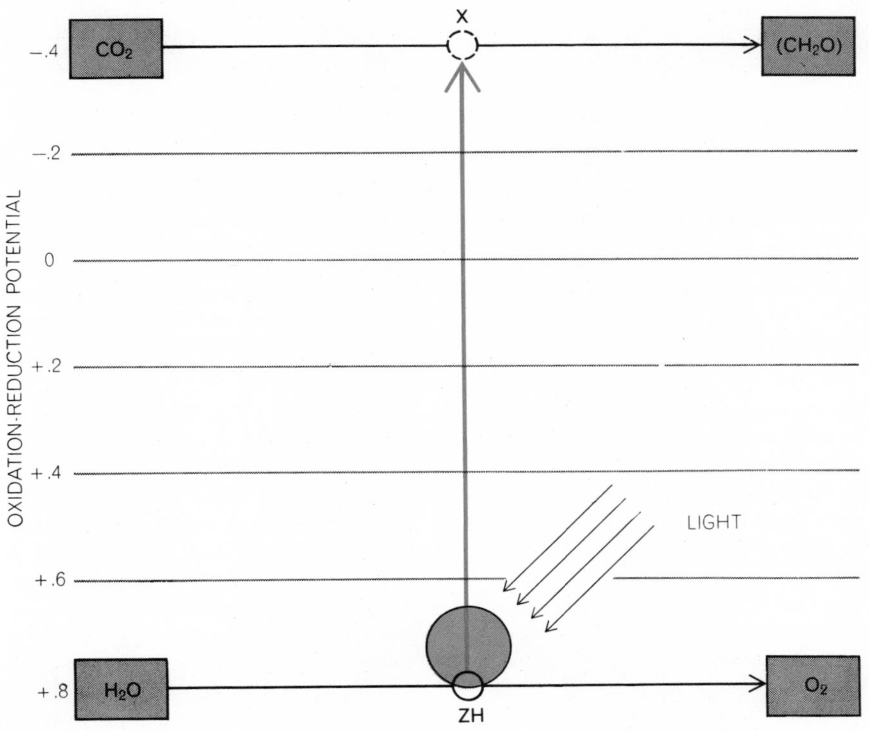

THREE STAGES of photosynthesis are the removal of hydrogen from water with the release of oxygen (*bottom arrow*), the transfer (*vertical arrow*) of the hydrogen by energy from light trapped by chlorophyll (*color*) and the use of the hydrogen to reduce carbon dioxide to carbohydrate (*top arrow*). In this scheme the oxidation-reduction potentials involved are indicated by the scale at the left, and the hypothetical "primary reductant" and "primary acceptor" intermediates are designated as ZH and X respectively.

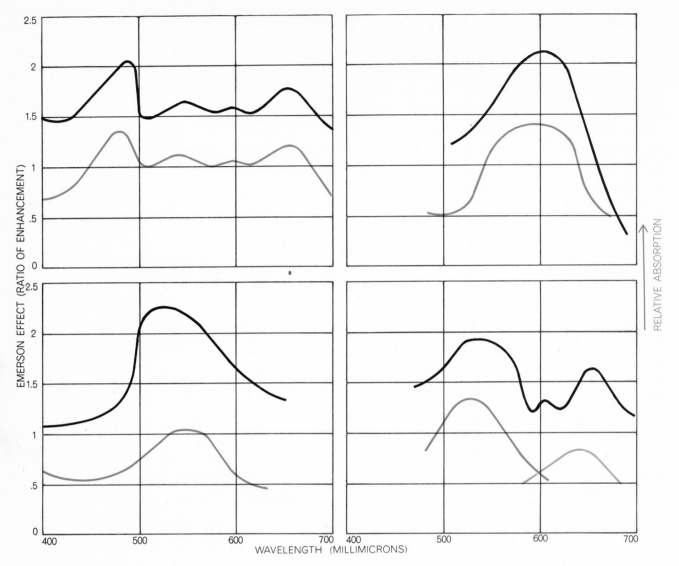

EMERSON EFFECT is shown for *Chlorella* (*top left*), the blue-green alga *Anacystis nidulans* (*top right*), *Porphyridium* (*bottom left*) and the diatom *Navicula minima* (*bottom right*). In each case the black curve shows the action spectrum of the Emerson effect, or the degree of enhancement in quantum yield as the wavelength of the supplementary illumination is varied. The curve of the action spectrum turns out to be parallel to the absorption curves (*color*) of the various accessory pigments: chlorophyll *b* in *Chlorella*, phycocyanin in *Anacystis*, phycoerythrin in *Porphyridium* and fucoxanthol (*solid color*) and chlorophyll *c* (*light color*) in *Navicula*.

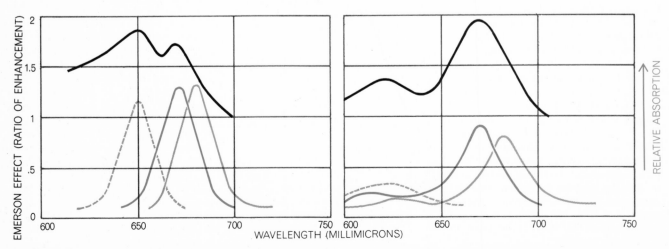

DETAILED ACTION SPECTRA of the Emerson effect reveal the presence of chlorophyll *a* 670 in *Chlorella* (*left*) and *Navicula* (*right*). The Emerson-effect peaks coincide with the absorption peaks of chlorophyll *a* 670 (*solid color*) as well as of chlorophyll *b* in *Chlorella* and chlorophyll *c* in *Navicula* (*broken curves*). The chlorophyll *a* absorption curve is also shown (*light-color curve*).

ond stage of photosynthesis manufactures both ATP and reduced NADP and feeds them into the third stage.

At first it was assumed that NADP is identical with X, the primary acceptor in our scheme. Subsequent experiments by various workers—notably Anthony San Pietro at Johns Hopkins University and Daniel I. Arnon and his colleagues at the University of California at Berkeley—suggested, however, that NADP is preceded in the "bucket brigade" of electron transfer by ferredoxin, a protein that contains iron. This compound has an oxidation-reduction potential of about —.42 volt; therefore if it is reduced in light it can bring about the reduction of NADP by a "dark" reaction requiring no additional energy supply.

More recently Bessel Kok of the Research Institute for Advanced Studies in Baltimore has found evidence suggesting that compound X may be a still stronger reductant, with a potential of about —.6 volt. If this is so, plants have the alternatives of either applying this stronger reductant directly to the reduction of carbon dioxide or letting it reduce first ferredoxin and then NADP and using reduced NADP to reduce carbon dioxide. It seems a roundabout procedure to create a reductant sufficiently strong for the task at hand, then to sacrifice a part of its reducing power and finally to use ATP to compensate for the loss. It is not unknown, however, for nature to resort to devious ways in order to achieve its aims.

For photosynthesis to be a self-contained process the required high-energy phosphate ATP must be itself manufactured by photosynthesis. The formation of ATP has in fact been detected in illuminated fragments of bacteria by Albert W. Frenkel of the University of Minnesota and in chloroplast fragments by Arnon and his co-workers [see "The Role of Light in Photosynthesis," by Daniel I. Arnon; SCIENTIFIC AMERICAN Offprint 75]. As a matter of fact, ATP is needed not only to act as a booster in the reduction of an intermediate in the carbon cycle by reduced NADP but also for another step in the third stage of photosynthesis. According to a sequence of reactions worked out in 1951 by Andrew A. Benson and his colleagues at the University of California at Berkeley, carbon dioxide enters photosynthesis by first reacting with a "carbon dioxide acceptor," a special sugar phosphate called ribulose diphosphate. It turns out that the production of this compound from its precursor—

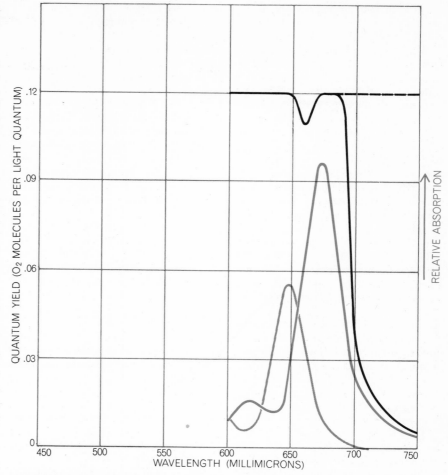

"RED DROP," the drop in quantum yield (*black curve*) of oxygen in photosynthesis under long-wave illumination, is demonstrated in the green alga *Chlorella pyrenoidosa*. Peak efficiency is restored (*broken line*) by supplementary shorter-wave illumination. Absorption curves of chlorophylls a (*solid color*) and b(*light color*) are also shown. This illustration and the next two are based on data of the late Robert Emerson of the University of Illinois.

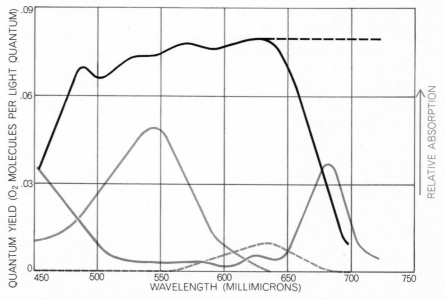

QUANTUM YIELD is similarly affected by long-wave illumination in the red alga *Porphyridium cruentum* (*black curve*). Yield drops to less than half of its maximum when absorption by chlorophyll a (*solid-color curve*) is at its peak. Absorption of the pigments phycoerythrin (*light-color curve*) and phycocyanin (*broken-color curve*) are also shown.

ribulose monophosphate—calls for a molecule of ATP.

ATP is produced both in chloroplasts and in mitochondria, the tiny intracellular bodies that are the site of the energy-liberating stage of respiration in animals as well as plants. The mitochondria produce ATP as their main function, exporting it as packaged energy for many life processes. The chloroplasts, on the other hand, make ATP only as an auxiliary source of energy for certain internal purposes. The energy of the light falling on the chloroplasts is stored mostly as oxidation-reduction energy by the uphill transfer of electrons. Only a relatively small fraction is diverted to the formation of ATP, and this fraction too ultimately becomes part of the oxidation-reduction energy of the final products of photosynthesis: oxygen and carbohydrate.

Let us now consider the uphill transport of electrons in greater detail. Recent investigations have yielded considerable information about this stage. Apparently the pumping of the electrons is a two-step affair, and among the most important intermediates in it are the catalysts called cytochromes.

The idea of a two-step electron-transfer process grew from a consideration of the energy economy of photosynthesis. Precise measurements, particularly those made by the late Robert Emerson and his co-workers at the University of Illinois, showed that the reduction of one molecule of carbon dioxide to carbohydrate, and the liberation of one molecule of oxygen, requires a minimum of eight quanta of light energy. The maximum quantum yield of photosynthesis, defined as the number of oxygen molecules that can be released for each quantum of light absorbed by the plant cell, is thus 1/8, or 12 percent. Since the transfer of four electrons is involved in the reduction of one carbon dioxide molecule, it was suggested that it takes two light quanta to move each electron. Emerson and his colleagues went on to determine the quantum yield of photosynthesis in monochromatic light of different wavelengths throughout the visible spectrum. They found that the yield, although it remained constant at about 12 percent in most of the spectrum, dropped sharply near the spectrum's far-red end [see illustrations on page 311]. This decline in the quantum yield, called the "red drop," begins at a wavelength of 680 millimicrons in green plants and at 650 millimicrons in red algae.

There are two chlorophylls present in green plants: chlorophyll a and chlorophyll b. Only chlorophyll a absorbs light at wavelengths longer than 680 millimicrons; the absorption of chlorophyll b rises to a peak at 650 millimicrons and becomes negligible at about 680 millimicrons. Emerson found that the quantum yield of photosynthesis at the far-red end of the spectrum beyond 680 millimicrons can be brought to the full efficiency of 12 percent by simultaneously exposing the plant to a second beam of light with a wavelength of 650 millimicrons. In other words, when light primarily absorbed by chlorophyll a was supplemented by light primarily absorbed by chlorophyll b, both beams gave rise to oxygen at the full rate. This relative excess in photosynthesis when a plant is exposed to two beams of light simultaneously, as compared with the yield produced by the same two beams separately, is known as the Emerson effect, or enhancement.

On the basis of his discovery Emerson concluded that photosynthesis involves two photochemical processes: one using energy supplied by chlorophyll a, the other using energy supplied by chlorophyll b or some other "accessory" pigment. Experimenting with various combinations of a constant far-red beam with beams of shorter wavelength, and using four different types of algae (green, red, blue-green and brown), Emerson's group found that the strongest enhancement always occurred when the second beam was absorbed mainly by the most important accessory pigment (the green pigment chlorophyll b in green cells, the red pigment phycoerythrin in red algae, the blue pigment phycocyanin in blue-green algae and the reddish pigment fucoxanthol in brown algae). Such results suggested that these other pigments are not mere accessories of chlorophyll a but have an important function of their own in photosynthesis [see top illustration on page 310].

Certain findings concerning the behavior of pigments in living plant cells, however, seemed to make this conclusion untenable. Illuminated plant cells fluoresce; that is, pigment molecules energized by the absorption of light quanta reemit some of the absorbed energy as fluorescent light. The source of fluorescence can be identified, because each substance has its own characteristic fluorescence spectrum. The main fluorescing pigment in plants always proves to be chlorophyll a, even when the light is absorbed by another pigment. This had first been shown for brown algae in a study conducted in

1943 by H. J. Dutton, W. H. Manning and B. B. Duggar at the University of Wisconsin; later the finding was extended to other organisms by L. N. M. Duysens of the University of Leiden. Known as sensitized fluorescence, the phenomenon indicates that the initial absorber has transferred its energy of excitation to chlorophyll a; the transfer is effected by a kind of resonance process. Careful measurements have shown that certain accessory pigments—chlorophyll b, phycoerythrin, phycocyanin and fucoxanthol—pass on to chlorophyll a between 80 and 100 percent of the light quanta they absorb. For some other accessory pigments—for example carotene—the transfer is less efficient.

This puts accessory pigments back in the role of being mere adjuncts to chlorophyll a. True, they can contribute, by means of resonance transfer, light energy to photosynthesis, thereby improving the supply of energy in regions of the spectrum where chlorophyll a is a poor absorber. Chlorophyll a, however, collects all this energy before it is used in the primary photochemical process. Why, then, the enhancement effect? Why should chlorophyll a need, in order to give rise to full-rate photosynthesis, one "secondhand" quantum obtained by resonance transfer from another absorber in addition to the one quantum it had absorbed itself?

A better understanding of this paradox resulted from the discovery that there apparently exist in the cell not only chlorophyll a and chlorophyll b but also two forms of chlorophyll a. These two forms have different light-absorption characteristics, and they probably also have different photochemical functions.

In the living cell chlorophyll a absorbs light most strongly in a broad band with its peak between 670 and 680 millimicrons. In our laboratory at the University of Illinois we undertook to plot the Emerson effect more carefully than before as a function of the wavelength of the enhancing light. We found that for green and brown cells the resulting curve showed, in addition to peaks corresponding to strong absorption by the accessory pigments, a peak at 670 millimicrons that must be due to chlorophyll a itself [see bottom illustration on page 310]. It was this finding that suggested the existence of two forms of chlorophyll a. The form that absorbs light at the longer wavelengths—mainly above 680 millimicrons—seemed to belong to one pigment system, now often called System I. The form that absorbs at 670 millimicrons seemed to belong to another pigment system: System II. In the second system the form of chlorophyll *a* that absorbs at 670 millimicrons is strongly assisted by accessory pigments, probably by resonance transfer of their excitation energy. Careful analysis of the absorption band of chlorophyll *a* by C. Stacy French of the Carnegie Institution of Washington's Department of Plant Biology, and also in our laboratory, confirmed that the band is double, with one peak near 670

millimicrons (at 668 millimicrons) and another band at 683 millimicrons [*see bottom illustration on page 310*].

If chlorophyll *a* is extracted from living plants, there is only one product; we must therefore assume that in the living cell the two forms differ in the way molecules of chlorophyll *a* are clumped together, or in the way they are associated with different chemical partners (proteins, lipids or other substances). Be

this as it may, the important implication of the new finding is that photosynthesizing cells possess two light-absorbing systems, one containing a form of chlorophyll *a* absorbing around 683 millimicrons and the other a form absorbing around 670. The latter system includes chlorophyll *b* (in green-plant cells) or other accessory pigments (in brown, red and blue-green algae). Further investigation—particularly of red algae—has suggested, however, that the distribu-

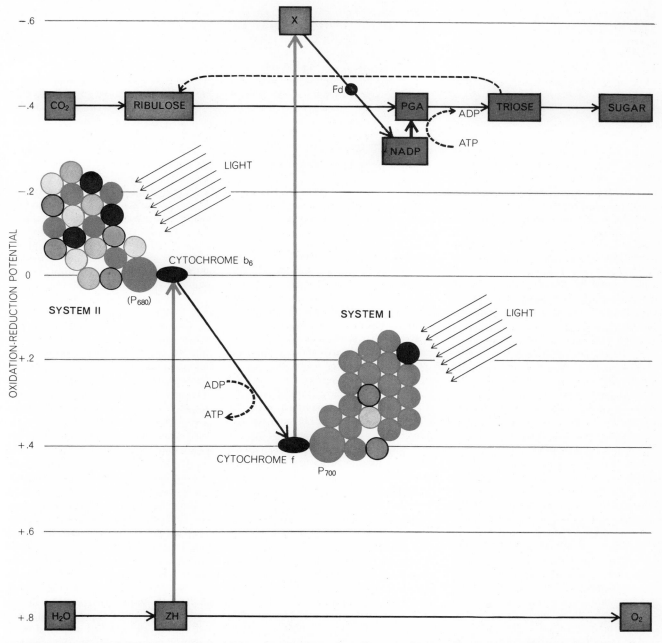

HYDROGEN TRANSFER in photosynthesis is now conceived of as a two-step process involving two pigment systems. Hydrogen atoms (or electrons) from the donor (ZH) are boosted to cytochrome b_6 by energy collected in System II and trapped by a hypothetical "pigment 680" ($P\ 680$). The pigments of System II include chlorophyll *a* 670 and such accessory pigments as chlorophyll *b* or *c*, phycoerythrin or phycocyanin, depending on the plant. The elec-

trons are passed "downhill" to cytochrome *f*, synthesizing adenosine triphosphate (ATP) in the process. Energy from System I (primarily chlorophyll *a*, with some accessory pigments), trapped by pigment 700 ($P\ 700$), boosts the electrons to a receptor (X), whence they move via ferredoxin (Fd) to nicotinamide adenine dinucleotide phosphate ($NADP$). Energy from ATP helps to move the electrons to phosphoglyceric acid (PGA) and into the carbon cycle.

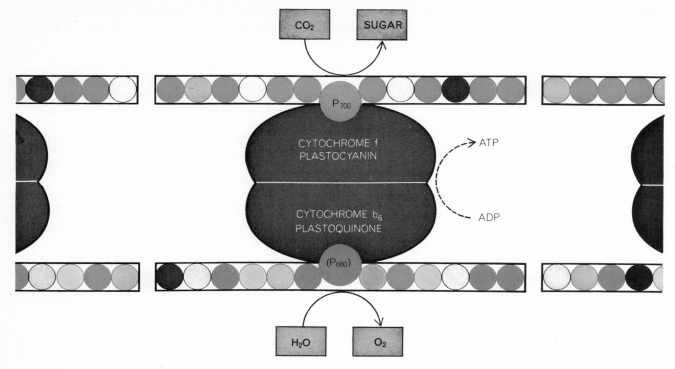

HYPOTHETICAL ARRANGEMENT of pigments in a chloroplast lamella would have System I in a monomolecular layer at the top and System II at the bottom. The space between the two pigment layers might contain the compounds responsible for the transport of hydrogen atoms (or electrons). The water-to-oxygen cycle would then be linked to System II and the carbon cycle to System I.

tion of these two components in the two systems may be less clear-cut. In red algae a large fraction of the chlorophyll *a* absorbing at 670 millimicrons seems to belong to System I rather than System II.

In all likelihood the two systems provide energy for two different photochemical reactions, and efficiency in photosynthesis requires that the rates of the two reactions be equal. What are these reactions? This question brings us to another significant finding, which suggested the participation of cytochromes in photosynthesis.

Cytochromes are proteins that carry an iron atom in an attached chemical group. They are found in all mitochondria, where they serve to catalyze the reactions of respiration. Robert Hill and his co-workers at the University of Cambridge first found that chloroplasts also contain cytochromes—two kinds of them. One, which they named cytochrome *f*, has a positive oxidation-reduction potential of about .4 volt. The other, which they named cytochrome b_6, has a potential of about 0 volt. In 1960 Hill, together with Fay Bendall, proposed an ingenious hypothesis as to how the two cytochromes might act as intermediate carriers of electrons and connect the two photochemical systems [*see illustration on preceding page*]. They suggested that cytochrome b_6 receives an

electron by a photochemical reaction from the electron donor *ZH;* the electron is then passed on to cytochrome *f* by a "downhill" reaction requiring no light energy. (The oxidation-reduction potential of cytochrome *f* is much more positive than that of cytochrome b_6.) A second photochemical reaction moves the electron uphill again, from cytochrome *f* to the electron-acceptor *X* in the third stage of photosynthesis. In this sequence the photochemical reactions store energy and the reaction between the two cytochromes releases energy. Some of the released energy, however, can be salvaged by the formation of an ATP molecule; this occurs in the transfer of electrons among cytochromes in respiration. In this way ATP is obtained without spending extra light quanta on its formation, which the tight energy economy of photosynthesis does not allow.

Experiments by Duysens and his associates confirmed this hypothesis, by showing that the absorption of light by System I causes the oxidation of a cytochrome, whereas the absorption of light by System II causes its reduction. This is exactly what we would expect. The illustration on the preceding page shows that the light reaction of System II should flood the intermediates between the two photochemical reactions with electrons taken from *ZH;* the light reaction of System I should drain these

electrons away, sending them up to the acceptor *X* and into the third stage of photosynthesis.

This, then, describes in a general way the oxidation-reduction process by which the chloroplasts store the energy of light in photosynthesis. Several other investigators have contributed evidence for the two-step mechanism; notable among them are French, Kok, Arnon, Horst Witt of the Max-Vollmer Institute in Berlin and their colleagues. In detail the process probably is much more complex than our scheme suggests. Its "downhill" central part seems to include, in addition to the two cytochromes, certain compounds of the group known as quinones and also plastocyanin, a protein that contains copper.

What is known of the submicroscopic structure in which the reactions of the second stage of photosynthesis take place? There is much evidence that the photosynthetic apparatus consists of "units" within the chloroplasts, each unit containing about 300 chlorophyll molecules. This picture first emerged from experiments conducted in 1932 by Emerson and William Arnold on photosynthesis during flashes of light; it was later supported by various other observations. The pigment molecules are packed so closely in the unit that when one of them is excited by light it readily transfers its excitation to a neighbor by resonance. The energy goes on traveling through the unit, rather as the steel ball in a pinball machine bounces around among the pins and turns on one light after another. Eventually the migrating energy quantum arrives at the entrance to an enzymatic "conveyor belt," where it is trapped and utilized either to load an electron onto the belt or to unload one from it. (The steel-ball analogy should not be taken literally; the migration of energy is a quantum-mechanical phenomenon, and the quantum's location can only be defined in terms of probability; its entrapment depends on the probability of finding it at the entrance to the conveyor belt.)

How is the quantum trapped? The trap must be a pigment molecule with what is called a lower excited state; the migrating quantum can stumble into such a molecule but cannot come out of it. Kok has found evidence that System I contains a small amount of a special form of chlorophyll called pigment 700 because it absorbs light at a wavelength of 700 millimicrons; this pigment could serve as a trap for the quantum bouncing around in System I. There seems to be a proper amount of pigment 700: about one molecule per unit. Furthermore, experiments suggest that pigment 700 is oxidized by light absorbed in System I and reduced by light absorbed in System II. It has an oxidation-reduction potential of about +.4 volt. All these properties fit the role we have assigned pigment 700 in our scheme: collecting energy from a 300-molecule unit in System I, using it to transfer an electron to the acceptor X and recovering the electron from cytochrome f [see illustration on page 313].

One suspects that there should be a counterpart of pigment 700 in System II, but so far none has been convincingly demonstrated. We believe, however, that a pigment we have tentatively named pigment 680—from the anticipated position of its absorption band—does serve as an energy trap in System II. Its existence is supported by the discovery of a new fluorescent emission band of chlorophyll at 693 millimicrons, which is compatible with absorption at 680 millimicrons. This band is emitted by certain algae when they are exposed to strong light of the wavelengths absorbed by System II.

What is the spatial organization of the pigment systems in the electron-boosting mechanism of the second stage of photosynthesis? It seems that the two systems may be arranged in two monomolecular layers, with a protein layer between them containing the enzymatic conveyor belt [see illustration on page 314]. The chloroplasts are known from electron microscope studies to consist of a set of lamellae: thin alternating layers of protein and fatty material piled one atop the other. Each layer appears to consist of particles arrayed rather like cobblestones in a pavement. The particles were first observed in electron micrographs made by E. Steinmann of the Technische Hochschule in Zurich; subsequently Roderic B. Park and John Biggins of the University of California at Berkeley made clearer micrographs of the particles and named them quantasomes [see illustration on page 308]. The units comprising Systems I and II may operate independently or they may be sufficiently close together to exchange energy by resonance, when

such exchange is needed to maintain a balanced rate of operation by the two systems.

The picture of the energy-storing second stage of photosynthesis presented in this article is, of course, still only a working hypothesis. Alternative hypotheses are possible, one of which we shall briefly describe. For many years the late James Franck, who shared the Nobel prize in physics for 1925, tried to develop a plausible physicochemical mechanism of photosynthesis. In 1963 he proposed, together with Jerome L. Rosenberg of the University of Pittsburgh, a concept according to which the two consecutive photochemical steps occur in one and the same energy trap. In other words, according to Franck, the same chlorophyll molecule that takes the electron away from the initial donor ZH and transfers it to a cytochrome then supplies energy for the transfer of the electron from the cytochrome to the acceptor X. In the first transfer, Franck suggested, the chlorophyll a molecule functions in the short-lived "singlet" excited state (in which the valence electrons have opposite spins); in the second transfer it functions in the long-lived "triplet" state (in which the valence electrons have parallel spins). Franck's hypothesis avoids certain difficulties of the "two trap" theory, but new difficulties arise in their place. On balance the two-trap picture seems to us the more plausible one at present.

No doubt this picture will change as more information emerges. It is merely a first effort to penetrate the inner sanctum of photosynthesis, the photocatalytic laboratory in which the energy of sunlight is converted into the chemical energy of life.

32 | The Evolution of Hemoglobin

EMILE ZUCKERKANDL · *May 1965*

Every living thing carries within itself a richly detailed record of its antecedents from the beginning of life on earth. This record is preserved in coded form in the giant molecules of deoxyribonucleic acid (DNA) that constitute the organism's genome, or total stock of genetic information. The genetic record is also expressed more tangibly in the protein molecules that endow the organism with its form and function.

These two kinds of molecule—DNA and protein—are living documents of evolutionary history. Although chemically very different, they have in common a fundamental characteristic: they are both made up of a one-dimensional succession of slightly differing subunits, like differently colored beads on a string. Each colored bead occupies a

place specifically assigned to it unless the heritable changes called mutations either change the color of a bead or displace, eliminate or add a bead (or several beads) at a time. In addition the protein molecules are folded in a specific way that enables them to carry out their specific functions.

To examine these molecular documents of evolutionary history a new discipline has emerged: chemical paleogenetics. It sets itself the ambitious goal of reconstructing, insofar as possible, how evolution proceeds at the molecular level. The new discipline is still in its infancy because almost nothing is yet known about the linear sequence of subunits that embody the code for a single gene in a molecule of DNA. Viruses, the smallest structures containing the blueprints for their own repli-

cation, possess from a few to several hundred genes. Each gene, in turn, consists of a string of several hundred code "letters." It has not been possible to isolate a single gene from any organism for chemical analysis.

It has been possible, however, to study and determine the chemical structure of a number of individual polypeptide chains that embody the coded information contained in individual genes. The term "polypeptide" refers to the principal chain of a protein molecule; it describes a sequence of amino acid molecules that are held together by peptide bonds. Such bonds are formed when two amino acid molecules link up with the release of a molecule of water; when they are linked in this way, the amino acids are called residues.

Because three code letters in DNA

HEMOGLOBIN CHAINS

HUMAN–BETA	VAL	HIS	LEU	THR	PRO	GLU	GLU	LYS	SER	ALA	VAL	THR	ALA	LEU	TRY	GLY	LYS	VAL	ASN		VAL	ASP	GLU	VAL	GLY	GLY	GLU	ALA	LEU	GLY	ARG	LEU	L
	1	2	3	4	5	6	7	8	9	10	11	12	13	14	15	16	17	18	19		20	21	22	23	24	25	26	27	28	29	30	31	3
HUMAN–DELTA	VAL	HIS	LEU	THR	PRO	GLU	GLU	LYS	THR	ALA	VAL	ASN	ALA	LEU	TRY	GLY	LYS	VAL	ASN		VAL	ASP	ALA	VAL	GLY	GLY	GLU	ALA	LEU	GLY	ARG	LEU	LE
	1	2	3	4	5	6	7	8	9	10	11	12	13	14	15	16	17	18	19		20	21	22	23	24	25	26	27	28	29	30	31	3
HUMAN–GAMMA	GLY	HIS	PHE	THR	GLU	GLU	ASP	LYS	ALA	THR	ILEU	THR	SER	LEU	TRY	GLY	LYS	VAL	ASN		VAL	GLU	ASP	ALA	GLY	GLY	GLU	THR	LEU	GLY	ARG	LEU	L
	1	2	3	4	5	6	7	8	9	10	11	12	13	14	15	16	17	18	19		20	21	22	23	24	25	26	27	28	29	30	31	3
HUMAN–ALPHA	VAL		LEU	SER	PRO	ALA	ASP	LYS	THR	ASN	VAL	LYS	ALA	ALA	TRY	GLY	LYS	VAL	GLY	ALA	HIS	ALA	GLY	GLU	TYR	GLY	ALA	GLU	ALA	LEU	GLU	ARG	MET	P
	1		2	3	4	5	6	7	8	9	10	11	12	14	15	16	17	18	19	20	21	22	23	24	25	26	27	28	29	30	31	32	3
GORILLA–BETA	VAL	HIS	LEU	THR	PRO	GLU	GLU	LYS	SER	ALA	VAL	THR	ALA	LEU	TRY	GLY	LYS	VAL	ASN		VAL	ASP	GLU	VAL	GLY	GLY	GLU	ALA	LEU	GLY	ARG	LEU	LE
	1	2	3	4	5	6	7	8	9	10	11	12	13	14	15	16	17	18	19		20	21	22	23	24	25	26	27	28	29	30	31	3
PIG–BETA	VAL	HIS	LEU	SER	ALA	GLU	GLU	LYS	SER	ALA	VAL	THR	ALA	LEU	TRY	GLY	LYS	VAL	ASN		VAL	ASP	GLU	VAL	GLY	GLY	GLU	ALA	LEU	GLY	ARG	LEU	LE
	1	2	3	4	5	6	7	8	9	10	11	12	13	14	15	16	17	18	19		20	21	22	23	24	25	26	27	28	29	30	31	3
HORSE–BETA	VAL	GLN	LEU	SER	GLY	GLU	GLU	LYS	ALA	ALA	VAL	LEU	ALA	LEU	TRY	ASP	LYS	VAL	ASN		GLU	GLU	GLU	VAL	GLY	GLY	GLU	ALA	LEU	GLY	ARG	LEU	LE
	1	2	3	4	5	6	7	8	9	10	11	12	13	14	15	16	17	18	19		20	21	22	23	24	25	26	27	28	29	30	31	3
WHALE MYOGLOBIN	VAL		LEU	SER	GLU	GLY	GLU	TRY	GLN	LEU	VAL	LEU	HIS	VAL	TRY	ALA	LYS	VAL	GLU	ALA	ASP	VAL	ALA	GLY	HIS	GLY	GLN	ASP	ILEU	LEU	ILEU	ARG	LEU	P
	1		2	3	4	5	6	7	8	9	10	11	12	14	15	16	17	18	19	21	22	23	24	25	26	27	28	29	30	31	32	3

FAMILY RESEMBLANCES are exhibited by the polypeptide chains found in several kinds of hemoglobin and by the polypeptide chain of sperm whale myoglobin. Hemoglobin is the oxygen-carrying molecule of the blood; myoglobin stores oxygen in muscle. Polypeptides are molecular chains whose links are amino acid units, usually called residues. The hemoglobin chains comprise either 141 or 146 residues; the myoglobin chain, 153. (The illustration is continued on pages 318 and 319.) Each molecule of

are required to make a "word" specifying one amino acid molecule, there is a certain compression of information between the gene and the polypeptide chain it encodes. A "structural" gene containing 600 code letters is required to specify a polypeptide containing 200 amino acid residues. The reason for the three-to-one ratio is that there are 20 kinds of amino acid and only four kinds of DNA code letters, embodied in subunits called bases, to identify them; a minimum of three code letters, or bases, is needed to specify each amino acid. (In fact, three code units can specify 64 different items, and there is evidence that more than one DNA triplet exists for some of the amino acids.)

Enough is now known about the amino acid sequence of certain polypeptides to enable the chemical paleontologist to test the validity of three basic postulates. The first asserts that polypeptide chains in present-day organisms have arisen by evolutionary divergence from similar polypeptide chains that existed in the past. The present and past chains would be similar in that many of their amino acid residues match; such chains are said to be homologous. The

second postulate is that a gene existing at some past epoch can occasionally be duplicated so that it appears at two or more sites in the genome of descendent organisms. Thus a contemporary organism can have two or more homologous genes represented by two or more homologous polypeptide chains, which have mutated independently and are therefore no longer identical in structure. The third postulate holds that the mutational events most commonly retained by natural selection are those that lead to the replacement of a single amino acid residue in a polypeptide chain.

In addition to these three postulates I would like to suggest a fourth that is much more controversial: Contemporary organisms that look much like ancient ancestral organisms probably contain a majority of polypeptide chains that resemble quite closely those of the ancient organisms. In other words, certain animals said to be "living fossils," such as the cockroach, the horseshoe crab, the shark and, among mammals, the lemur, probably manufacture a great many polypeptide molecules that differ only slightly from those manufactured by their ancestors millions of

years ago. This postulate is controversial because it is often said that evolution has been just as long for organisms that appear to have changed little as for those that have changed much; consequently it is held that the biochemistry of living fossils is probably very different from that of their remote ancestors. My own view is that it is unlikely that selective forces would favor the stability of morphological characteristics without at the same time favoring the stability of biochemical characteristics, which are more fundamental.

As an example of the application of chemical paleogenetics I shall describe how evolutionary changes are reflected in the molecular structure of hemoglobin, the oxygen-carrying protein of the blood. Hemoglobin is the most complex protein whose detailed molecular composition and structure are known in man, in his near relatives among the primates and in his more distant relatives such as horses and cattle. The composition and structure of hemoglobin molecules in more primitive organisms such as fishes are rapidly being worked out.

Hemoglobin is a particularly good

ALA	ALANINE	LEU	LEUCINE
ARG	ARGININE	LYS	LYSINE
ASN	ASPARAGINE	MET	METHIONINE
ASP	ASPARTIC ACID	PHE	PHENYLALANINE
CYS	CYSTEINE	PRO	PROLINE
GLN	GLUTAMINE	SER	SERINE
GLU	GLUTAMIC ACID	THR	THREONINE
GLY	GLYCINE	TRY	TRYPTOPHAN
HIS	HISTIDINE	TYR	TYROSINE
ILEU	ISOLEUCINE	VAL	VALINE

RESIDUE THE SAME IN ALL CHAINS SHOWN
RESIDUE THE SAME IN ALL KNOWN HEMOGLOBIN AND MYOGLOBIN CHAINS
RESIDUE THE SAME IN ALL HEMOGLOBIN CHAINS SHOWN
RESIDUE THE SAME IN ALL KNOWN HEMOGLOBIN CHAINS
RESIDUE THE SAME IN FOUR MAIN HUMAN HEMOGLOBIN CHAINS
RESIDUE THE SAME AS THAT IN HUMAN BETA CHAIN
RESIDUE DIFFERENT FROM THAT IN HUMAN BETA CHAIN
RESIDUE NOT DETERMINED
(SOME RESIDUE ASSIGNMENTS ARE TENTATIVE)

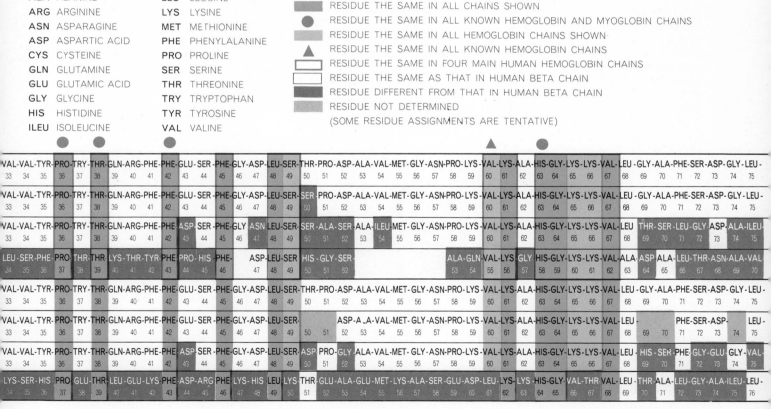

hemoglobin contains two subunits of a polypeptide chain called alpha (α) and two of a chain called beta (β). In human adults about 2 percent of the hemoglobin molecules contain delta (δ) chains in place of beta chains. Two other chains, gamma (γ) and epsilon (ε, not shown), are manufactured during fetal life and can also serve in place of the β-chain. The illustration enables one to compare the four principal chains (α, β, γ, δ) found in human hemoglobin with the β-chains found (caption continued on next page)

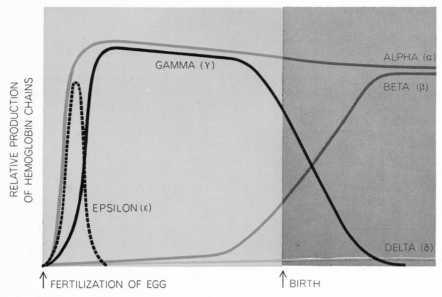

GAMMA (γ)

ALPHA (α)

BETA (β)

EPSILON (ε)

DELTA (δ)

RELATIVE PRODUCTION OF HEMOGLOBIN CHAINS

↑ FERTILIZATION OF EGG   ↑ BIRTH

OUTPUT OF HUMAN HEMOGLOBIN CHAINS shifts abruptly during fetal development. Throughout life two of the four subunits in normal hemoglobin are α-chains. These chains pair first with epsilon (ε) chains, then with γ-chains. Just before birth β-chains begin to replace γ-chains. Simultaneously δ-chains appear and also pair with some α-chains.

same. Both the similarities and the differences are of interest to the chemical paleontologist.

The reader may wonder at this point how one can assume that the alpha and beta chains of human hemoglobin have a common ancestry if they are now more different than they are alike. The answer is that it seems most improbable that two different and unrelated polypeptide chains could evolve in such a way as to have the same function, the same conformation and a substantial number of identical amino acid residues at corresponding molecular sites. Consequently the chemical paleontologist interprets their marked difference in amino acid sequence as evidence that a long time has elapsed since they diverged from a common ancestor.

subject for chemical paleogenetics because it is produced in several slightly variant forms even within an individual organism, and the study of these variants suggests how their components may have descended from a common ancestral form. A molecule of hemoglobin is composed of four large subunits, each a polypeptide chain. Each chain enfolds an iron-containing "heme" group that can pick up an atom of oxygen as hemoglobin passes through the lungs and release it in tissues where oxygen is needed.

The principal kind of hemoglobin found in the human adult is composed of two alpha chains and two beta chains, and it is believed that they too have a common ancestry. The alpha chain comprises 141 amino acid residues; the beta chain, 146. Although the two chains are quite similar in their three-dimensional conformation, they differ considerably in composition. When the two chains are placed side by side, there are 77 sites where the residues in the two chains are different and only 64 sites where the residues are the

The argument for a common ancestry is strengthened by the fact that in the hemoglobins of man the beta chain is sometimes replaced by chains with still other amino acid sequences known as gamma, delta and epsilon chains. The epsilon chain is manufactured only for a brief period early in fetal life. The gamma chain replaces the beta chain during most of embryonic development and disappears almost entirely shortly after birth. Throughout adult life a small fraction of the hemoglobin in circulation contains delta chains rather than beta chains [see top illustration on this page]. The beta, gamma and delta chains are all 146 units long and closely resemble one another in amino acid sequence. There are only 39 differences in amino acid residues between the beta

ALA	HIS	LEU	ASP	ASN	LEU	LYS	GLY	THR	PHE	ALA	THR	LEU	SER	GLU	LEU	HIS	CYS	ASP	LYS	LEU	HIS	VAL	ASP	PRO	GLU	ASN	PHE	ARG	LEU	LEU	GLY	ASN	VAL	LEU	VAL	CYS	VAL	LEU	ALA	HIS	HIS	PH
76	77	78	79	80	81	82	83	84	85	86	87	88	89	90	91	92	93	94	95	96	97	98	99	100	101	102	103	104	105	106	107	108	109	110	111	112	113	114	115	116	117	11
ALA	HIS	LEU	ASP	ASN	LEU	LYS	GLY	THR	PHE	SER	GLN	LEU	SER	GLU	LEU	HIS	CYS	ASP	LYS	LEU	HIS	VAL	ASP	PRO	GLU	ASN	PHE	ARG	LEU	LEU	GLY	ASN	VAL	LEU	VAL	CYS	VAL	LEU	ALA	ARG	ASN	PH
76	77	78	79	80	81	82	83	84	85	86	87	88	89	90	91	92	93	94	95	96	97	98	99	100	101	102	103	104	105	106	107	108	109	110	111	112	113	114	115	116	117	11
LYS	HIS	LEU	ASP	ASP	LEU	LYS	GLY	THR	PHE	ALA	GLN	LEU	SER	GLU	LEU	HIS	CYS	ASP	LYS	LEU	HIS	VAL	ASP	PRO	GLU	ASN	PHE	LYS	LEU	LEU	GLY	ASN	VAL	LEU	VAL	THR	VAL	LEU	ALA	ILEU	HIS	PH
76	77	78	79	80	81	82	83	84	85	86	87	88	89	90	91	92	93	94	95	96	97	98	99	100	101	102	103	104	105	106	107	108	109	110	111	112	113	114	115	116	117	11
ALA	HIS	VAL	ASP	ASP	MET	PRO	ASN	ALA	LEU	SER	ALA	LEU	SER	ASP	LEU	HIS	ALA	HIS	LYS	LEU	ARG	VAL	ASP	PRO	VAL	ASN	PHE	LYS	LEU	LEU	SER	HIS	CYS	LEU	LEU	VAL	THR	LEU	ALA	ALA	HIS	L
71	72	73	74	75	76	77	78	79	80	81	82	83	84	85	86	87	88	89	90	91	92	93	94	95	96	97	98	99	100	101	102	103	104	105	106	107	108	109	110	111	112	
ALA	HIS	LEU	ASP	ASN	LEU	LYS	GLY	THR	PHE	ALA	THR	LEU	SER	GLU	LEU	HIS	CYS	ASP	LYS	LEU	HIS	VAL	ASP	PRO	GLU	ASN	PHE	LYS	LEU	LEU	GLY	ASN	VAL	LEU	VAL	CYS	VAL	LEU	ALA	HIS	HIS	PH
76	77	78	79	80	81	82	83	84	85	86	87	88	89	90	91	92	93	94	95	96	97	98	99	100	101	102	103	104	105	106	107	108	109	110	111	112	113	114	115	116	117	11
LYS	HIS	LEU	ASP	ASN	LEU	LYS	GLY	THR	PHE	ALA	LYS	LEU	SER	GLU	LEU	HIS	CYS	ASP	GLU	LEU	HIS	VAL	ASP	PRO	GLU	ASN	PHE	ARG			GLY	ASN	VAL		VAL		VAL	LEU	ALA	ARG	ARG	PH
76	77	78	79	80	81	82	83	84	85	86	87	88	89	90	91	92	93	94	95	96	97	98	99	100	101	102	103	104			107	108	109	110		113	114		116	117	11
HIS	HIS	LEU	ASP	ASN	LEU	LYS	GLY	THR	PHE	ALA	ALA	LEU	SER	GLU	LEU	HIS	CYS	ASP	LYS	LEU	HIS	VAL	ASP	PRO	GLU	ASN	PHE	ARG	LEU	LEU	GLY	ASN	VAL	LEU	ALA	LEU	VAL	VAL	ALA	ARG	HIS	PH
76	77	78	79	80	81	82	83	84	85	86	87	88	89	90	91	92	93	94	95	96	97	98	99	100	101	102	103	104	105	106	107	108	109	110	111	112	113	114	115	116	117	11
LYS	LYS	LYS	GLY	HIS	HIS	GLU	ALA	GLU	LEU	LYS	PRO	LEU	ALA	GLN	SER	HIS	ALA	THR	LYS	HIS	LYS	ILEU	PRO	ILEU	LYS	TYR	LEU	GLU	PHE	ILEU	SER	GLU	ALA	ILEU	ILEU	HIS	VAL	LEU	HIS	SER	ARG	H
77	78	79	80	81	82	83	84	85	86	87	88	89	90	91	92	93	94	95	96	97	98	99	100	101	102	103	104	105	106	107	108	109	110	111	112	113	114	115	116	117	118	1

in the hemoglobin molecules of gorillas, pigs and horses. The δ-, γ- and α-chains are ranked below the human β-chain in order of increasing number of differences. The gorilla β-chain differs from the human β-chain at only one site. The pig β-chain appears to

differ at about 17 sites (based on the known differences), and the horse β-chain at 26 sites. The number of differences indicates roughly how far these animals are separated from man on the phylogenetic tree. Relatively few sites have been completely re-

and the gamma chains and only 10 between the beta and the delta chains. The sequence of the human epsilon chain has not yet been established.

One other oxygen-carrying protein molecule figures in this discussion of hemoglobin evolution: the protein known as myoglobin, which does not circulate in the blood but acts as an oxygen repository in muscle. Myoglobin is a single polypeptide chain of 153 amino acid residues that has nearly the same three-dimensional configuration as the various hemoglobin chains. In fact, the unraveling of the three-dimensional structure of sperm whale myoglobin in 1958 by John C. Kendrew and his colleagues at the University of Cambridge marked the first complete determination of the structure of any protein molecule. Two years later Kendrew's colleague M. F. Perutz announced the three-dimensional conformation of the alpha and beta chains of horse hemoglobin; their topological similarity to myoglobin was immediately apparent [see "The Three-dimensional Structure of a Protein Molecule," by John C. Kendrew, SCIENTIFIC AMERICAN Offprint 121, and "The Hemoglobin Molecule," by M. F. Perutz, which begins on page 39 in this book].

In amino acid sequence whale myoglobin and the alpha and beta chains of human hemoglobin are far apart. The sequence for human myoglobin is only now being determined, and it is apparent that it will be much closer to the sequence of whale myoglobin than to that of any of the human hemoglobin chains. Whale myoglobin and the alpha

chain of human hemoglobin have the same residues at 37 sites; whale myoglobin and the human beta chain are alike at 35 sites. Again the chemical paleontologist regards it as probable that myoglobin and the various hemoglobin chains have descended from a remote common ancestor and are therefore homologous.

Although I have been speaking loosely of the evolution and descent of polypeptide chains, the reader should keep in mind that the molecular mutations underlying the evolutionary process take place not in polypeptide molecules but in the structural genes of DNA that carry the blueprint for each polypeptide chain. The effect of a single mutation of the most common kind is to change a single base in a structural gene, with the result that one triplet code word is changed into a different code word. Unless the new code word happens to specify the same amino acid as the old code word (which is sometimes the case) the altered gene will specify a polypeptide chain in which one of the amino acid residues is replaced by a different one. The effect of such a substitution is usually harmful to the organism, but from time to time a one-unit alteration in a polypeptide chain will increase the organism's chances of survival in a particular environment and the organism will transmit its altered gene to its progeny. This is the basic mechanism of natural selection.

As I have mentioned, there are also types of mutation that produce deletions or additions in a polypeptide

chain. And there are the still more complex genetic events in which it is believed a structural gene is duplicated. One of the duplicates may later be shifted to a different location so that copies appear at two or more places in the genome. Such gene duplication, followed by independent mutation, would seem to account for the various homologues of hemoglobin found in all vertebrates.

Duplicate genes may have several values for an organism. For example, they may provide the organism with twice as much of a given polypeptide chain as it had before the duplication. They may also have subtler and more important values. It may be that the gamma chain found in fetal hemoglobin is particularly adapted to the needs of prenatal existence whereas the beta chain that replaces the gamma chain soon after birth is more suitable for life outside the womb. The precise value to the organism of having these two kinds of hemoglobin chain available at different stages of development remains to be discovered. It is somewhat puzzling that adult humans who have a certain genetically controlled abnormality go through life with gamma chains rather than beta chains in a significant fraction of their hemoglobin and show no ill effects.

Even without detailed knowledge of the role of duplicate genes it is clear that they are valuable both for the evolution of species and for the development of the individual organism. For purposes of evolution they provide two (or more) copies of genetic material that

HEMOGLOBIN CHAINS

Chain	Sequence (residue positions)
HUMAN–BETA	GLY(119)-LYS(120)-GLU(121)-PHE(122)-THR(123)-PRO(124)-PRO(125)-VAL(126)-GLN(127)-ALA(128)-ALA(129)-TYR(130)-GLN(131)-LYS(132)-VAL(133)-VAL(134)-ALA(135)-GLY(136)-VAL(137)-ALA(138)-ASN(139)-ALA(140)-LEU(141)-ALA(142)-HIS(143)-LYS(144)-TYR(145)-HIS(146)
HUMAN–DELTA	GLY(119)-LYS(120)-GLU(121)-PHE(122)-THR(123)-PRO(124)-GLN(125)-MET(126)-GLN(127)-ALA(128)-ALA(129)-TYR(130)-GLN(131)-LYS(132)-VAL(133)-VAL(134)-ALA(135)-GLY(136)-VAL(137)-ALA(138)-ASN(139)-ALA(140)-LEU(141)-ALA(142)-HIS(143)-LYS(144)-TYR(145)-HIS(146)
HUMAN–GAMMA	GLY(119)-LYS(120)-GLU(121)-PHE(122)-THR(123)-PRO(124)-GLU(125)-VAL(126)-GLN(127)-ALA(128)-SER(129)-TRY(130)-GLN(131)-LYS(132)-MET(133)-VAL(134)-THR(135)-GLY(136)-VAL(137)-ALA(138)-SER(139)-ALA(140)-LEU(141)-SER(142)-SER(143)-ARG(144)-TYR(145)-HIS(146)
HUMAN–ALPHA	PRO(114)-ALA(115)-GLU(116)-PHE(117)-THR(118)-PRO(119)-ALA(120)-VAL(121)-HIS(122)-ALA(123)-SER(124)-LEU(125)-ASP(126)-LYS(127)-PHE(128)-LEU(129)-ALA(130)-SER(131)-VAL(132)-SER(133)-THR(134)-VAL(135)-LEU(136)-THR(137)-SER(138)-LYS(139)-TYR(140)-ARG(141)
GORILLA–BETA	GLY(119)-LYS(120)-GLU(121)-PHE(122)-THR(123)-PRO(124)-PRO(125)-VAL(126)-GLN(127)-ALA(128)-ALA(129)-TYR(130)-GLN(131)-LYS(132)-VAL(133)-VAL(134)-ALA(135)-GLY(136)-VAL(137)-ALA(138)-ASN(139)-ALA(140)-LEU(141)-ALA(142)-HIS(143)-LYS(144)-TYR(145)-HIS(146)
PIG–BETA	GLY(119)- [. . .] -LYS(132)-VAL(133)-VAL(134)-ALA(135)-GLY(136)-VAL(137)-ALA(138)-ASN(139)-ALA(140)-LEU(141)-ALA(142)-HIS(143)-LYS(144)-TYR(145)-HIS(146)
HORSE–BETA	GLY(119)-LYS(120)-ASP(121)-PHE(122)-THR(123)-PRO(124)-GLU(125)-LEU(126)-GLN(127)-ALA(128)-SER(129)-TYR(130)-GLN(131)-LYS(132)-VAL(133)-VAL(134)-ALA(135)-GLY(136)-VAL(137)-ALA(138)-ASN(139)-ALA(140)-LEU(141)-ALA(142)-HIS(143)-LYS(144)-TYR(145)-HIS(146)
WHALE MYOGLOBIN	PRO(120)-GLY(121)-ASN(122)-PHE(123)-GLY(124)-ALA(125)-ASP(126)-ALA(127)-GLN(128)-GLY(129)-ALA(130)-MET(131)-ASN(132)-LYS(133)-ALA(134)-LEU(135)-GLU(136)-LEU(137)-PHE(138)-ARG(139)-LYS(140)-ASP(141)-ILEU(142)-ALA(143)-ALA(144)-LYS(145)-TYR(146)-LYS(147)-GLU(148)-LEU(149)-GLY(150)-TYR(151)-GLN(152)-GLY(153)

sistant to evolutionary change. Only 11 of the sites (*colored circles*) have the same residues in all known hemoglobin and myoglobin chains, and only 15 more sites (*colored triangles*) have the same residues in all known chains of hemoglobin. Among the four

principal chains of normal human hemoglobin the same residues are found at 49 sites. The β-, δ- and γ-chains, which are closely related, have 103 sites in common. The three-dimensional conformation of all these chains is illustrated at the top of the next page.

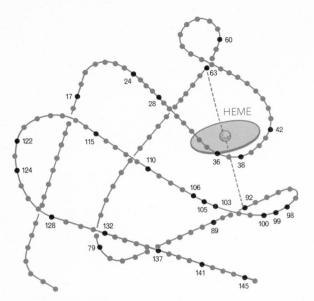
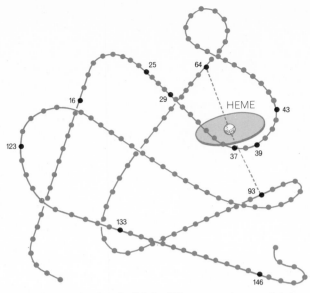

INVARIANT SITES are identified on knotlike shapes representing the three-dimensional structure of the polypeptide chains of hemoglobin and myoglobin. The 26 numbered sites at left are occupied by the same residues in all known hemoglobin chains. Eleven of these same sites (*assigned slightly different numbers at right*) are occupied by the same residues in all known chains of hemoglobin and myoglobin. Presumably the invariant sites are important in establishing the structure and function of these polypeptides.

are free to evolve separately. Thus a duplicate gene may be transformed so completely that it gives rise to a new type of polypeptide chain with a function entirely different from that of its ancestor. In the life history of an individual organism the existence of duplicate genes at different sites in the genome enables the organism to obtain a supply of an essential polypeptide without activation of the whole genome. In this way gene duplication makes possible a more complex pattern of gene activation and inactivation during an organism's development.

It is not always easy to decide when two polypeptide chains are homologous and when they are not. As long as one is dealing with rather similar chains that serve the same function—as in the case of the various hemoglobin chains—there is a strong *prima facie* case for homology. As the amino acid sequences of more and more polypeptides are deciphered, however, one can expect ambiguities to arise.

One potential source of ambiguity arises in the identification of "corresponding" molecular sites. Such sites are often made to correspond by shifting parts of one chain with respect to the homologous chain [*see illustration below*]. The shifts are justified on the grounds that deletions or additions of one to several residues in a row have occurred during the evolution of certain polypeptide chains. A shift is considered successful when it maximizes the number of identities between the segments of two chains. The argument, therefore, is somewhat circular in that the shifts are justified by the presumed deletions (or additions) and the deletions (or additions) by the shifts. The argument that breaks the circle is that by invoking a small number of shifts, homologous polypeptide chains can be brought to display remarkable coincidences, whereas nonhomologous chains cannot be. There remains, however, the problem of placing the concept of homology on an objective basis. An effort is being made to do this with

the help of a computer analysis of real and hypothetical polypeptide chains.

Now that the reader has this background I can provide a more detailed statement of the aims and methods of chemical paleogenetics. Fundamentally it attempts to discover the probable amino acid sequence of ancestral polypeptide chains and also the probable base sequence in the genes that controlled them. It is concerned with the fate of the descendent line of each gene. It inquires whether gene duplication has occurred and, if so, when it occurred; it asks what became of the duplicate genes, how they may have been shifted to various parts of the genome and how they have mutated. Finally it is concerned with the factors that regulate the rate and timing of the synthesis of the various polypeptide chains.

Present evidence suggests (although exceptions are known) that the number of differences between homologous polypeptide chains of a certain type found in different animals is roughly

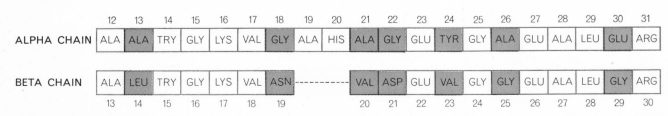

	12	13	14	15	16	17	18	19	20	21	22	23	24	25	26	27	28	29	30	31
ALPHA CHAIN	ALA	ALA	TRY	GLY	LYS	VAL	GLY	ALA	HIS	ALA	GLY	GLU	TYR	GLY	ALA	GLU	ALA	LEU	GLU	ARG
BETA CHAIN	ALA	LEU	TRY	GLY	LYS	VAL	ASN	---------	VAL	ASP	GLU	VAL	GLY	GLY	GLU	ALA	LEU	GLY	ARG	
		13	14	15	16	17	18	19	20	21	22	23	24	25	26	27	28	29	30	

CORRESPONDING REGIONS of the α- and β-chains of human hemoglobin show how a short deletion must be inferred in the β-chain to produce a good match at corresponding sites. An earlier one-unit deletion in the α-chain explains why α-site 12 corresponds to β-site 13. By postulating the two-unit deletion shown here the two chains can be made to have the same residues at 11 sites.

proportional to the relatedness of these animals as established by standard methods of phylogenetic classification. Indeed, the readily observable differences among living things must be to a significant extent the expression of differences in their enzymes—the proteins that catalyze the chemical reactions of life—and therefore of differences in the amino acid sequences of the polypeptide chains that form the enzymes. It is probable that observable differences also reflect differences in the regulation of rate and timing of the synthesis of polypeptide chains rather than differences in the amino acid sequence of these chains.

On the other hand, a difference in sequence may express itself primarily as a difference in rate and timing. It is quite probable that regulatory enzymes play an important role, and less obvious regulatory mechanisms may also exist. It has been suggested, for example, that differences in rate and timing may be attributable to certain sequences of bases in DNA that never find expression in a polypeptide chain. It seems in the last analysis, however, that the differences between organisms, if the environment is kept constant, boil down to differences in molecular sequences. These differences may reside in base sequences in genes, which are then expressed in amino acid sequences in polypeptide chains; they may reside in other base sequences that are not so expressed; finally they may reside in the sequential order in which genes are distributed within the genome.

Although chemical paleogenetics will ultimately have taxonomic value in providing a fundamental way of measuring the distance between living things on the evolutionary scale, this is not its prime objective. A major value of analyzing evolutionary changes at the molecular level will be to provide a deeper understanding of natural selection in relation to different types of mutation.

Let me proceed, then, to apply the methods of chemical paleogenetics to the myoglobin-hemoglobin family of polypeptide chains. The top illustration at the right shows the number of differences in amino acid sequence between four animal-hemoglobin alpha and beta chains and the corresponding human chains. For purposes of rough computation let us assume that the alpha and beta chains evolve at the same rate and pool the number of differences they exhibit. The reason for doing this is to

ANIMAL	NUMBER OF DIFFERENCES		MEAN NUMBER OF DIFFERENCES, ALL CHAINS	ESTIMATED TIME SINCE COMMON ANCESTOR
	ALPHA CHAIN	BETA CHAIN		
HORSE	17	26		
PIG	~ 18	~ 17	~ 22	80 MILLION YEARS
CATTLE	~ 27			
RABBIT	~ 27			

COMPARISON OF HEMOGLOBIN CHAINS offers a way to estimate the number of years required to produce an evolutionarily effective change at one site. The values given here for the number of differences represent a comparison with the α- and β-chains of human hemoglobin. The mean of 22 differences between any pair of human and animal chains implies an average of 11 mutations per chain, or about one change per seven million years.

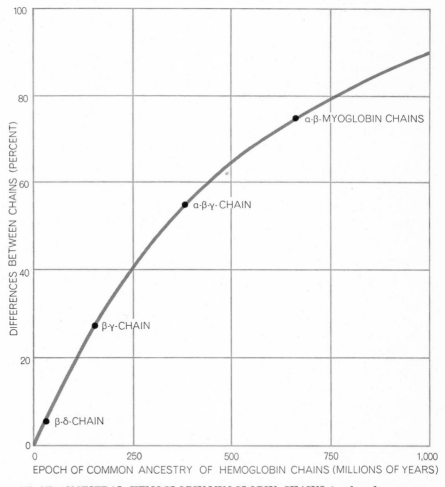

AGE OF ANCESTRAL HEMOGLOBIN-MYOGLOBIN CHAINS is plotted on a curve computed by Linus Pauling. Except for myoglobin the chains represented are those of humans. Where only a few differences are observed it is assumed that about seven million years are needed to establish an effective mutation. But where chains show large differences today it can be assumed that more than one mutation occurred at a given site in the course of evolution. For example, the α-chain and β-chain each differ from the myoglobin chain at about 110 sites. Thus the ancestral α-β-myoglobin chain appears on the curve where the vertical axis reads 75 percent (110/146 is about 3/4). This point corresponds to a period about 650 million years ago rather than the 385 million years that would be obtained if 55 mutations per gene line (110 ÷ 2) were simply multiplied by seven million.

establish a mean value for the number of apparent amino acid substitutions that have occurred in the alpha and beta chains of the four animal species (horse, pig, cattle and rabbit) since the time when the four species and man had a common ancestor. The mean difference is 22 apparent changes in the two chains, or an average of 11 changes per chain. If the common ancestor of man and the four other animals lived about 80 million years ago, as is thought to be the case, the average time required to establish a successful amino acid substitution in any species is about seven million years. Until more chains have been analyzed, however, 10 million years per substitution is a good order-of-magnitude figure.

Such a figure can now be used for a different purpose: to estimate very roughly the time elapsed since the four principal types of chain in human hemoglobin had a common ancestor. In making such a calculation one must employ statistical principles to allow for the following fact. The greater the number of differences in sequence be-

tween two homologous chains, the greater the chances that at some molecular sites more than one amino acid substitution will have been retained temporarily by evolution since the time of the common ancestor. An appropriate calculation was recently performed by Linus Pauling, with the result shown in the bottom illustration on the preceding page. The curve in the illustration allows one to read off the probable time of existence of the common molecular ancestor of various polypeptide chains as a function of the percentage of differences in amino acid sequence between the chains.

The two chains that are most nearly alike—the beta and delta chains—differ at only 10 sites and presumably were the most recent to arise by duplication of a common genetic ancestor. To exhibit 10 differences each gene line would have to undergo only five changes, which implies an elapsed time of roughly 35 million years on Pauling's chart. The beta and gamma chains are different at 37 sites and thus seem to have arisen by gene duplication about

150 million years ago. The beta and alpha chains are different at 76 sites and therefore their common ancestor goes back some 380 million years. If the calculation is valid as a rough approximation, the common genetic ancestor of the hemoglobin chains now circulating in the human bloodstream dates back to the Devonian period and to the appearance of the first amphibians.

The curve also indicates very roughly how long it has been since the chains of hemoglobin and myoglobin may have arisen as the result of duplication of a common ancestral gene. The differences in amino acid sequence between hemoglobin chains and myoglobin are so numerous that their common molecular ancestor may date back about 650 million years to the end of the Precambrian era, long before the appearance of the vertebrates. This suggests, in turn, that it may be possible to find in living invertebrates a distant relative of the vertebrate hemoglobins and myoglobins.

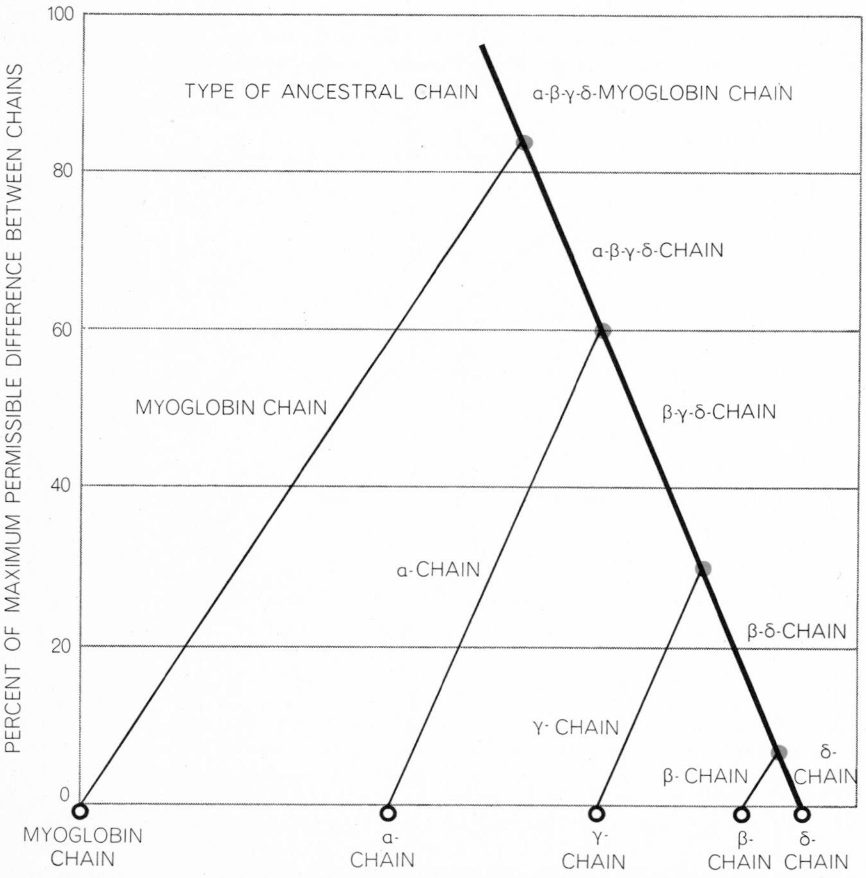

Let me turn now from discussing the overall differences between homologous polypeptide chains to the question of how one might construct a molecular "phylogenetic tree." Such a tree would show an evolutionary line of descent for an entire family of polypeptide molecules. One can also construct individual trees for individual molecular sites. Later this site-by-site information can be synthesized to obtain probable residue sequences for complete ancestral chains.

If the amino acid residue is the same in two homologous chains at a given molecular site, there is a certain probability that the same residue was also present in the common ancestor of the two chains. There is also a chance, of course, that the ancestral residue was different and that the identity observed in the two homologous existing chains was produced by molecular convergence or simply by coincidence. Traditional paleontology reveals many examples of convergences at the level of large-scale morphology. In chemical paleogenetics molecular convergence or coincidence is particularly troublesome because the path from difference to similarity runs directly counter to that needed to trace a molecular phylogenetic tree. About all one can say at this stage in the development of the new discipline is that convergence or coincidence do not seem to occur often enough to vitiate the effort of constructing such trees.

The illustration at the left shows

HEMOGLOBIN-MYOGLOBIN RELATIONSHIP is traced back through evolution, based on the number of differences in the various chains. The four colored dots indicate where ancestral genes were presumably duplicated, giving rise each time to a new gene line.

schematically, in the form of an inverted tree, the probable evolutionary relationships for the known chains of human hemoglobin and myoglobin. The tree also represents the relationships of any given molecular site in these chains. The epsilon chain has been omitted because too little is known about it. The vertical axis is not an absolute time scale but shows how chain differences rate on a scale in which the maximum permissible difference is 100 percent. Some of the branching points in the tree are assumed to coincide with a gene duplication. Following such duplication the resulting independent genes (and their polypeptide chains) evolve separately. The most ancient duplication presumably separated the myoglobin gene from the gene that ultimately gave rise, by repeated duplications, to the alpha, beta, gamma and delta genes of hemoglobin. Additional gene duplications will surely have to be postulated along various lines.

The next molecular phylogenetic tree [see top illustration at right] attempts to reconstruct the evolutionary changes at one particular site (site No. 4 in the human alpha chain) that led to the amino acid residues now observed at that site in various animal species, including man. As the genetic code is being worked out, it is becoming possible to distinguish amino acid substitutions that may have occurred in one step from those requiring two or more steps. It is a principle of chemical paleogenetics that in postulating a possible ancestral amino acid residue one should prefer the residue that can be reached by invoking the fewest number of mutations in the genetic message. In the tree just referred to the residue of the amino acid alanine has been selected as the residue at site No. 4 in the ancestral polypeptide chain from which the 17 present-day hemoglobin chains are descended. This selection may seem odd; among the 17 chains eight have proline in the No. 4 position and only four have alanine. (The remaining five chains have glycine, glutamic acid or serine in the No. 4 position.) The explanation is that if proline is assumed to be in the No. 4 position in the most remote ancestral chain, one has to postulate nine or 10 evolutionarily effective amino acid substitutions in the various descendent chains to reach the residues actually observed in the 17 present-day chains, but if alanine is selected as the ancestral residue, only eight effective substitutions are needed.

The choice of alanine becomes more impressive when it is shown that no

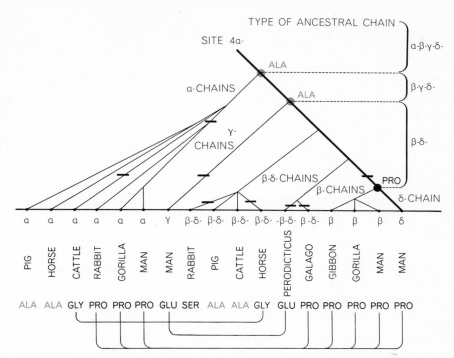

ANCESTRAL RESIDUE can be traced by trying to establish the simplest lines of descent for residues now found at a particular site in polypeptide chains of hemoglobin. The residues shown across the bottom occupy site No. 4 in the human α-chain. (Perodicticus and Galago are small monkeys commonly known as the potto and the bush baby.) Alanine (ala) is selected as the probable residue in the earliest ancestral chain because it provides a line of descent requiring fewer mutations than any other that might be selected: eight. They are represented by short horizontal bars. The lines at the bottom identify convergences or coincidences: identical residues that presumably resulted from independent mutations.

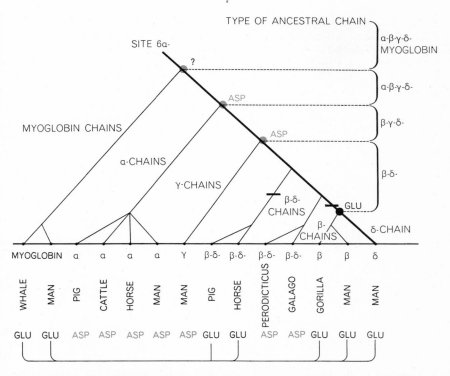

AMBIGUOUS ANCESTRAL RELATIONSHIP is encountered when the present-day residues at a particular site are those of two amino acids that frequently replace each other, such as glutamic acid (glu) and aspartic acid (asp). The sites compared are No. 6 in the α-chain of human hemoglobin. Note that myoglobin has been included in this evolutionary tree.

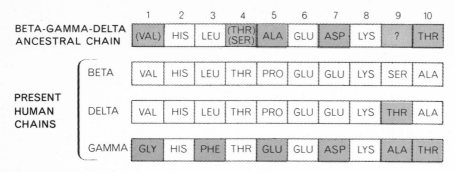

		1	2	3	4	5	6	7	8	9	10
BETA-GAMMA-DELTA ANCESTRAL CHAIN		(VAL)	HIS	LEU	(THR) (SER)	ALA	GLU	ASP	LYS	?	THR
PRESENT HUMAN CHAINS	BETA	VAL	HIS	LEU	THR	PRO	GLU	GLU	LYS	SER	ALA
	DELTA	VAL	HIS	LEU	THR	PRO	GLU	GLU	LYS	THR	ALA
	GAMMA	GLY	HIS	PHE	THR	GLU	GLU	ASP	LYS	ALA	THR

RECONSTRUCTION OF ANCESTRAL CHAIN represents a synthesis of evolutionary trees for individual sites as illustrated on the preceding page. This chart shows the first 10 sites in the ancestral β-γ-δ-chain and the corresponding region in its three present-day descendants. Residues in the δ-, γ- and ancestral chains that differ from those in the contemporary β-chain are shown in color. Gray indicates uncertain or unknown residues.

more than one amino acid substitution is needed in any single line of descent to explain the residues currently observed. If proline is made the ancestral choice, double substitutions—the ones least likely to occur—must be postulated in three of the lines of descent. The choice of any other amino acid for the ancestral position would necessitate many more substitutions. Alanine is therefore adopted as the most probable ancestral residue—a conclusion that is not likely to need revision unless the genetic code is revised with regard to proline. In this particular example molecular coincidence is represented in some of the chains that now contain proline, glutamic acid and glycine.

The problem of identifying a probable ancestral residue is often difficult. At a site where there are frequent interchanges between residues that seem to be more or less functionally equivalent, any conclusion about ancestry becomes doubtful. This is demonstrated at site

No. 6, as numbered in the human alpha chain, where there is a frequent interchange between aspartic acid and glutamic acid [see bottom illustration on preceding page].

The information from a series of molecular phylogenetic trees can finally be synthesized to produce a complete sequence of residues representing the composition of an ancestral polypeptide chain. The illustration above shows such a postulated sequence for the first 10 sites of the polypeptide chain that is presumed to be the ancestor of the beta, gamma and delta chains now present in human hemoglobin.

In order to establish by chemical paleogenetics the evolutionary relationship between two different organisms it should not be necessary to know the sequential composition of thousands or even hundreds of homologous polypeptide chains. To require such knowledge would be discouraging indeed. It can

reasonably be predicted, however, that a comparison of relatively few chains—perhaps a few dozen—should yield a large fraction of the maximum amount of information that polypeptide chains can provide. The reason is that even relatively few chains should yield a good statistical sample of the evolutionary behavior of many chains.

Chemical paleogenetics offers many new possibilities. For example, after one has reconstructed a number of ancestral polypeptides for some ancient organism one should be able to make various deductions about some of its physiological functions. One might be able to decide, for instance, whether it could live successfully in an atmosphere composed as we know it today or whether it was designed for a different atmosphere.

From similar polypeptide reconstructions it may be possible to make informed guesses about organisms, such as soft-bodied animals, that have left no fossil record. In this way the state of living matter in past evolutionary times can be pieced together, at least in part, without the help of fossil remains. But one of the main attractions of chemical paleogenetics is the possibility of deriving strictly from molecular sequences a phylogenetic tree that is entirely independent of phylogenetic evidence gathered by traditional methods. If this can be accomplished, one can compare the two kinds of phylogenetic tree—the molecular and the traditional—and see if they tell the same story of evolution. If they do, chemical paleogenetics will have provided a powerful and independent confirmation of the already well-documented theory of evolution.

33 | Chemical Fossils

GEOFFREY EGLINTON AND MELVIN CALVIN · January 1967

If you ask a child to draw a dinosaur, the chances are that he will produce a recognizable picture of such a creature. His familiarity with an animal that lived 150 million years ago can of course be traced to the intensive studies of paleontologists, who have been able to reconstruct the skeletons of extinct animals from fossilized bones preserved in ancient sediments. Recent chemical research now shows that minute quantities of organic compounds—remnants of the original carbon-containing chemical constituents of the soft parts of the animal—are still present in some fossils and in ancient sediments of all ages, including some measured in billions of years. As a result of this finding organic chemists and geologists have joined in a search for "chemical fossils": organic molecules that have survived unchanged or little altered from their original structure, when they were part of organisms long since vanished.

This kind of search does not require the presence of the usual kind of fossil—a shape or an actual hard form in the rock. The fossil molecules can be extracted and identified even when the organism has completely disintegrated and the organic molecules have diffused into the surrounding material. In fact, the term "biological marker" is now being applied to organic substances that show pronounced resistance to chemical change and whose molecular structure gives a strong indication that they could have been created in significant amounts only by biological processes.

One might liken such resistant compounds to the hard parts of organisms that ordinarily persist after the soft parts have decayed. For example, hydrocarbons, the compounds consisting only of carbon and hydrogen, are comparatively resistant to chemical and biological attack. Unfortunately many other biologically important molecules such as nucleic acids, proteins and polysaccharides contain many bonds that hydrolyze, or cleave, readily; hence these molecules rapidly decompose after an organism dies. Nevertheless, several groups of workers have reported finding constituents of proteins (amino acids and peptide chains) and even proteins themselves in special well-protected sites, such as between the thin sheets of crystal in fossil shells and bones [see "Paleobiochemistry," by Philip H. Abelson; SCIENTIFIC AMERICAN Offprint 101].

Where complete destruction of the organism has taken place one cannot, of course, visualize its original shape from the nature of the chemical fossils it has left behind. One may, however, be able to infer the biological class, or perhaps even the species, of organism that gave rise to them. At present such deductions must be extremely tentative because they involve considerable uncertainty. Although the chemistry of living organisms is known in broad outline, biochemists even today have identified the principal constituents of only a few small groups of living things. Studies in comparative biochemistry or chemotaxonomy are thus an essential parallel to organic geochemistry. A second uncertainty involves the question of whether or not the biochemistry of ancient organisms was generally the same as the biochemistry of present-day organisms. Finally, little is known of the chemical changes wrought in organic substances when they are entombed for long periods of time in rock or a fossil matrix.

In our work at the University of California at Berkeley and at the University of Glasgow we have gone on the assumption that the best approach to the study of chemical fossils is to analyze geological materials that have had a relatively simple biological and geological history. The search for suitable sediments requires a close collaboration between the geologist and the chemist. The results obtained so far augur well for the future.

Organic chemistry made its first major impact on the earth sciences in 1936, when the German chemist Alfred Treibs isolated metal-containing porphyrins from numerous crude oils and shales. Certain porphyrins are important biological pigments; two of the best-known are chlorophyll, the green pigment of plants, and heme, the red pigment of the blood. Treibs deduced that the oils were biological in origin and could not have been subjected to high temperatures, since that would have decomposed some of the porphyrins in them. It is only during the past decade, however, that techniques have been available for the rapid isolation and identification of organic substances present in small amounts in oils and ancient sediments. Further refinements and new methods will be required for detailed study of the tiny amounts of organic substances found in some rocks. The effort should be worthwhile, because such techniques for the detection and definition of the specific architecture of organic molecules should not only tell us much more about the origin of life on the earth but also help us to establish whether or not life has developed on other planets. Furthermore, chemical fossils present the organic chemist with a new range of organic compounds to study and may offer the geologist a new tool for determining the environment of the earth in various geological epochs and the conditions subsequently experienced by the sediments laid down in those epochs.

If one could obtain the fossil molecules from a single species of organism, one would be able to make a direct correlation between present-day biochemistry and organic geochemistry. For example, one could directly compare the lipids, or fatty compounds, isolated from a living organism with the lipids of its fossil ancestor. Unfortunately the fossil lipids and other fossil compounds found in sediments almost always represent the chemical debris from many organisms.

The deposition of a compressible fine-grained sediment containing mineral particles and disseminated organic matter takes place in an aquatic environment in which the organic content can be partially preserved; an example would be the bottom of a lake or a delta. The organic matter makes up something less than 1 percent of many ancient sediments. The small portion of this carbon-containing material that is soluble in organic solvents represents a part of the original lipid content, more or less modified, of the organisms that lived and died while the sediment was being deposited.

The organic content presumably consists of varying proportions of the components of organisms—terrestrial as well as aquatic—that have undergone chemical transformation while the sediment was being laid down and compressed. Typical transformations are reduction, which has the effect of removing oxygen from molecules and adding hydrogen, and decarboxylation, which removes the carboxyl radical (COOH). In addition, it appears that a variety of reactive unsaturated compounds (compounds having available chemical bonds) combine to form an insoluble amorphous material known as kerogen. Other chemical changes that occur with the passage of time are related to the temperature to which the rock is heated by geologic processes. Thus many petroleum chemists and geologists believe petroleum is created by progressive degradation, brought about by heat, of the organic matter that is finely disseminated throughout the original sediment. The organic matter that comes closest in structure to the chains and rings of carbon atoms found in the hydrocarbons of petroleum is the matter present in the lipid fraction of organisms. Another potential source of petroleum hydrocarbons is kerogen itself, presumably formed from a wide variety of organic molecules; it gives off a range of straight-chain, branched-chain and ring-containing hydrocarbons when it is strongly heated in the laboratory. One would also like to know more about the role of bacteria in the early steps of sediment formation. In the upper layers of most newly formed sediments there is strong bacterial activity, which must surely re-

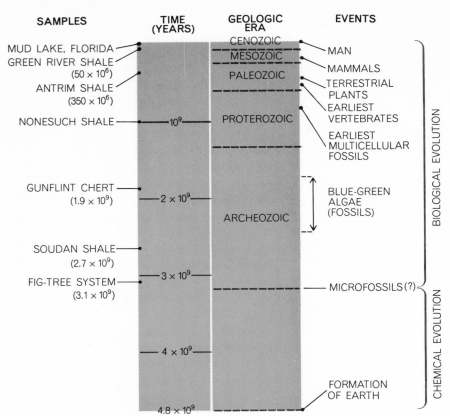

GEOLOGICAL TIME SCALE shows the age of some intensively studied sedimentary rocks (*left*) and the sequence of major steps in the evolution of life (*right*). The stage for biological evolution was set by chemical evolution, but the period of transition is not known.

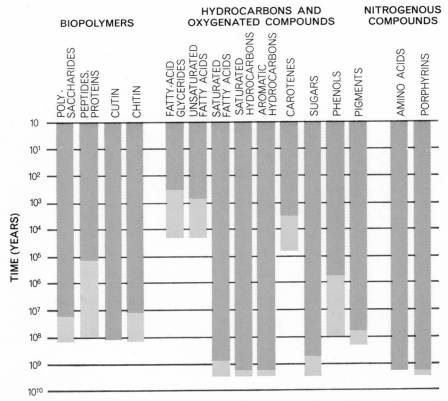

ORGANIC COMPOUNDS originally synthesized by living organisms and more or less modified have now been found in many ancient rocks that began as sediments. The dark bars indicate reasonably reliable identification; the light bars, unconfirmed reports. Cutin and chitin are substances present respectively in the outer structures of plants and of insects.

sult in extensive alteration of the initially deposited organic matter.

In this article we shall concentrate on the isolation of fossil hydrocarbons. The methods must be capable of dealing with the tiny quantity of material available in most rocks. Our general procedure is as follows.

After cutting off the outer surface of a rock specimen to remove gross contaminants, we clean the remaining block with solvents and pulverize it. We then place the powder in solvents such as benzene and methanol to extract the organic material. Before this step we sometimes dissolve the silicate and carbonate minerals of the rock with hydrofluoric and hydrochloric acids. We separate the

organic extract so obtained into acidic, basic and neutral fractions. The compounds in these fractions are converted, when necessary, into derivatives that make them suitable for separation by the technique of chromatography. For the initial separations we use column chromatography, in which a sample in solution is passed through a column packed with alumina or silica. Depending on their nature, compounds in the sample pass through the column at different speeds and can be collected in fractions as they emerge.

In subsequent stages of the analysis finer fractionations are achieved by means of gas-liquid chromatography. In this variation of the technique, the sam-

ple is vaporized into a stream of light gas, usually helium, and brought in contact with a liquid that tends to trap the compounds in the sample in varying degree. The liquid can be supported on an inorganic powder, such as diatomaceous earth, or coated on the inside of a capillary tube. Since the compounds are alternately trapped in the liquid medium and released by the passing stream of gas they progress through the column at varying speeds, with the result that they are separated into distinct fractions as they emerge from the tube. The temperature of the column is raised steadily as the separation proceeds, in order to drive off the more strongly trapped compounds.

The initial chromatographic separation is adjusted to produce fractions that consist of a single class of compound, for example the class of saturated hydrocarbons known as alkanes. Alkane molecules may consist either of straight chains of carbon atoms or of chains that include branches and rings. These subclasses can be separated with the help of molecular sieves: inorganic substances, commonly alumino-silicates, that have a fine honeycomb structure. We use a sieve whose mesh is about five angstrom units, or about a thousandth of the wavelength of green light. Straight-chain alkanes, which resemble smooth flexible rods about 4.5 angstroms in diameter, can enter the sieve and are trapped. Chains with branches and rings are too big to enter and so are held back. The straight-chain alkanes can be liberated from the sieve for further analysis by dissolving the sieve in hydrofluoric acid. Other families of molecules can be trapped in special crystalline forms of urea and thiourea, whose crystal lattices provide cavities with diameters of five angstroms and seven angstroms respectively.

The families of molecules isolated in this way are again passed through gas chromatographic columns that separate the molecular species within the family. For example, a typical chromatogram of straight-chain alkanes will show that molecules of increasing chain length emerge from the column in a regularly spaced sequence that parallels their increasing boiling points, thus producing a series of evenly spaced peaks. Although the species of molecule in a particular peak can often be identified tentatively on the basis of the peak's position, a more precise identification is usually desired. To obtain it one must collect the tiny amount of substance that produced the peak—often measured in micrograms—and examine it by one or more analytical methods such as ultraviolet and infrared

PULVERIZED SHALE

EXTRACTION

TOTAL LIPID EXTRACT

CHROMATOGRAPHY

TOTAL ALKANE FRACTION

5-ANGSTROM SIEVE

NORMAL ALKANES

BRANCHED AND RING ALKANES

GAS CHROMATOGRAPHY

SINGLE ALKANE

SINGLE ALKANE

MASS SPECTROSCOPY

ANALYTICAL PROCEDURE for identifying chemical fossils begins with the extraction of alkane hydrocarbons from a sample of pulverized shale. In normal alkanes the carbon atoms are arranged in a straight chain. (Typical alkanes are illustrated on page 329.) Molecular sieves are used to separate straight-chain alkanes from alkanes with branched chains and rings. The two broad classes are then further fractionated. Compounds responsible for individual peaks in the chromatogram are identified by mass spectrometry and other methods.

spectroscopy, mass spectrometry or nuclear magnetic resonance. In one case X-ray crystallography is being used to arrive at the structure of a fossil molecule.

A new and useful apparatus is one that combines gas chromatography and mass spectrometry [*see illustration at right*]. The separated components emerge from the chromatograph and pass directly into the ionizing chamber of the mass spectrometer, where they are broken into submolecular fragments whose abundance distribution with respect to mass is unique for each component. These various analytical procedures enable us to establish a precise structure and relative concentration for each organic compound that can be extracted from a sample of rock.

How is it that such comparatively simple substances as the alkanes should be worthy of geochemical study? There are several good reasons. Alkanes are generally prominent components of the soluble lipid fraction of sediments. They survive geologic time and geologic conditions well because the carbon-hydrogen and carbon-carbon bonds are strong and resist reaction with water. In addition, alkane molecules can provide more information than the simplicity of their constitution might suggest; even a relatively small number of carbon and hydrogen atoms can be joined in a large number of ways. For example, a saturated hydrocarbon consisting of 19 carbon atoms and 40 hydrogen atoms could exist in some 100,000 different structural forms that are not readily interconvertible. Analysis of ancient sediments has already shown that in some cases they contain alkanes clearly related to the long-chain carbon compounds of the lipids in present-day organisms [*see illustration on next page*]. Generally one finds a series of compounds of similar structure, such as the normal, or straight-chain, alkanes (called *n*-alkanes); the compounds extracted from sediments usually contain up to 35 carbon atoms. Alkanes isolated from sediments may have been buried as such or formed by the reduction of substances containing oxygen.

The more complicated the structure of the molecule, the more valuable it is likely to be for geochemical purposes: its information content is greater. Good examples are the alkanes with branches and rings, such as phytane and cholestane. It is unlikely that these complex alkanes could be built up from small subunits by processes other than biological ones, at least in the proportions found. Hence we are encouraged to look

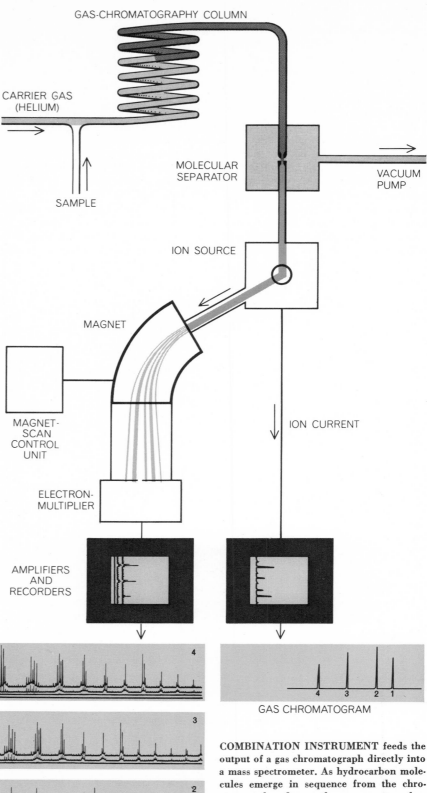

GAS-CHROMATOGRAPHY COLUMN

CARRIER GAS (HELIUM)

SAMPLE

MOLECULAR SEPARATOR

VACUUM PUMP

ION SOURCE

MAGNET

MAGNET-SCAN CONTROL UNIT

ION CURRENT

ELECTRON-MULTIPLIER

AMPLIFIERS AND RECORDERS

4
3
2
1

MASS SPECTRA

4   3   2   1

GAS CHROMATOGRAM

COMBINATION INSTRUMENT feeds the output of a gas chromatograph directly into a mass spectrometer. As hydrocarbon molecules emerge in sequence from the chromatograph and enter the spectrometer, they are ionized, or broken into charged fragments. The size of the ionization current is proportional to the amount of material present at each instant and can be converted into a chromatogram. In the spectrometer the charged fragments are directed through a magnetic field, which separates them according to mass. Each species of molecule produces a unique mass-distribution pattern.

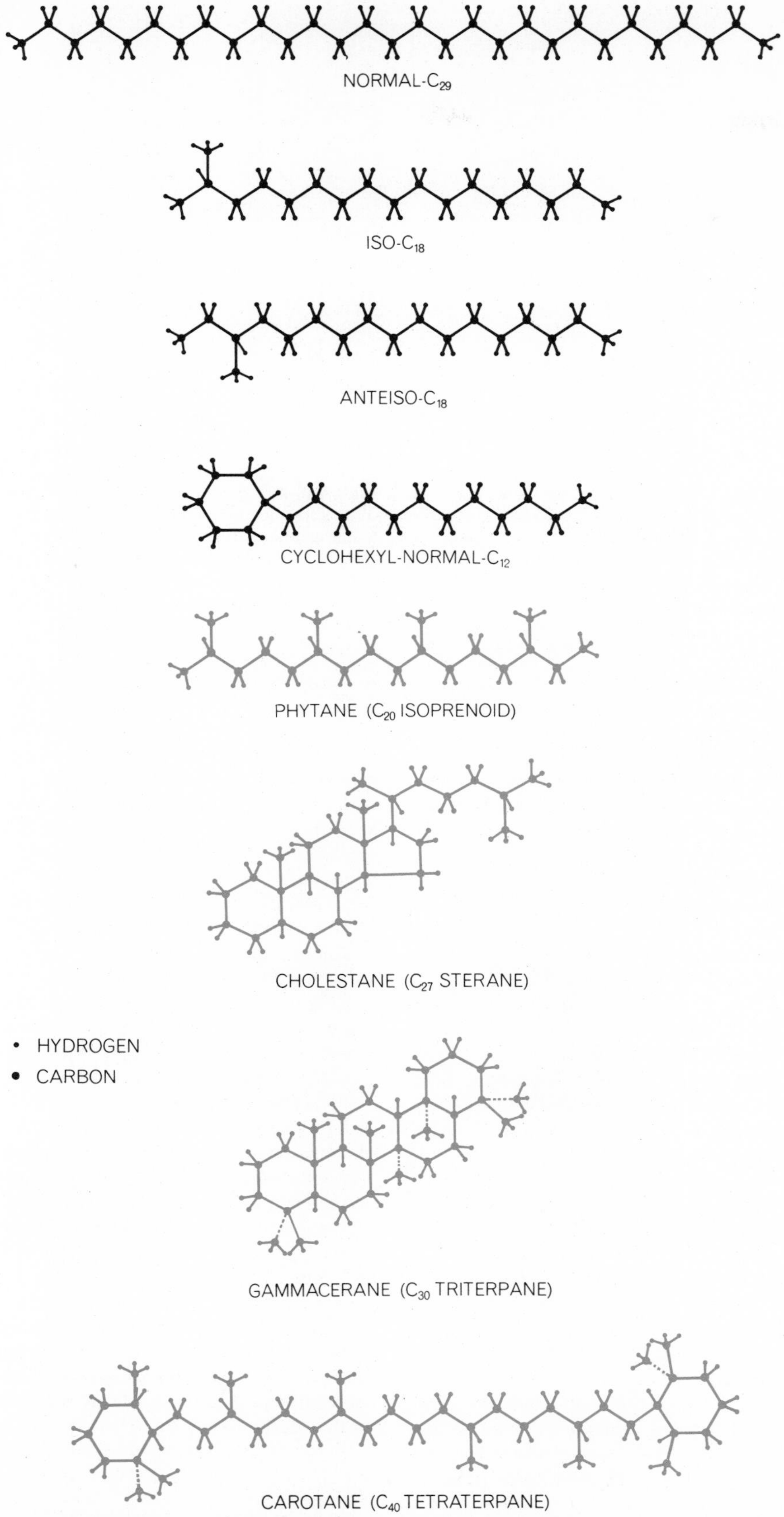

NORMAL-C$_{29}$

ISO-C$_{18}$

ANTEISO-C$_{18}$

CYCLOHEXYL-NORMAL-C$_{12}$

PHYTANE (C$_{20}$ ISOPRENOID)

CHOLESTANE (C$_{27}$ STERANE)

• HYDROGEN
• CARBON

GAMMACERANE (C$_{30}$ TRITERPANE)

CAROTANE (C$_{40}$ TETRATERPANE)

ALKANE HYDROCARBON MOLECULES can take various forms: straight chains (which are actually zigzag chains), branched chains and ring structures. Those depicted here have been found in crude oils and shales. The molecules shown in color are so closely related to well-known biological molecules that they are particularly useful in bespeaking the existence of ancient life. The broken lines indicate side chains that are directed into the page.

for biological precursors with appropriate preexisting carbon skeletons.

In conducting this kind of search one makes the assumption, at least at the outset, that the overall biochemistry of past organisms was similar to that of present-day organisms. When lipid fractions are isolated directly from modern biological sources, they are generally found to contain a range of hydrocarbons, fatty acids, alcohols, esters and so on. The mixture is diverse but by no means random. The molecules present in such fractions have structures that reflect the chemical reaction pathways systematically followed in biological organisms. There are only a few types of biological molecule wherein long chains of carbon atoms are linked together; two examples are the straight-chain lipids, the end groups of which may include oxygen atoms, and the lipids known as isoprenoids.

The straight-chain lipids are produced by what is called the polyacetate pathway [see illustration on the next page]. This pathway leads to a series of fatty acids with an even number of carbon atoms; the odd-numbered molecules are missing. One also finds in nature straight-chain alcohols (n-alkanols) that likewise have an even number of carbon atoms, which is to be expected if they are formed by simple reduction of the corresponding fatty acids. In contrast, the straight-chain hydrocarbons (n-alkanes) contain an odd number of carbon atoms. Such a series would be produced by the decarboxylation of the fatty acids.

The second type of lipid, the isoprenoids, have branched chains consisting of five-carbon units assembled in a regular order [see illustration on page 331]. Because these units are assembled in head-to-tail fashion the side-chain methyl groups (CH$_3$) are attached to every fifth carbon atom. (Tail-to-tail addition occurs less frequently but accounts for several important natural compounds, for example beta-carotene.) When the isoprenoid skeleton is found in a naturally occurring molecule, it is reasonable to assume that the compound has been formed by this particular biological pathway.

Chlorophyll is possibly the most widely distributed molecule with an isoprenoid chain; therefore it must make some contribution to the organic matter in sediments. Its fate under conditions of geological sedimentation is not known, but it may decompose into only two or three large fragments [see illustration on page 332]. The molecule of chlorophyll a consists of a system of interconnected rings and a phytyl side chain, which is an isoprenoid. When chlorophyll is decomposed, it seems likely that the phytyl chain is split off and converted to phytane (which has the same number of carbon atoms) and pristane (which is shorter by one carbon atom). When both of these branched alkanes are found in a sediment, one has reasonable presumptive evidence that chlorophyll was once present. The chlorophyll ring system very likely gives rise to the metal-containing porphyrins that are found in many crude oils and sediments.

Phytane and pristane may actually enter the sediments directly. Max Blumer of the Woods Hole Oceanographic Institution showed in 1965 that certain species of animal plankton that eat the plant plankton containing chlorophyll store quite large quantities of pristane and related hydrocarbons. The animal plankton act in turn as a food supply for bigger marine animals, thereby accounting for the large quantities of pristane in the liver of the shark and other fishes.

An indirect source for the isoprenoid alkanes could be the lipids found in the outer membrane of certain bacteria that live only in strong salt solutions, an environment that might be found where ancient seas were evaporating. Morris Kates of the National Research Council of Canada has shown that a phytyl-containing lipid (diphytyl phospholipid) is common to bacteria with the highest salt requirement but not to the other bacteria examined so far.

This last example brings out the point that in spite of the overall oneness of present-day biochemistry, organisms do differ in the compounds they make. They also synthesize the same compounds in different proportions. These differences are making it possible to classify living species on a chemotaxonomic, or chemical, basis rather than on a morphological, or shape, basis. Eventually it may be possible to extend chemical classification to ancient organisms, creating a discipline that could be called paleochemotaxonomy.

Our study of chemical fossils began in 1961, when we decided to probe the sedimentary rocks of the Precambrian period in a search for the earliest signs of life. This vast period of time, some four billion years, encompasses the beginnings of life on this planet and its early development to the stage of organisms consisting of more than one cell [see illustrations on page 326]. We hoped that our study would complement the efforts being made by a number of work-

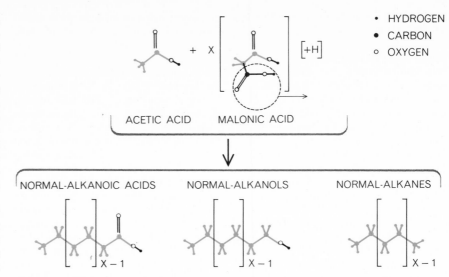

STRAIGHT-CHAIN LIPIDS are created in living organisms from simple two-carbon and three-carbon compounds: acetate and malonate, shown here as their acids. The complex biological process, which involves coenzyme A, is depicted schematically. The fatty acids (*n*-alkanoic acids) and fatty alcohols (*n*-alkanols) produced in this way have an even number of carbon atoms. The removal of carbon dioxide from the fatty acids, the net effect of decarboxylation, would give rise to a series of *n*-alkanes with an odd number of carbon atoms.

ers, including one of us (Calvin), to imitate in the laboratory the chemical evolution that must have preceded the appearance of life on earth. We also saw the possibility that our work could be adapted to the study of meteorites and of rocks obtained from the moon or nearby planets. Thus it even includes the possibility of uncovering exotic and alien biochemistries. The exploration of the ancient rocks of the earth provides a testing ground for the method and the concepts involved.

We chose the alkanes because one might expect them to resist fairly high temperatures and chemical attack for long periods of time. Moreover, J. G. Bendoraitis of the Socony Oil Company, Warren G. Meinschein of the Esso Research Laboratory and others had already identified individual long-chain alkanes, including a range of isoprenoid types, in certain crude oils. Even more encouraging, J. J. Cummins and W. E. Robinson of the U.S. Bureau of Mines had just made a preliminary announcement of their isolation of phytane, pristane and other isoprenoids from a relatively young sedimentary rock: the Green River shale of Colorado, Utah and Wyoming. Thus the alkanes seemed to offer the biological markers we were seeking. Robinson generously provided our laboratory with samples of the Green River shale, which was deposited some 50 million years ago and constitutes the major oil-shale reserve of the U.S.

The Green River shale, which is the

remains of large Eocene lakes in a rather stable environment, contains a considerable fraction (.6 percent) of alkanes. Using the molecular-sieve technique, we split the total alkane fraction into alkanes with straight chains and those with branched chains and rings and ran the resulting fractions through the gas chromatograph [see illustration at top left on page 333]. The straight-chain alkanes exhibit a marked dominance of molecules containing an odd number of carbon atoms, which is to be expected for straight-chain hydrocarbons from a biological source. The other fraction shows a series of prominent sharp peaks; we conclusively identified them as isoprenoids, confirming the results of Cummins and Robinson. The large proportion of phytane, the hydrocarbon corresponding to the entire side chain of chlorophyll, is particularly noteworthy. The oxygenated counterparts of the steranes and triterpanes (27 to 30 carbon atoms) and the high-molecular-weight *n*-alkanes (29 to 31 carbons) are typical constituents of the waxy covering of the leaves and pollen of land plants, leading to the inference that such plants made major contributions to the organic matter deposited in the Green River sediments.

Although the gross chemical structure (number of rings and side chains) of the steranes and triterpanes was established in this work, it was only recently that the precise structure of one of these hydrocarbons was conclusively established. E. V. Whitehead and his associates in the British Petroleum Company and Robinson and his collaborators in the Bureau of Mines have shown that one of the triterpanes extracted from the Green River shale is identical in all respects with gammacerane [*see illustration on page 329*]. Conceivably it is produced by the reduction of a compound known as gammaceran-3-beta-ol, which was recently isolated from the common protozoon *Tetrahymena pyriformis*. Other derivatives of gammacerane are rather widely distributed in the plant kingdom.

At our laboratory in Glasgow, Sister Mary T. J. Murphy and Andrew McCormick recently identified several steranes and triterpanes and also the tetraterpane called perhydro-beta-carotene, or carotane [*see top illustration on page 336*]. Presumably carotane is derived by reduction from beta-carotene, an important red pigment of plants. A similar reduction process could convert the familiar biological compound cholesterol into cholestane, one of the steranes found in the Green River shale [*see same illustration on page 336*]. The mechanism and sedimentary site of such geochemical reduction processes is an important problem awaiting attack.

W. H. Bradley of the U.S. Geological Survey has sought a contemporary counterpart of the richly organic ooze that presumably gave rise to the Green River shale. So far he has located only four lakes, two in the U.S. and two in Africa, that seem to be reasonable candidates. One of them, Mud Lake in Flor-

ida, is now being studied closely. A dense belt of vegetation surrounding the lake filters out all the sand and silt that might otherwise be washed into it from the land. As a result the main source of sedimentary material is the prolific growth of microscopic algae. The lake bottom uniformly consists of a grayish-green ooze about three feet deep. The bottom of the ooze was deposited about 2,300 years ago, according to dating by the carbon-14 technique.

Microscopic examination of the ooze shows that it consists mainly of minute fecal pellets, made up almost exclusively of the cell walls of blue-green algae. Some pollen grains are also present. Decay is surprisingly slow in spite of the ooze's high content of bound oxygen and the temperatures characteristic of Florida. Chemical analyses in several laboratories, reported this past November at a meeting of the Geological Society of America, indicate that there is indeed considerable correspondence between the lipids of the Mud Lake ooze and those of the Green River shale. Eugene McCarthy of the University of California at Berkeley has also found beta-carotene in samples of Mud Lake ooze that are about 1,100 years old. The high oxygen content of the Mud Lake ooze seems inconsistent, however, with the dominance of oxygen-poor compounds in the Green River shale. The long-term geological mechanisms that account for the loss of oxygen may have to be sought in sediments older than those in Mud Lake.

Sediments much older than the Green River shale have now been examined by our groups in Berkeley and Glasgow, and by workers in other universities and in oil-industry laboratories. We find that the hydrocarbon fractions in these more ancient samples are usually more complex than those of the Green River shale; the gas chromatograms of the older samples tend to show a number of partially resolved peaks centered around a single maximum. One of the older sediments we have studied is the Antrim shale of Michigan. A black shale probably 350 million years old, it resembles other shales of the Chattanooga type that underlie many thousands of square miles of the eastern U.S. Unlike the Green River shale, the straight-chain alkane fraction of the Antrim shale shows little or no predominance of an odd number of carbon atoms over an even number [*see the top lefthand illustration on page 334*]. The alkanes with branched chains and rings, however, continue to be rich in isoprenoids.

The fact that alkanes with an odd number of carbon atoms are not predominant in the Antrim shale and sediments of comparable antiquity may be owing to the slow cracking by heat of carbon chains both in the alkane component and in the kerogen component. The effect can be partially reproduced in the laboratory by heating a sample of the Green River shale for many hours above 300 degrees centigrade. After such treatment the straight-chain alkanes show a reduced dominance of odd-carbon molecules and the branched-chain-and-ring fraction is more complex.

The billion-year-old shale from the Nonesuch formation at White Pine, Mich., exemplifies how geological, geochemical and micropaleontological techniques can be brought to bear on the problem of detecting ancient life. With the aid of the electron microscope Elso S. Barghoorn and J. William Schopf of Harvard University have detected in the Nonesuch shale "disaggregated particles of condensed spheroidal organic matter." In collaboration with Meinschein the Harvard workers have also found evidence that the Nonesuch shale contains isoprenoid alkanes, steranes and porphyrins. Independently we have analyzed the Nonesuch shale and found that it contains pristane and phytane, in addition to iso-alkanes, anteiso-alkanes and cyclohexyl alkanes.

Barghoorn and S. A. Tyler have also detected microfossils in the Gunflint chert of Ontario, which is 1.9 billion years old, almost twice the age of the

ACETIC ACID (3 UNITS)   MEVALONIC ACID   ISOPENTENYL PYROPHOSPHATE

DIMER, $(C_5)_2$

TRIMER, $(C_5)_3$

TETRAMER, $(C_5)_4$

POLYMER $(C_5)_n$

BRANCHED-CHAIN LIPIDS are produced in living organisms by an enzymatically controlled process, also depicted schematically. In this process three acetate units link up to form a six-carbon compound (mevalonic acid), which subsequently loses a carbon atom and is combined with a high-energy phosphate. "Head to tail" assembly of the five-carbon subunits produces branched-chain molecules that are referred to as isoprenoid structures.

Nonesuch shale. They have reported that the morphology of the Gunflint microfossils "is similar to that of the existing primitive filamentous blue-green algae."

One of the oldest Precambrian sediments yet analyzed is the Soudan shale of Minnesota, which was formed about 2.7 billion years ago. Although its total hydrocarbon content is only .05 percent, we have found that it contains a mixture of straight-chain alkanes and branched-chain-and-ring alkanes not unlike those present in the much younger Antrim shale [*see the top righthand illustration appearing on page 334*]. In the branched-chain-and-ring fraction we have identified pristane and phytane. Steranes and triterpanes also seem to be present, but we have not yet established their precise three-dimensional structure. Preston E. Cloud of the University of California at Los Angeles has reported that the Soudan shale contains microstructures resembling bacteria or blue-green algae, but he is not satisfied that the evidence is conclusive.

A few reports are now available on the most ancient rocks yet examined: sediments from the Fig Tree system of Swaziland in Africa, some 3.1 billion years old. An appreciable fraction of the alkane component of these rocks consists of isoprenoid molecules. If one assumes that isoprenoids are chemical vestiges of chlorophyll, one is obliged to conclude that living organisms appeared on the earth only about 1.7 billion years after the earth was formed (an estimated 4.8 billion years ago).

Before reaching this conclusion, however, one would like to be sure that the isoprenoids found in ancient sediments have the precise carbon skeleton of the biological molecules from which they are presumed to be derived. So far no sample of pristane or phytane—the isoprenoids that may be derived from the phytyl side chain of chlorophyll—has been shown to duplicate the precise three-dimensional structure of a pure reference sample. Vigorous efforts are being made to clinch the identification.

Assuming that one can firmly establish the presence of biologically structured isoprenoid alkanes in a sediment, further questions remain. The most serious one is: Were the hydrocarbons or their precursors deposited when the sediment was formed or did they seep in later? This question is not easily answered. A sample can be contaminated at any point up to—and after—the time it reaches the laboratory bench. Fossil fuels, lubricants and waxes are omnipresent, and laboratory solvents contain

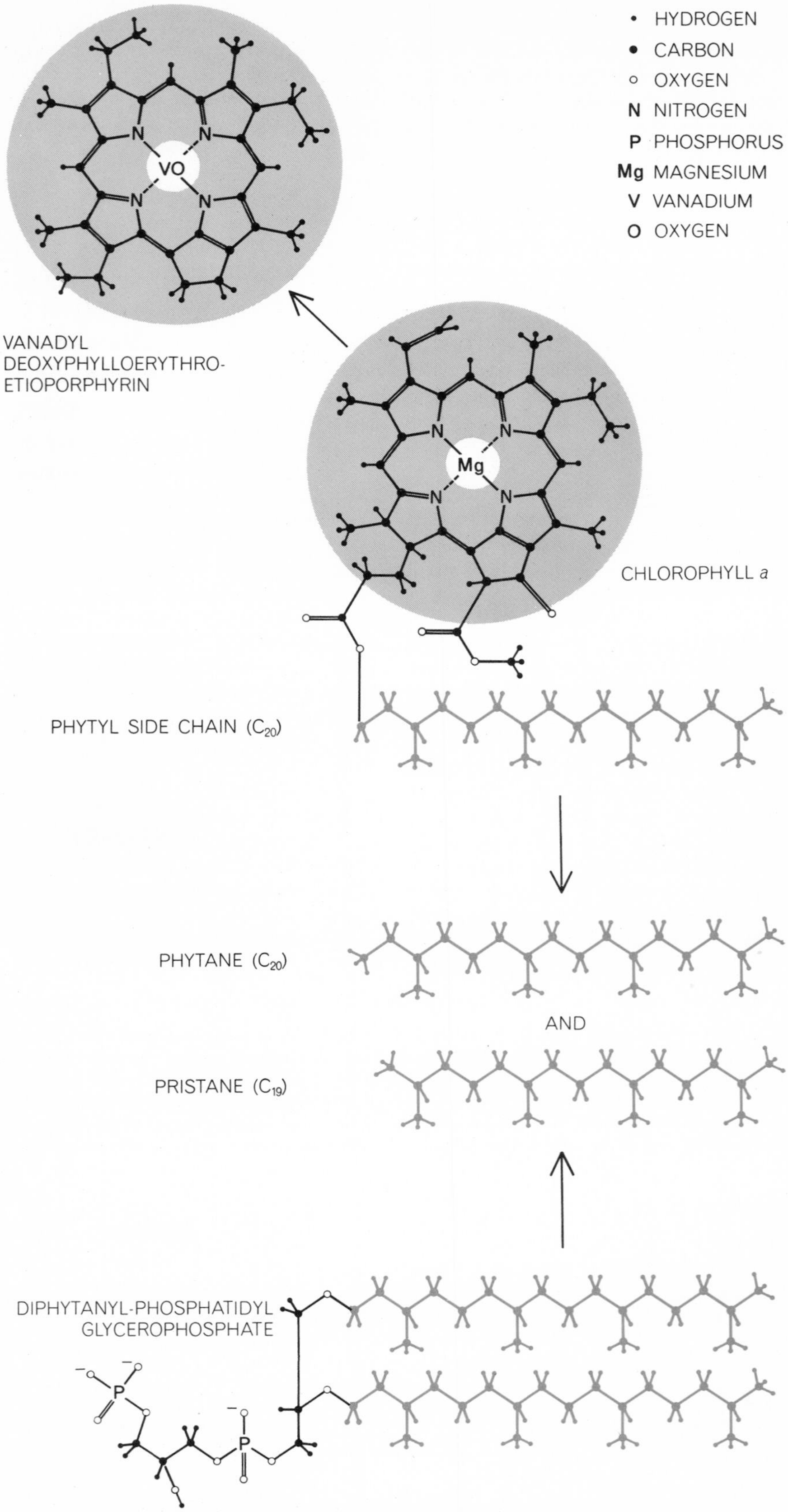

- HYDROGEN
- CARBON
- OXYGEN
N NITROGEN
P PHOSPHORUS
Mg MAGNESIUM
V VANADIUM
O OXYGEN

VANADYL
DEOXYPHYLLOERYTHRO-
ETIOPORPHYRIN

CHLOROPHYLL *a*

PHYTYL SIDE CHAIN (C$_{20}$)

PHYTANE (C$_{20}$)

AND

PRISTANE (C$_{19}$)

DIPHYTANYL-PHOSPHATIDYL
GLYCEROPHOSPHATE

DEGRADATION OF CHLOROPHYLL *A*, the green pigment in plants, may give rise to two kinds of isoprenoid molecules, phytane and pristane, that have been identified in many ancient sediments. It also seems likely that phytane and pristane can be derived from the isoprenoid side chains of a phosphate-containing lipid (*bottom structure*) that is a major constituent of salt-loving bacteria. The porphyrin ring of chlorophyll *a* is the probable source of vanadyl porphyrin (*upper left*) that is widely found in crude oils and shales.

tiny amounts of pristane and phytane unless they are specially purified.

One way to determine whether or not rock hydrocarbons are indigenous is to measure the ratio of the isotopes carbon 13 and carbon 12 in the sample. (The ratio is expressed as the excess of carbon 13 in parts per thousand compared with the isotope ratio in a standard: a sample of a fossil animal known as a belemnite.) The principle behind the test is that photosynthetic organisms discriminate against carbon 13 in preference to carbon 12. Although we have few clues to the abundance of the two isotopes throughout the earth's history, we can at least test various hydrocarbon fractions in a given sample to see if they have the same isotope ratio. As a simple assumption, one would expect to find the same ratio in the soluble organic fraction as in the insoluble kerogen fraction, which could not have seeped into the rock as kerogen.

Philip H. Abelson and Thomas C. Hoering of the Carnegie Institution of Washington have made such measurements on sediments of various geological ages and have found that the isotope ratios for soluble and insoluble fractions in most samples agree reasonably well. In some of the oldest samples, however, there are inconsistencies. In the Soudan shale, for example, the soluble hydrocarbons have an isotope ratio expressed as −25 parts per thousand compared with −34 parts per thousand for the kerogen. (In younger sediments and in present-day marine organisms the ratio is about midway between these two values: −29 parts per thousand.) The isotope divergence shown by hydrocarbons in the Soudan shale may indicate that the soluble hydrocarbons and the kerogen originated at different times. But since nothing is known of the mechanism of kerogen formation or of the alterations that take place in organic matter generally, the divergence cannot be regarded as unequivocal evidence of separate origin.

On the other hand, there is some reason to suspect that the isoprenoids did indeed seep into the Soudan shale sometime after the sediments had been laid down. The Soudan formation shows evidence of having been subjected to temperatures as high as 400 degrees C. The isoprenoid hydrocarbons pristane and phytane would not survive such conditions for very long. But since the exact date, extent and duration of the heating of the Soudan shale are not known, one can only speculate about whether the isoprenoids were indigenous and survived or seeped in later. In any event, they could not have seeped in much later because the sediment became compacted and relatively impervious within a few tens of millions of years.

A still more fundamental issue is whether or not isoprenoid molecules and others whose architecture follows that of known biological substances could have been formed by nonbiological processes. We and others are studying the kinds and concentrations of hydrocarbons produced by both biological and nonbiological sources. Isoprene itself, the hydrocarbon whose polymer constitutes natural rubber, is easily prepared in the laboratory, but no one has been able to

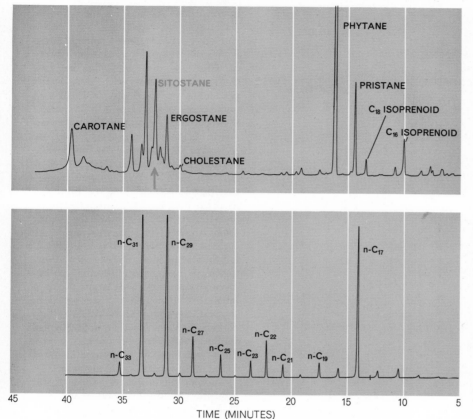

HYDROCARBONS IN YOUNG SEDIMENT, the 50-million-year-old Green River shale, produced these chromatograms. Alkanes with branched chains and rings appear in the top curve, normal alkanes in the bottom curve. The alkanes in individual peaks were identified by mass spectrometry and other methods. Such alkanes as phytane and pristane and the predominance of normal alkanes with an odd number of carbon atoms affirm that the hydrocarbons are biological in origin. The bimodal distribution of the curves is also significant.

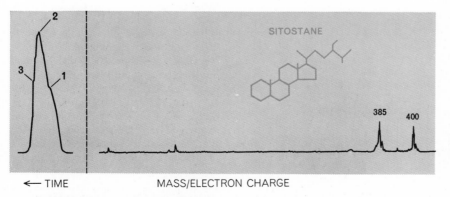

IDENTIFICATION OF SITOSTANE in the Green River shale was accomplished by "trapping" the alkanes that produced a major peak in the chromatogram (*colored arrow at top left on this page*) and passing them through the chromatograph-mass spectrometer. As the chromatograph drew the curve at the left, three scans were made with the spectrometer. Scan 1 (*partially shown at right*) is identical with the scan produced by pure sitostane.

demonstrate that isoprenoids can be formed nonbiologically under geologically plausible conditions. Using a computer approach, Margaret O. Dayhoff of the National Biomedical Research Foundation and Edward Anders of the University of Chicago and their colleagues have concluded that under certain restricted conditions isoprene should be one of the products of their hypothetical reactions. But this remains to be demonstrated in the laboratory.

It is well known, of course, that complex mixtures of straight-chain, branched-chain and even ring hydrocarbons can readily be synthesized in the laboratory from simple starting materials. For example, the Fischer-Tropsch process, used by the Germans as a source of synthetic fuel in World War II, produces a mixture of saturated hydrocarbons from carbon monoxide and water. The reaction requires a catalyst (usually nickel, cobalt or iron), a pressure of about 100 atmospheres and a temperature of from 200 to 350 degrees C. The hydrocarbons formed by this process, and several others that have been studied, generally show a smooth distribution of saturated hydrocarbons. Many of them have straight chains but lack the special characteristics (such as the predominance of chains with an odd number of carbons) found in the similar hydrocarbons present in many sediments. Isoprenoid alkanes, if they are formed at all, cannot be detected.

Paul C. Marx of the Aerospace Corporation has made the ingenious suggestion that isoprenoids may be produced by the hydrogenation of graphite. In the layered structure of graphite the carbon atoms are held in hexagonal arrays by carbon-carbon bonds. Marx has pointed out that if the bonds were broken in certain ways during hydrogenation, an isoprenoid structure might result. Again a laboratory demonstration is needed to support the hypothesis. What seems certain, however, is that nonbiological syntheses are extremely unlikely to produce those specific isoprenoid patterns found in the products of living cells.

Another dimension is added to this discussion by the proposal, made from time to time by geologists, that certain hydrocarbon deposits are nonbiological in origin. Two alleged examples of such a deposit are a mineral oil found enclosed in a quartz mineral at the Abbott mercury mine in California and a bitumen-like material called thucolite found in an ancient nonsedimentary rock in Ontario. Samples of both materials have been analyzed in our laboratory at Berkeley. The Abbott oil contains a significant isoprenoid fraction and probably constitutes an oil extracted and brought up from somewhat older sediments of normal biological origin. The thucolite consists chiefly of carbon from which only a tiny hydrocarbon fraction can be extracted. Our analysis shows, however, that the fraction contains trace amounts of pristane and phytane. Recognizing the hazards of contamination, we are repeating the analysis, but on the basis of our preliminary findings we suspect that the thucolite sample represents an oil of biological origin that has been almost completely carbonized. We are aware, of course, that one runs the risk of invoking

OLDER SEDIMENTS are represented by the Antrim shale (*left*), which is 350 million years old, and by the Soudan shale (*right*), which is 2.7 billion years old. Alkanes with branched chains and rings again are shown in the top curves; normal alkanes in the bottom curves. These chromatograms lack a pronounced bimodal distribution and the normal alkanes do not show a predominance of molecules with an odd number of carbon atoms. Nevertheless, the prevalence of isoprenoids argues for a biological origin.

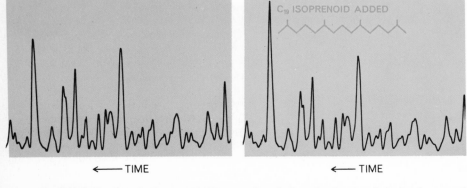

NINETEEN-CARBON ISOPRENOID was identified in the Antrim shale by the use of a coinjection technique together with a high-resolution gas chromatograph. These two high-resolution curves, each taken from a much longer trace, show the change in height of a specific peak when a small amount of pure 19-carbon isoprenoid was coinjected with the sample. Other peaks can be similarly identified by coinjecting known alkanes.

circular arguments in such discussions. Do isoprenoids demonstrate biological origin (as we and others are suggesting) or does the presence of isoprenoids in such unlikely substances indicate that they were formed nonbiologically? The debate may not be quickly settled.

There is little doubt, in any case, that organic compounds of considerable variety and complexity must have accumulated on the primitive earth during the prolonged period of nonbiological chemical development—the period of chemical evolution. With the appearance of the first living organisms biological evolution took command and presumably the "food stock" of nonbiological compounds was rapidly altered. If the changeover was abrupt on a geological time scale, one would expect to find evidence of it in the chemical composition of sediments whose age happens to bracket the period of transition. Such a discontinuity would make an intensely exciting find for organic geochemistry. The transition from chemical to biological evolution must have occurred earlier than three billion years ago. As yet, however, no criteria have been established for distinguishing between the two types of evolutionary process.

We suggest that an important distinction should exist between the kinds of molecules formed by the two processes. In the period of chemical evolution autocatalysis must have been one of the dominant mechanisms for creating large molecules. An autocatalytic system is one in which a particular substance promotes the formation of more of itself. In biological evolution, on the other hand, two different molecular systems are involved: an information-bearing system based on nucleic acids and a catalytic system based on proteins. The former directs the synthesis of the latter. A major problem, subject to laboratory experiment, is visualizing how the two systems originated and were linked.

The role of lipids in the transition may have been important. Today lipids form an important part of the membranes of all living cells. A. I. Oparin, the Russian investigator who was among the first to discuss in detail the chemical origin of life, has suggested that an essential step in the transition from chemical to biological evolution may have been the formation of membranes around droplets, which could then serve as "reaction vessels." Such self-assembling membranes might well have required lipid constituents for their function, which would be to allow some compounds to enter and leave the "cell" more readily than others. These membranes might have been formed nonbiologically by the polymerization of simple two-carbon and three-carbon units. According to this line of reasoning, the compounds that are now prominent constituents of living things are prominent precisely because they were prominent products of chemical evolution. We scarcely need add that this is a controversial and therefore stimulating hypothesis.

What one can say with some confidence is that autocatalysis alone seems unlikely to have been capable of producing the distribution pattern of hydrocarbons observed in ancient Precambrian rocks, even when some allowance is made for subsequent reactions over the course of geologic time. That it could have produced compounds of the observed type is undoubtedly possible, but

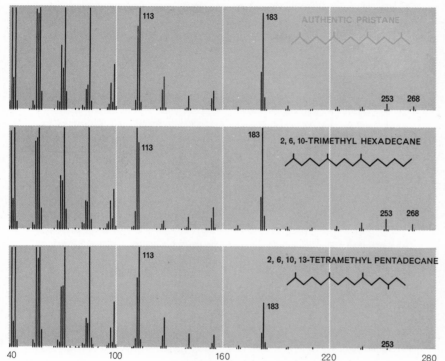

SIMILARITY OF MASS SPECTRA makes it difficult to distinguish the 19-carbon isoprenoid pristane from two of its many isomers (molecules with the same number of carbon and hydrogen atoms). The three records shown here are replotted from the actual tracings produced by pure compounds. When the sample contains impurities, as is normally the case, the difficulty of identifying authentic pristane by mass spectrometry is even greater.

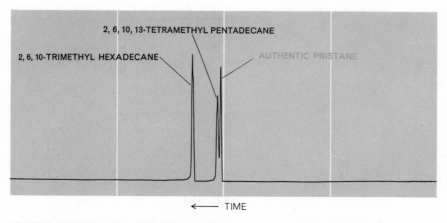

IDENTIFICATION OF PRISTANE can be done more successfully with the aid of a high-resolution gas chromatograph. When pure pristane and the isomers shown in the illustration above are fed into such an instrument, they produce three distinct peaks. This curve and the mass spectra were made by Eugene McCarthy of the University of California at Berkeley. He also made the isoprenoid study shown at the bottom of preceding two pages.

it seems to us that the observed pattern could not have arisen without the operation of those molecular systems we now recognize as the basis of living things. Eventually it should be possible to find in the geological record certain molecular fossils that will mark the boundary between chemical and biological evolution.

Another and more immediate goal for the organic geochemist is to attempt to trace on the molecular level the direction of biological evolution. For such a study one would like to have access to the actual nucleic acids and proteins synthesized by ancient organisms, but these are as yet unavailable (except perhaps in rare instances). We must therefore turn to the geochemically stable compounds, such as the hydrocarbons and oxygenated compounds that must have derived from the operation of the more perishable molecular systems. These "secondary metabolites," as we have referred to them, can be regarded as the signatures of the molecular systems that synthesized them or their close relatives.

It follows that the carbon skeletons found in the secondary metabolites of present-day organisms are the outcome of evolutionary selection. Thus it should be possible for the organic geochemist to arrange in a rough order of evolutionary sequence the carbon skeletons found in various sediments. There are some indications that this may be feasible. G. A. D. Haslewood of Guy's Hospital Medical School in London has proposed that the bile alcohols and bile acids found in present-day vertebrates can be arranged in an evolutionary sequence: the bile acids of the most primitive organisms contain molecules nearest chemically to cholesterol, their supposed biosynthetic precursor.

Within a few years the organic geochemist will be presented with a piece of the moon and asked to describe its organic contents. The results of this analysis will be awaited with immense curiosity. Will we find that the moon is a barren rock or will we discover traces of organic compounds—some perhaps resembling the complex carbon skeletons we had thought could be produced only by living systems? During the 1970's and 1980's we can expect to receive reports from robot sampling and analytical instruments landed on Mars, Venus and perhaps Jupiter. Whatever the results and their possible indications of alien forms of life, we shall be very eager to learn what carbon compounds are present elsewhere in the solar system.

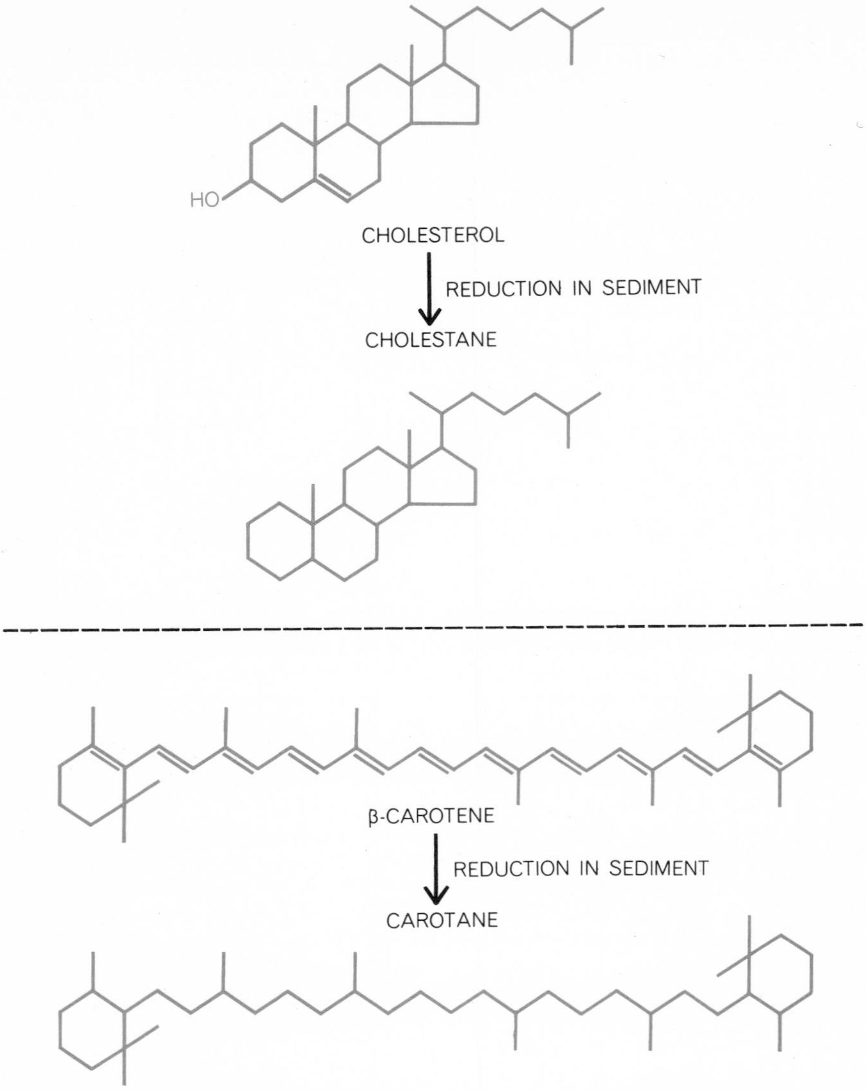

CHOLESTEROL

REDUCTION IN SEDIMENT

CHOLESTANE

β-CAROTENE

REDUCTION IN SEDIMENT

CAROTANE

TWO ALKANES IN GREEN RIVER SHALE, cholestane and carotane, probably have been derived from two well-known biological substances: cholesterol and beta-carotene. The former is closely related to the steroid hormones; the latter is a red pigment widely distributed in plants. These two natural substances can be converted to their alkane form by reduction: a process that adds hydrogen at the site of double bonds and removes oxygen.

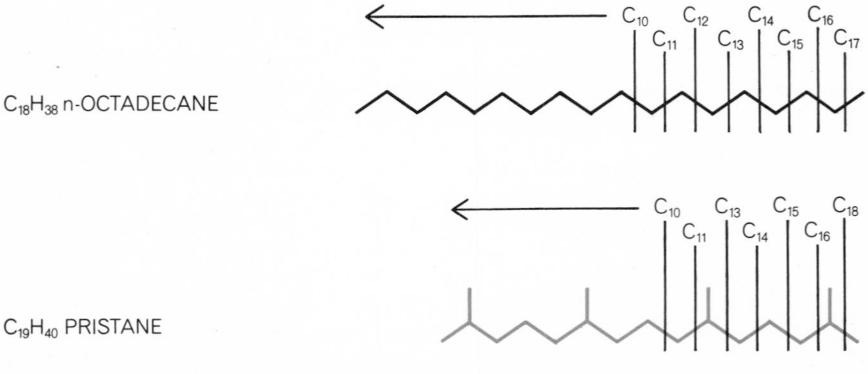

$C_{18}H_{38}$ n-OCTADECANE

$C_{19}H_{40}$ PRISTANE

EFFECT OF HEATING ALKANES is to produce a smoothly descending series of products (normal alkenes) if the starting material is a straight-chain molecule such as *n*-octadecane. (The term "alkene" denotes a hydrocarbon with one carbon-carbon double bond.) If, however, the starting material is an isoprenoid such as pristane, heating it to 600 degrees centigrade for .6 second produces an irregular series of alkenes because of the branched chain. Such degradation processes may take place in deeply buried sediments. These findings were made by R. T. Holman and his co-workers at the Hormel Institute in Minneapolis, Minn.

34 | The Origin of Life

GEORGE WALD · August 1954

About a century ago the question, How did life begin?, which has interested men throughout their history, reached an impasse. Up to that time two answers had been offered: one that life had been created supernaturally, the other that it arises continually from the nonliving. The first explanation lay outside science; the second was now shown to be untenable. For a time scientists felt some discomfort in having no answer at all. Then they stopped asking the question.

Recently ways have been found again to consider the origin of life as a scientific problem—as an event within the order of nature. In part this is the result of new information. But a theory never rises of itself, however rich and secure the facts. It is an act of creation. Our present ideas in this realm were first brought together in a clear and defensible argument by the Russian biochemist A. I. Oparin in a book called *The Origin of Life*, published in 1936. Much can be added now to Oparin's discussion, yet it provides the foundation upon which all of us who are interested in this subject have built.

The attempt to understand how life originated raises a wide variety of scientific questions, which lead in many and diverse directions and should end by casting light into many obscure corners. At the center of the enterprise lies the hope not only of explaining a great past event—important as that should be—but of showing that the explanation is workable. If we can indeed come to understand how a living organism arises from the nonliving, we should be able to construct one—only of the simplest description, to be sure, but still recognizably alive. This is so remote a possibility now

that one scarcely dares to acknowledge it; but it is there nevertheless.

One answer to the problem of how life originated is that it was created. This is an understandable confusion of nature with technology. Men are used to making things; it is a ready thought that those things not made by men were made by a superhuman being. Most of the cultures we know contain mythical accounts of a supernatural creation of life. Our own tradition provides such an account in the opening chapters of *Genesis*. There we are told that beginning on the third day of the Creation, God brought forth living creatures—first plants, then fishes and birds, then land animals and finally man.

Spontaneous Generation

The more rational elements of society, however, tended to take a more naturalistic view of the matter. One had only to accept the evidence of one's senses to know that life arises regularly from the nonliving: worms from mud, maggots from decaying meat, mice from refuse of various kinds. This is the view that came to be called spontaneous generation. Few scientists doubted it. Aristotle, Newton, William Harvey, Descartes, van Helmont, all accepted spontaneous generation without serious question. Indeed, even the theologians—witness the English Jesuit John Turberville Needham—could subscribe to this view, for *Genesis* tells us, not that God created plants and most animals directly, but that He bade the earth and waters to bring them forth; since this directive was never rescinded, there is nothing heretical in believing that the process has continued.

But step by step, in a great controversy that spread over two centuries, this belief was whittled away until nothing remained of it. First the Italian Francesco Redi showed in the 17th century that meat placed under a screen, so that flies cannot lay their eggs on it, never develops maggots. Then in the following century the Italian abbé Lazzaro Spallanzani showed that a nutritive broth, sealed off from the air while boiling, never develops microorganisms, and hence never rots. Needham objected that by too much boiling Spallanzani had rendered the broth, and still more the air above it, incompatible with life. Spallanzani could defend his broth; when he broke the seal of his flasks, allowing new air to rush in, the broth promptly began to rot. He could find no way, however, to show that the air in the sealed flask had not been vitiated. This problem finally was solved by Louis Pasteur in 1860, with a simple modification of Spallanzani's experiment. Pasteur too used a flask containing boiling broth, but instead of sealing off the neck he drew it out in a long, S-shaped curve with its end open to the air. While molecules of air could pass back and forth freely, the heavier particles of dust, bacteria and molds in the atmosphere were trapped on the walls of the curved neck and only rarely reached the broth. In such a flask the broth seldom was contaminated; usually it remained clear and sterile indefinitely.

This was only one of Pasteur's experiments. It is no easy matter to deal with so deeply ingrained and common-sense a belief as that in spontaneous generation. One can ask for nothing better in such a pass than a noisy and stubborn opponent, and this Pasteur had in the

BIBLICAL ACCOUNT of the origin of life is part of the Creation, here illustrated in a 16th-century Bible printed in Lyons. On the first day (*die primo*) God created heaven and the earth. On the second day (*die secundo*) He separated the firmament and the waters. On the third day (*die tertio*) He made the dry land and plants. On the fourth day (*die quarto*) He made the sun, the moon and the stars. On the fifth day (*die quinto*) He made the birds and the fishes. On the sixth day (*die sexto*) He made the land animals and man. In this account there is no theological conflict with spontaneous generation. According to *Genesis* God, rather than creating the animals and plants directly, bade the earth and waters bring them forth. One theological view is that they retain this capacity.

naturalist Félix Pouchet, whose arguments before the French Academy of Sciences drove Pasteur to more and more rigorous experiments. When he had finished, nothing remained of the belief in spontaneous generation.

We tell this story to beginning students of biology as though it represents a triumph of reason over mysticism. In fact it is very nearly the opposite. The reasonable view was to believe in spontaneous generation; the only alternative, to believe in a single, primary act of supernatural creation. There is no third position. For this reason many scientists a century ago chose to regard the belief in spontaneous generation as a "philosophical necessity." It is a symptom of the philosophical poverty of our time that this necessity is no longer appreciated. Most modern biologists, having reviewed with satisfaction the downfall of the spontaneous generation hypothesis, yet unwilling to accept the alternative belief in special creation, are left with nothing.

I think a scientist has no choice but to approach the origin of life through a hypothesis of spontaneous generation. What the controversy reviewed above showed to be untenable is only the belief that living organisms arise spontaneously under present conditions. We have now to face a somewhat different problem: how organisms may have arisen spontaneously under different conditions in some former period, granted that they do so no longer.

The Task

To make an organism demands the right substances in the right proportions and in the right arrangement. We do not think that anything more is needed—but that is problem enough.

The substances are water, certain salts—as it happens, those found in the ocean—and carbon compounds. The latter are called *organic* compounds because they scarcely occur except as products of living organisms.

Organic compounds consist for the most part of four types of atoms: carbon, oxygen, nitrogen and hydrogen. These four atoms together constitute about 99 per cent of living material, for hydrogen and oxygen also form water. The organic compounds found in organisms fall mainly into four great classes: carbohydrates, fats, proteins and nucleic acids. The illustrations on this and the next three pages give some notion of their composition and degrees of complexity. The fats are simplest, each consisting of three fatty acids joined to glycerol. The starches and glycogens are made of sugar units strung together to form long straight and branched chains. In general only one type of sugar appears in a single starch or glycogen; these molecules are large, but still relatively simple. The principal function of carbohydrates and fats in the organism is to serve as fuel—as a source of energy.

The nucleic acids introduce a further level of complexity. They are very large structures, composed of aggregates of at least four types of unit—the nucleotides—brought together in a great variety of proportions and sequences. An almost endless variety of different nucleic acids is possible, and specific differences among them are believed to be of the highest importance. Indeed, these structures are thought by many to be the main constituents of the genes, the bearers of hereditary constitution.

Variety and specificity, however, are most characteristic of the proteins, which include the largest and most complex molecules known. The units of

which their structure is built are about 25 different amino acids. These are strung together in chains hundreds to thousands of units long, in different proportions, in all types of sequence, and with the greatest variety of branching and folding. A virtually infinite number of different proteins is possible. Organisms seem to exploit this potentiality, for no two species of living organism, animal or plant, possess the same proteins.

Organic molecules therefore form a large and formidable array, endless in variety and of the most bewildering complexity. One cannot think of having organisms without them. This is precisely the trouble, for to understand how organisms originated we must first of all explain how such complicated molecules could come into being. And that is only the beginning. To make an organism requires not only a tremendous variety of these substances, in adequate amounts and proper proportions, but also just the right arrangement of them. Structure here is as important as composition—and what a complication of structure! The most complex machine man has devised—say an electronic brain—is child's play compared with the simplest of living organisms. The especially trying thing is that complexity here involves such small dimensions. It is on the molecular level; it consists of a detailed fitting of molecule to molecule such as no chemist can attempt.

The Possible and Impossible

One has only to contemplate the magnitude of this task to concede that the spontaneous generation of a living organism is impossible. Yet here we are—as a result, I believe, of spontaneous generation. It will help to digress for a mo-

CARBOHYDRATES comprise one of the four principal kinds of carbon compound found in living matter. This structural formula represents part of a characteristic carbohydrate. It is a polysaccharide consisting of six-carbon sugar units, three of which are shown.

ment to ask what one means by "impossible."

With every event one can associate a probability—the chance that it will occur. This is always a fraction, the proportion of times the event occurs in a large number of trials. Sometimes the probability is apparent even without trial. A coin has two faces; the probability of tossing a head is therefore 1/2. A die has six faces; the probability of throwing a deuce is 1/6. When one has no means of estimating the probability beforehand, it must be determined by counting the fraction of successes in a large number of trials.

Our everyday concept of what is impossible, possible or certain derives from our experience: the number of trials that may be encompassed within the space of a human lifetime, or at most within recorded human history. In this colloquial, practical sense I concede the spontaneous origin of life to be "impossible." It is impossible as we judge events in the scale of human experience.

We shall see that this is not a very meaningful concession. For one thing, the time with which our problem is concerned is geological time, and the whole extent of human history is trivial in the balance. We shall have more to say of this later.

But even within the bounds of our own time there is a serious flaw in our judgment of what is possible. It sounds impressive to say that an event has never been observed in the whole of human history. We should tend to regard such an event as at least "practically" impossible, whatever probability is assigned to it on abstract grounds. When we look a little further into such a statement, however, it proves to be almost meaningless. For men are apt to reject reports of very improbable occurrences. Persons of good

judgment think it safer to distrust the alleged observer of such an event than to believe him. The result is that events which are merely very extraordinary acquire the reputation of never having occurred at all. Thus the highly improbable is made to appear impossible.

To give an example: Every physicist knows that there is a very small probability, which is easily computed, that the table upon which I am writing will suddenly and spontaneously rise into the air. The event requires no more than that the molecules of which the table is composed, ordinarily in random motion in all directions, should happen by chance to move in the same direction. Every physicist concedes this possibility; but try telling one that you have seen it happen. Recently I asked a friend, a Nobel laureate in physics, what he would say if I told him that. He laughed and said that he would regard it as more probable that I was mistaken than that the event had actually occurred.

We see therefore that it does not mean much to say that a very improbable event has never been observed. There is a conspiracy to suppress such observations, not among scientists alone, but among all judicious persons, who have learned to be skeptical even of what they see, let alone of what they are told. If one group is more skeptical than others, it is perhaps lawyers, who have the harshest experience of the unreliability of human evidence. Least skeptical of all are the scientists, who, cautious as they are, know very well what strange things are possible.

A final aspect of our problem is very important. When we consider the spontaneous origin of a living organism, this is not an event that need happen again and again. It is perhaps enough for it to happen once. The probability with

which we are concerned is of a special kind; it is the probability that an event occur *at least once*. To this type of probability a fundamentally important thing happens as one increases the number of trials. However improbable the event in a single trial, it becomes increasingly probable as the trials are multiplied. Eventually the event becomes virtually inevitable. For instance, the chance that a coin will not fall head up in a single toss is 1/2. The chance that no head will appear in a series of tosses is $1/2 \times 1/2 \times 1/2$ . . . as many times over as the number of tosses. In 10 tosses the chance that no head will appear is therefore 1/2 multiplied by itself 10 times, or 1/1,000. Consequently the chance that a head will appear at least once in 10 tosses is 999/1,000. Ten trials have converted what started as a modest probability to a near certainty.

The same effect can be achieved with any probability, however small, by multiplying sufficiently the number of trials. Consider a reasonably improbable event, the chance of which is 1/1,000. The chance that this will not occur in one trial is 999/1,000. The chance that it won't occur in 1,000 trials is 999/1,000 multiplied together 1,000 times. This fraction comes out to be 37/100. The chance that it will happen at least once in 1,000 trials is therefore one minus this number—63/100—a little better than three chances out of five. One thousand trials have transformed this from a highly improbable to a highly probable event. In 10,000 trials the chance that this event will occur at least once comes out to be 19,999/20,000. It is now almost inevitable.

It makes no important change in the argument if we assess the probability that an event occur at least two, three, four or some other small number of

FATS are a second kind of carbon compound found in living matter. This formula represents the whole molecule of palmitin, one of the commonest fats. The molecule consists of glycerol (*11 atoms at the far left*) and fatty acids (*hydrocarbon chains at the right*).

times rather than at least once. It simply means that more trials are needed to achieve any degree of certainty we wish. Otherwise everything is the same.

In such a problem as the spontaneous origin of life we have no way of assessing probabilities beforehand, or even of deciding what we mean by a trial. The origin of a living organism is undoubtedly a stepwise phenomenon, each step with its own probability and its own conditions of trial. Of one thing we can be sure, however: whatever constitutes a trial, more such trials occur the longer the interval of time.

The important point is that since the origin of life belongs in the category of at-least-once phenomena, time is on its side. However improbable we regard this event, or any of the steps which it involves, given enough time it will almost certainly happen at least once. And for life as we know it, with its capacity for growth and reproduction, once may be enough.

Time is in fact the hero of the plot. The time with which we have to deal is of the order of two billion years. What we regard as impossible on the basis of human experience is meaningless here. Given so much time, the "impossible" becomes possible, the possible probable, and the probable virtually certain. One has only to wait: time itself performs the miracles.

Organic Molecules

This brings the argument back to its first stage: the origin of organic compounds. Until a century and a quarter ago the only known source of these substances was the stuff of living organisms. Students of chemistry are usually told that when, in 1828, Friedrich Wöhler synthesized the first organic compound, urea, he proved that organic compounds do not require living organisms to make

them. Of course it showed nothing of the kind. Organic chemists are alive; Wöhler merely showed that they can make organic compounds externally as well as internally. It is still true that with almost negligible exceptions all the organic matter we know is the product of living organisms.

The almost negligible exceptions, however, are very important for our argument. It is now recognized that a constant, slow production of organic molecules occurs without the agency of living things. Certain geological phenomena yield simple organic compounds. So, for example, volcanic eruptions bring metal carbides to the surface of the earth, where they react with water vapor to yield simple compounds of carbon and hydrogen. The familiar type of such a reaction is the process used in old-style bicycle lamps in which acetylene is made by mixing iron carbide with water.

Recently Harold Urey, Nobel laureate in chemistry, has become interested in the degree to which electrical discharges in the upper atmosphere may promote the formation of organic compounds. One of his students, S. L. Miller, performed the simple experiment of circulating a mixture of water vapor, methane (CH_4), ammonia (NH_3) and hydrogen—all gases believed to have been present in the early atmosphere of the earth—continuously for a week over an electric spark. The circulation was maintained by boiling the water in one limb of the apparatus and condensing it in the other. At the end of the week the water was analyzed by the delicate method of paper chromatography. It was found to have acquired a mixture of amino acids! Glycine and alanine, the simplest amino acids and the most prevalent in proteins, were definitely identified in the solution, and there were indications it contained aspartic acid and two others. The yield was surprisingly

high. This amazing result changes at a stroke our ideas of the probability of the spontaneous formation of amino acids.

A final consideration, however, seems to me more important than all the special processes to which one might appeal for organic syntheses in inanimate nature.

It has already been said that to have organic molecules one ordinarily needs organisms. The synthesis of organic substances, like almost everything else that happens in organisms, is governed by the special class of proteins called enzymes—the organic catalysts which greatly accelerate chemical reactions in the body. Since an enzyme is not used up but is returned at the end of the process, a small amount of enzyme can promote an enormous transformation of material.

Enzymes play such a dominant role in the chemistry of life that it is exceedingly difficult to imagine the synthesis of living material without their help. This poses a dilemma, for enzymes themselves are proteins, and hence among the most complex organic components of the cell. One is asking, in effect, for an apparatus which is the unique property of cells in order to form the first cell.

This is not, however, an insuperable difficulty. An enzyme, after all, is only a catalyst; it can do no more than change the *rate* of a chemical reaction. It cannot make anything happen that would not have happened, though more slowly, in its absence. Every process that is catalyzed by an enzyme, and every product of such a process, would occur without the enzyme. The only difference is one of rate.

Once again the essence of the argument is time. What takes only a few moments in the presence of an enzyme or other catalyst may take days, months or years in its absence; but given time, the end result is the same.

NUCLEIC ACIDS are a third kind of carbon compound. This is part of desoxyribonucleic acid, the backbone of which is five-carbon sugars alternating with phosphoric acid. The letter R is any one of four nitrogenous bases, two purines and two pyrimidines.

Indeed, this great difficulty in conceiving of the spontaneous generation of organic compounds has its positive side. In a sense, organisms demonstrate to us what organic reactions and products are *possible*. We can be certain that, given time, all these things must occur. Every substance that has ever been found in an organism displays thereby the finite probability of its occurrence. Hence, given time, it should arise spontaneously. One has only to wait.

It will be objected at once that this is just what one cannot do. Everyone knows that these substances are highly perishable. Granted that, within long spaces of time, now a sugar molecule, now a fat, now even a protein might form spontaneously, each of these molecules should have only a transitory existence. How are they ever to accumulate; and, unless they do so, how form an organism?

We must turn the question around. What, in our experience, is known to destroy organic compounds? Primarily two agencies: decay and the attack of oxygen. But decay is the work of living organisms, and we are talking of a time before life existed. As for oxygen, this introduces a further and fundamental section of our argument.

It is generally conceded at present that the early atmosphere of our planet contained virtually no free oxygen. Almost all the earth's oxygen was bound in the form of water and metal oxides. If this were not so, it would be very difficult to imagine how organic matter could accumulate over the long stretches of time that alone might make possible the spontaneous origin of life. This is a crucial point, therefore, and the statement that the early atmosphere of the planet was virtually oxygen-free comes forward so opportunely as to raise a suspicion of special pleading. I have for this reason taken care to consult a number of

geologists and astronomers on this point, and am relieved to find that it is well defended. I gather that there is a widespread though not universal consensus that this condition did exist. Apparently something similar was true also for another common component of our atmosphere—carbon dioxide. It is believed that most of the carbon on the earth during its early geological history existed as the element or in metal carbides and hydrocarbons; very little was combined with oxygen.

This situation is not without its irony. We tend usually to think that the environment plays the tune to which the organism must dance. The environment is given; the organism's problem is to adapt to it or die. It has become apparent lately, however, that some of the most important features of the physical environment are themselves the work of living organisms. Two such features have just been named. The atmosphere of our planet seems to have contained no oxygen until organisms placed it there by the process of plant photosynthesis. It is estimated that at present all the oxygen of our atmosphere is renewed by photosynthesis once in every 2,000 years, and that all the carbon dioxide passes through the process of photosynthesis once in every 300 years. In the scale of geological time, these intervals are very small indeed. We are left with the realization that all the oxygen and carbon dioxide of our planet are the products of living organisms, and have passed through living organisms over and over again.

Forces of Dissolution

In the early history of our planet, when there were no organisms or any free oxygen, organic compounds should have been stable over very long periods. This is the crucial difference between

the period before life existed and our own. If one were to specify a single reason why the spontaneous generation of living organisms was possible once and is so no longer, this is the reason.

We must still reckon, however, with another destructive force which is disposed of less easily. This can be called spontaneous dissolution—the counterpart of spontaneous generation. We have noted that any process catalyzed by an enzyme can occur in time without the enzyme. The trouble is that the processes which synthesize an organic substance are reversible: any chemical reaction which an enzyme may catalyze will go backward as well as forward. We have spoken as though one has only to wait to achieve syntheses of all kinds; it is truer to say that what one achieves by waiting is *equilibria* of all kinds—equilibria in which the synthesis and dissolution of substances come into balance.

In the vast majority of the processes in which we are interested the point of equilibrium lies far over toward the side of dissolution. That is to say, spontaneous dissolution is much more probable, and hence proceeds much more rapidly, than spontaneous synthesis. For example, the spontaneous union, step by step, of amino acid units to form a protein has a certain small probability, and hence might occur over a long stretch of time. But the dissolution of the protein or of an intermediate product into its component amino acids is much more probable, and hence will go ever so much more rapidly. The situation we must face is that of patient Penelope waiting for Odysseus, yet much worse: each night she undid the weaving of the preceding day, but here a night could readily undo the work of a year or a century.

How do present-day organisms manage to synthesize organic compounds against the forces of dissolution? They do so by a continuous expenditure of

PROTEINS are a fourth kind of carbon compound found in living matter. This formula represents part of a polypeptide chain, the backbone of a protein molecule. The chain is made up of amino acids. Here the letter R represents the side chains of these acids.

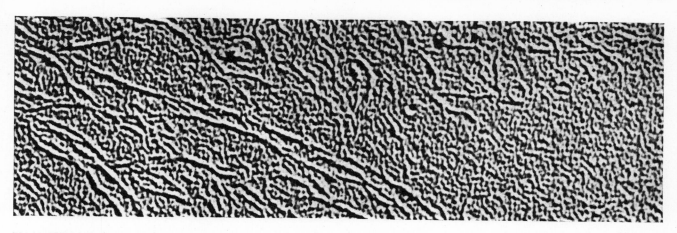

FILAMENTS OF COLLAGEN, a protein which is usually found in long fibrils, were dispersed by placing them in dilute acetic acid. This electron micrograph, which enlarges the filaments 75,000 times, was made by Jerome Gross of the Harvard Medical School.

energy. Indeed, living organisms commonly do better than oppose the forces of dissolution; they grow in spite of them. They do so, however, only at enormous expense to their surroundings. They need a constant supply of material and energy merely to maintain themselves, and much more of both to grow and reproduce. A living organism is an intricate machine for performing exactly this function. When, for want of fuel or through some internal failure in its mechanism, an organism stops actively synthesizing itself in opposition to the processes which continuously decompose it, it dies and rapidly disintegrates.

What we ask here is to synthesize organic molecules without such a machine. I believe this to be the most stubborn problem that confronts us—the weakest link at present in our argument. I do not think it by any means disastrous, but it calls for phenomena and forces some of which are as yet only partly understood and some probably still to be discovered.

Forces of Integration

At present we can make only a beginning with this problem. We know that it is possible on occasion to protect molecules from dissolution by precipitation or by attachment to other molecules. A wide variety of such precipitation and "trapping" reactions is used in modern chemistry and biochemistry to promote syntheses. Some molecules appear to acquire a degree of resistance to disintegration simply through their size. So, for example, the larger molecules composed of amino acids—polypeptides and proteins—seem to display much less tendency to disintegrate into their units than do smaller compounds of two or three amino acids.

Again, many organic molecules display still another type of integrating force—a spontaneous impulse toward structure formation. Certain types of fatty molecules—lecithins and cephalins—spin themselves out in water to form highly oriented and well-shaped structures—the so-called myelin figures. Proteins sometimes orient even in solution, and also may aggregate in the solid state in highly organized formations. Such spontaneous architectonic tendencies are still largely unexplored, particularly as they may occur in complex mixtures of substances, and they involve forces the strength of which has not yet been estimated.

What we are saying is that possibilities exist for opposing *intra*molecular dissolution by *inter*molecular aggregations of various kinds. The equilibrium between union and disunion of the amino acids that make up a protein is all to the advantage of disunion, but the aggregation of the protein with itself or other molecules might swing the equilibrium in the opposite direction: perhaps by removing the protein from access to the water which would be required to disintegrate it or by providing some particularly stable type of molecular association.

In such a scheme the protein appears only as a transient intermediate, an unstable way-station, which can either fall back to a mixture of its constituent amino acids or enter into the formation of a complex structural aggregate: amino acids $\leftrightarrows$ protein $\rightarrow$ aggregate.

Such molecular aggregates, of various degrees of material and architectural complexity, are indispensable intermediates between molecules and organisms. We have no need to try to imagine the spontaneous formation of an organism by one grand collision of its component molecules. The whole process must be gradual. The molecules form aggregates, small and large. The aggregates add further molecules, thus growing in size and complexity. Aggregates of various kinds interact with one another to form still larger and more complex structures. In this way we imagine the ascent, not by jumps or master strokes, but gradually, piecemeal, to the first living organisms.

First Organisms

Where may this have happened? It is easiest to suppose that life first arose in the sea. Here were the necessary salts and the water. The latter is not only the principal component of organisms, but prior to their formation provided a medium which could dissolve molecules of the widest variety and ceaselessly mix and circulate them. It is this constant mixture and collision of organic molecules of every sort that constituted in large part the "trials" of our earlier discussion of probabilities.

The sea in fact gradually turned into a dilute broth, sterile and oxygen-free. In this broth molecules came together in increasing number and variety, sometimes merely to collide and separate, sometimes to react with one another to produce new combinations, sometimes to aggregate into multimolecular formations of increasing size and complexity.

What brought order into such complexes? For order is as essential here as composition. To form an organism, molecules must enter into intricate designs and connections; they must eventually form a self-repairing, self-constructing dynamic machine. For a time this problem of molecular arrangement seemed to present an almost insuperable obstacle in the way of imagining a spontaneous origin of life, or indeed the laboratory

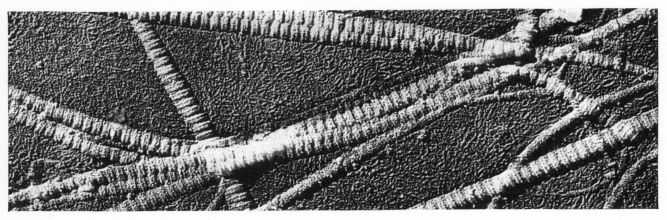

FIBRILS OF COLLAGEN formed spontaneously out of filaments such as those shown on the preceding page when 1 per cent of sodium chloride was added to the dilute acetic acid. These long fibrils are identical in appearance with those of collagen before dispersion.

synthesis of a living organism. It is still a large and mysterious problem, but it no longer seems insuperable. The change in view has come about because we now realize that it is not altogether necessary to *bring* order into this situation; a great deal of order is implicit in the molecules themselves.

The epitome of molecular order is a crystal. In a perfect crystal the molecules display complete regularity of position and orientation in all planes of space. At the other extreme are fluids—liquids or gases—in which the molecules are in ceaseless motion and in wholly random orientations and positions.

Lately it has become clear that very little of a living cell is truly fluid. Most of it consists of molecules which have taken up various degrees of orientation with regard to one another. That is, most of the cell represents various degrees of approach to crystallinity—often, however, with very important differences from the crystals most familiar to us. Much of the cell's crystallinity involves molecules which are still in solution—so-called liquid crystals—and much of the dynamic, plastic quality of cellular structure, the capacity for constant change of shape and interchange of material, derives from this condition. Our familiar crystals, furthermore, involve only one or a very few types of molecule, while in the cell a great variety of different molecules come together in some degree of regular spacing and orientation—*i.e.*, some degree of crystallinity. We are dealing in the cell with highly mixed crystals and near-crystals, solid and liquid. The laboratory study of this type of formation has scarcely begun. Its further exploration is of the highest importance for our problem.

In a fluid such as water the molecules are in very rapid motion. Any molecules dissolved in such a medium are under a constant barrage of collisions with water molecules. This keeps small and moderately sized molecules in a constant turmoil; they are knocked about at random, colliding again and again, never holding any position or orientation for more than an instant. The larger a molecule is relative to water, the less it is disturbed by such collisions. Many protein and nucleic acid molecules are so large that even in solution their motions are very sluggish, and since they carry large numbers of electric charges distributed about their surfaces, they tend even in solution to align with respect to one another. It is so that they tend to form liquid crystals.

We have spoken above of architectonic tendencies even among some of the relatively small molecules: the lecithins and cephalins. Such molecules are insoluble in water yet possess special groups which have a high affinity for water. As a result they tend to form surface layers, in which their water-seeking groups project into the water phase, while their water-repelling portions project into the air, or into an oil phase, or unite to form an oil phase. The result is that quite spontaneously such molecules, when exposed to water, take up highly oriented positions to form surface membranes, myelin figures and other quasi-crystalline structures.

Recently several particularly striking examples have been reported of the spontaneous production of familiar types of biological structure by protein molecules. Cartilage and muscle offer some of the most intricate and regular patterns of structure to be found in organisms. A fiber from either type of tissue presents under the electron microscope a beautiful pattern of cross striations of various widths and densities, very regularly spaced. The proteins that form these structures can be coaxed into free solution and stirred into completely random orientation. Yet on precipitating, under proper conditions, the molecules realign with regard to one another to regenerate with extraordinary fidelity the original patterns of the tissues [*see illustration above*].

We have therefore a genuine basis for the view that the molecules of our oceanic broth will not only come together spontaneously to form aggregates but in doing so will spontaneously achieve various types and degrees of order. This greatly simplifies our problem. What it means is that, given the right molecules, one does not have to do everything for them; they do a great deal for themselves.

Oparin has made the ingenious suggestion that natural selection, which Darwin proposed to be the driving force of organic evolution, begins to operate at this level. He suggests that as the molecules come together to form colloidal aggregates, the latter begin to compete with one another for material. Some aggregates, by virtue of especially favorable composition or internal arrangement, acquire new molecules more rapidly than others. They eventually emerge as the dominant types. Oparin suggests further that considerations of optimal size enter at this level. A growing colloidal particle may reach a point at which it becomes unstable and breaks down into smaller particles, each of which grows and redivides. All these phenomena lie within the bounds of known processes in nonliving systems.

The Sources of Energy

We suppose that all these forces and factors, and others perhaps yet to be revealed, together give us eventually the first living organism. That achieved, how does the organism continue to live?

We have already noted that a living organism is a dynamic structure. It is the site of a continuous influx and outflow of matter and energy. This is the very sign of life, its cessation the best evidence of death. What is the primal organism to use as food, and how derive the energy it needs to maintain itself and grow?

For the primal organism, generated under the conditions we have described, only one answer is possible. Having arisen in an oceanic broth of organic molecules, its only recourse is to live upon them. There is only one way of doing that in the absence of oxygen. It is called fermentation: the process by

which organisms derive energy by breaking organic molecules and rearranging their parts. The most familiar example of such a process is the fermentation of sugar by yeast, which yields alcohol as one of the products. Animal cells also ferment sugar, not to alcohol but to lactic acid. These are two examples from a host of known fermentations.

The yeast fermentation has the following over-all equation: $C_6H_{12}O_6 \rightarrow 2\ CO_2 + 2\ C_2H_5OH$ + energy. The result of fragmenting 180 grams of sugar into 88 grams of carbon dioxide and 92 grams of alcohol is to make available about 20,000 calories of energy for the use of the cell. The energy is all that the cell

derives by this transaction; the carbon dioxide and alcohol are waste products which must be got rid of somehow if the cell is to survive.

The cell, having arisen in a broth of organic compounds accumulated over the ages, must consume these molecules by fermentation in order to acquire the energy it needs to live, grow and reproduce. In doing so, it and its descendants are living on borrowed time. They are consuming their heritage, just as we in our time have nearly consumed our heritage of coal and oil. Eventually such a process must come to an end, and with that life also should have ended. It would have been necessary to start the entire development again.

Fortunately, however, the waste product carbon dioxide saved this situation. This gas entered the ocean and the atmosphere in ever-increasing quantity. Some time before the cell exhausted the supply of organic molecules, it succeeded in inventing the process of photosynthesis. This enabled it, with the energy of sunlight, to make its own organic molecules: first sugar from carbon dioxide and water, then, with ammonia and nitrates as sources of nitrogen, the entire array of organic compounds which it requires. The sugar synthesis equation is: $6\ CO_2 + 6\ H_2O$ + sunlight $\rightarrow C_6H_{12}O_6 + 6\ O_2$. Here 264 grams of carbon dioxide plus 108 grams of water plus about 700,000 calories of sunlight yield 180 grams of sugar and 192 grams of oxygen.

This is an enormous step forward. Living organisms no longer needed to depend upon the accumulation of organic matter from past ages; they could make their own. With the energy of sunlight they could accomplish the fundamental organic syntheses that provide their substance, and by fermentation they could produce what energy they needed.

Fermentation, however, is an extraordinarily inefficient source of energy. It leaves most of the energy potential of organic compounds unexploited; consequently huge amounts of organic material must be fermented to provide a modicum of energy. It produces also various poisonous waste products—alcohol, lactic acid, acetic acid, formic acid and so on. In the sea such products are readily washed away, but if organisms were ever to penetrate to the air and land, these products must prove a serious embarrassment.

One of the by-products of photosynthesis, however, is oxygen. Once this was available, organisms could invent a new way to acquire energy, many times as efficient as fermentation. This is the

EXPERIMENT of S. L. Miller made amino acids by circulating methane (CH_4), ammonia (NH_3), water vapor (H_2O) and hydrogen (H_2) past an electrical discharge. The amino acids collected at the bottom of apparatus and were detected by paper chromatography.

process of cold combustion called respiration: $C_6H_{12}O_6 + 6 O_2 \rightarrow 6 CO_2 + 6 H_2O$ + energy. The burning of 180 grams of sugar in cellular respiration yields about 700,000 calories, as compared with the approximately 20,000 calories produced by fermentation of the same quantity of sugar. This process of combustion extracts all the energy that can possibly be derived from the molecules which it consumes. With this process at its disposal, the cell can meet its energy requirements with a minimum expenditure of substance. It is a further advantage that the products of respiration—water and carbon dioxide—are innocuous and easily disposed of in any environment.

Life's Capital

It is difficult to overestimate the degree to which the invention of cellular respiration released the forces of living organisms. No organism that relies wholly upon fermentation has ever amounted to much. Even after the advent of photosynthesis, organisms could have led only a marginal existence. They could indeed produce their own organic materials, but only in quantities sufficient to survive. Fermentation is so profligate a way of life that photosynthesis could do little more than keep up with it. Respiration used the material of organisms with such enormously greater efficiency as for the first time to leave something over. Coupled with fermentation, photosynthesis made organisms self-sustaining; coupled with respiration, it provided a surplus. To use an economic analogy, photosynthesis brought organisms to the subsistence level; respiration provided them with capital. It is mainly this capital that they invested in the great enterprise of organic evolution.

The entry of oxygen into the atmosphere also liberated organisms in another sense. The sun's radiation contains ultraviolet components which no living cell can tolerate. We are sometimes told that if this radiation were to reach the earth's surface, life must cease. That is not quite true. Water absorbs ultraviolet radiation very effectively, and one must conclude that as long as these rays penetrated in quantity to the surface of the earth, life had to remain under water. With the appearance of oxygen, however, a layer of ozone formed high in the atmosphere and absorbed this radiation. Now organisms could for the first time emerge from the water and begin to populate the earth and air. Oxygen provided not only the means of obtaining adequate energy for evolution but the protective blanket of ozone which alone made possible terrestrial life.

This is really the end of our story. Yet not quite the end. Our entire concern in this argument has been to bring the origin of life within the compass of natural phenomena. It is of the essence of such phenomena to be repetitive, and hence, given time, to be inevitable.

This is by far our most significant conclusion—that life, as an orderly natural event on such a planet as ours, was inevitable. The same can be said of the whole of organic evolution. All of it lies within the order of nature, and apart from details all of it was inevitable.

Astronomers have reason to believe that a planet such as ours—of about the earth's size and temperature, and about as well-lighted—is a rare event in the universe. Indeed, filled as our story is with improbable phenomena, one of the least probable is to have had such a body as the earth to begin with. Yet though this probability is small, the universe is so large that it is conservatively estimated at least 100,000 planets like the earth exist in our galaxy alone. Some 100 million galaxies lie within the range of our most powerful telescopes, so that throughout observable space we can count apparently on the existence of at least 10 million million planets like our own.

What it means to bring the origin of life within the realm of natural phenomena is to imply that in all these places life probably exists—life as we know it. Indeed, I am convinced that there can be no way of composing and constructing living organisms which is fundamentally different from the one we know—though this is another argument, and must await another occasion. Wherever life is possible, given time, it should arise. It should then ramify into a wide array of forms, differing in detail from those we now observe (as did earlier organisms on the earth) yet including many which should look familiar to us—perhaps even men.

We are not alone in the universe, and do not bear alone the whole burden of life and what comes of it. Life is a cosmic event—so far as we know the most complex state of organization that matter has achieved in our cosmos. It has come many times, in many places—places closed off from us by impenetrable distances, probably never to be crossed even with a signal. As men we can attempt to understand it, and even somewhat to control and guide its local manifestations. On this planet that is our home, we have every reason to wish it well. Yet should we fail, all is not lost. Our kind will try again elsewhere.

BIOGRAPHICAL NOTES
AND BIBLIOGRAPHIES

Biographical Notes
and Bibliographies

I MACROMOLECULES
Molecular Structure as the Key to Biological Activity

1. Giant Molecules in Cells and Tissues

The Author

FRANCIS O. SCHMITT is Institute Professor of Biology at the Massachusetts Institute of Technology and has been elected to the National Academy of Sciences. Born in St. Louis in 1903, his first ambition was to be a surgeon and he took the pre-medical course at Washington University. There he became interested in cell structure and decided to give up surgery for cytology (his first paper on the subject was published in the year of his graduation, 1924). As a young graduate student at Washington University, Schmitt was inspired by the work of Jacques Loeb on proteins to abandon prepared slides and become a cell physiologist. But with the arrival of electron microscopy and polarization optics applied to cells, he began once more to study the molecular structure of life. After receiving his Ph.D. in 1927, he was a National Research Council Fellow for a year at the University of California, then did two more years of postdoctoral research in London and Berlin before returning to Washington University as a staff member. By 1940 Schmitt was head of the zoology department at Washington University. The following year he was made a professor at M.I.T., where he soon became head of the department of biology.

Bibliography

CONFERENCE ON TISSUE FINE STRUCTURE. *The Journal of Biophysical and Biochemical Cytology*, Vol. 2, No. 4, Part 2 (Supplement), pages 1–454; July 25, 1956.

MACROMOLECULAR INTERACTION PATTERNS IN BIOLOGICAL SYSTEMS. Francis O. Schmitt in *Proceedings of the American Philosophical Society*. Vol. 100, No. 5, pages 476–486; October 15, 1956.

DIE SUBMIKROSKOPISCHE STRUKTUR DES CYTOPLASMAS. A. Frey-Wyssling in *Protoplasmatologia*, Band 2A2. Springer-Verlag, 1955.

SYMPOSIA OF THE SOCIETY FOR EXPERIMENTAL BIOLOGY, NO. IX: FIBROUS PROTEINS AND THEIR BIOLOGICAL SIGNIFICANCE. Cambridge University Press, 1955.

SYMPOSIUM ON BIOMOLECULAR ORGANIZATION AND LIFE-PROCESSES. Francis O. Schmitt, Paul Doty, Cecil E. Hall, Robley C. Williams and Paul A. Weiss in *Proceedings of the National Academy of Sciences*, Vol. 42, No. 11, pages 789–830; November 15, 1956.

2. The Insulin Molecule

The Author

E. O. P. THOMPSON is a biochemist with the Commonwealth Scientific and Industrial Research Organization of Australia. Born in Sydney, he was graduated with first-class honors in organic chemistry from Sydney University in 1945 and after five years of teaching and research there obtained a fellowship which enabled him to go to England to work on insulin under Frederick Sanger at Cambridge University. Thompson carried out further studies on proteins during 1953 at the College of Medicine of the University of Utah at Salt Lake City. He is now investigating the chemistry of wool, "a complex protein material," in the Wool Textile Research Laboratories in Australia.

Bibliography

THE AMINO-ACID SEQUENCE IN THE GLYCYL CHAIN OF INSULIN. F. Sanger and E. O. P. Thompson in *The Biochemical Journal*, Vol. 53, No. 3, pages 353–374; February, 1953.

THE CHEMISTRY OF INSULIN. F. Sanger in *Annual Reports on the Chemical Society*, Vol. 45, pages 283–292; 1949.

THE PRINCIPLES OF CHROMATOGRAPHY. A. J. P. Martin in *Endeavour*, Vol. 6, No. 21, pages 21–28; January, 1947.

3. Proteins

The Author

PAUL DOTY, editor of the *Journal of Polymer Science*, is a Harvard University physical chemist who was once an assistant professor of chemistry at the Polytechnic Institute of Brooklyn. Born in Charleston, W. Va., in 1920, Doty studied at Pennsylvania State College and at Columbia University, where he took his Ph.D. under J. E. Mayer. At that time he had already begun his association with Brooklyn Poly; during his three years there he directed a research project for the U.S. Army Quartermaster Corps. In 1946 Doty went to the University of Cambridge as a Rockefeller Foundation Fellow. The following year he taught at the University of Notre Dame, and in 1948 he joined the Harvard faculty, where he soon rose to full professorship. He has served as chairman of the Federation of American Scientists, and is a member of the National Academy of Sciences.

Bibliography

THE NATIVE AND DENATURED STATES OF SOLUBLE COLLAGEN. Helga Boedtker and Paul Doty in *Journal of the American Chemical Society*, Vol. 78, No. 17, pages 4,267–4,280; September 5, 1956.

THE OPTICAL ROTATORY DISPERSION OF POLYPEPTIDES AND PROTEINS IN RELATION TO CONFIGURATION. Jen Tsi Yang and Paul Doty in *Journal of the American Chemical Society*, Vol. 79, No. 4, pages 761–775; February 27, 1957.

POLYPEPTIDES, VIII: MOLECULAR CONFIGURATIONS OF POLY-L-GLUTAMIC ACID IN WATER-DIOXANE SOLUTION. Paul Doty, A. Wada, Jen Tsi Yang and E. R. Blout in *Journal of Polymer Science*, Vol. 23, No. 104, pages 851–861; February, 1957.

SYNTHETIC POLYPEPTIDES: PREPARATION, STRUCTURE, AND PROPERTIES. C. H. Bamford, A. Elliott and W. E. Hanby. Academic Press Inc., 1956.

4.   The Hemoglobin Molecule

The Author

M. F. PERUTZ is chairman of the Laboratory of Molecular Biology in Cambridge, England and a Fellow of the Royal Society of London. Perutz was born in Vienna in 1914 and did his undergraduate work in chemistry at the University of Vienna. In 1936 he went to England to do research under J. D. Bernal at the Cavendish Laboratory of the University of Cambridge. He received a Ph. D. in X-ray crystallography from Cambridge in 1940. From 1939 to 1945 he worked as a research assistant to W. L. Bragg at the Cavendish Laboratory. In 1947 Perutz was made director of the newly constituted Medical Research Council Unit for Molecular Biology, a post he held until 1962, when the Medical Research Council built the Laboratory of Molecular Biology for him and his colleagues. Perutz' work on the structure of hemoglobin, he writes, "started as a result of a conversation with F. Haurowitz in Prague in September, 1937. G. A. Adair made me the first crystals of horse haemoglobin and Bernal and I. Fankuchen showed me how to take X-ray pictures and how to interpret them. Early in 1938 Bernal, Fankuchen and I published a joint paper on X-ray diffraction from crystals of haemoglobin and chymotrypsin. The chymotrypsin crystals were twinned and therefore difficult to work with, and so I continued with haemoglobin." It was not until 15 years later, in 1953, that Perutz finally discovered a method for solving the structure of the protein molecules. His method led to the solution of the structure of myoglobin by John C. Kendrew and of the structure of hemoglobin by Perutz himself. For these discoveries Perutz and Kendrew were awarded the Nobel prize in chemistry in 1962. On that occasion Perutz remarked: "I have had the good fortune of being joined by colleagues of great ability, several of whom have now been honored with the Nobel prize at the same time as myself. Kendrew came in 1946, [F. H. C.] Crick in 1948, and [J. D.] Watson arrived as a visitor in 1948. Recently F. Sanger, who received the Nobel prize in 1958, also joined forces with us. I am extremely happy at the generous recognition given by the Royal Caroline Institute to our great common adventures and hope that it will spur us to new endeavours."

Bibliography

THE CHEMISTRY AND FUNCTION OF PROTEINS. Felix Haurowitz. Academic Press, 1963.

RELATION BETWEEN STRUCTURE AND SEQUENCE OF HAEMOGLO-BIN. M. F. Perutz in *Nature*, Vol. 194, No. 4832, pages 914–918; June, 1962.

STRUCTURE OF HAEMOGLOBIN: A THREE-DIMENSIONAL FOURIER SYNTHESIS OF REDUCED HUMAN HAEMOGLOBIN AT 5.5 Å RESOLUTION. Hilary Muirhead and M. F. Perutz in *Nature*, Vol. 199, No. 4894, pages 633–639; August, 1963.

5.   The Three-Dimensional Structure of an Enzyme Molecule

The Author

DAVID C. PHILLIPS is professor of molecular biophysics at the University of Oxford. After taking bachelor's and doctor's degrees at the University of Wales, he worked at the National Research Laboratories in Ottawa for four years, investigating with X-rays the structure of small organic molecules. From 1956 until this year he was at the Royal Institution in London, working with Sir Lawrence Bragg, J. C. Kendrew, M. F. Perutz and others on X-ray analysis of protein structures.

Bibliography

BIOSYNTHESIS OF MACROMOLECULES. Vernon M. Ingram. W. A. Benjamin, Inc., 1965.

INTRODUCTION TO MOLECULAR BIOLOGY. G. H. Haggis, D. Michie, A. R. Muir, K. B. Roberts and P. M. B. Walker. John Wiley & Sons, Inc. 1964.

THE MOLECULAR BIOLOGY OF THE GENE. J. D. Watson. W. A. Benjamin, Inc., 1965.

PROTEIN AND NUCLEIC ACIDS: STRUCTURE AND FUNCTION. M. F. Perutz. American Elsevier Publishing Company, Inc., 1962.

STRUCTURE OF HEN EGG-WHITE LYSOZYME: A THREE-DIMENSIONAL FOURIER SYNTHESIS AT 2 Å. RESOLUTION. C. C. F. Blake, D. F. Koenig, G. A. Mair, A. C. T. North, D. C. Phillips and V. R. Sarma in *Nature*, Vol. 206, No. 4986, pages 757–763; May 22, 1965.

6.   The Structure of the Hereditary Material

The Author

F. H. C. CRICK is a molecular biologist who works for the British Medical Research Council's Laboratory of Molecular Biology at the University Postgraduate Medical School in Cambridge. He is also a Fellow of the Royal Society of London. He was originally a physicist but turned to basic research on the structure of viruses, collagen and the nucleic acids. In the early 1950's he worked on X-ray diffraction of crystals of ribonucleic acid at the Polytechnic Institute of Brooklyn. He is best known for putting forward (with James D. Watson) the idea that the molecule of the genetic material deoxyribonucleic acid (DNA) is a double helix; for work on the structure of DNA, Crick, Watson and M. H. F. Wilkins jointly received the Nobel prize for physiology and medicine in 1962.

Bibliography

THE BIOCHEMISTRY OF THE NUCLEIC ACIDS. J. N. Davidson. Methuen & Co., Ltd., 1954.

HELICAL STRUCTURE OF DEOXYPENTOSE NUCLEIC ACID. M. H. F. Wilkins and others in *Nature*, Vol. 172, No. 4382, pages 759–762; October 24, 1953.

SYMPOSIUM PAPERS ON THE NUCLEIC ACIDS. Proceedings of the National Academy of Sciences, 1954.

7.   The Nucleotide Sequence of a Nucleic Acid

The Author

ROBERT W. HOLLEY is professor of biochemistry and chairman of the section of biochemistry and molecular biology of the division of biological sciences at Cornell University. He was graduated from the University of Illinois in 1942 and obtained a Ph.D. at Cornell in 1947. He joined the Cornell faculty in 1948, and during his years there he has also worked with the U.S. Plant, Soil and Nutrition Laboratory at the university. Holley and his colleagues spent four years isolating one gram of pure transfer ribonucleic acid and three more years ascertaining its chemical structure. Holley received the 1965 Albert D. Lasker award for basic medical research for the work described in his article.

Bibliography

ISOLATION OF LARGE OLIGONUCLEOTIDE FRAGMENTS FROM THE ALANINE RNA. Jean Apgar, George A. Everett and Robert W. Holley in *Proceedings of the National Academy of Sciences,* Vol. 53, No. 3, pages 546–548; March, 1965.

LABORATORY EXTRACTION AND COUNTERCURRENT DISTRIBUTION. Lyman C. Craig and David Craig in *Technique of Organic Chemistry, Volume III, Part I: Separation and Purification,* edited by Arnold Weissberger. Interscience Publishers, Inc., 1956. See pages 149–332.

SPECIFIC CLEAVAGE OF THE YEAST ALANINE RNA INTO TWO LARGE FRAGMENTS. John Robert Penswick and Robert W. Holley in *Proceedings of the National Academy of Sciences,* Vol. 53, No. 3, pages 543–546; March, 1965.

STRUCTURE OF A RIBONUCLEIC ACID. Robert W. Holley, Jean Apgar, George A. Everett, James T. Madison, Mark Marquisee, Susan H. Merrill, John Robert Penswick and Ada Zamir in *Science,* Vol. 147, No. 3664, pages 1462–1465; March 19, 1965.

8. The Bacterial Chromosome

The Author

JOHN CAIRNS has recently served as director of the Cold Spring Harbor Laboratory of Quantitative Biology. He was born in England and obtained a medical degree at the University of Oxford. For several years he did research in Australia on the multiplication of influenza virus and vaccinia virus. Later he worked on the visualization of DNA molecules by autoradiography, a project he describes in part in the present article.

Bibliography

THE BACTERIAL CHROMOSOME AND ITS MANNER OF REPLICATION AS SEEN BY AUTORADIOGRAPHY. John Cairns in *Journal of Molecular Biology,* Vol. 6, No. 3, pages 208–213; March, 1963.

COLD SPRING HARBOR SYMPOSIA ON QUANTITATIVE BIOLOGY, VOLUME XXVIII: SYNTHESIS AND STRUCTURE OF MACROMOLECULES. Cold Spring Harbor Laboratory of Quantitative Biology, 1963.

MOLECULAR BIOLOGY OF THE GENE. James D. Watson. W. A. Benjamin, Inc., 1965. See pages 255–296.

9. The Repair of DNA

The Authors

PHILIP C. HANAWALT and ROBERT H. HAYNES are respectively associate professor of biological sciences at Stanford University and associate professor of biophysics and medical physics at the University of California at Berkeley. Hanawalt majored in physics at Oberlin College, from which he was graduated in 1954, and did graduate work in physics and biophysics at Yale University, from which he received a Ph.D. in 1959. Haynes obtained a bachelor's degree in physics and a Ph.D. in biophysics from the University of Western Ontario. Both Hanawalt and Haynes teach introductory courses in biology.

Bibliography

THE DISAPPEARANCE OF THYMINE DIMERS FROM DNA: AN ERROR-CORRECTING MECHANISM. R. B. Setlow and W. L. Carrier in *Proceedings of the National Academy of Sciences,* Vol. 51, No. 2, pages 226–231; February, 1964.

EVIDENCE FOR REPAIR REPLICATION OF ULTRAVIOLET-DAMAGED DNA IN BACTERIA. David Pettijohn and Philip C. Hanawalt in *Journal of Molecular Biology,* Vol. 9, No. 2, pages 395–410; August, 1964.

A GENETIC LOCUS IN E. COLI K 12 THAT CONTROLS THE REACTIVATION OF UV-PHOTOPRODUCTS ASSOCIATED WITH THYMINE IN DNA. P. Howard-Flanders, Richard P. Boyce, Eva Simson and Lee Theriot in *Proceedings of the National Academy of Sciences,* Vol. 48, No. 12, pages 2109–2115; December 15, 1962.

STRUCTURAL DEFECTS IN DNA AND THEIR REPAIR IN MICRO-ORGANISMS. Radiation Research, Supplement 6, edited by Robert H. Haynes, Sheldon Wolff and James E. Till. Academic Press, in press.

10. The Duplication of Chromosomes

The Author

J. HERBERT TAYLOR is professor of biology at the Institute for Molecular Biophysics of Florida State University, Tallahassee, and was formerly professor of cell biology at Columbia University. He has been using isotopes in biological research ever since high-resolution autoradiography was first developed in 1950. At that time he was teaching at the University of Tennessee and working as a consultant to the Oak Ridge National Laboratory. Taylor was graduated from Southeastern State College in Oklahoma and acquired a Ph.D. in biology from the University of Virginia.

Bibliography

THE BIOCHEMISTRY OF THE NUCLEIC ACIDS. J. N. Davidson. John Wiley & Sons, Inc., 1953.

THE NUCLEIC ACIDS. Edited by Erwin Chargaff and J. N. Davidson. Academic Press, Inc., 1955.

NUCLEIC ACIDS. F. H. C. Crick in *Scientific American,* Vol. 197, No. 3, pages 188–200; September; 1957.

THE ORGANIZATION AND DUPLICATION OF CHROMOSOMES AS REVEALED BY AUTORADIOGRAPHIC STUDIES USING TRITIUM-LABELED THYMIDINE. J. Herbert Taylor, Philip S. Woods and Walter L. Hughes in *Proceedings of the National Academy of Sciences,* Vol. 43, No. 1, pages 122–128; January, 1957.

PHYSICAL TECHNIQUES IN BIOLOGICAL RESEARCH. VOL. III: CELLS AND TISSUES. Edited by Gerald Oster and Arthur W. Pollister. Academic Press, Inc., 1956.

A SYMPOSIUM ON THE CHEMICAL BASIS OF HEREDITY. William D. McElroy and Bentley Glass. Johns Hopkins Press, 1957.

Suggestions for Further Reading

Bernhard, S. A. THE STRUCTURE AND FUNCTION OF ENZYMES. New York, W. A. Benjamin, Inc., 1968.

Kendrew, J. C. THE THREAD OF LIFE. Cambridge, Mass., Harvard University Press, 1966.

Perutz, M. F., PROTEINS AND NUCLEIC ACIDS. New York, American Elsevier, 1962.

Rich, Alexander, and Norman Davidson, Eds., STRUCTURAL CHEMISTRY AND MOLECULAR BIOLOGY, *A Volume Dedicated to Linus Pauling by his Students, Colleagues, and Friends.* San Francisco, W. H. Freeman and Company, 1968.

Watson, J. D., THE DOUBLE HELIX. New York, Atheneum, 1968.

II THE VIRUS
A Replicating Macromolecular Complex

11. Bacterial Viruses and Sex

The Authors

MAX DELBRÜCK is professor of biology at the California Institute of Technology. where he started the famous "Phage Group." A native of Berlin, he received his Ph.D. in physics from the University of Göttingen in 1930. He came to the United States in 1937 as a Rockefeller Foundation fellow in biology. He taught physics at Vanderbilt University until 1947, when he joined the biology department at Cal Tech. Dr. Delbrück is a member of the National Academy of Sciences. He was also one of the first molecular biologists to shift his attention from problems of genetics to those of neurobiology. MARY BRUCE DELBRÜCK is his wife.

Bibliography

EXPERIMENTS WITH BACTERIAL VIRUSES. M. Delbrück in the *Harvey Lecture Series,* Vol. 41, pages 161–187; 1945–46.
RECENT ADVANCES IN BACTERIAL GENETICS. S. E. Luria in the *Bacteriological Reviews,* Vol. 2; March, 1947.
HEREDITY AND VARIATION IN MICROORGANISMS. *Cold Spring Harbor Symposia on Quantitative Biology,* Vol. 11; 1946.

12. The Multiplication of Bacterial Viruses

The Author

GUNTHER S. STENT is a biologist who holds degrees in chemistry and owes his choice of career to a physicist. Born in Berlin in 1924, Stent came to the U.S. in 1940, worked as a waiter, office boy and soda jerk, and entered the University of Illinois. Just before he received his Ph.D. a friend gave him a copy of Erwin Schrödinger's *What Is Life?* Stent was "so impressed by what I read that I decided to have a try sometime at becoming a biologist." The opportunity soon came in the form of a two-year Merck fellowship awarded by the National Research Council, which sent him to the California Institute of Technology in 1948 to study viruses under Max Delbrück. Another two-year fellowship from the American Cancer Society permitted him to continue his studies in Denmark and at the Pasteur Institute in Paris. In Denmark he developed another interest. "No different from most of the bachelor scientists who have come to spend a year in Copenhagen," he writes, "I did not leave Denmark a single man. . . . As the only variation to the normal pattern, I married an Icelandic rather than a Danish girl." He is professor of molecular biology in the University of California, Berkeley, and since 1952 has been a member of the Virus Laboratory there. He has recently been honored as professor of arts and science at Berkeley.

Bibliography

BACTERIAL VIRUSES AND SEX. Max and Mary Bruce Delbrück in *Scientific American;* November, 1948.

13. The Structure of Viruses

The Author

R. W. HORNE is a member of the staff at the Institute of Animal Physiology in Cambridge, England. Horne, whose main interest is in developing new methods of combining electron microscopy with biochemical techniques, has since 1947 been closely associated with the development of electron microscopes and their applications. In 1958 he collaborated with Sydney Brenner of the University of Cambridge in a detailed study of the structure of the T2 virus, which infects the colon bacillus. The methods used in that study have subsequently been applied in elucidating the structure of a wide variety of viruses.

Bibliography

THE FINE STRUCTURE OF POLYOMA VIRUS. P. Wildy, M. G. P. Stoker, I. A. Macpherson and R. W. Horne in *Virology,* Vol. 11, No. 2, pages 444–457; June, 1960.
A HELICAL STRUCTURE IN MUMPS, NEWCASTLE DISEASE AND SENDAI VIRUSES. R. W. Horne and A. P. Waterson in *Journal of Molecular Biology,* Vol. 2, No. 1, pages 75–77; April, 1960.
THE ICOSAHEDRAL FORM OF AN ADENOVIRUS. R. W. Horne, S. Brenner, A. P. Waterson and P. Wildy in *Journal of Molecular Biology,* Vol. 1, No. 1, pages 84–86; April, 1959.
THE MORPHOLOGY OF HERPES VIRUS. P. Wildy, W. C. Russell and R. W. Horne in *Virology,* Vol. 12, No. 2, pages 204–222; October, 1960.
THE STRUCTURE AND COMPOSITION OF THE MYXOVIRUSES. R. W. Horne, A. P. Waterson, P. Wildy and A. E. Farnham in *Virology,* Vol. 11, No. 1, pages 79–98; May, 1960.
SYMMETRY IN VIRUS ARCHITECTURE. R. W. Horne and P. Wildy in *Virology,* Vol. 15, No. 3, pages 348–373; November, 1961.

14. The Fine Structure of the Gene

The Author

SEYMOUR BENZER was elected to the National Academy of Sciences while serving as professor of biophysics at Purdue University. After taking his B.A. at Brooklyn College in 1942, Benzer went to Purdue, where he acquired an M.S. the following year and a Ph.D. in physics in 1947. He then spent a year at the Oak Ridge National Laboratory, two years at the California Institute of Technology and a year at the Pasteur Institute in Paris before returning to Purdue in 1952. He is another of the outstanding molecular biologists who have been attracted to problems in neurobiology, and he is now a member of the biology division at Cal Tech.

Bibliography

THE ELEMENTARY UNITS OF HEREDITY. Seymour Benzer in *The Chemical Basis of Heredity,* edited by William D. McElroy and Bentley Glass, pages 70–93. The Johns Hopkins Press, 1957.
GENETIC RECOMBINATION BETWEEN HOST-RANGE AND PLAQUE-TYPE MUTANTS OF BACTERIOPHAGE IN SINGLE BACTERIAL CELLS. A. D. Hershey and Raquel Rotman in *Genetics,* Vol. 34, No. 1, pages 44–71; January, 1949.
INDUCTION OF SPECIFIC MUTATIONS WITH 5-BROMOURACIL. Seymour Benzer and Ernst Freese in *Proceedings of the National Academy of Sciences,* Vol. 44, No. 2, pages 112–119; February, 1958.

THE STRUCTURE OF THE HEREDITARY MATERIAL. F. H. C. Crick in *Scientific American*, Vol. 191, No. 4, pages 54–61; October, 1954.

ON THE TOPOGRAPHY OF THE GENETIC FINE STRUCTURE. Seymour Benzer in *Proceedings of the National Academy of Sciences*, Vol. 47, No. 3, pages 403–415; March, 1961.

15. The Genetics of a Bacterial Virus

The Authors

R. S. EDGAR and R. H. EPSTEIN are respectively associate professor of biology at the California Institute of Technology and an investigator at the Institute of Molecular Biology of the University of Geneva. They were graduate students together at the University of Rochester, where Epstein, who was born in Rochester, had done his undergraduate work; Edgar, a native of Canada, went to Rochester after undergraduate work at McGill University. Both obtained a Ph.D. at Rochester and then, in the late 1950's, went to the California Institute of Technology to study under Max Delbrück. Of the work reported in their article Edgar writes: "Epstein started the 'ambers' here and then went to Geneva to continue that work while I developed the temperature-sensitive system. The two systems were developed independently, with communication going on through an intermediary, an associate of Epstein's, since he is a notoriously bad letter writer (he doesn't)."

Bibliography

BACTERIOPHAGE REPRODUCTION. Sewell P. Champe in *Annual Review of Microbiology*, Vol. 17, 1963.

MOLECULAR BIOLOGY OF BACTERIAL VIRUSES. Gunther S. Stent. W. H. Freeman and Company, 1963.

PHYSIOLOGICAL STUDIES OF CONDITIONAL LETHAL MUTANTS OF BACTERIOPHAGE T4D. R. H. Epstein, A. Bolle, C. M. Steinberg, E. Kellenberger, E. Boy de la Tour, R. Chevalley, R. S. Edgar, M. Susman, G. H. Denhardt and A. Lielausis in *Cold Spring Harbor Symposia on Quantitative Biology*, Vol. XXVIII. 1963.

16. Building a Bacterial Virus

The Authors

WILLIAM B. WOOD and R. S. EDGAR are in the division of biology of the California Institute of Technology; Wood is assistant professor and Edgar is professor. Wood, who did his undergraduate work at Harvard College, received a doctorate in biochemistry from Stanford University in 1963 and spent a year and a half as a postdoctoral fellow in Switzerland before joining the Cal Tech faculty. Edgar, a graduate of McGill University, obtained his Ph.D. from the University of Rochester. Wood writes that they began discussing the experiments described in their article in 1963 and started work in 1965. "I suspect," he adds, "that either of us alone might never have initiated these experiments."

Bibliography

CONDITIONAL MUTATIONS IN BACTERIOPHAGE T4. R. S. Edgar and R. H. Epstein in *Genetics Today*, edited by S. J. Geerts. Pergamon Press, 1963.

GENE ACTION IN THE CONTROL OF BACTERIOPHAGE T4 MORPHOGENESIS. W. B. Wood in *Proceedings of the Thomas Hunt Morgan Centennial Symposium*. University of Kentucky, in press.

SOME STEPS IN THE MORPHOGENESIS OF BACTERIOPHAGE T4. R. S. Edgar and I. Lielausis in *Journal of Molecular Biology*, in press.

Suggestions for Further Reading

Cairns, J., G. S. Stent, and J. D. Watson, Eds., PHAGE AND THE ORIGINS OF MOLECULAR BIOLOGY. Cold Spring Harbor, New York, Cold Spring Harbor Laboratory of Quantitative Biology, 1966.

Hayes, W., THE GENETICS OF BACTERIA AND THEIR VIRUSES, New York, Wiley, 1964.

Luria, S. E., and J. E. Darnell, Jr., GENERAL VIROLOGY. New York, Wiley, 1967.

Stent, G. S., MOLECULAR BIOLOGY OF BACTERIAL VIRUSES. San Francisco, W. H. Freeman and Company, 1963.

III GENE ACTION IN PROTEIN SYNTHESIS
The Expression of Genetic Information

17. The Genes of Men and Molds

The Author

GEORGE BEADLE served for many years as head of the California Institute of Technology Division of Biology. He is a geneticist, whose most notable work was done with the bread mold *Neurospora*. In 1958, while on a visiting professorship at the University of Oxford, Beadle was summoned to Stockholm to receive a Nobel prize jointly with his collaborator Edward L. Tatum for the work on *Neurospora* described in this article. In 1961 Beadle left Cal Tech to become President of the University of Chicago.

Bibliography

GENES AND THE CHEMISTRY OF ORGANISM. G. W. Beadle in *American Scientist*, Vol. 34, pages 31–53; 1946.

THE PRINCIPLES OF HEREDITY, Third Edition. Laurence H. Snyder. D. C. Heath, 1946.

THE PHYSIOLOGY OF THE GENE. S. Wright in *Physiological Reviews*, Vol. 21, pages 487–527; 1941.

18. Hybrid Nucleic Acids

The Author

S. SPIEGELMAN is professor of microbiology at the University of Illinois and a member of the National Academy of Sciences. He acquired a B.S. in mathematics and physics from the College of the City of New York in 1938 and a Ph.D. in cellular physiology from Washington University in 1944. From 1942 to 1945 he was lecturer in physics and mathematics at Washington University and from 1946 to 1948 he was assistant professor of Microbiology at that university's College of Medicine. He did research as a special fellow of the U.S. Public Health Service at the University of Minnesota's Medical School from 1948 to 1949.

Bibliography

DISTINCT CISTRONS FOR THE TWO RIBOSOMAL RNA COMPONENTS. S. A. Yankofsky and S. Spiegelman in *Proceedings of the National Academy of Sciences*, Vol. 49, No. 4, pages 538–544; April, 1963.

ORIGIN AND BIOLOGIC INDIVIDUALITY OF THE GENETIC DIC-
TIONARY. Dario Giacomoni and S. Spiegelman in *Science*,
Vol. 138, No. 3547, pages 1328–1331; December, 1962.
STRAND SEPARATION AND SPECIFIC RECOMBINATION IN DEOXY-
RIBONUCLEIC ACIDS: BIOLOGICAL STUDIES. J. Marmur and
D. Lane in *Proceedings of the National Academy of Sci-
ences*, Vol. 46, No. 4, pages 453–461; April, 1960.
THERMAL RENATURATION OF DEOXYRIBONUCLEIC ACIDS. Julius
Marmur and Paul Doty in *Journal of Molecular Biology*,
Vol. 3, No. 5, pages 585–594; October, 1961.

19. Polyribosomes

The Author

ALEXANDER RICH is professor of biophysics at the Massachusetts Institute of Technology. A graduate of Harvard College,
Rich obtained an M.D. from the Harvard Medical School in
1949. He did research in chemistry at the California Institute of Technology from 1949 to 1954, when he became
chief of the section on physical chemistry at the National
Institutes of Health in Bethesda, Md. Rich was visiting scientist at the Cavendish Laboratory in Cambridge, England,
during 1955. He joined the M.I.T. faculty in 1958.

Bibliography

ELECTRON MICROSCOPE STUDIES OF RIBOSOMAL CLUSTERS SYN-
THESIZING HEMOGLOBIN. Jonathan R. Warner, Alexander
Rich and Cecil E. Hall in *Science*, Vol. 138, No. 3548,
pages 1399–1403; December 28, 1962.
FUNCTION OF AGGREGATED RETICULOCYTE RIBOSOMES IN PRO-
TEIN SYNTHESIS. Alfred Gierer in *Journal of Molecular
Biology*, Vol. 6, No. 2, pages 148–157; February, 1963.
MECHANISM OF POLYRIBOSOME ACTION DURING PROTEIN SYN-
THESIS. Howard M. Goodman and Alexander Rich in
Nature, Vol. 199, No. 4891, pages 318–322; July 27, 1963.
A MULTIPLE RIBOSOMAL STRUCTURE IN PROTEIN SYNTHESIS. Jo-
nathan R. Warner, Paul M. Knopf and Alexander Rich
in *Proceedings of the National Academy of Sciences of
the U.S.A.*, Vol. 49, No. 1, pages 122–129; January, 1963.

20. The Genetic Code

The Author

F. H. C. CRICK is a molecular biologist who works for the
British Medical Research Council's Laboratory of Molecular
Biology at the University Postgraduate Medical School in
Cambridge. He is also a Fellow of the Royal Society of London. He was originally a physicist but turned to basic research on the structure of viruses, collagen and the nucleic
acids. In the early 1950's he worked on X-ray diffraction of
crystals of ribonucleic acid at the Polytechnic Institute of
Brooklyn. He is best known for putting forward (with James
D. Watson) the idea that the molecule of the genetic material
deoxyribonucleic acid (DNA) is a double helix; for work on
the structure of DNA, Crick, Watson and M. H. F. Wilkins
jointly received the Nobel prize for physiology and medicine
in 1962.

Bibliography

THE FINE STRUCTURE OF THE GENE. Seymour Benzer in *Scientific American*, Vol. 206, No. 1, pages 70–84; January,
1962.
GENERAL NATURE OF THE GENETIC CODE FOR PROTEINS. F. H. C.
Crick, Leslie Barnett, S. Brenner and R. J. Watts-Tobin
in *Nature*, Vol. 192, No. 4809, pages 1227–1232; December 30, 1961.

MESSENGER RNA. Jerard Hurwitz and J. J. Furth in *Scientific
American*, Vol. 206, No. 2, pages 41–49; February, 1962.
THE NUCLEIC ACIDS: Vol. III. Edited by Erwin Chargaff and
J. N. Davidson. Academic Press Inc., 1960.

21. The Genetic Code: II

The Author

MARSHALL W. NIRENBERG is head of the Section of Biochemical Genetics at the National Heart Institute, one of the
nine National Institutes of Health. Nirenberg took a B.S. at
the University of Florida in 1948. After receiving an M.S. in
biology from the University of Florida in 1952, Nirenberg
went to the department of biological chemistry at the University of Michigan, where he acquired a Ph.D. in 1957. A two-
year postdoctoral fellowship from the American Cancer Society brought him to the National Institute of Arthritis and
Metabolic Diseases later the same year, where he remained
until he took his present post. He is a member of the National Academy of Sciences.

Bibliography

THE DEPENDENCE OF CELL-FREE PROTEIN SYNTHESIS IN E. COLI
UPON NATURALLY OCCURRING OR SYNTHETIC POLYRIBO-
NUCLEOTIDES. Marshall W. Nirenberg and J. Heinrich
Matthaei in *Proceedings of the National Academy of Sci-
ences of the U.S.A.*, Vol. 47, No. 10, pages 1588–1602;
October, 1961.
A PHYSICAL BASIS FOR DEGENERACY IN THE AMINO ACID CODE.
Bernard Weisblum, Seymour Benzer and Robert W. Hol-
ley in *Proceedings of the National Academy of Sciences
of the U.S.A.*, Vol. 48, No. 8, pages 1449–1453; August,
1962.
POLYRIBONUCLEOTIDE-DIRECTED PROTEIN SYNTHESIS USING AN
E. COLI CELL-FREE SYSTEM. M. S. Bretscher and M. Grun-
berg-Manago in *Nature*, Vol. 195, No. 4838, pages 283–
284; July 21, 1962.
QUALITATIVE SURVEY OF RNA CODEWORDS. Oliver W. Jones, Jr.,
and Marshall W. Nirenberg in *Proceedings of the National
Academy of Sciences of the U.S.A.*, Vol. 48, No. 12, pages
2115–2123; December, 1962.
SYNTHETIC POLYNUCLEOTIDES AND THE AMINO ACID CODE, IV.
J. F. Speyer, P. Lengyel, C. Basilio and S. Ochoa in *Pro-
ceedings of the National Academy of Sciences of the
U.S.A.*, Vol. 48, No. 3, pages 441–448; March, 1962.

22. The Genetic Code: III

The Author

F. H. C. CRICK is a molecular biologist who works for the
British Medical Research Council's Laboratory of Molecular
Biology at the University Postgraduate Medical School in
Cambridge. For additional information about him, see bio-
graphical note 20.

Bibliography

THE GENETIC CODE, VOL. XXXI: 1966 COLD SPRING HARBOR SYM-
POSIA ON QUANTITATIVE BIOLOGY. Cold Spring Harbor
Laboratory of Quantitative Biology.
MOLECULAR BIOLOGY OF THE GENE. James D. Watson. W. A.
Benjamin, Inc., 1965.
RNA CODEWORDS AND PROTEIN SYNTHESIS, VII: ON THE GENERAL
NATURE OF THE RNA CODE. M. Nirenberg, P. Leder, M.
Bernfield, R. Brimacombe, J. Trupin, F. Rottman and C.
O'Neal in *Proceedings of the National Academy of Sci-
ences*, Vol. 53, No. 5, pages 1161–1168; May, 1965.

STUDIES ON POLYNUCLEOTIDES, LVI: FURTHER SYNTHESES, IN VITRO, OF COPOLYPEPTIDES CONTAINING TWO AMINO ACIDS IN ALTERNATING SEQUENCE DEPENDENT UPON DNA-LIKE POLYMERS CONTAINING TWO NUCLEOTIDES IN ALTERNATING SEQUENCE. D. S. Jones, S. Nishimura and H. G. Khorana in *Journal of Molecular Biology*, Vol. 16, No. 2, pages 454–472; April, 1966.

23. Gene Structure and Protein Structure

The Author

CHARLES YANOFSKY is professor of biology at Stanford University. After his graduation from the City College of the City of New York in 1948 he did graduate work in the department of microbiology at Yale University, receiving a Ph.D. there in 1951. He remained at Yale until 1954, when he joined the faculty of the Western Reserve University School of Medicine. Four years later he went to the department of biological sciences at Stanford. Yanofsky has received several awards for his work in molecular biology. He was elected to the American Academy of Arts and Sciences in 1964 and to the National Academy of Sciences last year.

Bibliography

CO-LINEARITY OF β-GALACTOSIDASE WITH ITS GENE BY IMMUNOLOGICAL DETECTION OF INCOMPLETE POLYPEPTIDE CHAINS. Audree V. Fowler and Irving Zabin in *Science*, Vol. 154, No. 3752, pages 1027–1029; November 25, 1966.
CO-LINEARITY OF THE GENE WITH THE POLYPEPTIDE CHAIN. A. S. Sarabhai, A. O. W. Stretton, S. Brenner and A. Bolle in *Nature*, Vol. 201, No. 4914, pages 13–17; January 4, 1964.
THE COMPLETE AMINO ACID SEQUENCE OF THE TRYPTOPHAN SYNTHETASE A PROTEIN (α SUBUNIT) AND ITS CO-LINEAR RELATIONSHIP WITH THE GENETIC MAP OF THE A GENE. Charles Yanofsky, Gabriel R. Drapeau, John R. Guest and Bruce C. Carlton in *Proceedings of the National Academy of Sciences*, Vol. 57, No. 2, pages 296–298; February, 1967.
MUTATIONALLY INDUCED AMINO ACID SUBSTITUTIONS IN A TRYPTIC PEPTIDE OF THE TRYPTOPHAN SYNTHETASE A PROTEIN. John R. Guest and Charles Yanofsky in *Journal of Biological Chemistry*, Vol. 240, No. 2, pages 679–689; February, 1965.
ON THE COLINEARITY OF GENE STRUCTURE AND PROTEIN STRUC-TURE. C. Yanofsky, B. C. Carlton, J. R. Guest, D. R. Helinski and U. Henning in *Proceedings of the National Academy of Sciences*, Vol. 51, No. 2, pages 266–272; February, 1964.

24. How Proteins Start

The Authors

BRIAN F. C. CLARK and KJELD A. MARCKER work together at the British Medical Research Council's Laboratory of Molecular Biology in Cambridge. Clark has a Ph.D. in organic chemistry from the University of Cambridge. He has also done research in biochemistry at the Massachusetts Institute of Technology and in biochemical genetics at the National Heart Institute in Bethesda, Md. Marcker has a Ph.D. in biochemistry from the University of Copenhagen. He is at Cambridge on a Carlsberg-Wellcome Fellowship.

Bibliography

A GTP REQUIREMENT FOR BINDING INITIATOR tRNA TO RIBOSOMES. John S. Anderson, Mark S. Bretscher, Brian F. C. Clark and Kjeld A. Marcker in *Nature*, Vol. 215, No. 5100, pages 490–492; July 29, 1967.
N-FORMYL-METHIONYL-S-RNA. K. Marcker and F. Sanger in *Journal of Molecular Biology*, Vol. 8, No. 6, pages 835–840; June, 1964.
THE ROLE OF N-FORMYL-METHIONYL-S-RNA IN PROTEIN BIOSYNTHESIS. B. F. C. Clark and K. A. Marcker in *Journal of Molecular Biology*, Vol. 17, No. 2, pages 394–406; June, 1966.
STUDIES ON POLYNUCLEOTIDES, LXVII: INITIATION OF PROTEIN SYNTHESIS IN VITRO AS STUDIED BY USING RIBOPOLYNUCLEOTIDES WITH REPEATING NUCLEOTIDE SEQUENCES AS MESSENGERS. H. P. Ghosh, D. Söll and H. G. Khorana in *Journal of Molecular Biology*, Vol. 25, No. 2, pages 275–298; April 28, 1967.

Suggestions for Further Reading

COLD SPRING HARBOR SYMPOSIUM ON QUANTITATIVE BIOLOGY. Volume XXXI, "The Genetic Code." Cold Spring Harbor, New York, 1966.
Watson, J. D. MOLECULAR BIOLOGY OF THE GENE. New York, Benjamin, 1966.

IV MODIFICATION OF GENE ACTION
The Regulation of Cellular Activity

25. The Control of Biochemical Reactions

The Author

JEAN-PIERRE CHANGEUX is *maître-assistant* in biochemistry at the University of Paris. He describes his post as "something more than an assistant but less than a professor." Changeux also does research at the Pasteur Institute, where in 1959 he began an investigation of the mechanism by which the activity of enzymes is regulated. That work has led him into other investigations of cellular regulatory processes in an effort to elucidate the mechanisms by which a metabolite, or regulatory signal, controls a chemical reaction at the molecular level. Before he went to work at the Pasteur Institute, Changeux did research in marine zoology.

Bibliography

ALLOSTERIC PROTEINS AND CELLULAR CONTROL SYSTEMS. Jacques Monod, Jean-Pierre Changeux and François Jacob in *Journal of Molecular Biology*, Vol. 6, No. 4, pages 306–329; April, 1963.
GENETIC REGULATORY MECHANISMS IN THE SYNTHESIS OF PROTEINS. François Jacob and Jacques Monod in *Journal of Molecular Biology*, Vol. 3, No. 3, pages 318–356; June, 1961.
ON THE REGULATION OF DNA REPLICATION IN BACTERIA. François Jacob, Sydney Brenner and François Cuzin in *Cold Spring Harbor Symposia on Quantitative Biology*, Vol. XXVIII. 1963.

A PLAUSIBLE MODEL OF ALLOSTERIC TRANSITION. Jacques Monod, Jeffries Wyman and Jean-Pierre Changeux in *Journal of Molecular Biology*, in press.

26. Hormones and Genes

The Author

ERIC H. DAVIDSON is a research associate at the Rockefeller Institute, working in cell biology. As a high school student in Nyack, N.Y., he worked summers at the Marine Biological Laboratory in Woods Hole, Mass., and was one of the national winners of the Westinghouse Science Talent Search. Davidson was graduated from the University of Pennsylvania in 1958, having majored in zoology. For the next five years he was a graduate fellow at the Rockefeller Institute, obtaining a doctor's degree there in 1963. He writes that as a research fellow at the Institute he is "collaborating with Alfred E. Mirsky in the study of gene action in the initiation and control of embryological development."

Bibliography

EFFECT OF ACTINOMYCIN AND INSULIN ON THE METABOLISM OF ISOLATED RAT DIAPHRAGM. Ira G. Wool and Arthur N. Moyer in *Biochimica et Biophysica Acta*, Vol. 91, No. 2, pages 248–256; October 16, 1964.

ON THE MECHANISM OF ACTION OF ALDOSTERONE ON SODIUM TRANSPORT: THE ROLE OF RNA SYNTHESIS. George A. Porter, Rita Bogoroch and Isidore S. Edelman in *Proceedings of the National Academy of Sciences*, Vol. 52, No. 6, pages 1326–1333; December, 1964.

PREVENTION OF HORMONE ACTION BY LOCAL APPLICATION OF ACTINOMYCIN D. G. P. Talwar and Sheldon J. Segal in *Proceedings of the National Academy of Sciences*, Vol. 50, No. 1, pages 226–230; July 15, 1963.

SELECTIVE ALTERATIONS OF MAMMALIAN MESSENGER-RNA SYNTHESIS: EVIDENCE FOR DIFFERENTIAL ACTION OF HORMONES ON GENE TRANSCRIPTION. Chev Kidson and K. S. Kirby in *Nature*, Vol. 203, No. 4945, pages 599–603; August 8, 1964.

TRANSFER RIBONUCLEIC ACIDS. E. N. Carlsen, G. J. Trelle and O. A. Schjeide in *Nature*, Vol. 202, No. 4936, pages 984–986; June 6, 1964.

27. Antibiotics and the Genetic Code

The Author

LUIGI GORINI is American Cancer Society Professor of Bacteriology and Immunology at the Harvard Medical School. He is a native of Milan who was graduated from the University of Pavia in 1925 and began a career in scientific research at the University of Milan in 1928. Fascism caused a 20-year interruption of that career. As Gorini puts it: "For political reasons I was unable to hold an academic position in fascist Italy and resumed my scientific research after the war." In 1947 he accepted a research fellowship at the University of Paris (the Sorbonne). He came to the U.S. in 1955 as a visiting investigator at New York University, and in 1957 he joined the Harvard medical faculty. For his work on streptomycin he received last year the Ledlie Prize, which is awarded by Harvard University every two years for "the most valuable contribution to science or in any way for the benefit of mankind."

Bibliography

MECHANISM OF STREPTOMYCIN ACTION ON BACTERIA: A UNITARY HYPOTHESIS. Charles R. Spotts and R. Y. Stanier in *Nature*, Vol. 192, No. 4803, pages 633–637; November 18, 1961.

PHENOTYPIC REPAIR BY STREPTOMYCIN OF DEFECTIVE GENOTYPES IN E. COLI. Luigi Gorini and Eva Kataja in *Proceedings of the National Academy of Sciences*, Vol. 51, No. 3, pages 487–493; March, 1964.

ROLE OF RIBOSOMES IN STREPTOMYCIN-ACTIVATED SUPPRESSION. W. French Anderson, Luigi Gorini and Lee Breckenridge in *Proceedings of the National Academy of Sciences*, Vol. 54, No. 4, pages 1076–1083; October, 1965.

28. The Induction of Cancer by Viruses

The Author

RENATO DULBECCO is resident fellow at the Salk Institute for Biological Studies. Born in Italy, he took a medical degree at the University of Torino in 1936 and remained there as a teacher and researcher until 1947. Moving to the U.S. in that year, he was at Indiana University for two years and at the California Institute of Technology for 14, including nine years as professor of biology. Dulbecco joined the Salk Institute in 1963 but spent the academic year 1963–1964 as Royal Society Visiting Professor at the University of Glasgow. Since 1964 he has served as a trustee of the Salk Institute while continuing his research activities there.

Bibliography

CELL TRANSFORMATION BY DIFFERENT FORMS OF POLYOMA VIRUS DNA. Lionel Crawford, Renato Dulbecco, Mike Fried, Luc Montagnier and Michael Stoker in *Proceedings of the National Academy of Sciences*, Vol. 52, No. 1, pages 148–152; July, 1964.

IMMUNOLOGICAL DETERMINANTS OF POLYOMA VIRUS ONCOGENESIS. Karl Habel in *The Journal of Experimental Medicine*, Vol. 115, No. 1, pages 181–193; January 1, 1962.

STUDIES ON SPECIFIC TRANSPLANTATION RESISTANCE TO POLYOMA-VIRUS-INDUCED TUMORS, I: TRANSPLANTATION RESISTANCE INDUCED BY POLYOMA VIRUS INFECTION. Hans Olof Sjögren in *Journal of the National Cancer Institute*, Vol. 32, No. 2, pages 361–393; February, 1964.

TRANSFORMATION OF CELLS IN VITRO BY DNA-CONTAINING VIRUSES. Renato Dulbecco in *The Journal of the American Medical Association*, Vol. 190, No. 8, pages 721–726; November 23, 1964.

TRANSFORMATION OF PROPERTIES OF AN ESTABLISHED CELL LINE BY SV 40 AND POLYOMA VIRUS. George J. Todaro, Howard Green and Burton D. Goldberg in *Proceedings of the National Academy of Sciences*, Vol. 51, No. 1, pages 66–73; January, 1964.

VIRUS-CELL INTERACTION WITH A TUMOR-PRODUCING VIRUS. Marguerite Vogt and Renato Dulbecco in *Proceedings of the National Academy of Sciences*, Vol. 46, No. 3, pages 365–370; March 15, 1960.

29. The Structure of Antibodies

The Author

R. R. PORTER was recently appointed Whitley Professor of Biochemistry at the University of Oxford and director of a Medical Research Council Unit for research into immunochemistry that is being set up at the university. Previously he had been for seven years Pfeizer Professor of Immunology at St. Mary's Hospital Medical School of the University of London. Porter, who was elected a Fellow of the Royal Society in 1964, studied at the University of Liverpool and the University of Cambridge. From 1949 to 1960 he was a member of the scientific staff at the National Institute for Medical Research in London. He lists his recreations as walking and fishing.

Bibliography

IMMUNOGLOBULINS. Julian B. Fleischman in *Annual Review of Biochemistry*, Part II, Vol. 35, pages 835–872; 1966.
IMMUNOGLOBULINS. E. S. Lennox and M. Cohn in *Annual Review of Biochemistry*, Part I, Vol. 36, 1967.
THE STRUCTURE OF IMMUNOGLOBULINS. R. R. Porter in *Essays in Biochemistry:* Vol. 3, edited by P. N. Campbell and G. D. Greville. Academic Press, in press.

Suggestions for Further Reading

Kalmus, H., Ed., REGULATION AND CONTROL IN LIVING SYSTEMS. New York, Wiley, 1966.
Maaløe, O., and N. O. Kjeldgaard, CONTROL OF MACROMOLECULAR SYNTHESIS. New York, Benjamin, 1966.

V RADIANT ENERGY AND THE ORIGIN OF LIFE
Molecular Evolution

30. Life and Light

The Author

GEORGE WALD is Harvard University's well-known authority on the chemistry of vision. Born in New York, he graduated from New York University in 1927, then did graduate work in zoology at Columbia University under Selig Hecht. After receiving his Ph.D. in 1932, he traveled to Germany on a National Research Council fellowship. While studying in Otto Warburg's laboratory at the Kaiser Wilhelm Institute in Berlin, Wald made his first notable contribution to knowledge of the eye—his discovery of vitamin A in the retina. After another year of postdoctoral study at the University of Chicago, he went to Harvard, where he is now professor of biology. He is a member of the National Academy of Sciences and was recently awarded the Nobel Prize for his work on the molecular basis of vision.

Bibliography

PHOTOSYNTHESIS AND RELATED PROCESSES. Eugene I. Rabinowitch. Interscience Publishers, Inc., 1945–1956.
RADIATION BIOLOGY. VOLUME III: VISIBLE AND NEAR-VISIBLE LIGHT. Edited by Alexander Hollaender. McGraw-Hill Book Company, Inc., 1956.
VISION AND THE EYE. M. H. Pirenne. The Pilot Press Ltd., 1948.
THE VISUAL PIGMENTS. H. J. A. Dartnall. Methuen & Co. Ltd., 1957.

31. The Role of Chlorophyll in Photosynthesis

The Authors

EUGENE I. RABINOWITCH and GOVINDJEE are respectively professor of botany and biophysics and assistant professor of botany at the University of Illinois. Rabinowitch was born in Russia, received a Ph.D. in inorganic chemistry at the University of Berlin in 1926 and worked in Germany, Denmark and Britain before coming to the U.S. in 1938. During World War II he worked on the Manhattan project. He joined the staff of the University of Illinois in 1947. Rabinowitch is the author of many books and papers, editor of the *Bulletin of the Atomic Scientists* and a translator of Russian poetry. In addition a book of poems that he has written in Russian is being published in Paris. Govindjee, who has no other name, is a graduate of the University of Allahabad in India; he obtained a Ph.D. in biophysics at the University of Illinois in 1960. His father dropped the family name, Asthana, in an effort to wipe out caste distinctions; one can often judge the caste or subcaste of Indians by their family names. Rabinowitch says he has "often suggested to Govindjee that he should invent a first name to make life easier for abstracters and indexers, but he seems to enjoy the distinction."

Bibliography

ACTION SPECTRUM OF THE "SECOND EMERSON EFFECT." Govindjee and E. Rabinowitch in *Biophysical Journal*, Vol. 1, No. 1, pages 1–14; September, 1960.
FLUORESCENCE CHANGES IN PORPHYRIDIUM EXPOSED TO GREEN LIGHT OF DIFFERENT INTENSITY: A NEW EMISSION BAND AT 693 Mμ AND ITS SIGNIFICANCE TO PHOTOSYNTHESIS. A. Krey and Govindjee in *Proceedings of the National Academy of Sciences*, Vol. 52, No. 6, pages 1568–1572; December, 1964.
PRIMARY PROCESSES IN PHOTOSYNTHESIS. Martin D. Kamen. Academic Press, 1963.

32. The Evolution of Hemoglobin

The Author

EMILE ZUCKERKANDL is an investigator with the French National Center for Scientific Research, working at the Physico-Chemical Colloidal Laboratory in Montpellier. A native of Vienna, he became a French citizen in 1938. After he was graduated from the Sorbonne, he obtained a master's degree at the University of Illinois and then returned to the Sorbonne for his doctorate. For several years he served at a marine biological station in Brittany, investigating proteins. From 1959 to 1964 he worked with Linus Pauling at the California Institute of Technology, investigating hemoglobin.

Bibliography

EVOLUTIONARY DIVERGENCE AND CONVERGENCE IN PROTEINS. Emile Zuckerkandl and Linus Pauling in *Evolving Genes and Proteins*, edited by Henry J. Vogel. Academic Press, in press.
GENE EVOLUTION AND THE HAEMOGLOBINS. Vernon M. Ingram in *Nature*, Vol. 189, No. 4766, pages 704–708; March 4, 1961.
THE HEMOGLOBINS. G. Braunitzer, K. Hilse, V. Rudloff and N. Hilschmann in *Advances in Protein Chemistry:* Vol. XIX, edited by C. B. Anfinsen, Jr., John T. Edsall, M. L. Anson and Frederic M. Richards. Academic Press, 1964.
MOLECULAR DISEASE, EVOLUTION, AND GENIC HETEROGENEITY. Emile Zuckerkandl and Linus Pauling in *Horizons in Biochemistry*, edited by Michael Kasha and Bernard Pullman. Academic Press, 1962.

33. Chemical Fossils

The Authors

GEOFFREY EGLINTON and MELVIN CALVIN are respectively senior lecturer in chemistry at the University of Glasgow and professor of chemistry at the University of California at Berkeley. Eglinton obtained a Ph.D. from the University of

Manchester in 1951. He writes: "I once mountaineered in the Alps and the Rockies but now feel nervous peering through the protective glass at the top of the Empire State Building." Calvin, winner of the Nobel prize for chemistry in 1961 for his work in elucidating the chemical pathways of carbon in photosynthesis, is a member of the President's Science Advisory Committee and a foreign member of the Royal Society. He was graduated from the Michigan College of Mining and Technology in 1931 and received a Ph.D. from the University of Minnesota in 1935. From 1935 to 1937 he was a research fellow at the University of Manchester; he joined the faculty of the University of California at Berkeley as an instructor in chemistry in 1937.

Bibliography

CHEMICAL EVOLUTION. M. Calvin in *Proceedings of the Royal Society*, Series A, Vol. 288, No. 1415, pages 441–466; November 30, 1965.

OCCURRENCE OF ISOPRENOID FATTY ACIDS IN THE GREEN RIVER SHALE. J. N. Ramsay, James R. Maxwell, A. G. Douglas and Geoffrey Eglinton in *Science*, Vol. 153, No. 3740, pages 1133–1134; September 2, 1966.

ORGANIC PIGMENTS: THEIR LONG-TERM FATE. Max Blumer in *Science*, Vol. 149, No. 3685, pages 722–726; August 13, 1965.

34. The Origin of Life

The Author

GEORGE WALD is professor of biology at Harvard. For additional information about him, see biographical note 30, under "Life and Light."

Bibliography

THE ORIGIN OF LIFE. A. I. Oparin. Dover Publications, Inc., 1953.

A PRODUCTION OF AMINO ACIDS UNDER POSSIBLE PRIMITIVE EARTH CONDITIONS. Stanley L. Miller in *Science*, Vol. 117, No. 3046, page 528; May 15, 1953.

TIME'S ARROW AND EVOLUTION. Harold F. Blum. Princeton University Press, 1951.

Suggestions for Further Reading

Bernal, J. D., THE ORIGINS OF LIFE. New York, World, 1968.

Oparin, A. I., LIFE, ITS NATURE, ORIGIN AND DEVELOPMENT. New York, Academic Press, 1962.

INDEXES

Index of Names

Numbers that appear in boldface type after a name indicate the page on which that person's article begins.

Index of Subjects